SPECULATIONS

**an introduction
to literature
through fantasy
and science fiction**

an introduction
to literature
through fantasy
and science fiction

Thomas E. Sanders
University of
South Florida

Glencoe Press
A division of Benziger Bruce & Glencoe, Inc.
New York • Beverly Hills

SPECULATIONS

for Louise Forshaw,
a thrilling wonder
story, a fantasy
captured forever
in the amber of
memory

Glencoe Press
A division of Benziger Bruce & Glencoe, Inc.
8701 Wilshire Boulevard
Beverly Hills, California   90211

Collier-Macmillan Canada, Ltd., Toronto, Canada

Library of Congress catalog card number: 72–86794

First printing, 1973

ACKNOWLEDGMENTS

Acknowledgment is gratefully made to the following authors, agents, and publishers who have granted permission to use selections from their publications.

FORREST J. ACKERMAN, *for:* "Automation" by A. E. van Vogt. Copyright 1950 by Clark Publishing Co; by permission of the author's agent, Forrest J. Ackerman (SFWA), 915 So. Sherbourne Dr., Los Angeles, Calif. 90035.
"It's a Good Life" by Jerome Bixby. Copyright 1953 by Ballantine Books; by arrangement with Forrest J. Ackerman (SFWA), 915 So. Sherbourne Dr., Los Angeles, Calif. 90035.

CONTENTS

FICTION   45

AN ESSAY, AN EXPLANATION, AND AN EXCERPT   583

THEMATIC CONTENTS

TO COMMUNICATE WITH OTHERS OR THE SELF: THE SEARCH FOR IDENTITY

OUR ENEMY, OUR FRIEND, METAL OR MENTAL: THE MACHINE

BEAUTY, TRUTH, IMPORTANCE:
THE CONSTANT SEARCH

OUR AMBIVALENCE REVEALED:
DESIRE AND FEAR

WE HAVE MET THE ENEMY AND HE IS—US:
THE APOCALYPSE

WE COME TRAILING CLOUDS:
THE FRIGHTENING CHILD

WHEN ALL ELSE FAILS: RELIGION

THE NATURE OF THE ALIEN:
STRANGERS IN STRANGE LANDS

PREFACE

The year was 1934; the place, Picher, Oklahoma, on the crayfish flats of the tri-state lead and zinc fields, Quapaw Indian country. My Cherokee father was riding a streak of hot dice at the illegal table in an illegal tavern on Connell Avenue. Probably a little worried I would leave the car and walk the eight blocks home to tell my mother where he was and what he was doing, he rested the dice long enough for the boys to get a refill of the Corona weed killer that sold for whiskey and jogged out to the parked car where I slept happily in the backseat as only an eight-year-old waiting for his dad can sleep. He gave me a coin (I can't remember the denomination—all money was very big in those days) and said I could buy whatever I wanted at the Connell Drug.

In that splendid emporium smelling of lilac and gardenia soap that was piled in unwrapped heaps, I assayed the wonders of candy counter and soda fountain, but they lacked the hypnotic pull of the magazine rack. Oh, the excitement of those incredible magazines with their brilliantly splashed covers, with the great, fat words announcing WEIRD TALES, AMAZING, ASTOUNDING. Strange creatures crawled across the glossy covers and seemed to disappear even as I watched into the dangerous-smelling pages. And the paper—what paper! It was thick and fluffy and dingy white. Only on that cheapest of pulp paper could those stories have come alive, for it was a part of the mystery and the magic of them. I think I was sure the ink was made from the juice of berries grown in cemeteries and picked in the dark of the moon.

And there were *Flash Gordon* comic books with Gale Arden in a dress like no one in my town would ever wear. With Flash Gordon in yellow ringlets, rippling muscles, and mortal combat with Ming the Merciless, Emperor of Mongo. The difficulties of making choices from that feast of wonder! I looked through every magazine until the druggist asked if I planned to shuffle the print off the pages. Then, embarrassed, I chose the two I had set my heart on: *Weird Tales* and *Flash Gordon.* And I gave him the coin and ran back to the car. There, in the dim light of an overhead thing called a dome light, I left the crayfish flats, I left Oklahoma, I left Earth. In the middle of the comic book was a four-page, triple-column story about Flash Gordon in a dungeon deep under the castle of Ming the Merciless. Somewhere above him, Gale was being ravished by the galactic Mandarin, and all around, men were moaning in hunger as gray, predatory rats prowled the corridors just out of reach of the hands that darted out to grab them.

Outside the car, night crouched in doorways as the drugstore closed and the theater turned off the box office light. Inside the car, I was a part of Flash Gordon, that clean, blond-haired god among the decimated prisoners of Ming the Merciless. I can, in memory, see the dingy page on which the words were printed. I remember one of the *d*'s in the font of type was broken:

> As Flash watched, one of the gray shapes veered near the bars. A hand snaked out to close round the dripping fur. Then it was gone. A high, thin squeak filled the corridor for a moment. Then all was still except for the crunching of a hundred tiny bones. . . .

I knew what those rats looked like. They prowled the two-by-fours that held the outhouse above the pit in the backyard of every house in town. I had grown up with them, thrown rocks at them, feared their sharp teeth when, occasionally, I would get one cornered and watch my dog move in for the kill. And suddenly I was sick—very sick. But it passed after I had stumbled into the night air and leaned gasping against the rear fender. Night noises, Earth noises, the comfortable noises of an Oklahoma summer replaced the crunching of a hundred tiny bones. And when I had quit shaking, when my stomach had settled down again, I climbed back in the car, opened the comic book and found the passage beginning, "As Flash watched, one of the gray shapes. . . ."

I make no attempt to explain this memory to you. I only hope you have one that is as important to you. If you have, you may already know most or all of the stories in this collection. If you do not, you may find one that will somehow serve the same function mine does.

Many people have shared the excitements, the insights, the journeys into madness, terror, and revelation of these stories—many people my life would be something of a prison without. Among them: Louise Forshaw who shared the star basin of Watonga; Scott Kirby, Chris Thiessen, and Judy Hulnick who shared the wonder of youth; Paige Graham and Gabe Horn who shared the generosity of friendship. And Walter W. Peek who shares them because blood brothers just share.

Thomas E. Sanders

INTRODUCTION

Crackling across the black miles of space on July 20, 1969, Neil A. Armstrong's voice assured a fascinated world it had just seen one of the epic footprints being made on the sands of time as the astronaut's moon-suited boot sank into the dust beneath the ladder of his lunar module: "That's one small step for a man, one giant leap for mankind." Later lunar landings seemed not only anticlimactic but a little tedious, lacking as they did the drama of "firstness." Such has it always been with man. Armstrong's successors were destined to share that near-anonymity accorded the conquerors of Mt. Everest after Edmund P. Hillary's initial conquest or the outright namelessness of the elaborate zoo that traveled the space paths pioneered by Laika in *Sputnik I.* Elation at finally reaching an imaginative goal is almost ephemeral because ennui sets in almost immediately and demands, "So what are you doing for an encore?"

Even before the question was asked after Armstrong's moon landing, one answer had come. In the June, 1960, issue of *Science Digest,* Arthur C. Clarke asserted by way of title for an essay, "We'll Never Conquer Space." At no point did that distinguished dean of science fiction writers suggest man would not map, cross, and occupy space outside Earth's atmosphere; he did extrapolate a human probability: Man's spiritual ties to Earth are too strong to be broken by the lure of the exotic in some distant sky. His prediction:

> When you are next outdoors on a summer night, turn your head toward the zenith. Almost vertically above you will be shining the brightest star of the northern skies—Vega of the Lyre, twenty-six years away at the speed of light, near enough the point of no return for us short-lived creatures. Past this blue-white beacon, fifty times as brilliant as our sun, we may send our minds and bodies, but never our hearts.
>
> For no man will ever turn homewards from beyond Vega, to greet again those he knew and loved on the earth.

Shortly after Armstrong's walk, C. P. Snow, that realistic, intellectual spokesman for mankind, was to lament in "The Moon Landing" (*Look,* August 26, 1969) that the distances from Earth to any other solar system are so great "that it would take the entire history of mankind from paleolithic man to the present day to traverse—at the speed of *Apollo 11*—the distance to the nearest star." Consequently, he reasoned, "This is forever the end of the mortal frontier." Within one hundred years the realization should become general, and then "disappointment, the sense of confinement, a kind of cosmic claustrophobia will set in." Man has needed limitless horizons, and the moon landing makes ours "desolately limited." In the period between Columbus and Armstrong, those horizons were geographically narrowed and, in actuality, closed. Snow contends, "Science-fiction writers (at least those who have scientific knowledge and insight, of whom there are plenty) have been fighting a rearguard action against the inevitable." The result? "One of the casualties of the moon landing will be science fiction, at least as applied to space travel." As a further result, "Science-fiction writers will be driven inward, not outward, and will turn their attention to human biology and psychology. There is plenty to occupy them there for more than a hundred years."

Snow sees that turning inward as the paradox of the moon landing. The moon promised new pioneering, new exploration; but the landing dashed such hopes with a new realization, "The realization that, as well as being the greatest exploration, it was very near the final one." If Snow is correct, diminished hope is the tragic victim of technological enterprise. And man has always needed hope—or the promise of it. Snow concludes:

> We badly need something to take us out—not constantly but for part of our time—out of this, our mundane life. The naïve idea of heaven did that for generation after generation, when people could believe that heaven was somewhere above us, up there beyond the sky. It was a naïve idea but very powerful, and nothing more sophisticated has been so powerful. To secular minds, the prospect of space, other worlds to find, other lives to meet, has been a substitute. To many, a substitute of almost equal power. Now that will fail us too. As a result of supreme technological skill and heroism, we are faced not with the infinite but with the immovable limits. The limits of our practical condition. We now know that the only lives we shall ever meet turn out to be our own.

And still a third loud voice echoed the theme. Kurt Vonnegut, Jr., has long been the *enfant terrible* of underground literature in America. Now his black humor, his keen ear for the satirical have made him a writer for all readers and caused such a mainstream author as Graham Greene to declare him "one of the best living American writers." On March 13, 1972, the Public Broadcasting System presented Vonnegut's *Between Time and Timbuktu* to a fascinated audience. In a "Background" interview for *TV Guide* (March 11, 1972), Vonnegut commented on his feelings about the space program:

> Just look at any big picture book on the universe where the distances between heavenly bodies are indicated, and the natures of the atmospheres of some of the other planets. One must conclude that exploration is not a particularly hopeful enterprise.
>
> I think many people are encouraged to believe that we can use up this planet and dispose of it like a Kleenex because we are going to wonderful new planets which are all green and moist and nourishing—and that we can continue to do this indefinitely. Well, that isn't the case. I think we are permanent prisoners on this planet. It's the only planet we'll ever have.

Vonnegut's conclusion sounds very like a paraphrase of Snow's:

> I think that the only extraordinary trips we can take now
> will have to be in our own minds. Man's principal human
> enterprise is going to be to endure, as long as he can,
> under worsening conditions.

Man's most extraordinary trips have always been charted and traveled in his mind, however. For every Marco Polo, Christopher Columbus, or Neil Armstrong who has made the literal journey, millions of vicarious voyagers have passed the same way through the media of poetry, fiction, history, travel accounts, radio, movies, or television. The lunar landscape was, for many, disappointing because they had, in earlier visits with such astronauts as Lucian of Samosata, Jules Verne, and Flash Gordon seen a more challenging geography. The plains of Mars and the seas of Venus can never be as exciting in reality as they have been in the imaginative meanderings of Edgar Rice Burroughs and dozens of forgotten writers who first led many geographically homebound voyagers to distant planets, to distant galaxies, to the edge of space itself. Whether or not time warps will ever allow the metal conveyers of man to defeat time is of little consequence. The star gates of the Navajo religious accounts and such writers as Arthur C. Clarke have already shown man superior beings, incredibly advanced civilizations, and spiritual achievements that create a homesickness in him even as he sits at home. Often, he can hardly wait to return to Earth to begin the new life that will ultimately lead man to find the mental utopia here that he has glimpsed in literary space.

Curiously, no matter if his intention on setting forth was to escape from his own tedious reality, man more often than not finds himself a prisoner of a harsher reality than he left; instead of escaping into a suspension of thought, he has escaped into a metaphorical or speculative situation that illuminates the facets of his world in ways that mainstream fiction cannot. He is forced to ask, "Are we heading in this direction? Will our future be this perilous as a result of our present?" Whether or not he wants to, he is forced to assess his religious attitudes, his beliefs about science and technology, his ideas about socio-political activities in his time. And the act of assessing creates change in him.

Aesthetic distance between the literary voyager and Emma Bovary or Jake Barnes is limited by geographical proximity. The trivia of daily incident does affect our lives, but it also distracts our literary attention from the larger problem, "the human condition," and centers it on a unique character, one so individualized we can never really identify with him as a model. He may exemplify some of our strengths and weaknesses, his life may be very much like ours, his furniture, his world are the elements of now—a present so absolute that we are not impelled to take steps to avoid his tragedies or enjoy his triumphs because his life is concurrent with ours and nothing about his environment or ours will be changed as a result of what he did. The act of reading about him imprisons him in a past that we recognize as being any time before today, therefore incapable of giving us reason to change this moment which is a result of *his* past. He is history, and history is set, its results immutable.

Fantasy-science fiction is quite another matter, however. Fantasy allows us to see the reality of *now*, stripped of the distractions of actual experience. The exaggerations of character traits, natural laws, geography create metaphorical reality wherein evil is truly evil without the necessity of rational study of extenuating circumstances, wherein good is good because irrational evil can be circumvented if not completely vanquished. Science fiction allows us to see possible results of today in some future made by the history that is our lives—a history free of distracting trivia. If we see the future results of personal or group action or non-action, that future is merely an extrapolation; it can be changed by now in ways that Hamlet's history cannot change our present. Could Hamlet have acted in our present, the reader (whose present Hamlet's world would become) could have taken steps to change it. But looking back at Hamlet's past does not change our present—unless man does profit from the mistakes of history, a possibility that, philosophers feel, should occur but, historians realize, does not.

Fantasy-science fiction is by no means a recent innovation. Resting on his need to postulate explanations for the inexplicable past, the confusing present, and the mystifying future, man has always been a fantast as he creates religions and constructs myths to explain his basic beliefs and perpetuate his ideals. The golden age of fantasy, the classical period of this literature, may well have come to a close with the composition of the *Koran*, the last major religious code including a hierarchy of immortals dedicated to the preservation of an eternal utopia.

Certainly the classical age of science fiction was to come much later, though it had its genesis in the fifth century B.C. with Democritus's postulation of the atomic structure of matter and Leucippus's postulation of causality in nature, the belief that every natural event has a natural cause. In the next three centuries Euclid compiled his *Elements*, the first formal statement of geometric principles; Archimedes established the discipline of hydrostatics; Eratosthenes measured the Earth's circumference; Aristarchus of Samos concluded the Earth is smaller than the sun around which it revolves as it rotates on an inclined axis; and Hipparchus measured the size and distance of the sun and the moon.

The next seventeen centuries were the province of the fantast in man, for he concerned himself with those primordial fears and dim memories that chronically plague him. Two scientific achievements in all those centuries must be noted, however: Ptolemy's synthesis of astronomical knowledge which provided a system of celestial mechanics in the second century A.D., and Al-Khowarizmi's theory of numbers in the ninth century A.D. Without such scientific laws and assumptions, a body of fiction resting on them could, obviously, not emerge. However, as early as Plato's fourth century B.C. *Timaeus* and *Critias*, the "scientific wonders of Atlantis" came into existence, and Lucian of Samosata recounts an extravagantly fantastic voyage to the moon in his *Veracious History* in the second century A.D. To minimize the fantasy-science fiction elements of Plato's Atlantis references or Lucian's mock narrative of travel is the humor of a mainstream scholar who feels they must be removed from the "disreputable" category of speculative fiction if their archetypal qualities are to be reserved for the "special" categories of mainstream literature designed to include Aristophanes' *The Birds* or Jonathan Swift's *Gulliver's Travels*—works so firmly entrenched as "possessing literary value" that they must not be judged by standards reserved for "escapist writers." And neither can we let that happen to Voltaire's *Micromégas* in which an alien visits Earth. *The Odyssey* might even have to be reassessed if such were allowed to happen! Is not Circe an enchantress worthy of a *Star Trek* script? Or Polyphemus as much an alien as one might encounter in Edmond Hamilton's *The Monster-God of Mamurth*? And that trip to Hades! Well, it certainly cannot be associated with Jules Verne's *A Journey to the Center of the Earth* even if that is where Hades was located by Homer. One might as well seek the archetype for Verne's *Twenty Thousand Leagues under the Sea* in Beowulf's battle with Grendel's mother!

Such haggling serves only to separate from fantasy-science fiction that reader who probably most needs it—the unimaginative, the unadventurous, the one so frightened that he fears further disturbance. When comfortable rules and unassailable dicta make small confines pleasant, zoo cages seem spacious. Whether or not man will find his destiny in the stars or in William Blake's "grain of sand" does not seem particularly important. That he continues to seek and, not finding, to speculate on the ultimate possibility—that is important.

Are there sirens on Titan? Giants in the Earth? Sea creatures that respond to the plaintive call of foghorns? The unequivocal answers to such questions are no more important than the unequivocal answers to such questions as, "Can Hamlet destroy the evil of his stepfather without becoming evil himself?" or "Can Nora find liberation by exchanging her doll's house for a furnished flat?" That the questions need to be asked is important, for the answers to all of them are speculations. The major difference in the two types of questions lies in the realization that mainstream literature poses questions concerned with a kind of overwhelming immediacy so close to the asker that he must respond or refuse to respond almost at once, for the immediate circumstances change immediately, and decisions (for good or ill) must be made at once. The urgencies faced by Nora or Hamlet are generated by the moment that allows for little vision or revision—either in the literary character or the reader.

On the other hand, the questions raised by speculative fiction concern themselves with vague, formless anxieties and aspirations that shape life over a span of years, chronically scraping the intellect and the heart with an abrasive action that allows growth of a response to the general condition rather than to a specific problem. In short, man needs mainstream fiction to help him arrive at the immediate answers to specific personal questions; he needs speculative fiction to prepare him, as a member of his race, to see that that race has a future in which it can read mainstream literature. As Ray Bradbury suggests in *Fahrenheit 451*, an unread book is a burned book. Readers and writers never suggest mainstream literature should be so burned—if they are fantasy-science fiction readers and writers. And they find it curious that mainstream scholars should suggest the fate for a literature that includes such names as Shakespeare (*The Tempest* and *Macbeth*), Marlowe (*The Tragical History of Dr. Faustus)* in the past; Orwell *(1984)* and Huxley *(Brave New World)* in the recent present.

The creator of Caliban and Hecate's followers, William Shakespeare, knew man's need of the fantastic that, metaphorically, creates an awareness of reality that the mundane cannot. And he obviously knew that some kinds of reality are not communicable except through the speculative image. He would have agreed with John Steinbeck's observation in *The Log from the Sea of Cortez* (New York, 1951):

> Men really need sea-monsters in their personal oceans
> ...for the ocean, deep and black in the depths, is like
> the dark levels of our minds in which the dream symbols
> incubate and sometimes rise up to sight like the Old Man
> of the Sea. And even if the symbol vision be horrible,
> it is there and it is ours. An ocean without its unnamed
> monsters would be like a completely dreamless sleep.

Space is also deep and black in the depths—and as strong in its lure. Whether monsters are rushing up from unfathomable grottos to swallow the suddenly-nervous swimmer or dropping from the deeps of space on the unwary night stroller of the land, an ambivalence compounded of eager anticipation and dread fear draws him always back into bottomless water and dark night. Swimming pools with their clean view of the bottom, daylight with its limitless view —these are functional but unsatisfying, for they conceal nothing.

Nothing? Because they *seem* so innocent, so transparent, they *must* harbor the unseen—the suspicious nature of man deems it so. As early as Plato's *The Republic*, invisibility as a cloak to allow man to behave unethically occupies Glaucon and Socrates, an idea further explored by Marlowe's Dr. Faustus and expanded by H. G. Wells in his 1897 classic *The Invisible Man*. That daylight might fail to reveal the alien being is an even more shattering prospect, however, a prospect plumbed by H. P. Lovecraft in "The Colour out of Space" and Algernon Blackwood in "The Willows."

As a group, scientists are both pragmatic and skeptical, preferring to believe established natural laws are both accurate and universal, but as recently as 1967, *Time* magazine published the findings of a Gallup poll that revealed the following remarkable statistics. Over 5,000,000 Americans are *certain* they have seen "flying saucers or other UFOs" and "46% of American adults believe that UFOs are something real." In the essay, "A Fresh Look at Flying Saucers" (August 4, 1967), *Time* asked, "What of the possibility that an advanced culture may somehow have learned to circumvent the Einstein limit, and thus be able to send craft to distant stars at incredible speeds?" The question was not answered by *Time*, but it was immediately followed by, "Says one physicist, 'My God, could our whole science just be a fiction completely unrelated to what the UFOs might have? All this earthly science—F equals *ma* and all the rest that I so much believe in—could it really be something else?' "

That question by a physicist who obviously refused to be quoted by name lies at the heart of "hard science fiction," a fiction that has never attempted to answer questions but which has devoted itself to extrapolation and to speculation. Are there other intelligences "out there"? Is man a primitive being among the countless possible beings in a universe that may contain 100 billion galaxies of which the Milky Way galaxy is only an average member of about 100 billion stars of which our sun is only one? Have superior beings visited Earth, programmed primitive Earthlings to become intelligent beings or to destroy themselves, seen man as a potential equal, a potential threat? Such questions are as unanswerable as they are undismissable, but they do concern both scientists and laymen. Astronomer J. Allen Hynek, director of Northwestern University's Dearborn Observatory is quoted in the *Time* essay: "There is a tendency in the 20th century to forget that there will be a 21st century science, and indeed a 30th century science, from which vantage points our knowledge of the universe may appear quite different. We suffer, perhaps, from temporal provincialism, a form of arrogance that has always irritated posterity."

That provincialism is nowhere more apparent than among the literary critics, scholars, professors who find fantasy-science fiction outside the bounds of their provincial considerations. That they would have refused to consider Shakespeare's plays lacking merit because they were not a part of the "respectable and acceptable" forms in Elizabethan England is its own best argument for their provincialism. Not that all fantasy-science fiction is worthy of consideration. A very small portion of it is. But, then, a very small portion of mainstream literature is of value. Most of the endless mouthings of man are undeserving of consideration or study.

In 1952, Isaac Asimov, a respected scientist (Ph.D. in chemistry) and prolific author of science fiction and non-fiction, defined science fiction as "that branch of literature which is concerned with the impact of scientific advance upon human beings," a definition he modified in 1953, saying, "I would like to say that my definition applies not to 'science fiction' but to a subdivision of the field which I find it convenient to speak of as 'social science fiction.' It is my opinion that social science fiction is the only branch of science fiction that is sociologically significant, and that those stories which are generally accepted as science fiction (at least to the point where skilled editors accept them for inclusion in their science fiction magazines) but do not fall within the definition I have given above, are *not* significant, however amusing they may be and however excellent as pieces of fiction." ("Social Science Fiction" in Reginald Bretnor, ed., *Modern Science Fiction.* New York, 1953.) Summarizing his article, Asimov concludes:

1. For the first time in history mankind is faced with a rapidly changing society, due to the advent of modern technology.
2. Science fiction is a form of literature that has grown out of this fact.
3. The contribution that science fiction can make to society is that of accustoming its readers to the thought of the inevitability of continuing change and the necessity of directing and shaping that change rather than opposing it blindly or blindly permitting it to overwhelm us.

Not all science fiction writers and critics would agree with Asimov in his definition though most would agree with his assessment of the value of such fiction. In a lecture delivered at The University of Chicago in 1957 and published in modified form under the title "Science Fiction: Its Nature, Faults and Virtues" (in *The Science Fiction Novel.* Chicago, 1969), Robert A. Heinlein, author of *Stranger in a Strange Land,* summarizes some of his contemporaries' attitudes:

Damon Knight, a distinguished critic in this field, argues
that there is no clear distinction between fantasy and science fiction, in which opinion August Derleth seems to
agree. . . . Theodore Sturgeon, a giant in this field, defines
a science fiction story as one in which the story would
not exist if it were not for the scientific element.
. . . Reginald Bretnor, author, editor and acute critic of
this field, gives what is to me the most thoughtful, best
reasoned, and most useful definition of science fiction.
He sees it as a field of literature much broader than that
often termed "mainstream" literature—or "non-science
fiction," if you please—science fiction being that sort in
which the author shows awareness of the nature and
importance of the human activity known as the scientific
method, shows equal awareness of the great body of
human knowledge already collected through that activity,
and takes into account in his stories the effects and possible future effects on human beings of scientific method
and scientific fact. . . . When I say "fantasy fiction" I shall
mean "imaginary-and-not-possible" in the world as we
know it; conversely all fiction which I regard as
"imaginary-but-possible" I shall refer to as "realistic
fiction," i.e., imaginary but could be real so far as we
know the real universe. Science fiction is in the latter
class. It is not fantasy.

John W. Campbell, editor of the Condé-Nast science fiction
magazine *Analog*, made this distinction in his introduction to *Analog
6* (Garden City, New York, 1966):

The major distinction between fantasy and science fiction
is, simply, that science fiction uses one, or a very, very
few new postulates, and develops the rigidly consistent
logical consequences of those limited postulates. Fantasy
makes up its rules as it goes along. . . . The basic nature
of fantasy is "The only rule is, make up a new rule any
time you need one!" The basic rule of science fiction is
"Set up a basic proposition—then develop its consistent,
logical consequences."

Were mainstream authors and critics in harmony in defining a
novel as opposed to a social novel, a satire as opposed to a burlesque,
a poem of any kind, this disagreement about the two ends of the
fantasy-science fiction continuum would be distressing. Happily,
the nature of literature—all literature—allows the author latitude to
so readily shape and change his medium to suit the purposes of

his communication that Homer's *The Odyssey,* Milton's *Paradise Lost,* and Virgil's *The Aeneid* can all fit comfortably within the general confines of the definition of an epic. And how easily epics fall into almost any definition of fantasy! Consequently, a rigid definition of speculative fiction is not really important; the results of that fiction are.

In Isaac Asimov's "Misbegotten Missionary" (the first story in this book), we encounter an alien creature that has stowed away on an Earthbound spaceship. From a society that is complete and whole, one single entity, the "misbegotten missionary" seeks to bring a sense of completeness to Earth if he can remain undetected until the ship lands and he can establish himself on Earth.

> But he was weary of the ship. It was such a futile phenomenon. These life fragments were skillful in their constructions, yet it was only a measure of their unhappiness, after all. They strove to find in the control of inanimate matter what they could not find in themselves. In their unconscious yearning for completion, they built machines and scoured space, seeking, seeking. . . .

That observable feature in man—that striving to find in the control of inanimate matter what he cannot find in himself—lies at the heart of all speculative fiction. And the exploration of man's need to find that which seems to exist outside himself is nowhere better presented than in fantasy-science fiction. If it seems important to you, by all means debate the nature of the works in this book. In deciding whether or not Mary Shelley's *The Last Man* is fantasy or science fiction, you will discover Mary Shelley's primary communication. In compartmentalizing Saki's "Sredni Vashtar," you will learn a great deal about yourself because you will be forced to distinguish between science and religion—a distinction you probably have never made, even though you have vague ideas about what you think you think.

Alexander Pope's advice in *An Essay on Man* may even assume new meaning—and you may understand it for the first time:

> Know then thyself, presume not God to scan,
> The proper study of mankind is man.
> Placed on this isthmus of a middle state,
> A being darkly wise, and rudely great:
> With too much knowledge for the skeptic side,
> With too much weakness for the stoic's pride,
> He hangs between; in doubt to act, or rest;
> In doubt to deem himself a god, or beast;
> In doubt his mind or body to prefer;

Born but to die, and reasoning but to err;
Alike in ignorance, his reason such,
Whether he thinks too little or too much;
Chaos of thought and passion, all confused;
Still by himself abused or disabused;
Created half to rise and half to fall;
Great lord of all things, yet a prey to all;
Sole judge of truth, in endless error hurled:
The glory, jest, and riddle of the world!

Somewhere in Pope's advice are the reasons man has written speculative fiction, the reasons it is important to all men, the reasons it is specifically important to you.

We require a dimension like sky . . .

CID CORMAN

POETRY

When Edgar Allan Poe apostrophized, "Science! true daughter of Old Time . . . hast thou not torn . . . from me the summer dream beneath the tamarind tree?" he stated that ambivalent fear and wonder that had earlier been the poet's unique response to God. Centuries before Poe, the Psalmist had asserted, "The heavens declare the glory of God; and the firmament sheweth his handywork," but the awe was not directed at the natural laws that create the order and harmony of the universe. Instead, "The law of the Lord *is* perfect." Poe's acceptance of the reality of science was shared by his contemporary Emily Dickinson whose dictum in "Faith is a fine invention" that microscopes are more practical than faith in emergencies is a logical outgrowth of Pope's imperative "Know then thyself, presume not God to scan."

Pope's argument for science is inextricably bound up in religion, however. Perhaps the deeply rooted religious needs of man are the fantast's statement of undiscovered science and, since religion has always been a poetic statement, the poets after Poe and Dickinson may have felt a new obligation to provide the vision man would need if he was ever to know himself. Self-reliance rather than reliance on the back-up team of God would certainly be necessary if he were to discover the link between himself and the universe, especially if, as Stephen Crane felt, man's existence does not create a sense of obligation in the universe.

In "A Defence of Poetry," Percy Bysshe Shelley anticipated Poe, Dickinson, Crane, and their followers: "Poets are the hierophants of an unapprehended inspiration; the mirrors of the gigantic shadows which futurity casts upon the present." Worthwhile poets are of their time, but poetic vision makes them citizens of all time as it releases them from the confines of their age. Thomas Carlyle was aware of this truth when he wrote "On Boswell's Life of Johnson" in 1832. He said, "Whoso belongs only to his own age, and reverences only its gilt Popinjays or soot-smeared Mumbojumbos, must needs die with it."

Not all poets have been convinced that science and poetry can serve each other, however. Samuel Taylor Coleridge declared in his "Definitions of Poetry" that "Poetry is not the proper antithesis to prose, but to science. Poetry is opposed to science, and prose to metre. The proper and immediate object of science is the acquirement, or communication, of truth; the proper and immediate object of poetry is the communication of immediate pleasure." Poetry that grows out of fantasy-science fiction concerns is, by no means, pleasure-inducing in the sense that Coleridge's "Kubla Khan" is. Confined by the rules of prosody, it is harmonious and rhythmically pleasing, but the possibilities it postulates, the realizations it forces are enjoyable only in the way that picking a scab from an almost healed sore is enjoyable—the pain and the promise of new waiting periods urge us on in spite of our determination to ignore the source of irritation. We can not allow a scab to be what it is: a protective covering for new skin growth. We must see it as an alien appendage. In *Jurgen*, James Branch Cabell noted, "Poetry is man's rebellion against being what he is." As long as man possesses poetry, a concept of science, and his own human nature he will look to some future—especially if he is a part of a democracy, for, as Alexis de Tocqueville observed about Americans in 1840, "Democratic nations care but little for what has been, but they are haunted by visions of what will be; in this direction their unbounded imagination grows and dilates beyond all measure.... Democracy, which shuts the past against the poet, opens the future before him."

The poets in this section do, indeed, turn toward that future....

Science Fiction
Kingsley Amis

What makes us rove that starlit corridor
May be the impulse to meet face to face
Our vice and folly shaped into a thing,
And so at last ourselves; what lures us there
Is simpler versions of disaster:
A web confounding time and space,
A world of ocean without shore,
A sentence to perpetual journeying,
And simplest, flapping down the poisoned air,
A ten-clawed monster.

In him, perhaps, we see the general ogre
Who rode our ancestors to nightmare,
And in his habitat their maps of hell;
But climates and geographies soon change,
Spawning mutations none can quell
With silver sword or necromancer's ring,
Worse than their sires, of wider range,
And much more durable.

The Misfit
A. R. Ammons

The unassimilable fact leads us on:
round the edges
   where broken shapes make poor masonry
the synthesis
fails (and succeeds) into limitation
   or extending itself too far
becomes a different synthesis:
law applies
   consistently to the molecule,
not to the ocean, unoriented, unprocessed,
it floats in, that floats in it:
   we are led on

to the boundaries
where relations loosen into chaos
   or where the nucleus fails to control,
fragments in odd shapes
expressing more and more the interstitial sea:
   we are led on

to peripheries, to the raw blocks of material,
where mortar and trowel can convert
   diversity into enlarging unity:
not the million oriented facts
but the one or two facts,
   out of place,

recalcitrant, the one observed fact
that tears us into questioning:
   what has not
joined dies into order to redeem, with
loss of singleness extends the form,
   or, unassimilable, leads us on.

Six Haiku
Karen Anderson

1

The white vapor trail
   Scrawls slowly on the sky
      Without any squeak.

2

Gilt and painted clouds
   Float back through the shining air,
      What, are there stars, too?

3

In the heavy world's
   Shadow, I watch the sputnik
      Coasting in sunlight.

4

Those crisp cucumbers
  Not yet planted in Syrtis—
    How I desire one!

5

In the fantastic
  Seas of Venus, who would dare
    To imagine gulls?

6

When Proxima sets
  What constellation do they
    Dream around our sun?

Moon Landing
W. H. Auden

It's natural the Boys should whoop it up for
so huge a phallic triumph, an adventure
    it would not have occurred to women
    to think worth while, made possible only

because we like huddling in gangs and knowing
the exact time: yes, our sex may in fairness
    hurrah the deed, although the motives
    that primed it were somewhat less than *menschlich*.

A grand gesture. But what does it period?
What does it osse? We were always adroiter
    with objects than lives and more facile
    at courage than kindness: from the moment

the first flint was flaked, this landing was merely
a matter of time. But our selves, like Adam's,
    still don't fit us exactly, modern
    only in this—our lack of decorum.

Homer's heroes were certainly no braver
than our Trio, but more fortunate: Hector
   was excused the insult of having
   his valor covered by television.

Worth *going* to see? I can well believe it.
Worth *seeing?* Mneh! I once rode through a desert
   and was not charmed: give me a watered
   lively garden, remote from blatherers

about the New, the von Brauns and their ilk, where
on August mornings I can count the morning
   glories, where to die has a meaning,
   and no engine can shift my perspective.

Unsmudged, thank God, my Moon still queens the Heavens
as She ebbs and fulls, a Presence to glop at,
   Her Old Man, made of grit not protein,
   still visits my Austrian several

with His old detachment, and the old warnings
still have power to scare me: Hybris comes to
   an ugly finish, Irreverence
   is a greater oaf than Superstition.

Our apparatniks will continue making
the usual squalid mess called History:
   all we can pray for is that artists,
   chefs and saints may still appear to blithe it.

The Unknown Citizen

(To JS/07/M/378 This Marble Monument Is Erected by the State)

W. H. Auden

He was found by the Bureau of Statistics to be
One against whom there was no official complaint,
And all the reports on his conduct agree
That, in the modern sense of an old-fashioned word, he was a saint,
For in everything he did he served the Greater Community.
Except for the War till the day he retired

He worked in a factory and never got fired,
But satisfied his employers, Fudge Motors Inc.
Yet he wasn't a scab or odd in his views,
For his Union reports that he paid his dues,
(Our report on his Union shows it was sound)
And our Social Psychology workers found
That he was popular with his mates and liked a drink.
The Press are convinced that he bought a paper every day
And that his reactions to advertisements were normal in every way.
Policies taken out in his name prove that he was fully insured,
And his Health-card shows he was once in hospital but left it cured.
Both Producers Research and High-Grade Living declare
He was fully sensible to the advantages of the Installment Plan
And had everything necessary to Modern Man,
A phonograph, a radio, a car and a frigidaire.
Our researchers into Public Opinion are content
That he held the proper opinions for the time of year;
When there was peace, he was for peace; when there was war, he
            went.
He was married and added five children to the population,
Which our Eugenist says was the right number for a parent of his
            generation,
And our teachers report that he never interfered with their educa-
            tion.
Was he free? Was he happy? The question is absurd:
Had anything been wrong, we certainly should have heard.

Nightmare Number Three
Stephen Vincent Benét

We had expected everything but revolt
And I kind of wonder myself when they started thinking—
But there's no dice in that now.
                              I've heard fellows say
They must have planned it for years and maybe they did.
Looking back, you can find little incidents here and there,
Like the concrete-mixer in Jersey eating the wop
Or the roto press that printed "Fiddle-dee-dee!"
In a three-color process all over Senator Sloop,
Just as he was making a speech. The thing about that
Was, how could it walk upstairs? But it was upstairs,
Clicking and mumbling in the Senate Chamber.

They had to knock out the wall to take it away
And the wrecking-crew said it grinned.
                                        It was only the best
Machines, of course, the superhuman machines,
The ones we'd built to be better than flesh and bone,
But the cars were in it, of course . . .
                                        and they hunted us
Like rabbits through the cramped streets on that Bloody Monday,
The Madison Avenue busses leading the charge.
The busses were pretty bad—but I'll not forget
The smash of glass when the Duesenberg left the show-room
And pinned three brokers to the Racquet Club steps
Or the long howl of the horns when they saw men run,
When they saw them looking for holes in the solid ground . . .

I guess they were tired of being ridden in
And stopped and started by pygmies for silly ends,
Of wrapping cheap cigarettes and bad chocolate bars
Collecting nickels and waving platinum hair
And letting six million people live in a town.
I guess it was that. I guess they got tired of us
And the whole smell of human hands.
                                        But it was a shock
To climb sixteen flights of stairs to Art Zuckow's office
(Nobody took the elevators twice)
And find him strangled to death in a nest of telephones,
The octopus-tendrils waving over his head,
And a sort of quiet humming filling the air. . . .
Do they eat? . . . There was red . . . But I did not stop to look.
I don't know yet how I got to the roof in time
And it's lonely, here on the roof.
                                        For a while, I thought
That window-cleaner would make it, and keep me company.
But they got him with his own hoist at the sixteenth floor
And dragged him in, with a squeal.
You see, they cooperate. Well, we taught them that
And it's fair enough, I suppose. You see, we built them.
We taught them to think for themselves.
It was bound to come. You can see it was bound to come.
And it won't be so bad, in the country. I hate to think
Of the reapers, running wild in the Kansas fields,
And the transport planes like hawks on a chickenyard,
But the horses might help. We might make a deal with the horses.
At least, you've more chance, out there.

                                    And they need us, too.
They're bound to realize that when they once calm down.
They'll need oil and spare parts and adjustments and tuning up.
Slaves? Well, in a way, you know, we were slaves before.
There won't be so much real difference—honest, there won't.
(I wish I hadn't looked into that beauty-parlor
And seen what was happening there.
But those are female machines and a bit high-strung.)
Oh, we'll settle down. We'll arrange it. We'll compromise.
It won't make sense to wipe out the whole human race.
Why, I bet if I went to my old Plymouth now
(Of course you'd have to do it the tactful way)
And said, "Look here! Who got you the swell French horn?"
He wouldn't turn me over to those police cars;
At least I don't think he would.
                                    Oh, it's going to be jake.
There won't be so much real difference—honest, there won't—
And I'd go down in a minute and take my chance—
I'm a good American and I always liked them—
Except for one small detail that bothers me
And that's the food proposition. Because, you see,
The concrete-mixer may have made a mistake,
And it looks like just high spirits.
But, if it's got so they like the flavor... well...

E=mc²

Morris Bishop

What was our trust, we trust not;
    What was our faith, we doubt;
Whether we must or must not,
    We may debate about.
The soul, perhaps, is a gust of gas
    And wrong is a form of right—
But we know that Energy equals Mass
    By the Square of the Speed of Light.

What we have known, we know not;
   What we have proved, abjure;
Life is a tangled bowknot,
   But one thing still is sure.
Come, little lad; come, little lass—
   Your docile creed recite:
"We know that Energy equals Mass
   By the Square of the Speed of Light."

Let the Trees
Philip Booth

Let the trees be full.
                    Full,
you ask, for God's sake of *what?*
Leaves in due season, or snow;
a moon, if it comes to that.
Or, lacking as much, a night
after clouds full of wind.
                              What
do you mean you don't know
what I mean? Get out
of the house and into
the trees. You, through
fall-out and smoke, who
for six gravid days
have program'd yourselves
into space, tracking
your progress through
wave-lengths converged
on hundreds of lenses. . . .

It's no great matter what
starlings have already
flown, or stiffly still wait
in the branches; the seeds,
from their warm apogee,
have spun toward hard
re-entry. Refusing
how winter answers
your doubt, you might
even want, toward new

growth, to kneel at the root
of what you look up at.
Look, I say, to the trees,
and let your two eyes
fill them, even as then
your own two eyes may
be filled.
      We've looked
long enough at ourselves:
for six brave days without
love, computing cold pride
through a hundred lenses.
Proud of voyage less than
return, we've left no
hero in space; nor is
there a tree on the moon,
to feast on or look up to.

The computers whirr and blaze
in their own trajectory,
plotting how men return
to Texas to tell their story
to punchcards. Conditioned
to die, we watch ourselves
orbit on padded couches, banking
on tapes to program our
last defenses.
      Look
out the window, you
who have planted a tree
in your yard, or live
on the edge of a hedgerow;
you, whom computers have
fired, and gravity finally
tugged home: I pray you,
come to your senses.

The Outer Becoming Inner
William Bronk

Sometimes, I could go in anywhere, not
to see the stars, not to be as we
are always, not only under them
but in them. The outer spaces push against
us, all their vastnesses apart, they crowd
us. They become our world. I could go hide
like Adam in his garden. How
would it matter? No, we are in the stars. Not
for us ever any familiar and definite world.

The Compass
Cid Corman

The sky is a pro-
position we
cannot take and can
not quite leave. It's of an

order that exceeds
order, as if
the city hung up
under it were a trick,

an imitation
chaos. Fixed on
one plane, hugging a
wish to fall together.

We require a di-
mension like sky,
as that of heaven,
to eradicate our

pomposity, to
compel us to
see how pointless is
any compass where air

is not pivotal.
Not to deny
what we are, for that
is patently beyond us,

but rather to let
ourselves into
a universe, a
poetry, a pity.

A Man Said to the Universe
Stephen Crane

A man said to the universe:
"Sir, I exist!"
"However," replied the universe,
"The fact has not created in me
A sense of obligation."

pity this busy monster, manunkind
e e cummings

pity this busy monster,manunkind

not.   Progress is a comfortable disease:
your victim(death and life safely beyond)

plays with the bigness of his littleness
—electrons deify one razorblade
into a mountainrange;lenses extend

unwish through curving wherewhen till unwish
returns on its unself.
                              A world of made
is not a world of born—pity poor flesh

and trees,poor stars and stones,but never this
fine specimen of hypermagical

ultraomnipotence.   We doctors know

a hopeless case if—listen:there's a hell
of a good universe next door;let's go

Rhymes for a Modern Nursery
Paul Dehn

Hey diddle diddle,
The physicists fiddle,
  The Bleep jumped over the moon.
The little dog laughed to see such fun
  And died the following June.

Jack and Jill went up the hill
  To fetch some heavy water.
They mixed it with the dairy milk
  And killed my youngest daughter.

Two blind mice
See how they run!
They each ran out of the lab with an oath,
For the scientist's wife had injected them both.
Did you ever see such a neat little growth
On two blind mice?

  Little Miss Muffet
  Crouched on a tuffet,
Collecting her shell-shocked wits.
  There dropped (from a glider)
  An H-bomb beside her—
Which frightened Miss Muffet to *bits*.

In a cavern, in a canyon
  Lay an unexploded mine,
Which was tripped on by Miss Shipton.
  Dreadful sorry, Clementine.

To the Moon, 1969

Babette Deutsch

You are not looked for through the smog, you turn blindly
Behind that half palpable poison—you who no longer
Own a dark side, yet whose radiance falters, as if it were
    fading.
Now you have been reached, you are altered
                                beyond belief—
As a stranger spoken to, remaining remote, changes from
    being a stranger.
Astronomers know you a governor of tides, women as the
    mistress
Of menstrual rhythms, poets have called you Hecate,
    Astarte, Artemis—huntress whose arrows
Fuse into a melt of moonlight as they pour
                        upon earth, upon water.
We all know you a danger
    to the thief in the garden, the pilot
In the enemy plane, to lovers embraced in your promise
    of a shining security. Are you a monster?
A noble being? Or simply a planet that men have,
    almost casually, cheapened?
The heavens do not answer.
Once, it was said, the cry: "Pan is dead! Great Pan
    is dead!"
       shivered, howled, through the forests: the gentle
Christ had killed him.
There is no lament for you—who are silent
    as the dead always are.
You have left the mythologies, the old ones, our own.
But, for a few, what has happened is the death of a divine
    Person, is a betrayal, is a piece of
The cruelty that the Universe is witness to
                    while displaying its glories.

Apollo
James Dickey

I   For the First Manned Moon Orbit

*...whoever lives out there in space
must surely call Earth the blue planet...*

—Ed White

So long as the void
Is hysterical, bolted out, you float on nothing

But procedure alone,

Eating, sleeping like a man
Deprived of the weight of his own
And all humanity in the name

Of a new life
             and through this, making new
Time slowly, the moon comes.
                         Its mountains bulge
They crack they hold together
Closer   spreading   smashed crust
Of uncanny rock   ash-glowing   alchemicalizing the sun
With peace: with the peace of a country
Bombed-out by the universe.
                   You lean back from the great light-
shattered face   the pale blaze
of God-stone coming

Close   too close, and the dead seas turn
             The craters hover   turn
             Their dark side to kill
             The radio, and the one voice
Of earth.
             You and your computers have brought out
The silence of mountains the animal
Eye has not seen since the earth split,
Since God first found geometry
             Would move   move
In mysterious ways. You hang

Mysteriously, pulling   the moon-dark pulling,
             And solitude breaks down
Like an electrical system: it is something

Else: nothing is something
Something I am trying
To say O God
Almighty! To come back! To complete the curve to come
back
Singing with procedure   back through the last dark
of the moon, past the dim ritual
Random stones of oblivion, and through
the blinding edge
of Moonlight into the sun

And behold

The blue planet steeped in its dream

Of reality, its calculated vision shaking with
The only love.

II   The Moon Ground

You look as though
You know me, though the world we came from is striking
You in the forehead like Apollo. Buddy,
We have brought the gods. We know what it is to shine
Far off, with earth. We alone
Of all men, could take off
Our shoes and fly. One-sixth of our weight, we have
gathered,
Both of us, under another one
Of us overhead. He is reading the dials he is understanding
Time, to save our lives. You and I are in earth
light and deep moon
shadow on magic ground
Of the dead new world, and we do not but we could
Leap over each other like children in the universal
playground
Of stones
but we must not play
At being here: we must look
We must look for it: the stones are going to tell us
Not the why but the how of all things. Brother, your gold
face flashes
On me. It is the earth. I hear your deep voice rumbling
from the body
Of its huge clothes   Why did we come here
It does not say, but the ground looms, and the secret
Of time is lying

Within amazing reach. It is everywhere
We walk, our glass heads shimmering with absolute heat
And cold. We leap slowly
Along it. We will take back the very stones
Of Time, and build it where we live. Or in the cloud
striped blue of home, will the secret crumble
In our hands with air? Will the moon-plague kill
our children
In their beds? The Human Planet trembles in its black
Sky with what we do   I can see it hanging
in the god-gold only
Brother of your face. We are this world: we are
The only men. What hope is there at home
In the azure of breath, or here with the stone
Dead secret? My massive clothes bubble around me
Crackling with static and Gray's
Elegy helplessly coming
From my heart, and I say I think something
From high school I remember Now
Fades the glimmering landscape on the sight,
and all the air
A solemn stillness holds. Earth glimmers
And in its air-color a solemn stillness holds
It. O brother! Earth-faced god! APOLLO! My eyes
blind
With unreachable tears   my breath goes all over
Me and cannot escape. We are here to do one
Thing only, and that is rock by rock to carry the moon
to take it
Back. Our clothes embrace we cannot touch we cannot
Kneel. We stare into the moon
dust, the earth-blazing ground. We laugh,
with the beautiful craze
Of static. We bend, we pick up stones.

Poem
Rocket

Allen Ginsberg

'Be a Star-screwer!'—Gregory Corso

Old moon my eyes are new moon with human footprint
no longer Romeo Sadface in drunken river Loony Pierre eyebrow,
       goof moon
O possible moon in Heaven we get to first of ageless constellations
       of names
as God is possible as All is possible so we'll reach another life.

Moon politicians earth weeping and warring in eternity

tho not one star disturbed by screaming madmen from Hollywood
oil tycoons from Romania making secret deals with flabby green
       Plutonians—
slave camps on Saturn Cuban revolutions on Mars?
Old life and new side by side, will Catholic church find Christ on
       Jupiter
Mohammed rave in Uranus will Buddha be acceptable on the stolid
       planets
or will we find Zoroastrian temples flowering on Neptune?
What monstrous new ecclesiastical designs on the entire universe
       unfold in the dying Pope's brain?
Scientist alone is true poet he gives us the moon
he promises the stars he'll make us a new universe if it comes to
       that
O Einstein I should have sent you my flaming mss.
O Einstein I should have pilgrimaged to your white hair!
O fellow travellers I write you a poem in Amsterdam in the Cosmos
where Spinoza ground his magic lenses long ago
I write you a poem long ago
already my feet are washed in death
Here I am naked without identity
with no more body than the fine black tracery of pen mark on soft
       paper
as star talks to star multiple beams of sunlight all the same myriad
       thought
in one fold of the universe where Whitman was
and Blake and Shelley saw Milton dwelling as in a starry temple
brooding in his blindness seeing all—
Now at last I can speak to you beloved brothers of an unknown
       moon

real Yous squatting in whatever form amidst Platonic Vapors of
          Eternity
I am another Star.
Will you eat my poems or read them
or gaze with aluminum blind plates on sunless pages?
do you dream or translate & accept data with indifferent droopings
          of antennae?
do I make sense to your flowery green receptor eyesockets? do you
          have visions of God?
Which way will the sunflower turn surrounded by millions of suns?

This is my rocket my personal rocket I send up my message Beyond
Someone to hear me there
My immortality
without steel or cobalt basalt or diamond gold or mercurial fire
without passports filing cabinets bits of paper warheads
without myself finally
pure thought
message all and everywhere the same
I send up my rocket to land on whatever planet awaits it
preferably religious sweet planets no money
fourth dimensional planets where Death shows movies
plants speak (courteously) of ancient physics and poetry itself is
          manufactured by the trees
the final Planet where the Great Brain of the Universe sits waiting
          for a poem to land in His golden pocket
joining the other notes mash-notes love-sighs complaints-musical
          shrieks of despair and the million unutterable thoughts
          of frogs
I send you my rocket of amazing chemical
more than my hair my sperm or the cells of my body
the speeding thought that flies upward with my desire as instantane-
          ous as the universe and faster than light
and leave all other questions unfinished for the moment to turn
          back to sleep in my dark bed on earth.

The Great Bear

John Hollander

Even on clear nights, lead the most supple children
Out onto hilltops, and by no means will
They make it out. Neither the gruff round image

From a remembered page nor the uncertain
Finger tracing that image out can manage
To mark the lines of what ought to be there,
Passing through certain bounding stars, until
The whole massive expanse of bear appear
Swinging, across the ecliptic; and, although
The littlest ones say nothing, others respond,
Making us thankful in varying degrees
For what we would have shown them: "There it is!"
"I see it now!" Even "Very like a bear!"
Would make us grateful. Because there is no bear

We blame our memory of the picture: trudging
Up the dark, starlit path, stooping to clutch
An anxious hand, perhaps the outline faded
Then; perhaps could we have retained the thing
In mind ourselves, with it we might have staged
Something convincing. We easily forget
The huge, clear, homely dipper that is such
An event to reckon with, an object set
Across the space the bear should occupy;
But even so, the trouble lies in pointing
At any stars. For one's own finger aims
Always elsewhere: the man beside one seems
Never to get the point. "No! The bright star
Just above my fingertip." The star,

If any, that he sees beyond one's finger
Will never be the intended one. To bring
Another's eye to bear in such a fashion
On any single star seems to require
Something very like a constellation
That both habitually see at night;
Not in the stars themselves, but in among
Their scatter, perhaps, some old familiar sight
Is always there to take a bearing from.
And if the smallest child of all should cry
Out on the wet, black grass because he sees
Nothing but stars, though claiming that there is
Some bear not there that frightens him, we need
Only reflect that we ourselves have need

Of what is fearful (being really nothing)
With which to find our way about the path
That leads back down the hill again, and with
Which to enable the older children standing
By us to follow what we mean by "This
Star," "That one," or "The other one beyond it."
But what of the tiny, scared ones?—Such a bear,
Who needs it? We can still make do with both
The dipper that we always knew was there
And the bright, simple shapes that suddenly
Emerge on certain nights. To understand
The signs that stars compose, we need depend
Only on stars that are entirely there
And the apparent space between them. There

Never need be lines between them, puzzling
Our sense of what is what. What a star does
Is never to surprise us as it covers
The center of its patch of darkness, sparkling
Always, a point in one of many figures.
One solitary star would be quite useless,
A frigid conjecture, true but trifling;
And any single sign is meaningless
If unnecessary. Crab, bull, and ram,
Or frosty, irregular polygons of our own
Devising, or finally the Great Dark Bear
That we can never quite believe is there—
Having the others, any one of them
Can be dispensed with. The bear, of all of them,

Is somehow most like any one, taken
At random, in that we always tend to say
That just because it might be there; because
Some Ancients really traced it out, a broken
And complicated line, webbing bright stars
And fainter ones together; because a bear
Habitually appeared—then even by day
It is for us a thing that should be there.
We should not want to train ourselves to see it.
The world is everything that happens to
Be true. The stars at night seem to suggest
The shapes of what might be. If it were best,
Even, to have it there (such a great bear!
All hung with stars!), there still would be no bear.

Science
Robinson Jeffers

Man, introverted man having crossed
In passage and but a little with the nature of things this latter century
Has begot giants; but being taken up
Like a maniac with self-love and inward conflicts cannot manage
　　　　his hybrids.
Being used to deal with edgeless dreams,
Now he's bred knives on nature turns them also inward: they have
　　　　thirsty points though.
His mind forbodes his own destruction;
Actaeon who saw the goddess naked among leaves and his hounds
　　　　tore him.
A little knowledge, a pebble from the shingle,
A drop from the oceans: who would have dreamed this infinitely
　　　　little too much?

Planetary Exchange
LeRoi Jones

We are meat in the air. Flying into night space.
Meat complexified by evolution from the original
stuff. Re-evolved and retread, grown, bolted, hands
feet working, like they do, from slimy water, even now,
shot out the peter, through the crisscross round mileage
of speed and explosion.

I am.

Burst of the planet, burst through years I see on a hill
in electric your death and am puzzled. I am. I am. Milliards
of millions of no thing, blank, zero, indian time. To go.
And me. My feeling, and clicking brain. Zero. From nothing.
To nothing. Just speed and adventure, sensation. But truth,
real shit, where is it. I am. I am. I am. Through the dazzling
lives of the planets and stars. I am. sings.

Space
for Martin Green
X. J. Kennedy

I

Who could have thought, but for eight days in space,
The heart might learn to thrive on weightlessness,
As though with no flesh holding it in place,
Yearning by choice, not made to by distress,
Turning in free fall on reprieve from earth
We tug-of-war with daily for the sakes
Of those we long for, those we help bring forth.
How will it be when all the strength it takes
To rip moons loose from planet boughs, or send
Engines of slag careening from their track
Into the unending dark, end over slow end,
Is in the twist that opens a door a crack?
Who will need long to savor his desire
When wishes no more blunt them against bulk,
But pierce straight through; when acts, once dreamt, transpire?
Man may imagine man's own mother's milk.

II

Heads bowed in fetal crouch, the Gemini
Float in their pear-shaped comfort. Data grows
By little clicks, as pine cones, drying free
And dropping, pile up. Enter, through a hose,
Essence of roast beef. Signs that flash ABORT
Bespeak a tube's break. If all hold, instead,
The moon's thin skin shall cringe under their boots—
Just as we always thought, the thing's stone dead.

III

Hope to be disembodied reconciles
Our drifted hearts to that exacting beat.
We clerks-without-church look on while slide-rules
Render our lusts and madnesses concrete.
It may well be that when I rev my car
And let it overtake and pass my thinking,
It's space I crave; when my electric bar
Sets up a moonshot, lemon-oiled and clinking,
And gulp by gulp, I shrug the world's dull weight,
Out after what I had long thought I'd hate.

The Flight of Apollo
Stanley Kunitz

I

   Earth was my home, but even there I was a
stranger. This mineral crust. I walk like a
swimmer. What titanic bombardments in those old
astral wars! I know what I know: I shall never
escape from strangeness or complete my journey.
Think of me as nostalgic, afraid, exalted. I am
your man on the moon, a speck of megalomania, restless for the leap towards island universes pulsing
beyond where the constellations set. Infinite
space overwhelms the human heart, but in the middle
of nowhere life inexorably calls to life. Forward
my mail to Mars. What news from the Great Spiral
Nebula in Andromeda and the Magellanic Clouds?

II

I was a stranger on earth.

Stepping on the moon, I begin

the gay pilgrimage to new

Jerusalems

in foreign galaxies.

Heat. Cold. Craters of silence.

The Sea of Tranquillity

rolling on the shores of entropy.

And, beyond,

the intelligence of the stars.

Star-gaze Poem
Sandford Lyne

In whatever galaxy,
I believe there must be creatures like ourselves,
dreamers,
savages,
poets,
builders of canoes,
far-scattered eyes moving
against the twinkling darkness of the heavens,
pilgrims
in equivalents of dust,
singers of small laments:
the ones we also know,
so well.

So,
for one such as me
this earth is enough of the possibility of grace.

I step out on my small porch, gaze:

these tiny lights, these beacons, bobbing
so far away in the night
we
cannot hear their bells
marking
the shallows of the universe.

Sonnet: To Science
Edgar Allan Poe

Science! true daughter of Old Time thou art!
Who alterest all things with thy peering eyes.
Why preyest thou thus upon the poet's heart,
Vulture, whose wings are dull realities?
How should he love thee? or how deem thee wise,
Who wouldst not leave him in his wandering

To seek for treasure in the jewelled skies,
Albeit he soared with an undaunted wing?
Hast thou not dragged Diana from her car?
And driven the Hamadryad from the wood
To seek a shelter in some happier star?
Hast thou not torn the Naiad from her flood,
The Elfin from the green grass, and from me
The summer dream beneath the tamarind tree?

The Coming
A. Poulin, Jr.

They're coming. Every night
I hear them coming: the whine
of their ships' incredible

annunciations far above
the cornfields at the city's
edge in the enormous dark,

among the stars. Only dogs
and others like me hear them.
Their fantastic engines ring

grace in our bones. One day
they won't simply hover over
fields, visions for a few

insomniacs. But they'll land.
They'll land swiftly, without
warning, right in the centers

of cities. As if promised
for centuries, they will dis-
embark, radiant, inhuman and

glorious as gods stalking virgins.

Earth Will Not Let Go
May Swenson

Earth will not let go our foot
except in her sea
cup she lets us float.

Thistle seed first parachute
and dragonfly the glider
use wind for skate.

So does flying squirrel
and helicopter humming
bird and winged lizard. But wind

is earth's streamered wake
where she whirls and where
in leather suit pterodactyl

and soaring albatross white yacht
proved not grace
nor corpulence to extremes brought

breaks the sac earth wraps
her creatures in marsupial.
"Only mammal capable of true

flight the bat"
equipped with sensory parts
like modern instrument craft

swoops blind of blue
unconscious a closet his orbit
or a cave construes

by echo which is radio.
For Icarus is not yet. The Wright
Aeroplane of 1903

was nothing but a big box kite
"in which the pilot lay prone
head forward his left hand

operating the lever his hips
in a saddle. Shifting
the hips sideways pulled

wires by which the wing tips
were warped and the rudder
turned ... a double action from one

movement controlling balance
and direction." Blue pilot cap
cocked like kingfisher's beak

and heavy round-toed
shoes how droll he wore.
Belly-down on the floor

of the long frail open
box he steered
with his hips' wiggle. Not merely

the magic carpet
but the whole room
he took with him trusting

loops and fickle twists of air.
Lindbergh sat in a wicker chair
in The Cabin of the Spirit

and solo-crossed the Atlantic
in 1927. " ... Impossible
to photograph the cabin in one view

the actual distance from the back
of the seat to the face
of the instrument

board being only thirty-two
inches.... His feet
rested on the rudder control

pedals under the instrument
panel. To see ahead
he either used the periscope

or steered to one side
while looking out the window."
Enclosed in a sort of kayak

in wicker to save weight
the single wing his roof
head bonneted and goggled

like a plucky scaup
with swivelled neck he swam
on swells of ocean wind.

Not unencumbered ever or by
muscle and buoyancy alone
may we climb loose

out of earth's rings
her atmospheres ionospheres
the pastures to our lungs.

Rejecting wings
props wheels for landing all bird
and insect things

John Glenn
snug in the tip of a cartridge
was discharged in 1962

like a spore
within its pod was launched
by blowgun of pure

energy. His lungfood
he took with him. His suit
an embryonic sac

the capsule hugged him
uterus-tight. So tumbling
backward by propulsion he tore

the planet's web to the edge.
But a last elastic caught him
kept him to its circle. Implosion

inbuilt homeward sucked him back
to splashdown in her sea cup
that salty womb

that spewed the stillborn moon.
To that rock Apollo
astronauts would reach

they must take the earthpouch
simulated. And it may not breach.
For earth will not let go

our foot though
headfirst to be born
in angel space

we make wings
jets rockets orbit tables
spider-landing legs.

When I Heard the Learn'd Astronomer
Walt Whitman

When I heard the learn'd astronomer,
When the proofs, the figures, were ranged in columns before me,
When I was shown the charts and diagrams, to add, divide, and
       measure them,
When I sitting heard the astronomer where he lectured with much
      applause in the lecture-room,
How soon unaccountable I became tired and sick,
Till rising and gliding out I wander'd off by myself,
In the mystical moist night-air, and from time to time,
Look'd up in perfect silence at the stars.

Heel & Toe to the End
William Carlos Williams

Gagarin says, in ecstasy,
he could have
gone on forever

he floated
ate and sang
and when he emerged from that

one hundred eight minutes off
the surface of
the earth he was smiling

Then he returned
to take his place
among the rest of us

from all that division and
subtraction a measure
toe and heel

heel and toe he felt
as if he had
been dancing

I am the voice of today, the herald of tomorrow... I coin for you the enchanting tale, the
philosopher's moralizing, and the poet's visions.
... I am the leaden army that conquers the
world—I am TYPE.

FREDERIC WILLIAM GOUDY,
"The Type Speaks"

FICTION

Movable type is all of the things claimed by Frederic William
Goudy—and it is one other thing: a transportation system unlike
any other. It may take us to the edge of space or deep into the
core of our inner selves with equal speed and facility, for the distance
to the first is no greater than the distance to the second. Only the
methods of measuring are different. If we go to distant galaxies or
immediate fears, we cannot escape our present worlds for our bodies
are our worlds. In "The Boredom of Fantasy" (*The Trail of the
Dinosaur and Other Essays*, New York, 1955), Arthur Koestler
declared, "Travel is no cure for melancholia; space-ships and time-
machines are no escape from the human condition. Let Othello subject Desdemona to a lie-detector test; his jealousy will still blind
him to the evidence. Let Oedipus triumph over gravity; he won't
triumph over his fate."

The fantasy-science fiction writer would be the first to agree with
Koestler. The human condition is the first concern of fantasy-science
fiction, for the author seeks not to afford the reader an escape from
it as much as he seeks to make him explore it from a new vantage
point, with new vision. Forward in time, the viewer can look back
at possibility and, in the new view, he may see that thing that he
could not see in close proximity, that thing that caused his human
condition to be less satisfactory than he would have it be. With
new perspective, he may even be able to begin the slow process
involved in any change.

Whether or not he goes all the way back to Plato to begin that
exploration, whether or not he begins with the most recent offering
of the Science Fiction Book Club, he will find the human condition
unchanged and unchanging. Within the confines of these pages,
he will find the earliest story (Mary Wollstonecraft Shelley's *The Last*

Man, 1826) an exploration of the varieties of human ambition and an ecological speculation about the end of mankind. A few years later in time, Nathaniel Hawthorne will show him the folly of possession even as his contemporary Herman Melville reveals the demoniac nature of the machine—"The Tartarus of Maids" being the second half of a two-part work, "The Paradise of Bachelors and the Tartarus of Maids," which contrasts the opulent ease of the wealthy lawyers of London with the mechanical slavery of the female New England factory worker. Edgar Allan Poe's "Mellonta Tauta" (published in 1849) will take the reader on a balloon trip in the year 2848, a trip as satirical as it is emotionally uncomfortable, as humorous as it is perceptive. And H. G. Wells's "The Chronic Argonauts" (1888) will take him through the first version of Wells's classic of science fiction *The Time Machine* which was published in 1895.

As close in time as 1971, the reader will encounter a cure for cancer and watch bonsai performed on the human soul in Theodore Sturgeon's "Slow Sculpture." He will find himself caught in the new wave as Robert Silverberg shows him one extrapolation of the future of black Americans in "Black Is Beautiful" and another of the very distant future of the American Indian in "Sundance." And between the years 1826 and 1971, he will find the fantasy-science fiction voyages of such mainstream writers as Stephen Vincent Benét, Walter Van Tilburg Clark, Howard Fast, Graham Greene, Rudyard Kipling, H. H. Munro (Saki), and Ray Bradbury who is mainstream because he occupies space with J. M. Barrie and A. A. Milne as easily as he does with his contemporaries, J. G. Ballard and Jerome Bixby, who share space in this book with him.

Bradbury's lonely sea monster and Isaac Asimov's alien invader with good intentions are as understandable in their hold on the reader's sympathies as are Mark Clifton's Star Bright and Gordon Dickson's Hilifter, a supra-normally bright kid and a morally legal space hijacker. The security-mad society ("Frances Harkins" by Richard Goggin) and the society terrified by Martians (Howard Koch's radio-script version of H. G. Wells's *The War of the Worlds*) coexist with a society of archaeologists (R. A. Lafferty's "Continued on Next Rock") and a schoolroom in Terre Haute where a strip-teaser materializes in Mr. Tedder's first-period physics class. The ultimate catastrophe (Fritz Leiber's "A Pail of Air") is followed by the ultimate horror (H. P. Lovecraft's "The Outsider") before the ultimate beast appears—or doesn't appear in this case (Katherine MacLean's "Pictures Don't Lie").

The richly gothic style of Lovecraft; the spare, clean style of Arthur C. Clarke; the poetic-prose of Ray Bradbury mark the boundaries of literary excellence in the art and craft of these stories—art and craft as defensible and meritorious as any to be found in mainstream fiction. Dickson's "Hilifter" is as tightly plotted and as action-packed as any Jack London story, and Sturgeon's characterizations are as thoroughly realized in far fewer words as are any of Henry James's. In short, the writing, structure, and literary merit of these stories are as impeccable as any comparable group of stories from the mainstream.

Not that any of them need defending—they just need reading. . . .

Misbegotten Missionary

Isaac Asimov

He had slipped aboard the ship! There had been dozens waiting outside the energy barrier when it had seemed that waiting would do no good. Then the barrier had faltered for a matter of two minutes (which showed the superiority of unified organisms over life fragments) and he was across.

None of the others had been able to move quickly enough to take advantage of the break, but that didn't matter. All alone, he was enough. No others were necessary.

And the thought faded out of satisfaction and into loneliness. It was a terribly unhappy and unnatural thing to be parted from all the rest of the unified organism, to be a life fragment oneself. How could these aliens stand being fragments?

It increased his sympathy for the aliens. Now that he experienced fragmentation himself, he could feel, as though from a distance, the terrible isolation that made them so afraid. It was fear born of that isolation that dictated their actions. What but the insane fear of their condition could have caused them to blast an area, one mile in diameter, into dull-red heat before landing their ship? Even the organized life ten feet deep in the soil had been destroyed in the blast.

He engaged reception, listening eagerly, letting the alien thought saturate him. He enjoyed the touch of life upon his consciousness. He would have to ration that enjoyment. He must not forget himself.

But it could do no harm to listen to thoughts. Some of the fragments of life on the ship thought quite clearly, considering that they were such primitive, incomplete creatures. Their thoughts were like tiny bells.

Roger Oldenn said, "I feel contaminated. You know what I mean? I keep washing my hands and it doesn't help."

Jerry Thorn hated dramatics and didn't look up. They were still maneuvering in the stratosphere of Saybrook's Planet and he preferred to watch the panel dials. He said, "No reason to feel contaminated. Nothing happened."

"I hope not," said Oldenn. "At least they had all the field men discard their spacesuits in the air lock for complete disinfection. They had a radiation bath for all men entering from outside. I *suppose* nothing happened."

"Why be nervous, then?"

"I don't know. I wish the barrier hadn't broken down."

"Who doesn't? It was an accident."

"I wonder." Oldenn was vehement. "I was here when it happened. My shift, you know. There was no reason to overload the power line. There was equipment plugged into it that had no damn business near it. None whatsoever."

"All right. People are stupid."

"Not that stupid. I hung around when the Old Man was checking into the matter. None of them had reasonable excuses. The armor-baking circuits, which were draining off two thousand watts, had been put into the barrier line. They'd been using the second subsidiaries for a week. Why not this time? They couldn't give any reason."

"Can you?"

Oldenn flushed. "No, I was just wondering if the men had been"—he searched for a word—"hypnotized into it. By those things outside."

Thorn's eyes lifted and met those of the other levelly. "I wouldn't repeat that to anyone else. The barrier was down only two minutes. If anything had happened, if even a spear of grass had drifted across it would have shown up in our bacteria cultures within half an hour, in the fruit-fly colonies in a matter of days. Before we got back it would show up in the hamsters, the rabbits, maybe the goats. Just get it through your head, Oldenn, that nothing happened. Nothing."

Oldenn turned on his heel and left. In leaving, his foot came within two feet of the object in the corner of the room. He did not see it.

He disengaged his reception centers and let the thoughts flow past him unperceived. These life fragments were not important, in any case, since they were not fitted for the continuation of life. Even as fragments, they were incomplete.

The other types of fragments now—they were different. He had to be careful of them. The temptation would be great, and he must give no indication, none at all, of his existence on board ship till they landed on their home planet.

He focused on the other parts of the ship, marveling at the diversity of life. Each item, no matter how small, was sufficient to itself. He forced himself to contemplate this, until the unpleasantness of the thought grated on him and he longed for the normality of home.

Most of the thoughts he received from the smaller fragments were vague and fleeting, as you would expect. There wasn't much to be had from them, but that meant their need for completeness was all the greater. It was that which touched him so keenly.

There was the life fragment which squatted on its haunches and fingered the wire netting that enclosed it. Its thoughts were clear, but limited. Chiefly, they concerned the yellow fruit a companion fragment was eating. It wanted the fruit very deeply. Only the wire netting that separated the fragments prevented its seizing the fruit by force.

He disengaged the reception in a moment of complete revulsion. *These fragments competed for food!*

He tried to reach far outward for the peace and harmony of home, but it was already an immense distance away. He could reach only into the nothingness that separated him from sanity.

He longed at the moment even for the feel of the dead soil between the barrier and the ship. He had crawled over it last night. There had been no life upon it, but it had been the soil of home, and on the other side of the barrier there had still been the comforting feel of the rest of organized life.

He could remember the moment he had located himself on the surface of the ship, maintaining a desperate suction grip until the air lock opened. He had entered, moving cautiously between the outgoing feet. There had been an inner lock and that had been passed later. Now he lay here, a life fragment himself, inert and unnoticed.

Cautiously, he engaged reception again at the previous focus. The squatting fragment of life was tugging furiously at the wire netting. It still wanted the other's food, though it was the less hungry of the two.

Larsen said, "Don't feed the damn thing. She isn't hungry; she's just sore because Tillie had the nerve to eat before she herself was crammed full. The greedy ape! I wish we were back home and I never had to look another animal in the face again."

He scowled at the older female chimpanzee frowningly and the chimp mouthed and chattered back to him in full reciprocation.

Rizzo said, "Okay, okay. Why hang around here, then? Feeding time is over. Let's get out."

They went past the goat pens, the rabbit hutches, the hamster cages.

Larsen said bitterly, "You volunteer for an exploration voyage. You're a hero. They send you off with speeches—and make a zoo keeper out of you."

"They give you double pay."

"All right, so what? I didn't sign up just for the money. They said at the original briefing that it was even odds we wouldn't come back, that we'd end up like Saybrook. I signed up because I wanted to do something important."

"Just a bloomin' bloody hero," said Rizzo.

"I'm not an animal nurse."

Rizzo paused to lift a hamster out of the cage and stroke it. "Hey," he said, "did you ever think that maybe one of these hamsters has some cute little baby hamsters inside, just getting started?"

"Wise guy! They're tested every day."

"Sure, sure." He nuzzled the little creature, which vibrated its nose at him. "But just suppose you came down one morning and found them there. New little hamsters looking up at you with soft, green patches of fur where the eyes ought to be."

"Shut up, for the love of Mike," yelled Larsen.

"Little soft, green patches of shining fur," said Rizzo, and put the hamster down with a sudden loathing sensation.

He engaged reception again and varied the focus. There wasn't a specialized life fragment at home that didn't have a rough counterpart on shipboard.

There were the moving runners in various shapes, the moving swimmers, and the moving fliers. Some of the fliers were quite large, with perceptible thoughts; others were small, gauzy-winged creatures. These last transmitted only patterns of sense perception, imperfect patterns at that, and added nothing intelligent of their own.

There were the non-movers, which, like the non-movers at home, were green and lived on the air, water, and soil. These were a mental blank. They knew only the dim, dim consciousness of light, moisture, and gravity.

And each fragment, moving and non-moving, had its mockery of life.

Not yet. Not yet. . . .

He clamped down hard upon his feelings. Once before, these life fragments had come, and the rest at home had tried to help them—too quickly. It had not worked. This time they must wait.

If only these fragments did not discover him.

They had not, so far. They had not noticed him lying in the corner of the pilot room. No one had bent down to pick up and discard him. Earlier, it had meant he could not move. Someone might have turned and stared at the stiff wormlike thing, not quite six inches long. First stare, then shout, and then it would all be over.

But now, perhaps, he had waited long enough. The takeoff was long past. The controls were locked; the pilot room was empty.

It did not take him long to find the chink in the armor leading to the recess where some of the wiring was. They were dead wires.

The front end of his body was a rasp that cut in two a wire of just the right diameter. Then, six inches away, he cut it in two again. He pushed the snipped-off section of the wire ahead of him packing it away neatly and invisibly into a corner of recess. Its outer covering was a brown elastic material and its core was gleaming, ruddy metal. He himself could not produce the core, of course, but that was not necessary. It was enough that the pellicle that covered him had been carefully bred to resemble a wire's surface.

He returned and grasped the cut sections of the wire before and behind. He tightened against them as his little suction disks came into play. Not even a seam showed.

They could not find him now. They could look right at him and see only a continuous stretch of wire.

Unless they looked very closely indeed and noted that, in a certain spot on this wire, there were two tiny patches of soft and shining green fur.

"It is remarkable," said Dr. Weiss, "that little green hairs can do so much."

Captain Loring poured the brandy carefully. In a sense, this was a celebration. They would be ready for the jump through hyperspace in two hours, and after that, two days would see them back on Earth.

"You are convinced, then, the green fur is the sense organ?" he asked.

"It is," said Weiss. Brandy made him come out in splotches, but he was aware of the need of celebration—quite aware. "The experiments were conducted under difficulties, but they were quite significant."

The captain smiled stiffly. " 'Under difficulties' is one way of phrasing it. I would never have taken the chances you did to run them."

"Nonsense. We're all heroes aboard this ship, all volunteers, all great men with trumpet, fife, and fanfarade. You took the chance of coming here."

"You were the first to go outside the barrier."

"No particular risk was involved," Weiss said. "I burned the ground before me as I went, to say nothing of the portable barrier that surrounded me. Nonsense, Captain. Let's all take our medals when we come back; let's take them without attempt at gradation. Besides, I'm a male."

"But you're filled with bacteria to here." The captain's hand made a quick, cutting gesture three inches above his head. "Which makes you as vulnerable as a female would be."

They paused for drinking purposes.

"Refill?" asked the captain.

"No, thanks. I've exceeded my quota already."

"Then one last for the spaceroad." He lifted his glass in the general direction of Saybrook's Planet, no longer visible, its sun only a bright star in the visiplate. "To the little green hairs that gave Saybrook his first lead."

Weiss nodded. "A lucky thing. We'll quarantine the planet, of course."

The captain said, "That doesn't seem drastic enough. Someone might always land by accident someday and not have Saybrook's insight, or his guts. Suppose he did not blow up his ship, as Saybrook did. Suppose he got back to some inhabited place."

The captain was somber. "Do you suppose they might ever develop interstellar travel on their own?"

"I doubt it. No proof, of course. It's just that they have such a completely different orientation. Their entire organization of life has made tools unnecessary. As far as we know, even a stone ax doesn't exist on the planet."

"I hope you're right. Oh, and, Weiss, would you spend some time with Drake?"

"The Galactic Press fellow?"

"Yes. Once we get back, the story of Saybrook's Planet will be released for the public and I don't think it would be wise to oversensationalize it. I've asked Drake to let you consult with him on the story. You're a biologist and enough of an authority to carry weight with him. Would you oblige?"

"A pleasure."

The captain closed his eyes wearily and shook his head.

"Headache, Captain?"

"No. Just thinking of poor Saybrook."

He was weary of the ship. Awhile back there had been a queer, momentary sensation, as though he had been turned inside out. It was alarming and he had searched the minds of the keen-thinkers for an explanation. Apparently the ship had leaped across vast stretches of empty space by cutting across something they knew as "hyper-space." The keen-thinkers were ingenious.

But—he was weary of the ship. It was such a futile phenomenon. These life fragments were skillful in their constructions, yet it was only a measure of their unhappiness, after all. They strove to find in the control of inanimate matter what they could not find in themselves. In their unconscious yearning for completeness, they built machines and scoured space, seeking, seeking. . . .

These creatures, he knew, could never, in the very nature of things, find that for which they were seeking. At least not until such time as he gave it to them. He quivered a little at the thought.

Completeness!

These fragments had no concept of it, even. "Completeness" was a poor word.

In their ignorance they would even fight it. There had been the ship that had come before. The first ship had contained many of the keen-thinking fragments. There had been two varieties, life producers and the sterile ones. (How different this second ship was. The keen-thinkers were all sterile, while the other fragments, the fuzzy-thinkers and the no-thinkers, were all producers of life. It was strange.)

How gladly that first ship had been welcomed by all the planet! He could remember the first intense shock at the realization that the visitors were fragments and not complete. The shock had given way to pity, and the pity to action. It was not certain how they would fit into the community, but there had been no hesitation. All life was sacred and somehow room would have been made for them—for all of them, from the large keen-thinkers to the little multipliers in the darkness.

But there had been a miscalculation. They had not correctly analyzed the course of the fragments' ways of thinking. The keen-thinkers became aware of what had been done and resented it. They were frightened, of course; they did not understand.

They had developed the barrier first, and then, later, had destroyed themselves, exploding their ship to atoms.

Poor, foolish fragments.

This time, at least, it would be different. They would be saved, despite themselves.

John Drake would not have admitted it in so many words, but he was very proud of his skill on the photo-typer. He had a travel-kit model, which was a six-by-eight, featureless dark plastic slab, with cylindrical bulges on either end to hold the roll of thin paper. It fitted into a brown leather case, equipped with a beltlike contraption that held it closely about the waist and at one hip. The whole thing weighed less than a pound.

Drake could operate it with either hand. His fingers would flick quickly and easily, placing their light pressure at exact spots on the blank surface, and, soundlessly, words would be written.

He looked thoughtfully at the beginning of his story, then up at Dr. Weiss. "What do you think, Doc?"

"It starts well."

Drake nodded. "I thought I might as well start with Saybrook himself. They haven't released his story back home yet. I wish I could have seen Saybrook's original report. How did he ever get it through, by the way?"

"As near as I could tell, he spent one last night sending it through the sub-ether. When he was finished, he shorted the motors, and converted the entire ship into a thin cloud of vapor a millionth of a second later. The crew and himself along with it."

"What a man! You were in this from the beginning, Doc?"

"Not from the beginning," corrected Weiss gently. "Only since the receipt of Saybrook's report."

He could not help thinking back. He had read that report, realizing even then how wonderful the planet must have seemed when Saybrook's colonizing expedition first reached it. It was practically a duplicate of Earth, with an abounding plant life and a purely vegetarian animal life.

There had been only the little patches of green fur (how often had he used that phrase in his speaking and thinking!) which seemed strange. No living individual on the planet had eyes. Instead, there was this fur. Even the plants, each blade or leaf or blossom, possessed the two patches of richer green.

Then Saybrook had noticed, startled and bewildered, that there was no conflict for food on the planet. All plants grew pulpy appendages which were eaten by the animals. These were regrown in a matter of hours. No other parts of the plants were touched. It was as though the plants fed the animals as part of the order of nature. And the plants themselves did not grow in overpowering profusion. They might almost have been cultivated, they were spread across the available soil so discriminately.

How much time, Weiss wondered, had Saybrook had to observe the strange law and order on the planet?—the fact that insects kept their numbers reasonable, though no birds ate them; that the rodent-like things did not swarm, though no carnivores existed to keep them in check.

And then there had come the incident of the white rats.

That prodded Weiss. He said, "Oh, one correction, Drake. Hamsters were not the first animals involved. It was the white rats."

"White rats," said Drake, making the correction in his notes.

"Every colonizing ship," said Weiss, "takes a group of white rats for the purpose of testing any alien foods. Rats, of course, are very similar to human beings from a nutritional viewpoint. Naturally, only female white rats are taken."

Naturally. If only one sex was present, there was no danger of unchecked multiplication in case the planet proved favorable. Remember the rabbits in Australia.

"Incidentally, why not use males?" asked Drake.

"Females are hardier," said Weiss, "which is lucky, since that gave the situation away. It turned out suddenly that all the rats were bearing young."

"Right. Now that's where I'm up to, so here's my chance to get some things straight. For my own information, Doc, how did Saybrook find out they were in a family way?"

"Accidentally, of course. In the course of nutritional investigations, rats are dissected for evidence of internal damage. Their condition was bound to be discovered. A few more were dissected; same results. Eventually, all that lived gave birth to young—with *no* male rats aboard!"

"And the point is that all the young were born with little green patches of fur instead of eyes."

"That is correct. Saybrook said so and we corroborate him. After the rats, the pet cat of one of the children was obviously affected. When it finally kittened, the kittens were not born with closed eyes but with little patches of green fur. There was no tomcat aboard.

"Eventually Saybrook had the women tested. He didn't tell them what for. He didn't want to frighten them. Every single one of them was in the early stages of pregnancy, leaving out of consideration those few who had been pregnant at the time of embarkation. Saybrook never waited for any child to be born, of course. He knew they would have no eyes, only shining patches of green fur.

"He even prepared bacterial cultures (Saybrook was a thorough man) and found each bacillus to show microscopic green spots."

Drake was eager. "That goes way beyond our briefing—or, at least, the briefing I got. But granted that life on Saybrook's Planet is organized into a unified whole, how is it done?"

"How? How are your cells organized into a unified whole? Take an individual cell out of your body, even a brain cell, and what is it by itself? Nothing. A little blob of protoplasm with no more capacity for anything human than an amoeba. Less capacity, in fact, since it couldn't live by itself. But put the cells together and you have something that could invent a spaceship or write a symphony."

"I get the idea," said Drake.

Weiss went on, "*All* life on Saybrook's Planet is a *single* organism. In a sense, all life on Earth is too, but it's a fighting dependence, a dog-eat-dog dependence. The bacteria fix nitrogen; the plants fix carbon; animals eat plants and each other; bacterial decay hits everything. It comes full circle. Each grabs as much as it can, and is, in turn, grabbed.

"On Saybrook's Planet, each organism has its place, as each cell in our body does. Bacteria and plants produce food, on the excess of which animals feed, providing in turn carbon dioxide and nitrogenous wastes. Nothing is produced more or less than is needed. The scheme of life is intelligently altered to suit the local environment. No group of life forms multiplies more or less than is needed, just as the cells in our body stop multiplying when there are enough of them for a given purpose. When they don't stop multiplying, we call it cancer. And that's what life on Earth really is, the kind of organic organization we have, compared to that on Saybrook's Planet. One big cancer. Every species, every individual doing its best to thrive at the expense of every other species and individual."

"You sound as if you approve of Saybrook's Planet, Doc."

"I do, in a way. It makes sense out of the business of living. I can see their viewpoint toward us. Suppose one of the cells of your body could be conscious of the efficiency of the human body as compared with that of the cell itself, and could realize that this was only the result of the union of many cells into a higher whole. And then suppose it became conscious of the existence of free-living cells, with bare life and nothing more. It might feel a very strong desire to drag the poor thing into an organization. It might feel sorry for it, feel perhaps a sort of missionary spirit. The things on Saybrook's Planet—or the thing; one should use the singular—feels just that, perhaps."

"And went ahead by bringing about virgin births, eh, Doc? I've got to go easy on that angle of it. Post-office regulations, you know."

"There's nothing ribald about it, Drake. For centuries we've been able to make the eggs of sea urchins, bees, frogs, et cetera develop without the intervention of male fertilization. The touch of a needle was sometimes enough, or just immersion in the proper salt solution. The thing on Saybrook's Planet can cause fertilization by the controlled use of radiant energy. That's why an appropriate energy barrier stops it; interference, you see, or static.

"They can do more than stimulate the division and development of an unfertilized egg. They can impress their own characteristics upon its nucleo-proteins, so that the young are born with the little patches of green fur, which serve as the planet's sense organ and means of communication. The young, in other words, are not individuals, but become part of the thing on Saybrook's Planet. The thing on the planet, not at all incidentally, can impregnate any species—plant, animal, or microscopic."

"Potent stuff," muttered Drake.

"Totipotent," Dr. Weiss said sharply. "Universally potent. Any fragment of it is totipotent. Given time, a single bacterium from Saybrook's Planet can convert *all of Earth* into a single organism! We've got the experimental proof of that."

Drake said unexpectedly, "You know, I think I'm a millionaire, Doc. Can you keep a secret?"

Weiss nodded, puzzled.

"I've got a souvenir from Saybrook's Planet," Drake told him, grinning. "It's only a pebble, but after the publicity the planet will get, combined with the fact that it's quarantined from here on in, the pebble will be all any human being will ever see of it. How much do you suppose I could sell the thing for?"

Weiss stared. "A pebble?" He snatched at the object shown him, a hard, gray ovoid. "You shouldn't have done that, Drake. It was strictly against regulations."

"I know. That's why I asked if you could keep a secret. If you could give me a signed note of authentication——*What's the matter, Doc?*"

Instead of answering, Weiss could only chatter and point. Drake ran over and stared down at the pebble. It was the same as before——

Except that the light was catching it at an angle, and it showed up two little green spots. Look very closely; they were patches of green hairs.

He was disturbed. There was a definite air of danger within the ship. There was the suspicion of his presence aboard. How could that be? He had done nothing yet. Had another fragment of home come aboard and been less cautious? That would be impossible without his knowledge, and though he probed the ship intensely, he found nothing.

And then the suspicion diminished, but it was not quite dead. One of the keen-thinkers still wondered, and was treading close to the truth.

How long before the landing? Would an entire world of life fragments be deprived of completeness? He clung closer to the severed ends of the wire he had been specially bred to imitate, afraid of detection, fearful for his altruistic mission.

Dr. Weiss had locked himself in his own room. They were already within the solar system, and in three hours they would be landing. He had to think. He had three hours in which to decide.

Drake's devilish "pebble" had been part of the organized life on Saybrook's Planet, of course, but it was dead. It was dead when he had first seen it, and if it hadn't been, it was certainly dead after they fed it into the hyper-atomic motor and converted it into a blast of pure heat. And the bacterial cultures still showed normal when Weiss anxiously checked.

That was not what bothered Weiss now.

Drake had picked up the "pebble" during the last hours of the stay on Saybrook's Planet—*after* the barrier breakdown. What if the breakdown had been the result of a slow, relentless mental pressure on the part of the thing on the planet? What if parts of its being waited to invade as the barrier dropped? If the "pebble" had not been fast enough and had moved only after the barrier was re-established, it would have been killed. It would have lain there for Drake to see and pick up.

It was a "pebble," not a natural life form. But did that mean it was not *some* kind of life form? It might have been a deliberate production of the planet's single organism—a creature deliberately designed to look like a pebble, harmless-seeming, unsuspicious. Camouflage, in other words—a shrewd and frighteningly successful camouflage.

Had any other camouflaged creature succeeded in crossing the barrier *before* it was re-established—with a suitable shape filched from the minds of the humans aboard ship by the mind-reading organism of the planet? Would it have the casual appearance of a paperweight? Of an ornamental brass-head nail in the captain's old-fashioned chair? And how would they locate it? Could they search every part of the ship for the telltale green patches—even down to individual microbes?

And why camouflage? Did it intend to remain undetected for a time? Why? So that it might wait for the landing on Earth?

An infection *after landing* could not be cured by blowing up a ship. The bacteria of Earth, the molds, yeasts, and protozoa, would go first. Within a year the non-human young would begin arriving by the uncountable billions.

Weiss closed his eyes and told himself it might not be such a bad thing. There would be no more disease, since no bacterium would multiply at the expense of its host, but instead would be satisfied with its fair share of what was available. There would be no more overpopulation; the hordes of East Asia would decline to adjust themselves to the food supply. There would be no more wars, no crime, no greed.

But there would be no more individuality, either.

Humanity would find security by becoming a cog in a biological machine. A man would be brother to a germ, or to a liver cell.

He stood up. He would have a talk with Captain Loring. They would send their report and blow up the ship, just as Saybrook had done.

He sat down again. Saybrook had had proof, while he had only the conjectures of a terrorized mind, rattled by the sight of two green spots on a pebble. Could he kill the two hundred men on board ship because of a feeble suspicion?

He had to *think!*

He was straining. Why did he have to wait? If he could only welcome those who were aboard now. *Now!*

Yet a cooler, more reasoning part of himself told him that he could not. The little multipliers in the darkness would betray their new status in fifteen minutes, and the keen-thinkers had them under continual observation. Even one mile from the surface of their planet would be too soon, since they might still destroy themselves and their ship out in space.

Better to wait for the main air locks to open, for the planetary air to swirl in with millions of the little multipliers. Better to greet each one of them into the brotherhood of unified life and let them swirl out again to spread the message.

Then it would be done! Another world organized, complete!

He waited. There was the dull throbbing of the engines working mightily to control the slow dropping of the ship; the shudder of contact with planetary surface, then——

He let the jubilation of the keen-thinkers sweep into reception, and his own jubilant thoughts answered them. Soon they would be able to receive as well as himself. Perhaps not these particular fragments, but the fragments that would grow out of those which were fitted for the continuation of life.

The main air locks were about to be opened——

And all thought ceased.

Jerry Thorn thought, Damn it, something's wrong *now*.

He said to Captain Loring, "Sorry. There seems to be a power breakdown. The locks won't open."

"Are you sure, Thorn? The lights are on."

"Yes, sir. We're investigating it now."

He tore away and joined Roger Oldenn at the air-lock wiring box. "What's wrong?"

"Give me a chance; will you?" Oldenn's hands were busy. Then he said, "For the love of Pete, there's a six-inch break in the twenty-amp lead."

"What? That can't be!"

Oldenn held up the broken wires with their clean, sharp, sawn-through ends.

Dr. Weiss joined them. He looked haggard and there was the smell of brandy on his breath.

He said shakily, "What's the matter?"

They told him. At the bottom of the compartment, in one corner, was the missing section.

Weiss bent over. There was a black fragment on the floor of the compartment. He touched it with his finger and it smeared, leaving a sooty smudge on his finger tip. He rubbed it off absently.

There might have been something taking the place of the missing section of wire. Something that had been alive and only looked like wire, yet something that would heat, die, and carbonize in a tiny fraction of a second once the electrical circuit which controlled the air lock had been closed.

He said, "How are the bacteria?"

A crew member went to check, returned and said, "All normal, Doc."

The wires had meanwhile been spliced, the locks opened, and Dr. Weiss stepped out into the anarchic world of life that was Earth.

"Anarchy," he said, laughing a little wildly. "And it will stay that way."

The Garden of Time

J. G. Ballard

Towards evening, when the great shadow of the Palladian villa filled the terrace, Count Axel left his library and walked down the wide rococo steps among the time flowers. A tall, imperious figure in black velvet jacket, a gold tie pin glinting below his George V beard, cane held stiffly in a white-gloved hand, he surveyed the exquisite crystal flowers without emotion, listening to the sounds of his wife's harpsichord, as she played a Mozart rondo in the music room, echo and vibrate through the translucent petals.

The garden of the villa extended for some two hundred yards below the terrace, sloping down to a miniature lake spanned by a white bridge, a slender pavilion on the opposite bank. Axel rarely ventured as far as the lake, most of the time flowers grew in a small grove just below the terrace, sheltered by the high wall which encircled the estate. From the terrace he could see over the wall to the plain beyond, a continuous expanse of open ground that rolled in great swells to the horizon, where it rose slightly before finally dipping from sight. The plain surrounded the house on all sides, its drab emptiness emphasising the seclusion and mellowed magnificence of the villa. Here, in the garden, the air seemed brighter, the sun warmer, while the plain was always dull and remote.

As was his custom before beginning his regular evening stroll, Count Axel looked out across the plain to the final rise, where the horizon was illuminated like a distant stage by the fading sun. As the Mozart chimed delicately around him, flowing from his wife's graceful hands, he saw that the advance columns of an enormous army were moving slowly over the horizon. At first glance, the long ranks seemed to be progressing in orderly lines, but on closer inspection, it was apparent that, like the obscured detail of a Goya landscape, the army was composed of a vast confused throng of people,

62

men and women, interspersed with a few soldiers in ragged uniforms, pressing forward in a disorganised tide. Some laboured under heavy loads suspended from crude yokes around their necks, others struggled with cumbersome wooden carts, their hands wrenching at the wheel spokes, a few trudged on alone, but all moved on at the same pace, bowed backs illuminated in the fleeting sun.

The advancing throng was almost too far away to be visible, but even as Axel watched, his expression aloof yet observant, it came perceptibly nearer, the vanguard of an immense rabble appearing from below the horizon. At last, as the daylight began to fade, the front edge of the throng reached the crest of the first swell below the horizon, and Axel turned from the terrace and walked down among the time flowers.

The flowers grew to a height of about six feet, their slender stems, like rods of glass, bearing a dozen leaves, the once transparent fronds frosted by the fossilised veins. At the peak of each stem was the time flower, the size of a goblet, the opaque outer petals enclosing the crystal heart. Their diamond brilliance contained a thousand faces, the crystal seeming to drain the air of its light and motion. As the flowers swayed slightly in the evening air, they glowed like flame-tipped spears.

Many of the stems no longer bore flowers, and Axel examined them all carefully, a note of hope now and then crossing his eyes as he searched for any further buds. Finally he selected a large flower on the stem nearest the wall, removed his gloves and with his strong fingers snapped it off.

As he carried the flower back onto the terrace, it began to sparkle and deliquesce, the light trapped within the core at last released. Gradually the crystal dissolved, only the outer petals remaining intact, and the air around Axel became bright and vivid, charged with slanting rays that flared away into the waning sunlight. Strange shifts momentarily transformed the evening, subtly altering its dimensions of time and space. The darkened portico of the house, its patina of age stripped away, loomed with a curious spectral whiteness as if suddenly remembered in a dream.

Raising his head, Axel peered over the wall again. Only the furthest rim of the horizon was lit by the sun, and the great throng, which before had stretched almost a quarter of the way across the plain, had now receded to the horizon, the entire concourse abruptly flung back in a reversal of time, and now appearing to be stationary.

The flower in Axel's hand had shrunk to the size of a glass thimble, the petals contracting around the vanishing core. A faint sparkle flickered from the centre and extinguished itself, and Axel felt the flower melt like an ice-cold bead of dew in his hand.

Dusk closed across the house, sweeping its long shadows over the plain, the horizon merging into the sky. The harpsichord was silent, and the time flowers, no longer reflecting its music, stood motionlessly, like an embalmed forest.

For a few minutes Axel looked down at them, counting the flowers which remained, then greeted his wife as she crossed the terrace, her brocade evening dress rustling over the ornamental tiles.

"What a beautiful evening, Axel." She spoke feelingly, as if she were thanking her husband personally for the great ornate shadow across the lawn and the dark brilliant air. Her face was serene and intelligent, her hair, swept back behind her head into a jewelled clasp, touched with silver. She wore her dress low across her breast, revealing a long slender neck and high chin. Axel surveyed her with fond pride. He gave her his arm and together they walked down the steps into the garden.

"One of the longest evenings this summer," Axel confirmed, adding: "I picked a perfect flower, my dear, a jewel. With luck it should last us for several days." A frown touched his brow, and he glanced involuntarily at the wall. "Each time now they seem to come nearer."

His wife smiled at him encouragingly and held his arm more tightly.

Both of them knew that the time garden was dying.

Three evenings later, as he had estimated (though sooner than he secretly hoped), Count Axel plucked another flower from the time garden.

When he first looked over the wall the approaching rabble filled the distant half of the plain, stretching across the horizon in an unbroken mass. He thought he could hear the low, fragmentary sounds of voices carried across the empty air, a sullen murmur punctuated by cries and shouts, but quickly told himself that he had imagined them. Luckily, his wife was at her harpsichord, and the rich contrapuntal patterns of a Bach fugue cascaded lightly across the terrace, masking other noises.

Between the house and the horizon the plain was divided into four huge swells, the crest of each one clearly visible in the slanting light. Axel had promised himself that he would never count them, but the number was too small to remain unobserved, particularly when it so obviously marked the progress of the advancing army. By now the forward line had passed the first crest and was well on its way to the second; the main bulk of the throng pressed behind it, hiding the crest and the even vaster concourse spreading from the horizon. Looking to left and right of the central body, Axel could see the apparently limitless extent of the army. What had seemed at first to be the central mass was no more than a minor advance guard, one of many similar arms reaching across the plain. The true centre had not yet emerged, but from the rate of extension Axel estimated that when it finally reached the plain it would completely cover every foot of ground.

Axel searched for any large vehicles or machines, but all was amorphous and uncoordinated as ever. There were no banners or flags, no mascots or pike-bearers. Heads bowed, the multitude pressed on, unaware of the sky.

Suddenly, just before Axel turned away, the forward edge of the throng appeared on top of the second crest, and swarmed down across the plain. What astounded Axel was the incredible distance it had covered while out of sight. The figures were now twice the size, each one clearly within sight.

Quickly, Axel stepped from the terrace, selected a time flower from the garden and tore it from the stem. As it released its compacted light, he returned to the terrace. When the flower had shrunk to a frozen pearl in his palm he looked out at the plain, with relief saw that the army had retreated to the horizon again.

Then he realised that the horizon was much nearer than previously, and that what he assumed to be the horizon was the first crest.

When he joined the Countess on their evening walk he told her nothing of this, but she could see behind his casual unconcern and did what she could to dispel his worry.

Walking down the steps, she pointed to the time garden. "What a wonderful display, Axel. There are so many flowers still."

Axel nodded, smiling to himself at his wife's attempt to reassure him. Her use of 'still' had revealed her own unconscious anticipation of the end. In fact a mere dozen flowers remained of the many hundred that had grown in the garden, and several of these were little more than buds—only three or four were fully grown. As they walked down to the lake, the Countess's dress rustling across the cool turf, he tried to decide whether to pick the larger flowers first or leave them to the end. Strictly, it would be better to give the smaller flowers additional time to grow and mature, and this advantage would be lost if he retained the larger flowers to the end, as he wished to do, for the final repulse. However, he realised that it mattered little either way; the garden would soon die and the smaller flowers required far longer than he could give them to accumulate their compressed cores of time. During his entire lifetime he had failed to notice a single evidence of growth among the flowers. The larger blooms had always been mature, and none of the buds had shown the slightest development.

Crossing the lake, he and his wife looked down at their reflections in the still black water. Shielded by the pavilion on one side and the high garden wall on the other, the villa in the distance, Axel felt composed and secure, the plain with its encroaching multitude a nightmare from which he had safely awakened. He put one arm around his wife's smooth waist and pressed her affectionately to his shoulder, realising that he had not embraced her for several years, though their lives together had been timeless and he could remember as if yesterday when he first brought her to live in the villa.

"Axel," his wife asked with sudden seriousness. "Before the garden dies... may I pick the last flower?"

Understanding her request, he nodded slowly.

One by one over the succeeding evenings, he picked the remaining flowers, leaving a single small bud which grew just below the terrace for his wife. He took the flowers at random, refusing to count or ration them, plucking two or three of the smaller buds at the same time when necessary. The approaching horde had now reached the second and third crests, a vast concourse of labouring humanity that blotted out the horizon. From the terrace Axel could see clearly the shuffling, straining ranks moving down into the hollow towards the final crest, and occasionally the sounds of their voices carried across to him, interspersed with cries of anger and the cracking of whips. The wooden carts lurched from side to side on tilting wheels, their drivers struggling to control them. As far as Axel could tell, not a single member of the throng was aware of its overall direction. Rather, each one blindly moved forward across the ground directly below the heels of the person in front of him, and the only unity was that of the cumulative compass. Pointlessly, Axel hoped that the true centre, far below the horizon, might be moving in a different direction, and that gradually the multitude would alter course, swing away from the villa and recede from the plain like a turning tide.

On the last evening but one, as he plucked the time flower, the forward edge of the rabble had reached the third crest, and was swarming past it. While he waited for the Countess, Axel looked down at the two flowers left, both small buds which would carry them back through only a few minutes of the next evening. The glass stems of the dead flowers reared up stiffly into the air, but the whole garden had lost its bloom.

Axel passed the next morning quietly in his library, sealing the rarer of his manuscripts into the glass-topped cases between the galleries. He walked slowly down the portrait corridor, polishing each of the pictures carefully, then tidied his desk and locked the door behind him. During the afternoon he busied himself in the drawing rooms, unobtrusively assisting his wife as she cleaned their ornaments and straightened the vases and busts.

By evening, as the sun fell behind the house, they were both tired and dusty, and neither had spoken to the other all day. When his wife moved towards the music room, Axel called her back.

"Tonight we'll pick the flowers together, my dear," he said to her evenly. "One for each of us."

He peered only briefly over the wall. They could hear, less than half a mile away, the great dull roar of the ragged army, the ring of iron and lash, pressing on towards the house.

Quickly, Axel plucked his flower, a bud no bigger than a sapphire. As it flickered softly, the tumult outside momentarily receded, then began to gather again.

Shutting his ears to the clamour, Axel looked around at the villa, counting the six columns in the portico, then gazed out across the lawn at the silver disc of the lake, its bowl reflecting the last evening light, and at the shadows moving between the tall trees, lengthening across the crisp turf. He lingered over the bridge where he and his wife had stood arm in arm for so many summers—

"Axel!"

The tumult outside roared into the air, a thousand voices bellowed only twenty or thirty yards away. A stone flew over the wall and landed among the time flowers, snapping several of the brittle stems. The Countess ran towards him as a further barrage rattled along the wall. Then a heavy tile whirled through the air over their heads and crashed into one of the conservatory windows.

"Axel!" He put his arms around her, straightening his silk cravat when her shoulder brushed it between his lapels.

"Quickly, my dear, the last flower!" He led her down the steps and through the garden. Taking the stem between her jewelled fingers, she snapped it cleanly, then cradled it within her palms.

For a moment the tumult lessened slightly and Axel collected himself. In the vivid light sparkling from the flower he saw his wife's white, frightened eyes. "Hold it as long as you can, my dear, until the last grain dies."

Together they stood on the terrace, the Countess clasping the brilliant dying jewel, the air closing in upon them as the voices outside mounted again. The mob was battering at the heavy iron gates, and the whole villa shook with the massive impact.

While the final glimmer of light sped away, the Countess raised her palms to the air, as if releasing an invisible bird, then in a final access of courage put her hands in her husband's, her smile as radiant as the vanished flower.

"Oh, Axel!" she cried.

Like a sword, the darkness swooped down across them.

Heaving and swearing, the outer edge of the mob reached the knee-high remains of the wall enclosing the ruined estate, hauled their carts over it and along the dry ruts of what had once been an ornate drive. The ruin, formerly a spacious villa, barely interrupted the ceaseless tide of humanity. The lake was empty, fallen trees rotting at its bottom, an old bridge rusting into it. Weeds

flourished among the long grass in the lawn, overrunning the ornamental pathways and carved stone screens.

Much of the terrace had crumbled, and the main section of the
mob cut straight across the lawn, bypassing the gutted villa, but
one or two of the more curious climbed up and searched among
the shell. The doors had rotted from their hinges and the floors
had fallen through. In the music room an ancient harpsichord had
been chopped into firewood, but a few keys still lay among the
dust. All the books had been toppled from the shelves in the library,
the canvases had been slashed, and gilt frames littered the floor.

As the main body of the mob reached the house, it began to cross
the wall at all points along its length. Jostled together, the people
stumbled into the dry lake, swarmed over the terrace and pressed
through the house towards the open doors on the north side.

One area alone withstood the endless wave. Just below the terrace,
between the wrecked balcony and the wall, was a dense, six-
foot-high growth of heavy thornbushes. The barbed foliage formed
an impenetrable mass, and the people passing stepped around it
carefully, noticing the belladonna entwined among the branches.
Most of them were too busy finding their footing among the
upturned flagstones to look up into the centre of the thornbushes,
where two stone statues stood side by side, gazing out over the
grounds from their protected vantage point. The larger of the figures
was the effigy of a bearded man in a high-collared jacket, a cane
under one arm. Beside him was a woman in an elaborate full-skirted
dress, her slim serene face unmarked by the wind and rain. In her
left hand she lightly clasped a single rose, the delicately formed petals so thin as to be almost transparent.

As the sun died away behind the house a single ray of light
glanced through a shattered cornice and struck the rose, reflected
off the whorl of petals onto the statues, lighting up the grey stone
so that for a fleeting moment it was indistinguishable from the long-
vanished flesh of the statues' originals.

By the Waters of Babylon

Stephen Vincent Benét

The north and the west and the south are good hunting ground, but it is forbidden to go east. It is forbidden to go to any of the Dead Places except to search for metal, and then he who touches the metal must be a priest or the son of a priest. Afterward, both the man and the metal must be purified. These are the rules and the laws; they are well made. It is forbidden to cross the great river and look upon the place that was the Place of the Gods; this is most strictly forbidden. We do not even say its name, though we know its name. It is there that spirits live, and demons; it is there that there are the ashes of the Great Burning. These things are forbidden; they have been forbidden since the beginning of time.

My father is a priest; I am the son of a priest. I have been in the Dead Places near us with my father. At first I was afraid. When my father went into the house to search for the metal, I stood by the door, and my heart felt small and weak. It was a dead man's house, a spirit house. It did not have the smell of man, though there were old bones in a corner. But it is not fitting that a priest's son should show fear. I looked at the bones in the shadow and kept my voice still.

Then my father came out with the metal—a good, strong piece. He looked at me with both eyes, but I had not run away. He gave me the metal to hold. I took it and did not die. So he knew that I was truly his son and would be a priest in my time. That was when I was very young. Nevertheless, my brothers would not have done it, though they are good hunters. After that, they gave me the good piece of meat and the warm corner by the fire. My father watched over me; he was glad that I should be a priest. But when I boasted or wept without reason, he punished me more strictly than my brothers. That was right.

After a time, I myself was allowed to go into the dead houses and search for metal. So I learned the ways of those houses, and if I saw bones, I was no longer afraid. The bones are light and old; sometimes they will fall into dust if you touch them. But that is a great sin.

I was taught the chants and the spells. I was taught how to stop the running of blood from a wound, and many secrets. A priest must know many secrets—that was what my father said. If the hunters think we know all things by chants and spells, they may believe so; it does not hurt them. I was taught how to read in the old books and how to make the old writings; that was hard and took a long time. My knowledge made me happy; it was like a fire in my heart. Most of all, I liked to hear of the Old Days and the stories of the gods. I asked myself many questions that I could not answer, but it was good to ask them. At night, I would lie awake and listen to the wind; it seemed to me that it was the voice of the gods as they flew through the air.

We are not ignorant like the Forest People; our women spin wool on the wheel, our priests wear a white robe. We do not eat grubs from the tree, we have not forgotten the old writings, although they are hard to understand. Nevertheless, my knowledge and my lack of knowledge burned in me; I wished to know more. When I was a man at last, I came to my father and said, "It is time for me to go on my journey. Give me leave."

He looked at me for a long time, stroking his beard, then he said at last, "Yes. It is time."

That night, in the house of priesthood, I asked for and received purification. My body hurt, but my spirit was a cool stone. It was my father himself who questioned me about my dreams.

He bade me look into the smoke of the fire and see. I saw and told what I saw. It was what I have always seen—a river and, beyond it, a great Dead Place, and in it the gods walking. I have always thought about that. His eyes were stern when I told him; he was no longer my father but a priest. He said, "This is a strong dream."

"It is mine," I said, while the smoke waved and my head felt light. They were singing the Star song in the outer chamber, and it was like the buzzing of bees in my head.

He asked me how the gods were dressed, and I told him how they were dressed. We know how they were dressed from the book, but I saw them as if they were before me. When I had finished, he threw the sticks three times and studied them as they fell.

"This is a very strong dream," he said. "It may eat you up."

"I am not afraid," I said, and looked at him with both eyes. My voice sounded thin in my ears, but that was because of the smoke.

He touched me on the breast and the forehead. He gave me the bow and the three arrows.

"Take them," he said. "It is forbidden to travel east. It is forbidden to cross the great river. It is forbidden to go to the Place of the Gods. All these things are forbidden."

"All these things are forbidden," I said, but it was my voice that spoke, and not my spirit. He looked at me again.

"My son," he said, "once I had young dreams. If your dream does not eat you up, you may be a great priest. If it eats you, you are still my son. Now go on your journey."

I went fasting, as is the law. My body hurt, but not my heart. When the dawn came, I was out of sight of the village. I prayed and purified myself, waiting for a sign. The sign was an eagle. It flew east.

Sometimes signs are sent by bad spirits. I waited again on the flat rock, fasting, taking no food. I was very still; I could feel the sky above me and the earth beneath. I waited till the sun was beginning to sink. Then three deer passed in the valley, going east; they did not wind me or see me. There was a white fawn with them—a very great sign.

I followed them at a distance, waiting for what would happen. My heart was troubled about going east, yet I knew that I must go. My head hummed with my fasting; I did not even see the panther spring upon the white fawn. But before I knew it, the bow was in my hand. I shouted and the panther lifted his head from the fawn. It is not easy to kill a panther with one arrow, but the arrow went through his eye and into his brain. He died as he tried to spring; he rolled over, tearing at the ground. Then I knew I was meant to go east; I knew that was my journey. When the night came, I made my fire and roasted meat.

It is eight suns' journey to the east and a man passes by many Dead Places. The Forest People are afraid of them, but I am not. Once I made my fire on the edge of a Dead Place at night and, next morning, in the dead house, I found a good knife, little rusted. That was small to what came afterward, but it made my heart feel big. Always when I looked for game, it was in front of my arrow, and twice I passed hunting parties of the Forest People without their knowing. So I knew my magic was strong and my journey clean, in spite of the law.

Toward the setting of the eighth sun, I came to the banks of the great river. It was half a day's journey after I had left the god road; we do not use the god roads now, for they are falling apart into great blocks of stone, and the forest is safer going. A long way off, I had seen the water through trees, but the trees were thick. At last I came out upon an open place at the top of a cliff. There was the great river below, like a giant in the sun. It is very long, very wide. It could eat all the streams we know and still be thirsty. Its name is Ou-dis-sun, the Sacred, the Long. No man of my tribe has seen it; not even my father, the priest. It was magic and I prayed.

Then I raised my eyes and looked south. It was there—the Place of the Gods.

How can I tell what it was like? You do not know. It was there, in the red light, and they were too big to be houses. It was there, with the red light upon it, mighty and ruined. I knew that in another moment the gods would see me. I covered my eyes with my hands and crept back into the forest.

Surely, that was enough to do, and live. Surely, it was enough to spend the night upon the cliff. The Forest People themselves do not come near. Yet, all through the night, I knew that I should have to cross the river and walk in the Place of the Gods, although the gods ate me up. My magic did not help me at all, and yet there was a fire in my bowels, a fire in my mind. When the sun rose, I thought, "My journey has been clean. Now I will go home from my journey." But even as I thought so, I knew I could not. If I went to the Place of the Gods, I would surely die, but if I did not go, I could never be at peace with my spirit again. It is better to lose one's life than one's spirit, if one is a priest and the son of a priest.

Nevertheless, as I made the raft, the tears ran out of my eyes. The Forest People could have killed me without fight, if they had come upon me then, but they did not come. When the raft was made, I said the sayings for the dead and painted myself for death. My heart was cold as a frog and my knees like water, but the burning in my mind would not let me have peace. As I pushed the raft from the shore, I began my death song; I had the right. It was a fine song. I sang:

> "I am John, son of John. My people are the Hill People.
>   They are the men.
> I go into the Dead Places, but I am not slain.
> I take the metal from the Dead Places, but I am not
>   blasted.
> I travel upon the god roads and am not afraid. E-yah!
>   I have killed the panther, I have killed the fawn!
> E-yah! I have come to the great river. No man has come
>   there before.
> It is forbidden to go east, but I have gone; forbidden
>   to go on the great river, but I am there.
> Open your hearts you spirits, and hear my song.

> Now I go to the Place of the Gods; I shall not return.
> My body is painted for death and my limbs weak, but
> my heart is big as I go to the Place of the Gods!"

All the same, when I came to the Place of the Gods, I was afraid, afraid. The current of the great river is very strong; it gripped my raft with its hands. That was magic, for the river itself is wide and calm. I could feel evil spirits about me in the bright morning; I could feel their breath on my neck as I was swept down the stream. Never have I been so much alone. I tried to think of my knowledge, but it was a squirrel's heap of winter nuts. There was no strength in my knowledge any more and I felt small and naked as a new-hatched bird—alone upon the great river, the servant of the gods.

Yet, after a while, my eyes were opened and I saw. I saw both banks of the river; I saw that once there had been god roads across it, though now they were broken and fallen like broken vines. Very great they were, and wonderful and broken—broken in the time of the Great Burning, when the fire fell out of the sky. And always the current took me nearer to the Place of the Gods, and the huge ruins rose higher before my eyes.

I do not know the customs of rivers; we are the People of the Hills. I tried to guide my raft with the pole, but it spun about. I thought the river meant to take me past the Place of the Gods and out into the Bitter Water of the legends.

I grew angry then; my heart felt strong. I said aloud, "I am a priest and the son of a priest!" The gods heard me; they showed me how to paddle with the pole on one side of the raft. The current changed itself; I drew near to the Place of the Gods.

When I was very near, my raft struck and turned over. I can swim in our lakes; I swam to the shore. There was a great spike of rusted metal sticking out into the river; I hauled myself up upon it and sat there, panting. I had saved my bow and two arrows and the knife I found in the Dead Place, but that was all. My raft went whirling downstream toward the Bitter Water. I looked after it, and thought if it had trod me under, at least I would be safely dead. Nevertheless, when I had dried my bowstring and restrung it, I walked forward to the Place of the Gods.

It felt like ground underfoot; it did not burn me. It is not true—what some of the tales say—that the ground there burns forever, for I have been there. Here and there were the marks and stains of the Great Burning on the ruins, that is true. But they were old marks and old stains. It is not true, either—what some of our priests say—that it is an island covered with fogs and enchantments. It is not. It is a great Dead Place—greater than any Dead Place we know. Everywhere in it there are god roads; though most are cracked and broken. Everywhere there are the ruins of the high towers of the gods.

How shall I tell what I saw? I went carefully, my strung bow in my hand, my skin ready for danger. There should have been the wailings of spirits and the shrieks of demons, but there were not. It was very silent and sunny where I had landed; the wind and the rain and the birds that drop seeds had done their work; the grass grew in the cracks of the broken stone. It is a fair island; no wonder the gods built there. If I had come there a god, I also would have built.

How shall I tell what I saw? The towers are not all broken; here and there one still stands, like a great tree in a forest, and the birds nest high. But the towers themselves look blind, for the gods are gone. I saw a fish hawk, catching fish in the river. I saw a little dance of white butterflies over a great heap of broken stones and columns. I went there and looked about me; there was a carved stone with cut letters, broken in half. I can read letters, but I could not understand these. They said UBTREAS. There was also the shattered image of a man or a god. It had been made of white stone and he wore his hair tied back like a woman's. His name was ASHING, as I read on the cracked half of a stone. I thought it wise to pray to ASHING, though I do not know that god.

How shall I tell what I saw? There was no smell of man left on stone or metal. Nor were there many trees in that wilderness of stone. There are many pigeons, nesting and dropping in the towers; the gods must have loved them, or, perhaps, they used them for sacrifice. There are wild cats that roam the god roads, green-eyed, unafraid of man. At night they wail like demons, but they are not demons. The wild dogs are more dangerous, for they hunt in a pack, but them I did not meet till later. Everywhere there are the carved stones, carved with magical numbers and words.

I went north; I did not try to hide myself. When a god or a demon saw me, then I would die, but meanwhile I was no longer afraid. My hunger for knowledge burned in me; there was so much that I could not understand. After a while, I knew that my belly was hungry. I could have hunted for my meat, but I did not hunt. It is known that the gods did not hunt as we do; they got their food from enchanted boxes and jars. Sometimes these are still found in the Dead Places. Once, when I was a child and foolish, I opened such a jar and tasted it and found the food sweet. But my father found out and punished me for it strictly; for, often, that food is death. Now, though, I had long gone past what was forbidden, and I entered the likeliest towers, looking for the food of the gods.

I found it at last in the ruins of a great temple in the midcity. A mighty temple it must have been, for the roof was painted like the sky at night with its stars—that much I could see, though the colors were faint and dim. It went down into great caves and tunnels—perhaps they kept their slaves there. But when I started to climb down, I heard the squeaking of rats, so I did not go. Rats are unclean, and there must have been many tribes of them, from the squeaking. But near there I found food, in the heart of a ruin, behind a door that still opened. I ate only the fruits from the jars; they had a very sweet taste. There was drink, too, in bottles of glass; the drink of the gods is strong and made my head swim. After I had eaten and drunk, I slept on the top of a stone, my bow at my side.

When I woke, the sun was low. Looking down from where I lay, I saw a dog sitting on his haunches. His tongue hung out of his mouth; he looked as if he were laughing. He was a big dog with a gray-brown coat, as big as a wolf. I sprang up and shouted at him, but he did not move; he just sat there as if he were laughing. I did not like that. When I reached for a stone to throw, he moved swiftly out of the way of the stone. He was not afraid of me; he looked at me as if I were meat. No doubt I could have killed him with an arrow, but I did not know if there were others. Moreover, night was falling.

I looked about me. Not far away there was a great, broken god road, leading north. The towers were high enough, but not so high, and while many of the dead houses were wrecked, there were some that stood. I went toward this god road, keeping to the heights of the ruins, while the dog followed. When I had reached the god road, I saw that there were others behind him. If I had slept later, they would have come upon me asleep and torn out my throat. As it was, they were sure enough of me; they did not hurry. When I went into the dead house, they kept watch at the entrance; doubtless they thought they would have a fine hunt. But a dog cannot open a door, and I knew, from the books, that the gods did not like to live on the ground but on high.

I had just found a door I could open when the dogs decided to rush. Ha! They were surprised when I shut the door in their faces; it was a good door, of strong metal. I could hear their foolish baying beyond it, but I did not stop to answer them. I was in darkness; I found stairs and climbed. There were many stairs, turning around till my head was dizzy. At the top was another door; I found the knob and opened it. I was in a long small chamber. On one side of it was a bronze door that could not be opened, for it had no handle. Perhaps there was a magic word to open it, but I did not have the word. I turned to the door in the opposite side of the wall. The lock of it was broken and I opened it and went in.

Within, there was a place of great riches. The god who lived there must have been a powerful god. The first room was a small anteroom. I waited there for some time, telling the spirits of the place that

I came in peace and not as a robber. When it seemed to me that they had had time to hear me, I went on. Ah, what riches! Few, even, of the windows had been broken; it was all as it had been. The great windows that looked over the city had not been broken at all, though they were dusty and streaked with many years. There were coverings on the floors, the colors not greatly faded, and the chairs were soft and deep. There were pictures upon the walls, very strange, very wonderful. I remember one of a bunch of flowers in a jar; if you came close to it, you could see nothing but bits of color, but if you stood away from it, the flowers might have been picked yesterday. It made my heart feel strange to look at this picture, and to look at the figure of a bird, in some hard clay, on a table and see it so like our birds. Everywhere there were books and writings, many in tongues that I could not read. The god who lived there must have been a wise god, and full of knowledge. I felt I had a right there, as I sought knowledge also.

Nevertheless, it was strange. There was a washing place, but no water; perhaps the gods washed in air. There was a cooking place, but no wood, and though there was a machine to cook food, there was no place to put fire in it. Nor were there candles or lamps. There were things that looked like lamps, but they had neither oil nor wick. All these things were magic, but I touched them and lived; the magic had gone out of them. Let me tell one thing to show. In the washing place, a thing said "Hot," but it was not hot to the touch; another thing said "Cold," but it was not cold. This must have been a strong magic, but the magic was gone. I do not understand—they had ways—I wish that I knew.

It was close and dry and dusty in the house of the god. I have said the magic was gone, but that is not true; it had gone from the magic things, but it had not gone from the place. I felt the spirits about me, weighing upon me. Nor had I ever slept in a Dead Place before, and yet, tonight, I must sleep there. When I thought of it, my tongue felt dry in my throat, in spite of my wish for knowledge. Almost I would have gone down again and faced the dogs, but I did not.

I had not gone through all the rooms when the darkness fell. When it fell, I went back to the big room looking over the city and made fire. There was a place to make fire and a box with wood in it, though I do not think they cooked there. I wrapped myself in a floor covering and slept in front of the fire.

Now I tell what is very strong magic. I woke in the midst of the night. When I woke, the fire had gone out and I was cold. It seemed to me that all around me there were whisperings and voices. I closed my eyes to shut them out. Some will say that I slept again, but I do not think that I slept. I could feel the spirits drawing my spirit out of my body as a fish is drawn on a line.

Why should I lie about it? I am a priest and the son of a priest. If there are spirits, as they say, in the small Dead Places near us, what spirits must there not be in that great Place of the Gods? And would not they wish to speak after such long years? I know that I felt myself drawn as a fish is drawn on a line. I had stepped out of my body; I could see my body asleep in front of the cold fire, but it was not I. I was drawn to look out upon the city of the gods.

It should have been dark, for it was night, but it was not dark. Everywhere there were lights—lines of light, circles and blurs of light—ten thousand torches would not have been the same. The sky itself was alight; you could barely see the stars for the glow in the sky. I thought to myself, "This is strong magic," and trembled. There was a roaring in my ears like the rushing of rivers. Then my eyes grew used to the light and my ears to the sound. I knew that I was seeing the city as it had been when the gods were alive.

That was a sight indeed! Yes, that was a sight! I could not have seen it in the body—my body would have died. Everywhere went the gods, on foot and in chariots; there were gods beyond number and counting, and their chariots blocked the streets. They had turned night to day for their pleasure; they did not sleep with the sun. The noise of their coming and going was the noise of many waters. It was magic what they could do; it was magic what they did.

I looked out of another window; the great vines of their bridges were mended and the god roads went east and west. Restless, restless were the gods, and always in motion! They burrowed tunnels under rivers; they flew in the air. With unbelievable tools they did giant works; no part of the earth was safe from them, for, if they wished for a thing, they summoned it from the other side of the world. And always, as they labored and rested, as they feasted and made love, there was a drum in their ears—the pulse of the giant city, beating and beating like a man's heart.

Were they happy? What is happiness to the gods? They were great, they were mighty, they were wonderful and terrible. As I looked upon them and their magic, I felt like a child; but a little more, it seemed to me, and they would lay their hands upon the stars. I saw them with wisdom beyond wisdom and knowledge beyond knowledge. And yet not all they did was well done, and yet their wisdom could not but grow until all was peace.

Then I saw their fate come upon them, and that was terrible past speech. It came upon them as they walked the streets of their city. I have been in the fights with the Forest People; I have seen men die. But this was not like that. When gods war with gods, they use weapons we do not know. It was fire falling out of the sky and a mist that poisoned. It was the time of the Great Burning and the Destruction. They ran about like ants in the streets—poor gods, poor gods! Then the towers began to fall. A few escaped—yes, a

few. The legends tell it. But even after the city had become a Dead
Place, for many years the poison was still in the ground. I saw it
happen; I saw the last of them die. It was darkness over the broken
city and I wept.

All this, I saw. I saw it as I have told it; though not in the body.
When I woke in the morning, I was hungry, but I did not think
first of my hunger, for my heart was perplexed and confused. I knew
the reason for the Dead Places, but I did not see why it had happened. It seemed to me it should not have happened, with all the
magic they had. I went through the house looking for an answer.
There was so much in the house I could not understand, and yet
I am a priest and the son of a priest. It was like being on the side
of the great river at night, with no light to show the way.

Then I saw the dead god. He was sitting in his chair by the window, in a room I had not entered before, and, for the first moment,
I thought that he was alive. Then I saw the skin on the back of
his hand—it was like dry leather. The room was shut, hot and dry;
no doubt that had kept him as he was. At first I was afraid to
approach him; then the fear left me. He was sitting, looking out
over his city; he was dressed in the clothes of the gods. His age
was neither young nor old; I could not tell his age. But there was
wisdom in his face, and great sadness. You could see that he would
not run away. He had sat at his window, watching his city die;
then he himself had died. But it is better to lose one's life than
one's spirit; and you could see from the face that his spirit had
not been lost. I knew that, if I touched him, he would fall into dust;
and yet, there was something unconquered in the face.

That is all of my story, for then I knew he was a man. I knew
then that they had been men, neither gods nor demons. It is a great
knowledge, hard to tell and believe. They were men; they went a
dark road, but they were men. I had no fear after that. I had no
fear going home, though twice I fought off the dogs and once I
was hunted for two days by the Forest People. When I saw my
father again, I prayed and was purified.

He touched my lips and my breast; he said, "You went away
a boy. You come back a man and a priest."

I said, "Father, they were men! I have been in the Place of the
Gods and seen it! Now slay me if it is the law, but still I know
they were men."

He looked at me out of both eyes. He said, "The law is not always
the same shape. You have done what you have done. I could not
have done it in my time, but you come after me. Tell!"

I told and he listened. After that, I wished to tell all the people,
but he showed me otherwise. He said, "Truth is a hard deer to
hunt. If you eat too much truth at once, you may die of the truth.
It was not idly that our fathers forbade the Dead Places." He was

right; it is better the truth should come little by little. I have learned that, being a priest. Perhaps, in the old days they ate knowledge too fast.

Nevertheless, we make a beginning. It is not for the metal alone we go to the Dead Places now; there are the books and the writings. They are hard to learn. And the magic tools are broken, but we can look at them and wonder. At least, we make a beginning. And, when I am chief priest we shall go beyond the great river. We shall go to the Place of the Gods—the place Newyork—not one man but a company. We shall walk in the broken streets and say its name aloud, without fear. We shall look for the images of gods and find the god ASHING and the others—the gods LINCOLN and BILTMORE and MOSES. But they were men who built the city; they were not gods or demons. They were men. I remember the dead man's face. They were men who were here before us. We must build again.

It's a <u>Good</u> Life

Jerome Bixby

Aunt Amy was out on the front porch, rocking back and forth in the highbacked chair and fanning herself, when Bill Soames rode his bicycle up the road and stopped in front of the house.

Perspiring under the afternoon "sun," Bill lifted the box of groceries out of the big basket over the front wheel of the bike, and came up the front walk.

Little Anthony was sitting on the lawn, playing with a rat. He had caught the rat down in the basement—he had made it think that it smelled cheese, the most rich-smelling and crumbly-delicious cheese a rat had ever thought it smelled, and it had come out of its hole, and now Anthony had hold of it with his mind and was making it do tricks.

When the rat saw Bill Soames coming, it tried to run, but Anthony thought at it, and it turned a flip-flop on the grass and lay trembling, its eyes gleaming in small black terror.

Bill Soames hurried past Anthony and reached the front steps, mumbling. He always mumbled when he came to the Fremont house, or passed it by, or even thought of it. Everybody did. They thought about silly things, things that didn't mean very much, like two-and-two-is-four-and-twice-is-eight and so on; they tried to jumble up their thoughts and keep them skipping back and forth, so Anthony couldn't read their minds. The mumbling helped. Because if Anthony got anything strong out of your thought, he might take a notion to do something about it—like curing your wife's sick headaches or your kid's mumps, or getting your old cow back on schedule, or fixing the privy. And while Anthony mightn't actually mean any harm, he couldn't be expected to have much notion of what was the right thing to do in such cases.

That was if he liked you. He might try to help you, in his way. And that could be pretty horrible.

If he didn't like you . . . well, that could be worse.

Bill Soames set the box of groceries on the porch railing, and stopped his mumbling long enough to say, "Everythin' you wanted, Miss Amy."

"Oh, fine, William," Amy Fremont said lightly. "My ain't it terrible hot today?"

Bill Soames almost cringed. His eyes pleaded with her. He shook his head violently *no*, and then interrupted his mumbling again, though obviously he didn't want to: "Oh, don't say that, Miss Amy ... it's fine, just fine. A real *good* day!"

Amy Fremont got up from the rocking chair, and came across the porch. She was a tall woman, thin, a smiling vacancy in her eyes. About a year ago, Anthony had gotten mad at her, because she'd told him he shouldn't have turned the cat into a cat-rug, and although he had always obeyed her more than anyone else, which was hardly at all, this time he'd snapped at her. With his mind. And that had been the end of Amy Fremont's bright eyes, and the end of Amy Fremont as everyone had known her. And that was when word got around in Peaksville (population: 46) that even the members of Anthony's own family weren't safe. After that, everyone was twice as careful.

Someday Anthony might undo what he'd done to Aunt Amy. Anthony's Mom and Pop hoped he would. When he was older, and maybe sorry. If it was possible, that is. Because Aunt Amy had changed a lot, and besides, now Anthony wouldn't obey anyone.

"Land alive, William," Aunt Amy said, "you don't have to mumble like that. Anthony wouldn't hurt you. My goodness, Anthony likes you!" She raised her voice and called to Anthony, who had tired of the rat and was making it eat itself. "Don't you, dear? Don't you like Mr. Soames?"

Anthony looked across the lawn at the grocery man—a bright, wet, purple gaze. He didn't say anything. Bill Soames tried to smile at him. After a second Anthony returned his attention to the rat. It had already devoured its tail, or at least chewed it off—for Anthony had made it bite faster than it could swallow, and little pink and red furry pieces lay around it on the green grass. Now the rat was having trouble reaching its hindquarters.

Mumbling silently, thinking of nothing in particular as hard as he could, Bill Soames went stiff-legged down the walk, mounted his bicycle and pedalled off.

"We'll see you tonight, William," Aunt Amy called after him.

As Bill Soames pumped the pedals, he was wishing deep down that he could pump twice as fast, to get away from Anthony all the faster, and away from Aunt Amy, who sometimes just forgot how *careful* you had to be. And he shouldn't have thought that. Because Anthony caught it. He caught the desire to get away from the Fremont house as if it was something *bad*, and his purple gaze

blinked, and he snapped a small, sulky thought after Bill Soames
—just a small one, because he was in a good mood today, and
besides, he liked Bill Soames, or at least didn't dislike him, at least
today. Bill Soames wanted to go away—so, petulantly, Anthony
helped him.

Pedalling with superhuman speed—or rather, appearing to,
because in reality the bicycle was pedalling *him*—Bill Soames vanished down the road in a cloud of dust, his thin, terrified wail drifting back across the summerlike heat.

Anthony looked at the rat. It had devoured half its belly, and
had died from pain. He thought it into a grave out deep in the
cornfield—his father had once said, smiling, that he might as well
do that with the things he killed—and went around the house, casting his odd shadow in the hot, brassy light from above.

In the kitchen, Aunt Amy was unpacking the groceries. She put
the Mason-jarred goods on the shelves, and the meat and milk in
the icebox, and the beet sugar and coarse flour in big cans under
the sink. She put the cardboard box in the corner, by the door,
for Mr. Soames to pick up next time he came. It was stained and
battered and torn and worn fuzzy, but it was one of the few left
in Peaksville. In faded red letters it said *Campbell's Soup*. The last
cans of soup, or of anything else, had been eaten long ago, except
for a small communal hoard which the villagers dipped into for special occasions—but the box lingered on, like a coffin, and when it
and the other boxes were gone, the men would have to make some
out of wood.

Aunt Amy went out in back, where Anthony's Mom—Aunt Amy's
sister—sat in the shade of the house, shelling peas. The peas, every
time Mom ran a finger along a pod, went *lollop-lollop-lollop* into
the pan on her lap.

"William brought the groceries," Aunt Amy said. She sat down
wearily in the straight-backed chair beside Mom, and began fanning
herself again. She wasn't really old; but ever since Anthony had
snapped at her with his mind, something had seemed to be wrong
with her body as well as her mind, and she was tired all the time.

"Oh, good," said Mom. *Lollop* went the fat peas into the pan.

Everybody in Peaksville always said "Oh fine," or "Good," or
"Say, that's swell!" when almost anything happened or was mentioned—even unhappy things like accidents or even deaths. They'd
always say "Good," because if they didn't try to cover up how they
really felt, Anthony might overhear with his mind and then nobody
knew what might happen. Like the time Mrs. Kent's husband, Sam,
had come walking back from the graveyard, because Anthony liked
Mrs. Kent and had heard her mourning.

Lollop.

"Tonight's television night," said Aunt Amy. "I'm glad. I look forward to it so much every week. I wonder what we'll see tonight?"

"Did Bill bring the meat?" asked Mom.

"Yes." Aunt Amy fanned herself, looking up at the featureless brassy glare of the sky. "Goodness, it's so hot! I wish Anthony would make it just a little cooler—"

"_Amy!_"

"Oh!" Mom's sharp tone had penetrated, where Bill Soames' agonized expression had failed. Aunt Amy put one thin hand to her mouth in exaggerated alarm. "Oh ... I'm sorry, dear." Her pale blue eyes shuttled around, right and left, to see if Anthony was in sight. Not that it would make any difference if he was or wasn't—he didn't have to be near you to know what you were thinking. Usually, though, unless he had his attention on somebody, he would be occupied with thoughts of his own.

But some things attracted his attention—you could never be sure just what.

"This weather's just _fine_," Mom said.

Lollop.

"Oh, yes," Aunt Amy said. "It's a wonderful day. I wouldn't want it changed for the world!"

Lollop.

Lollop.

"What time is it?" Mom asked.

Aunt Amy was sitting where she could see through the kitchen window to the alarm clock on the shelf above the stove. "Four-thirty," she said.

Lollop.

"I want tonight to be something special," Mom said. "Did Bill bring a good lean roast?"

"Good and lean, dear. They butchered just today, you know, and sent us over the best piece."

"Dan Hollis will be _so_ surprised when he finds out that tonight's television party is a birthday party for him too!"

"Oh _I_ think he will! Are you sure nobody's told him?"

"Everybody swore they wouldn't."

"That'll be real nice," Aunt Amy nodded, looking off across the cornfield. "A birthday party."

"Well—" Mom put the pan of peas down beside her, stood up and brushed her apron. "I'd better get the roast on. Then we can set the table." She picked up the peas.

Anthony came around the corner of the house. He didn't look at them, but continued on down through the carefully kept garden— _all_ the gardens in Peaksville were carefully kept, very carefully kept —and went past the rusting, useless hulk that had been the Fremont family car, and went smoothly over the fence and out into the cornfield.

"Isn't this a lovely day!" said Mom, a little loudly, as they went toward the back door.

Aunt Amy fanned herself. "A beautiful day, dear. Just *fine!*"

Out in the cornfield, Anthony walked between the tall, rustling rows of green stalks. He liked to smell the corn. The alive corn overhead, and the old dead corn underfoot. Rich Ohio earth, thick with weeds and brown, dry-rotting ears of corn, pressed between his bare toes with every step—he had made it rain last night so everything would smell and feel nice today.

He walked clear to the edge of the cornfield, and over to where a grove of shadowy green trees covered cool, moist, dark ground and lots of leafy undergrowth and jumbled moss-covered rocks and a small spring that made a clear, clean pool. Here Anthony liked to rest and watch the birds and insects and small animals that rustled and scampered and chirped about. He liked to lie on the cool ground and look up through the moving greenness overhead, and watch the insects flit in the hazy soft sunbeams that stood like slanting, glowing bars between ground and treetops. Somehow, he liked the thoughts of the little creatures in this place better than the thoughts outside; and while the thoughts he picked up here weren't very strong or very clear, he could get enough out of them to know what the little creatures liked and wanted, and he spent a lot of time making the grove more like what they wanted it to be. The spring hadn't always been here; but one time he had found thirst in one small furry mind, and had brought subterranean water to the surface in a clear cold flow, and had watched blinking as the creature drank, feeling its pleasure. Later he had made the pool, when he found a small urge to swim.

He had made rocks and trees and bushes and caves, and sunlight here and shadows there, because he had felt in all the tiny minds around him the desire—or the instinctive want—for this kind of resting place, and that kind of mating place, and this kind of place to play, and that kind of home.

And somehow the creatures from all the fields and pastures around the grove had seemed to know that this was a good place, for there were always more of them coming in—every time Anthony came out here there were more creatures than the last time, and more desires and needs to be tended to. Every time there would be some kind of creature he had never seen before, and he would find its mind, and see what it wanted, and then give it to it.

He liked to help them. He liked to feel their simple gratification.

Today, he rested beneath a thick elm, and lifted his purple gaze to a red and black bird that had just come to the grove. It twittered on a branch over his head, and hopped back and forth, and thought its tiny thoughts, and Anthony made a big, soft nest for it, and pretty soon it hopped in.

A long, brown, sleek furred animal was drinking at the pool. Anthony found its mind next. The animal was thinking about a smaller creature that was scurrying along the ground on the other side of the pool, grubbing for insects. The little creature didn't know that it was in danger. The long, brown animal finished drinking and tensed its legs to leap, and Anthony thought it into a grave in the cornfield.

He didn't like those kinds of thoughts. They reminded him of the thoughts outside the grove. A long time ago some of the people outside had thought that way about *him*, and one night they'd hidden and waited for him to come back from the grove—and he'd just thought them all into the cornfield. Since then, the rest of the people hadn't thought that way—at least, very clearly. Now their thoughts were all mixed up and confusing whenever they thought about him or near him, so he didn't pay much attention.

He watched all the birds and insects and furry creatures for a while, and played with a bird, making it soar and dip and streak madly around tree trunks until, accidentally, when another bird caught his attention for a moment, he ran it into a rock. Petulantly, he thought the rock into a grave in the cornfield; but he couldn't do anything more with the bird. Not because it was dead, though it was; but because it had a broken wing. So he went back to the house. He didn't feel like walking back through the cornfield, so he just *went* to the house, right down into the basement.

It was nice down here. Nice and dark and damp and sort of fragrant, because once Mom had been making preserves in a rack along the far wall and then she'd stopped coming down ever since Anthony had started spending time here, and the preserves had spoiled and leaked down and spread over the dirt floor, and Anthony liked the smell.

He caught another rat, making it smell cheese, and after he played with it, he thought it into a grave right beside the long animal he'd killed in the grove. Aunt Amy hated rats, and so he killed a lot of them, because he liked Aunt Amy most of all and sometimes did things that Aunt Amy wanted. Her mind was more like the little furry minds out in the grove. She hadn't thought anything bad at all about him for a long time.

After the rat, he played with a big black spider in the corner under the stairs, making it run back and forth until its web shook and shimmered in the light from the cellar window like a reflection in silvery water. Then he drove fruit flies into the web until the spider was frantic trying to wind them all up. The spider liked flies, and its thoughts were stronger than theirs, so he did it. There was something bad in the way it liked flies, but it wasn't clear—and besides, Aunt Amy hated flies too.

He heard footsteps overhead—Mom moving around in the kitchen. He blinked his purple gaze, and almost decided to make her hold still—but instead he went up to the attic, and, after looking out the circular window for a while at the front lawn and the dusty road and Henderson's tip-waving wheatfield beyond, he curled into an unlikely shape and went partly to sleep.

Soon people would be coming for television, he heard Mom think.

He went more to sleep. He liked television night. Aunt Amy had always liked television a lot, so one time he had thought some for her, and a few other people had been there at the time, and Aunt Amy had felt disappointed when they wanted to leave. He'd done something to them for that—and now everybody came to television.

He liked all the attention he got when they did.

Anthony's father came home around six-thirty, looking tired and dirty and bloody. He'd been over in Dunn's pasture with the other men, helping pick out the cow to be slaughtered this month and doing the job, and then butchering the meat and salting it away in Soames's icehouse. Not a job he cared for, but every man had his turn. Yesterday, he had helped scythe down old McIntyre's wheat. Tomorrow, they would start threshing. By hand. Everything in Peaksville had to be done by hand.

He kissed his wife on the cheek and sat down at the kitchen table. He smiled and said, "Where's Anthony?"

"Around someplace," Mom said.

Aunt Amy was over at the wood-burning stove, stirring the big pot of peas. Mom went back to the oven and opened it and basted the roast.

"Well, it's been a *good* day," Dad said. By rote. Then he looked at the mixing bowl and breadboard on the table. He sniffed at the dough. "M'm," he said. "I could eat a loaf all by myself, I'm so hungry."

"No one told Dan Hollis about its being a birthday party, did they?" his wife asked.

"Nope. We kept as quiet as mummies."

"We've fixed up such a lovely surprise!"

"Um? What?"

"Well... you know how much Dan likes music. Well, last week Thelma Dunn found a *record* in her attic!"

"No!"

"Yes! And we had Ethel sort of ask—you know, without really *asking*—if he had that one. And he said no. Isn't that a wonderful surprise?"

"Well, now, it sure is. A record, imagine! That's a real nice thing to find! What record is it?"

"Perry Como, singing *You Are My Sunshine.*"

"Well, I'll be darned. I always liked that tune." Some raw carrots were lying on the table. Dad picked up a small one, scrubbed it on his chest, and took a bite. "How did Thelma happen to find it?"

"Oh, you know—just looking around for new things."

"M'm." Dad chewed the carrot. "Say, who has that picture we found a while back? I kind of liked it—that old clipper sailing along—"

"The Smiths. Next week the Sipichs get it and they give the Smiths old McIntyre's music-box, and we give the Sipichs—" And she went down the tentative order of things that would exchange hands among the women at church this Sunday.

He nodded. "Looks like we can't have the picture for a while, I guess. Look, honey, you might try to get that detective book back from the Reillys. I was so busy the week we had it, I never got to finish all the stories."

"I'll try," his wife said doubtfully. "But I hear the van Husens have a stereoscope they found in the cellar." Her voice was just a little accusing. "They had it two whole months before they told anybody about it—"

"Say," Dad said, looking interested. "That'd be nice, too. Lots of pictures?"

"I suppose so. I'll see on Sunday. I'd like to have it—but we still owe the van Husens for their canary. I don't know why that bird had to pick *our* house to die... it must have been sick when we got it. Now there's just no satisfying Betty van Husen—she even hinted she'd like our *piano* for a while!"

"Well, honey, you try for the stereoscope—or just anything you think we'll like." At last he swallowed the carrot. It had been a little young and tough. Anthony's whims about the weather made it so that people never knew what crops would come up, or what shape they'd be in if they did. All they could do was plant a lot; and always enough of something came up any one season to live on. Just once there had been a grain surplus; tons of it had been hauled to the edge of Peaksville and dumped off into the nothingness. Otherwise, nobody could have breathed when it started to spoil.

"You know," Dad went on. "It's nice to have the new things around. It's nice to think that there's probably still a lot of stuff nobody's found yet, in cellars and attics and barns and down behind things. They help, somehow. As much as anything can help—"

"Sh-h!" Mom glanced nervously around.

"Oh," Dad said, smiling hastily. "It's all right! The new things are *good!* It's *nice* to be able to have something around you've never seen before, and know that something you've given somebody else is making them happy ... that's a real *good* thing."

"A good thing," his wife echoed.

"Pretty soon," Aunt Amy said, from the stove, "there won't be any more new things. We'll have found everything there is to find. Goodness, that'll be too bad—"

"*Amy!*"

"Well—" Her pale eyes were shallow and fixed, a sign of her recurrent vagueness. "It will be kind of a shame—no new things—"

"Don't *talk* like that," Mom said, trembling. "Amy, be *quiet!*"

"It's *good*," said Dad, in the loud familiar, wanting-to-be-overheard tone of voice. "Such talk is *good*. It's okay, honey—don't you see? It's good for Amy to talk any way she wants. It's good for her to feel bad. Everything's good. Everything *has* to be good ..."

Anthony's mother was pale. And so was Aunt Amy—the peril of the moment had suddenly penetrated the clouds surrounding her mind. Sometimes it was difficult to handle words so that they might not prove disastrous. You just never *knew*. There were so many things it was wise not to say, or even think—but remonstration for saying or thinking them might be just as bad, if Anthony heard and decided to do anything about it. You could just never tell what Anthony was liable to do.

Everything had to be good. Had to be fine just as it was, even if it wasn't. Always. Because any change might be worse. So terribly much worse.

"Oh, my goodness, yes, of course it's good," Mom said. "You talk any way you want to, Amy, and it's just fine. Of course, you want to remember that some ways are *better* than others ..."

Aunt Amy stirred the peas, fright in her pale eyes.

"Oh, yes," she said. "But I don't feel like talking right now. It ... it's *good* that I don't feel like talking."

Dad said tiredly, smiling, "I'm going out and wash up."

They started arriving around eight o'clock. By that time, Mom and Aunt Amy had the big table in the dining room set, and two more tables off to the side. The candles were burning, and the chairs situated, and Dad had a big fire going in the fireplace.

The first to arrive were the Sipichs, John and Mary. John wore his best suit, and was well-scrubbed and pink-faced after his day in McIntyre's pasture. The suit was neatly pressed, but getting threadbare at elbows and cuffs. Old McIntyre was working on a loom, designing it out of schoolbooks, but so far it was slow going. McIntyre was a capable man with wood and tools, but a loom was a big order when you couldn't get metal parts. McIntyre had been one of the ones who, at first, had wanted to try to get Anthony to make things the villagers needed, like clothes and canned goods and medical supplies and gasoline. Since then, he felt that what had happened to the whole Terrance family and Joe Kinney was his fault, and he worked hard trying to make it up to the rest of them. And since then, no one had tried to get Anthony to do anything.

Mary Sipich was a small, cheerful woman in a simple dress. She immediately set about helping Mom and Aunt Amy put the finishing touches on the dinner.

The next arrivals were the Smiths and Dunns, who lived right next to each other down the road, only a few yards from the nothingness. They drove up in the Smiths' wagon, drawn by their old horse.

Then the Reillys showed up, from across the darkened wheatfield, and the evening really began. Pat Reilly sat down at the big upright in the front room, and began to play from the popular sheet music on the rack. He played softly, as expressively as he could—and nobody sang. Anthony liked piano playing a whole lot, but not singing; often he would come up from the basement, or down from the attic, or just *come*, and sit on top of the piano, nodding his head as Pat played *Lover* or *Boulevard of Broken Dreams* or *Night and Day*. He seemed to prefer ballads, sweet-sounding songs—but the one time somebody had started to sing, Anthony had looked over from the top of the piano and done something that made everybody afraid of singing from then on. Later they'd decided that the piano was what Anthony had heard first, before anybody had ever tried to sing, and now anything else added to it didn't sound right and distracted him from his pleasure.

So, every television night, Pat would play the piano, and that was the beginning of the evening. Wherever Anthony was, the music would make him happy, and put him in a good mood, and he would know that they were gathering for television and waiting for him.

By eight-thirty everybody had shown up, except for the seventeen children and Mrs. Soames who was off watching them in the schoolhouse at the far end of town. The children of Peaksville were never, never allowed near the Fremont house—not since little Fred Smith had tried to play with Anthony on a dare. The younger children weren't even told about Anthony. The others had mostly forgotten about him, or were told that he was a nice, nice goblin but they must never go near him.

Dan and Ethel Hollis came late, and Dan walked in not suspecting a thing. Pat Reilly had played the piano until his hands ached—he'd worked pretty hard with them today—and now he got up, and everybody gathered around to wish Dan Hollis a happy birthday.

"Well, I'll be darned," Dan grinned. "This is swell, I wasn't expecting this at all ... gosh, this is *swell!*"

They gave him his presents—mostly things they had made by hand, though some were things that people had possessed as their own and now gave him as his. John Sipich gave him a watch charm, hand-carved out of a piece of hickory wood. Dan's watch had broken down a year or so ago, and there was nobody in the village who knew how to fix it, but he still carried it around because it had been his grandfather's and was a fine old heavy thing of gold and silver. He attached the charm to the chain, while everybody laughed and said John had done a nice job of carving. Then Mary Sipich gave him a knitted necktie, which he put on, removing the one he'd worn.

The Reillys gave him a little box they had made, to keep things in. They didn't say what things, but Dan said he'd keep his personal jewelry in it. The Reillys had made it out of a cigar box, carefully peeled of its paper and lined on the inside with velvet. The outside had been polished, and carefully if not expertly carved by Pat—but his carving got complimented too. Dan Hollis received many other gifts—a pipe, a pair of shoelaces, a tie pin, a knit pair of socks, some fudge, a pair of garters made from old suspenders.

He unwrapped each gift with vast pleasure, and wore as many of them as he could right there, even the garters. He lit up the pipe, and said he'd never had a better smoke, which wasn't quite true, because the pipe wasn't broken in yet. Pete Manners had had it lying around ever since he'd received it as a gift four years ago from an out-of-town relative who hadn't known he'd stopped smoking.

Dan put the tobacco into the bowl very carefully. Tobacco was precious. It was only pure luck that Pat Reilly had decided to try to grow some in his backyard just before what had happened to Peaksville had happened. It didn't grow very well, and then they had to cure it and shred it and all, and it was just precious stuff. Everybody in town used wooden holders old McIntyre had made, to save on butts.

Last of all, Thelma Dunn gave Dan Hollis the record she had found.

Dan's eyes misted even before he opened the package. He knew it was a record.

"Gosh," he said softly. "What one is it? I'm almost afraid to look . . ."

"You haven't got it, darling," Ethel Hollis smiled. "Don't you remember, I asked about *You Are My Sunshine?*"

"Oh, gosh," Dan said again. Carefully he removed the wrapping and stood there fondling the record, running his big hands over the worn grooves with their tiny, dulling crosswise scratches. He looked around the room, eyes shining, and they all smiled back, knowing how delighted he was.

"Happy birthday, darling!" Ethel said, throwing her arms around him and kissing him.

He clutched the record in both hands, holding it off to one side
as she pressed against him. "Hey," he laughed, pulling back his
head. "Be careful... I'm holding a priceless object!" He looked
around again, over his wife's arms, which were still around his neck.
His eyes were hungry. "Look... do you think we could play it?
Lord, what I'd give to hear some new music... just the first part,
the orchestra part, before Como sings?"

Faces sobered. After a minute, John Sipich said, "I don't think
we'd better, Dan. After all, we don't know just where the singer
comes in—it'd be too much of a chance. Better wait till you get
home."

Dan Hollis reluctantly put the record on the buffet with all his
other presents. "It's *good*," he said automatically, but disappointedly, "that I can't play it here."

"Oh, yes," said Sipich. "It's good." To compensate for Dan's disappointed tone, he repeated, "It's *good*."

They ate dinner, the candles lighting their smiling faces, and ate
it all right down to the last delicious drop of gravy. They complimented Mom and Aunt Amy on the roast beef, and the peas and
carrots, and the tender corn on the cob. The corn hadn't come from
the Fremont's cornfield, naturally—everybody knew what was out
there, and the field was going to weeds.

Then they polished off the dessert—homemade ice cream and
cookies. And then they sat back, in the flickering light of the candles,
and chatted waiting for television.

There never was a lot of mumbling on television night—everybody
came and had a good dinner at the Fremonts', and that was nice,
and afterwards there was television, and nobody really thought
much about that—it just had to be put up with. So it was a pleasant
enough get-together, aside from your having to watch what you
said just as carefully as you always did every place. If a dangerous
thought came into your mind, you just started mumbling, even right
in the middle of a sentence. When you did that, the others just
ignored you until you felt happier again and stopped.

Anthony liked television night. He had done only two or three
awful things on television night in the whole past year.

Mom had put a bottle of brandy on the table, and they each had
a tiny glass of it. Liquor was even more precious than tobacco. The
villagers could make wine, but the grapes weren't right, and certainly the techniques weren't, and it wasn't very good wine. There
were only a few bottles of real liquor left in the village—four rye,
three Scotch, three brandy, nine real wine and half a bottle of Dram-
buie belonging to old McIntyre (only for marriages)—and when
those were gone, that was it.

Afterward, everybody wished that the brandy hadn't been
brought out. Because Dan Hollis drank more of it than he should

have, and mixed it with a lot of the homemade wine. Nobody thought anything about it at first, because he didn't show it much outside, and it was his birthday party and a happy party, and Anthony liked these get-togethers and shouldn't see any reason to do anything even if he was listening.

But Dan Hollis got high, and did a fool thing. If they'd seen it coming, they'd have taken him outside and walked him around.

The first thing they knew, Dan stopped laughing right in the middle of the story about how Thelma Dunn had found the Perry Como record and dropped it and it hadn't broken because she'd moved faster than she ever had before in her life and caught it. He was fondling the record again, and looking longingly at the Fremonts' gramophone over in the corner, and suddenly he stopped laughing and his face got slack, and then it got ugly, and he said, "Oh, *Christ!*"

Immediately the room was still. So still they could hear the whirring movement of the grandfather's clock out in the hall. Pat Reilly had been playing the piano, softly. He stopped, his hands poised over the yellowed keys.

The candles on the dining-room table flickered in a cool breeze that blew through the lace curtains over the bay window.

"Keep playing, Pat," Anthony's father said softly.

Pat started again. He played *Night and Day*, but his eyes were sidewise on Dan Hollis, and he missed notes.

Dan stood in the middle of the room, holding the record. In his other hand he held a glass of brandy so hard his hand shook.

They were all looking at him.

"*Christ,*" he said again, and he made it sound like a dirty word.

Reverend Younger, who had been talking with Mom and Aunt Amy by the dining-room door, said "Christ" too—but he was using it in a prayer. His hands were clasped, and his eyes were closed.

John Sipich moved forward. "Now, Dan . . . it's *good* for you to talk that way. But you don't want to talk too much, you know."

Dan shook off the hand Sipich put on his arm.

"Can't even play my record," he said loudly. He looked down at the record, and then around at their faces. "Oh, my *God* . . ."

He threw the glassful of brandy against the wall. It splattered and ran down the wallpaper in streaks.

Some of the women gasped.

"Dan," Sipich said in a whisper. "Dan, cut it out—"

Pat Reilly was playing *Night and Day* louder, to cover up the sounds of the talk. It wouldn't do any good, though, if Anthony was listening.

Dan Hollis went over to the piano and stood by Pat's shoulder, swaying a little.

"Pat," he said. "Don't play *that*. Play *this*." And he began to sing. Softly, hoarsely, miserably: "Happy birthday to me.... Happy birthday to me..."

"*Dan!*" Ethel Hollis screamed. She tried to run across the room to him. Mary Sipich grabbed her arm and held her back. "Dan," Ethel screamed again. "Stop—"

"My God, be quiet!" hissed Mary Sipich, and pushed her toward one of the men, who put his hand over her mouth and held her still.

"—Happy birthday, dear Danny," Dan sang. "Happy birthday to me!" He stopped and looked down at Pat Reilly. "Play it, Pat. Play it, so I can sing right... you know I can't carry a tune unless somebody plays it!"

Pat Reilly put his hands on the keys and began *Lover*—in a low waltz tempo, the way Anthony liked it. Pat's face was white. His hands fumbled.

Dan Hollis stared over at the dining-room door. At Anthony's mother, and at Anthony's father who had gone to join her.

"You had him," he said. Tears gleamed on his cheeks as the candlelight caught them. "*You* had to go and *have* him..."

He closed his eyes, and the tears squeezed out. He sang loudly, "You are my sunshine... my only sunshine... you make me happy... when I am blue..."

Anthony came into the room.

Pat stopped playing. He froze. Everybody froze. The breeze rippled the curtains. Ethel Hollis couldn't even try to scream—she had fainted.

"Please don't take my sunshine... away..." Dan's voice faltered into silence. His eyes widened. He put both hands out in front of him, the empty glass in one, the record in the other. He hiccupped, and said, "*No—*"

"Bad man," Anthony said, and thought Dan Hollis into something like nothing anyone would have believed possible, and then he thought the thing into a grave deep, deep in the cornfield.

The glass and record thumped on the rug. Neither broke.

Anthony's purple gaze went around the room.

Some of the people began mumbling. They all tried to smile. The sound of mumbling filled the room like a far-off approval. Out of the murmuring came one or two clear voices:

"Oh, it's a very *good* thing," said John Sipich.

"A good thing," said Anthony's father, smiling. He'd had more practice in smiling than most of them. "A wonderful thing."

"It's swell... just swell," said Pat Reilly, tears leaking from eyes and nose, and he began to play the piano again, softly, his trembling hands feeling for *Night and Day*.

Anthony climbed up on top of the piano, and Pat played for two hours.

Afterward, they watched television. They all went into the front room, and lit just a few candles, and pulled up chairs around the set. It was a small-screen set, and they couldn't all sit close enough to it to see, but that didn't matter. They didn't even turn the set on. It wouldn't have worked anyway, there being no electricity in Peaksville.

They just sat silently, and watched the twisting, writhing shapes on the screen, and listened to the sounds that came out of the speaker, and none of them had any idea of what it was all about. They never did. It was always the same.

"It's real nice," Aunt Amy said once, her pale eyes on the meaningless flickers and shadows. "But I liked it a little better when there were cities outside and we could get real—"

"Why, Amy!" said Mom. "It's good for you to say such a thing. Very good. But how can you mean it? Why, this television is *much* better than anything we ever used to get!"

"Yes," chimed in John Sipich. "It's fine. It's the best show we've ever seen!"

He sat on the couch, with two other men, holding Ethel Hollis flat against the cushions, holding her arms and legs and putting their hands over her mouth, so she couldn't start screaming again.

"It's really *good!*" he said again.

Mom looked out of the front window, across the darkened road, across Henderson's darkened wheatfield to the vast, endless, gray nothingness in which the little village of Peaksville floated like a soul—the huge nothingness that was most evident at night, when Anthony's brassy day had gone.

It did no good to wonder where they were . . . no good at all. Peaksville was just someplace. Someplace away from the world. It was wherever it had been since that day three years ago when Anthony had crept from her womb and old Doc Bates—God rest him—had screamed and dropped him and tried to kill him, and Anthony had whined and done the thing. Had taken the village someplace. Or had destroyed the world and left only the village, nobody knew which.

It did no good to wonder about it. Nothing at all did any good—except to live as they must live. Must always, always live, if Anthony would let them.

These thoughts were dangerous, she thought.

She began to mumble. The others started mumbling too. They had all been thinking, evidently.

The men on the couch whispered and whispered to Ethel Hollis and when they took their hands away, she mumbled too.

While Anthony sat on top of the set and made television, they sat around and mumbled and watched the meaningless, flickering shapes far into the night.

Next day it snowed, and killed off half the crops—but it was a *good* day.

The Fog Horn
Ray Bradbury

Out there in the cold water, far from land, we waited every night for the coming of the fog, and it came, and we oiled the brass machinery and lit the fog light up in the stone tower. Feeling like two birds in the gray sky, McDunn and I sent the light touching out, red, then white, then red again, to eye the lonely ships. And if they did not see our light, then there was always our Voice, the great deep cry of our Fog Horn shuddering through the rags of mist to startle the gulls away like decks of scattered cards and make the waves turn high and foam.

"It's a lonely life, but you're used to it now, aren't you?" asked McDunn.

"Yes," I said. "You're a good talker, thank the Lord."

"Well, it's your turn on land tomorrow," he said, smiling, "to dance the ladies and drink gin."

"What do you think, McDunn, when I leave you out here alone?"

"On the mysteries of the sea." McDunn lit his pipe. It was a quarter past seven of a cold November evening, the heat on, the light switching its tail in two hundred directions, the Fog Horn bumbling in the high throat of the tower. There wasn't a town for a hundred miles down the coast, just a road which came lonely through dead country to the sea, with few cars on it, a stretch of two miles of cold water out to our rock, and rare few ships.

"The mysteries of the sea," said McDunn thoughtfully. "You know, the ocean's the biggest damned snowflake ever? It rolls and swells a thousand shapes and colors, no two alike. Strange. One night, years ago, I was here alone, when all of the fish of the sea surfaced out there. Something made them swim in and lie in the bay, sort of trembling and staring up at the tower light going red, white, red, white, across them so I could see their funny eyes. I turned cold. They were like a big peacock's tail, moving out there until midnight. Then, without so much as a sound, they slipped away, the million of them was gone. I kind of think maybe, in some sort of way, they came all those miles to worship. Strange. But think how the tower must look to them, standing seventy feet above the water, the God-light flashing out from it, and the tower declaring itself with a monster voice. They never came back, those fish, but don't you think for a while they thought they were in the Presence?"

I shivered. I looked out at the long gray lawn of the sea stretching away into nothing and nowhere.

"Oh, the sea's full." McDunn puffed his pipe nervously, blinking. He had been nervous all day and hadn't said why. "For all our engines and so-called submarines, it'll be ten thousand centuries before we set foot on the real bottom of the sunken lands, in the fairy kingdoms there, and know *real* terror. Think of it, it's still the year 300,000 before Christ down under there. While we've paraded around with trumpets, lopping off each other's countries and heads, they have been living beneath the sea twelve miles deep and cold in a time as old as the beard of a comet."

"Yes, it's an old world."

"Come on. I got something special I been saving up to tell you."

We ascended the eighty steps, talking and taking our time. At the top, McDunn switched off the room lights so there'd be no reflection in the plate glass. The great eye of the light was humming, turning easily in its oiled socket. The Fog Horn was blowing steadily, once every fifteen seconds.

"Sounds like an animal, don't it?" McDunn nodded to himself. "A big lonely animal crying in the night. Sitting here on the edge of ten billion years calling out to the Deeps, I'm here, I'm here, I'm here. And the Deeps do answer, yes, they do. You been here now for three months, Johnny, so I better prepare you. About this time of year," he said, studying the murk and fog, "something comes to visit the lighthouse."

"The swarms of fish like you said?"

"No, this is something else. I've put off telling you because you might think I'm daft. But tonight's the latest I can put it off, for if my calendar's marked right from last year, tonight's the night it comes. I won't go into detail, you'll have to see it yourself. Just sit down there. If you want, tomorrow you can pack your duffel and take the motorboat in to land and get your car parked there at the dinghy pier on the cape and drive on back to some little inland town and keep your lights burning nights, I won't question or blame you. It's happened three years now, and this is the only time anyone's been here with me to verify it. You wait and watch."

Half an hour passed with only a few whispers between us. When we grew tired waiting, McDunn began describing some of his ideas to me. He had some theories about the Fog Horn itself.

"One day many years ago a man walked along and stood in the sound of the ocean on a cold sunless shore and said, 'We need a voice to call across the water, to warn ships; I'll make one. I'll make a voice like all of time and all of the fog that ever was; I'll make a voice that is like an empty bed beside you all night long, and like an empty house when you open the door, and like trees in autumn with no leaves. A sound like the birds flying south, crying, and a sound like November wind and the sea on the hard, cold shore. I'll make a sound that's so alone that no one can miss it, that whoever hears it will weep in their souls, and hearths will seem warmer, and being inside will seem better to all who hear it in the distant towns. I'll make me a sound and an apparatus and they'll call it a Fog Horn and whoever hears it will know the sadness of eternity and the briefness of life.' "

The Fog Horn blew.

"I made up that story," said McDunn quietly, "to try to explain why this thing keeps coming back to the lighthouse every year. The Fog Horn calls it, I think, and it comes. . . ."

"But—" I said.

"Sssst!" said McDunn. "There!" He nodded out to the Deeps.

Something was swimming toward the lighthouse tower.

It was a cold night, as I have said; the high tower was cold, the light coming and going, and the Fog Horn calling and calling through the raveling mist. You couldn't see far and you couldn't see plain, but there was the deep sea moving on its way about the night earth, flat and quiet, the color of gray mud, and here were the two of us alone in the high tower, and there, far out at first, was a ripple, followed by a wave, a rising, a bubble, a bit of froth. And then, from the surface of the cold sea came a head, a large head, dark-colored, with immense eyes, and then a neck. And then—not a body —but more neck and more! The head rose a full forty feet above the water on a slender and beautiful dark neck. Only then did the body, like a little island of black coral and shells and crayfish, drip up from the subterranean. There was a flicker of tail. In all, from head to tip of tail, I estimated the monster at ninety or a hundred feet.

I don't know what I said. I said something.

"Steady, boy, steady," whispered McDunn.

"It's impossible!" I said.

"No, Johnny, *we're* impossible. *It's* like it always was ten million years ago. *It* hasn't changed. It's *us* and the land that've changed, become impossible. *Us!*"

It swam slowly and with a great dark majesty out in the icy waters, far away. The fog came and went about it, momentarily erasing its shape. One of the monster eyes caught and held and flashed back our immense light, red, white, red, white, like a disk held high and sending a message in primeval code. It was as silent as the fog through which it swam.

"It's a dinosaur of some sort!" I crouched down, holding to the stair rail.

"Yes, one of the tribe."

"But they died out!"

"No, only hid away in the Deeps. Deep, deep down in the deepest Deeps. Isn't *that* a word now, Johnny, a real word, it says so much: the Deeps. There's all the coldness and darkness and deepness in a word like that."

"What'll we do?"

"Do? We got our job, we can't leave. Besides, we're safer here than in any boat trying to get to land. That thing's as big as a destroyer and almost as swift."

"But here, why does it come *here?*"

The next moment I had my answer.

The Fog Horn blew.

And the monster answered.

A cry came across a million years of water and mist. A cry so anguished and alone that it shuddered in my head and my body. The monster cried out at the tower. The Fog Horn blew. The monster roared again. The Fog Horn blew. The monster opened its great toothed mouth and the sound that came from it was the sound of the Fog Horn itself. Lonely and vast and far away. The sound of isolation, a viewless sea, a cold night, apartness. That was the sound.

"Now," whispered McDunn, "do you know why it comes here?"

I nodded.

"All year long, Johnny, that poor monster there lying far out, a thousand miles at sea, and twenty miles deep maybe, biding its time, perhaps it's a million years old, this one creature. Think of it, waiting a million years; could *you* wait that long? Maybe it's the last of its kind. I sort of think that's true. Anyway, here come men on land and build this lighthouse, five years ago. And set up their Fog Horn and sound it and sound it out toward the place where you bury yourself in sleep and sea memories of a world where there were thousands like yourself, but now you're alone, all alone in a world not made for you, a world where you have to hide.

"But the sound of the Fog Horn comes and goes, comes and goes, and you stir from the muddy bottom of the Deeps, and your eyes open like the lenses of two-foot cameras and you move, slow, slow, for you have the ocean sea on your shoulders, heavy. But that Fog Horn comes through a thousand miles of water, faint and familiar, and the furnace in your belly stokes up, and you begin to rise, slow, slow. You feed yourself on great slakes of cod and minnow, on rivers of jellyfish, and you rise slow through the autumn months, through September when the fogs started, through October with more fog and the horn still calling you on, and then, late in November, after pressurizing yourself day by day, a few feet higher every hour, you are near the surface and still alive. You've got to go slow; if you surfaced all at once you'd explode. So it takes you all of three months to surface, and then a number of days to swim through the cold waters to the lighthouse. And there you are, out there, in the night, Johnny, the biggest damn monster in creation. And here's the lighthouse calling to you, with a long neck like your neck sticking way up out of the water, and a body like your body, and, most important of all, a voice like your voice. Do you understand now, Johnny, do you understand?"

The Fog Horn blew.

The monster answered.

I saw it all, I knew it all—the million years of waiting alone, for someone to come back who never came back. The million years of isolation at the bottom of the sea, the insanity of time there, while the skies cleared of reptile-birds, the swamps dried on the continental lands, the sloths and saber-tooths had their day and sank in tar pits, and men ran like white ants upon the hills.

The Fog Horn blew.

"Last year," said McDunn, "that creature swam round and round, round and round, all night. Not coming too near, puzzled, I'd say. Afraid, maybe. And a bit angry after coming all this way. But the next day, unexpectedly, the fog lifted, the sun came out fresh, the sky was as blue as a painting. And the monster swam off away from the heat and the silence and didn't come back. I suppose it's been brooding on it for a year now, thinking it over from every which way."

The monster was only a hundred yards off now, it and the Fog Horn crying at each other. As the lights hit them, the monster's eyes were fire and ice, fire and ice.

"That's life for you," said McDunn. "Someone always waiting for someone who never comes home. Always someone loving some thing more than that thing loves them. And after a while you want to destroy whatever that thing is, so it can't hurt you no more."

The monster was rushing at the lighthouse.

The Fog Horn blew.

"Let's see what happens," said McDunn.

He switched the Fog Horn off.

The ensuing minute of silence was so intense that we could hear our hearts pounding in the glassed area of the tower, could hear the slow greased turn of the light.

The monster stopped and froze. Its great lantern eyes blinked. Its mouth gaped. It gave a sort of rumble, like a volcano. It twitched its head this way and that, as if to seek the sounds now dwindled off into the fog. It peered at the lighthouse. It rumbled again. Then its eyes caught fire. It reared up, threshed the water, and rushed at the tower, its eyes filled with angry torment.

"McDunn!" I cried. "Switch on the horn!"

McDunn fumbled with the switch. But even as he flicked it on, the monster was rearing up. I had a glimpse of its gigantic paws, fishskin glittering in webs between the finger-like projections, clawing at the tower. The huge eye on the right side of its anguished head glittered before me like a caldron into which I might drop, screaming. The tower shook. The Fog Horn cried; the monster cried. It seized the tower and gnashed at the glass, which shattered in upon us.

McDunn seized my arm. "Downstairs!"

The tower rocked, trembled, and started to give. The Fog Horn and the monster roared. We stumbled and half fell down the stairs. "Quick!"

We reached the bottom as the tower buckled down toward us. We ducked under the stairs into the small stone cellar. There were a thousand concussions as the rocks rained down; the Fog Horn stopped abruptly. The monster crashed upon the tower. The tower fell. We knelt together, McDunn and I, holding tight, while our world exploded.

Then it was over, and there was nothing but darkness and the wash of the sea on the raw stones.

That and the other sound.

"Listen," said McDunn quietly. "Listen."

We waited a moment. And then I began to hear it. First a great vacuumed sucking of air, and then the lament, the bewilderment, the loneliness of the great monster, folded over and upon us, above us, so that the sickening reek of its body filled the air, a stone's thickness away from our cellar. The monster gasped and cried. The tower was gone. The light was gone. The thing that had called to it across a million years was gone. And the monster was opening its mouth and sending out great sounds. The sounds of a Fog Horn, again and again. And ships far at sea, not finding the light, not seeing anything, but passing and hearing late that night, must've thought: There it is, the lonely sound, the Lonesome Bay horn. All's well. We've rounded the cape.

And so it went for the rest of that night.

The sun was hot and yellow the next afternoon when the rescuers came out to dig us from our stoned-under cellar.

"It fell apart, is all," said Mr. McDunn gravely. "We had a few bad knocks from the waves and it just crumbled." He pinched my arm.

There was nothing to see. The ocean was calm, the sky blue. The only thing was a great algaic stink from the green matter that covered the fallen tower stones and the shore rocks. Flies buzzed about. The ocean washed empty on the shore.

The next year they built a new lighthouse, but by that time I had a job in the little town and a wife and a good small warm house that glowed yellow on autumn nights, the doors locked, the chimney puffing smoke. As for McDunn, he was master of the new lighthouse, built to his own specifications, out of steel-reinforced concrete. "Just in case," he said.

The new lighthouse was ready in November. I drove down alone one evening late and parked my car and looked across the gray waters and listened to the new horn sounding, once, twice, three, four times a minute far out there, by itself.

The monster?

It never came back.

"It's gone away," said McDunn. "It's gone back to the Deeps. It's learned you can't love anything too much in this world. It's gone into the deepest Deeps to wait another million years. Ah, the poor thing! Waiting out there, and waiting out there, while man comes and goes on this pitiful little planet. Waiting and waiting."

I sat in my car, listening. I couldn't see the lighthouse or the light standing out in Lonesome Bay. I could only hear the Horn, the Horn, the Horn. It sounded like the monster calling.

I sat there wishing there was something I could say.

The Waveries

Fredric Brown

DEFINITIONS from school-abridged Webster-Hamlin Dictionary, 2088 edition:

> **wavery** (WĀ-ver-ĭ) *n.* a vader—*slang*
> **vader** (VĀ-dêr) *n.* inorgan of the class Radio
> **inorgan** (ĭn-ÔR-găn) *n.* noncorporeal ens, a vader
> **radio** (RĀ-dĭ-ōh, ră-DĒ-ōh) *n.* 1. Class of inorgans.
> 2. Etheric frequency between light and electricity.
> 3. (obsolete) Method of communication used up to 1947.

The opening guns of invasion were not at all loud, although they were heard by many people. George Bailey was one of the many; I choose George Bailey because he was the only one who came within a googol of light-years of guessing what they were.

George Bailey was drunk, and under the circumstances one can't blame him. He was listening to radio advertisements of the most verbose and annoying kind. Not because he *wanted* to listen to them, but because he'd been told to listen by his boss, J. R. McGee, of the MID network.

George Bailey wrote advertising for the radio. The only thing he hated worse than advertising was radio. And here, on his own time in the late evening, he was listening to fulsome and saccharine drippings on a rival network, at J. R. McGee's suggestion—which George very rightly took for an order.

"Bailey, you should be more familiar with what others are doing. Particularly those of our own accounts which use several networks. I'd suggest that—"

One doesn't quarrel with suggestions and keep a hundred-and-fifty-dollar-a-week job. But one can drink whisky sours while listening. One George Bailey did.

Also, one could play gin rummy with Maisie Hetterman, a cute little redheaded typist from the studio. One could do no more than that, but Maisie was worth just looking at across a card table. It was Maisie's apartment and Maisie's radio, but George had brought the liquor.

"—only the best tobaccos," said the radio, "go *dit-dit-dit*—the nation's favorite cigarettes—"

George glanced at the radio. "Marconi," he said.

He meant Morse, naturally, but the whisky sours had muddled him a bit, so he was nearer right than most people who heard that dit-dit-dit. It *was* Marconi, in a way; in, as it turned out, a very peculiar way.

"Marconi?" asked Maisie.

George Bailey, who hated to talk while a radio was going, leaned over and switched it off.

"I mean Morse," he said. "Morse, as in Boy Scouts or the Signal Corps. I used to be a Boy Scout once."

"You don't look it."

George sighed. "Somebody going to catch hell," he said, "broadcasting code on that wave length."

"What did it mean?"

"Mean? Oh, you mean what did it mean. Uh... S, letter S. *Dit-dit-dit*. SOS is *dit-dit-dit, dah-dah-dah, dit-dit-dit*."

"O is *dah-dah-dah*?"

George grinned. "Say it again, Maisie. I like it. I think 'oo is *dah-dah-dah*, too."

"George! Maybe it's really an SOS message. Turn it back on, please."

He turned it back on. The tobacco ad was still going. "—gentlemen of the most... *dit-dit-dit*... ing taste prefer the finer taste of Golden Harvest... *dit-dit-dit*... arettes. In the new package that keeps them... *dit-dit-dit*... and ultrafresh—"

"It's just S-S-S-S," said George. "Like a teakettle. Or maybe somebody s-s-stutters. But the Golden Harvest people are going to raise—Say—"

"What, George?"

"Maybe it's deliberate, an advertising gag like L.S.M.F.T. used to be. Just a minute till I—"

He reached over and turned the dial of the radio a bit to the right, then a bit to the left, and an incredulous look came over his face. He turned the dial to the extreme right, as far as it would go. There wasn't any station there—not even the hum of a carrier wave.

"*Dit-dit-dit*," said the radio, "*—dit-dit-dit*."

George turned it to the other end of the dial. "*Dit-dit-dit*," said the radio.

He switched it off and stared at Maisie, without even seeing her, which was hard to do.

"Something wrong, George?"

"I hope so," said George Bailey. "I certainly hope so."

He started to reach for another drink, then changed his mind. He had a sudden hunch that something big was happening, and wanted to sober up to appreciate it.

He didn't have the faintest idea *how* big it was.

"George, what do you mean?"

"I don't know. But Maisie, let's take a run down to the studio, huh? There ought to be some excitement."

April 5, 1947; that was the night the waveries came.

It was a gay night, except for radio technicians. New York was at its best and gayest, and the main stem, which is Broadway, running high, wide, and expensive. The streets were full of uniforms, mostly uniforms of men already demobilized, due to recent reduction in the armies of occupation—so recently demobilized that they hadn't taken time to buy civvies. Discharge pay burning in their pockets, they wanted Broadway and they took Broadway; or Broadway took them. Fresh shiploads of them daily.

The gaiety was hectic, but it was a surface gaiety, even greater than that of the boom years of 1928 and '29. Workers dead weary from overtime in the reconverted factories trying to supply the peak demand for automobiles and radios and jukeboxes and pinball games left the factories for a hasty meal, then went out in their automobiles—with car radios blaring—and spent their overtime pay in the jukeboxes and pinball machines. Which, of course, increased the demand for those commodities, which increased the overtime of the factories, which increased the overtime pay, which increased the spending and the demand and—Well, you see what I mean.

It was a vicious circle that would eventually have bitten itself.

But the waveries bit first.

April 5, 1947; that was the night the waveries came.

George and Maisie tried in vain to get a cab and took the subway instead. Oh, yes, the subways were still running then. It took them within a block of the MID Network Building.

It was a madhouse. George, grinning, strolled through the lobby with Maisie on his arm, took the elevator to five, and for no reason at all gave the elevator boy a dollar. He'd never before in his life tipped an elevator operator.

The boy grinned. "Better stay away from the big shots, Mr. Bailey," he said. "They're ready to chew off anybody's ears that looks at 'em cockeyed."

"Swell," said George. He left the elevator and headed straight for the office of J. R. McGee, himself. There were strident voices behind the glass door.

"But George," protested Maisie, "you'll be fired!"

" 'When in the course of human events,' " said George. "Oh, well, it's worth it. I got money saved up."

"But what are you going to do, George?"

"Stand back away from that door, honey." Gently, but firmly, he moved her to a safe position.

"But what *are* you—"

"This," said George Bailey soberly.

The frantic voices stopped as he opened the glass door a bit. All eyes turned as he stuck his head in through the crack of the door.

"*Dit-dit-dit*," he said. "*Dit-dit-dit*."

He ducked back and to one side just in time to escape the flying glass, as a paperweight and an inkwell came through the pane.

He grabbed Maisie and ran for the stairs.

"Now we get a drink," he told her.

The bar across from the Network Building was crowded, but it was a strangely silent crowd. Most of them were bunched around the big cabinet radio at one end of the bar.

"*Dit*," said the cabinet radio, "*dit-dah-d'dah-dit-dahditditdah . . . d'd'dahditdddititdah—*"

Somebody fiddled with the dial. Somebody asked, "What band is that?" and somebody said, "Police." Somebody said, "Try the foreign band," and somebody did. "This ought to be Buenos Aires," somebody said. The radio said, "*dit-dit-dahditititdditah.*"

George squeezed Maisie's arm.

"Lovely," he said. Maybe he meant her and maybe not; it didn't matter at the moment.

Somebody ran fingers through his hair and yelled, "Shut that thing off." Somebody did. Somebody else turned it back on.

George grinned and led the way to a back booth where he'd spotted Pete Mulvaney sitting alone with a tall bottle in front of him.

George seated Maisie and himself across from Pete Mulvaney.

"Hello," he said gravely.

"Hello," said Pete, who was head of the technical research staff of the MID.

"A beautiful night, Mulvaney. Did you see the moon riding high in the fleecy clouds like a golden galleon tossed upon silver-crested whitecaps in a stormy—"

"Shut up," said Pete. "I'm thinking."

"Whisky sours," said George to the waiter. He turned back to the brooding man across the table. "Think out loud," he said. "We sit at your feet. But first, how did you escape the looney bin?"

"I'm bounced, fired, discharged."

"Shake," said George, "and then explain."

"I told them what I thought it was, and they said I was crazy."

"Are you?"

"Yes," said Mulvaney.

"Good," said George. "I don't care what it is, as long as it's nothing trivial. But what the devil *is* it?"

"I don't know. Space, I think. Space is warped."

"Good old space," said George Bailey.

"George," said Maisie, "please shut up. I want to hear this."

"Space is also finite. You go far enough in any direction, and you get back where you started." Pete Mulvaney poured himself another drink. "Like an ant crawling around an apple."

"Make it an orange," said George.

"All right, an orange. Suppose the first radio waves ever sent out have just made the round trip. In forty-six years."

"Forty-six years? But I thought radio waves traveled at the speed of light. In forty-six years they could go only forty-six light-years, and *that* can't be around the Universe, because there are Galaxies known to be thousands of light-years away, or maybe millions; I don't know. But more than forty-six, Pete."

Pete Mulvaney sighed deeply. "We," he said, "are in the middle of a super-Galaxy that is two million light-years in diameter. That is just one Galaxy, a medium-sized one, they tell us. Yes, it's more than forty-six light-years around the orange."

"But—"

"But listen to that stuff. Can you read code?"

"Nope, not that fast, anyway."

"Well, I can. That's early American ham. Lingo and all. That's the kind of stuff the air was full of before *broadcasting*. It's the lingo, the abbreviations, the barnyard-to-attic chitchat of amateurs with keys, with Marconi coherers or Fessenden barreters—and you can listen for a violin solo pretty soon now. And you know what the first phonograph record ever broadcast was? Handel's *Largo* sent out by Fessenden from Brant Rock in 1906. You'll hear his CQ-CQ any minute now. Bet you a drink."

"Sure, but what was the *dit-dit-dit* that started what's turned into hash since?"

Mulvaney grinned and then his face went blank. He said, "Marconi, George. What was the first *powerful* signal ever broadcast, and by whom and when?"

"Marconi? *Dit-dit-dit?* Forty-six years ago?"

"Head of the class. The first transatlantic signal on December 12, 1901. For three hours Marconi's big station at Poldhu with two-hundred-foot masts sent out an intermittent S . . . *dit-dit-dit* . . . while Marconi and two assistants at St. Johns in Newfoundland got a kite-borne aerial four hundred feet in the air and finally got the signal. Across the Atlantic, George, with sparks jumping from the big Leyden jars at Poldhu and 20,000-volt juice jumping off the tremendous aerials—"

"Wait a minute, Pete, you're off the beam. If that was in 1901 and the first broadcast about 1906, it'll be five years before the Fessenden stuff gets here, on the same route. Even if there's a forty-six-light-year short cut across space, and even if those signals didn't get so weak en route that we couldn't hear them. It's crazy."

"I told you I was crazy," said Mulvaney. "Those signals should be so infinitesimal you couldn't hear them with the best set on Earth. Furthermore, they're all over the band on everything from microwave to ten kilocycles, and equally strong on each. Furthermore, we've come five years in two hours, which isn't possible. I told you I was crazy."

"But—"

"Listen," said Pete.

A blurred but unmistakably human voice was coming from the radio, mingling with the cracklings of code. And then music, faint and scratchy and punctuated by *dit-dah*, but nevertheless music. Handel's *Largo*.

Only it suddenly climbed in pitch, as though modulating from key to key, until it became so horribly shrill as to hurt the ear, like an orchestra made up of nothing but piccolos. And kept on going, past the high limit of audibility, until they could hear it no more.

Somebody said, "Shut that thing off." Somebody did, and this time nobody turned the thing back on.

George and Maisie looked at Pete Mulvaney, and Pete Mulvaney looked back at them.

"But it can't be," said Pete Mulvaney. "There must be some other explanation. The more I think of it, now, the more I think I'm wrong."

He was right: he was wrong.

"Preposterous," said Mr. Ogilvie. He took off his glasses, frowned fiercely, and put them back on again. He looked through them at the several sheets of copy paper in his hand and tossed them contemptuously to the top of his desk. They slid to rest against the triangular name plate that read:

B. R. Ogilvie
Editor-in-Chief

"Preposterous," he said again.

Casey Blair, his star reporter, blew a smoke ring and poked his index finger through it. "Why?" he asked.

"Because... why, it's preposterous!"

Casey Blair said, "It is now three o'clock in the morning. The radio interference has gone on for five hours and has reached the point where not a single current program is getting through. Every major broadcasting station in the world has gone off the air.

"For two reasons. One: It wasn't doing a bit of good to stay on the air and waste current, no matter what wave length they were

on. Two: The communications bureaus of their respective governments requested them to get off to aid their campaigns with the
direction finders. For five hours now—since the first note of interference—they've been working with everything they've got. And
what have they got?"

"Preposterous," said the editor.

"Exactly. Greenwich at eleven P.M.—New York time—got a bearing in about the direction of Miami. It shifted northward until at
two o'clock the direction was approximately that of Richmond, Virginia. Now, San Francisco at eleven got a bearing in about the direction of Denver; three hours later it shifted southward toward Tucson.
Southern hemisphere: bearings from Capetown, South Africa,
shifted from approximate direction of Buenos Aires to direction of
Montevideo, a thousand miles north. New York had trouble with
direction finders; weak indications at eleven were toward Madrid;
by two o'clock they could get no bearings at all." He blew another
smoke ring. "Maybe because the loop antennas they use turn only
on a horizontal plane."

"Absurd," said Mr. Ogilvie.

Casey said, "I liked 'preposterous' better, Mr. Ogilvie. It's not
absurd; I'm scared stiff. Those lines converge on about the constellation Leo, if you take them as straight lines instead of curving them
around the surface. I did it with a little globe and a star map."
He leaned forward and tapped a forefinger on the top copy page.
"Stations directly under that point in the sky get no bearings at
all. Stations on, as it were, the perimeter of the Earth get strong
bearings in the horizontal plane."

"But the Heaviside layer, Blair—isn't that supposed to stop all
radio waves—bounce 'em back, or something?"

"Uh-huh. It does. But maybe it leaks. Maybe some waves got
through. It isn't a solid wall."

"But—"

"I know; it's preposterous. But there it is. Only there's an hour
before press time and you ought to turn the observatories on it and
get it more accurately. Get *them* to extend those bearing lines. I
did it by rule of thumb. Further, I didn't have the data for checking
planet positions. Leo's on the ecliptic; a planet could be in line
between here and there. Like Mars, maybe."

Mr. Ogilvie's eyes brightened, then clouded again.

He said, "We'll be the laughingstock of the world, Blair, if we're
wrong."

"And if I'm right?"

Ogilvie picked up the phone and snapped an order that sent every
rewrite man into his office for orders.

April 6th headline of the New York *Morning Messenger*, final (5
A.M.) edition:

RADIO INTERFERENCE COMES FROM SPACE:
ORIGINATES IN LEO, SAY SCIENTISTS

May Be Attempt at Communication by Beings Outside Solar System!

ALL BROADCASTING SUSPENDED

RKO and Radio Corporation stocks, having closed the previous day at 10¼ and 11½ respectively, opened at 9¾ and 9½ and dropped sharply. By noon they were off four and five points respectively, when a moderate buying rally brought each of them back a fraction over two points.

Public action was mixed; people who had no radios rushed out to buy them, and there was a boom market in portable and table-top receivers. Those who had radios listened as long as their curiosity enabled them to stand it, and then turned them off. Extraterrestrial or not, the programs were a horrible hash.

Oh, there were flashes—times when, for several seconds at a time, a listener could recognize the voices of Will Rogers or Geraldine Farrar or could catch a scrap of the Dempsey-Carpentier fight. But things worth hearing—even for seconds at a time—were rare. Mostly it was a jumble of soap opera, advertising, and off-key snatches of what had once been music. It was utterly indiscriminate and utterly unbearable for any length of time.

But curiosity is a powerful motive. There *was* a brief boom in radio sets that morning.

There were other booms, less explicable, less capable of analysis. Reminiscent of the Wells-Welles Martian scare was a sudden up-swing in the sale of shotguns and sidearms. Bibles sold as readily as books on astronomy—and books on astronomy sold like hot cakes. One section of the country showed a sudden interest in lightning rods—builders were deluged with orders for immediate demonstration.

For some reason which has never been clearly ascertained, there was a run on fishhooks in Mobile, Alabama; every hardware and Sporting-goods store in that city was sold out of them before noon.

The public libraries had a run on books on astrology and books on Mars. Yes, on Mars—despite the fact that Mars was at the moment on the other side of the Sun and that every newspaper article on the subject stressed the fact that *no* planet was between Earth and the constellation Leo.

And not a radio station on Earth was on the air that morning.

Newspapers were passed from hand to hand because the presses couldn't keep up with the demand. *No news on the radio*—and something big was happening. People waited, in mobs, outside the newspaper offices for each new edition to appear. Circulation managers went quietly mad.

People gathered in curious little knots about the broadcasting studios. MID Network doors were locked, although there was a doorman on duty to admit technicians, who were trying to find an answer to the unprecedented difficulty. Some, who had been on duty the previous day, had now spent twenty-four hours without sleep.

George Bailey woke at noon, with only a slight headache. He turned on his radio and turned it off again quickly.

He shaved and showered, went out and drank a light breakfast, and was himself again. He bought early editions of the afternoon papers, read them, and grinned. His hunch had been right; whatever was wrong with radio, it was nothing trivial.

But *what* was wrong?

The later editions of the evening papers had it.

EARTH INVADED, SAYS SCIENTIST

Thirty-six line type was the biggest they had; they used it. Not a home-edition copy of a newspaper was delivered that evening. Newsboys starting on their routes were practically mobbed. They sold papers instead of delivering them; the smart ones got a quarter apiece for them. The foolish ones who didn't want to sell, because the papers had been bought for their routes, lost them anyway; people grabbed them.

The later home editions and the finals changed the heading only slightly—from a typographical viewpoint. But it was a big change, just the same:

EARTH INVADED, SAY SCIENTISTS

Funny what moving an S from the ending of a verb to the ending of a noun can do.

Carnegie Hall shattered precedents that evening with a lecture given at midnight. An unscheduled and unadvertised lecture. Professor Helmetz had stepped off the train at eleven-thirty, and a mob of reporters had been waiting for him. Helmetz, of Harvard, had been the scientist—singular—who had made the first headlines.

Harvey Ambers, Director of the Board of Carnegie Hall, had pushed his way through the mob. He arrived minus glasses, hat, and breath, but got hold of Helmetz's arm and hung on until he could talk again. "We want you to talk at Carnegie, Professor," he shouted into Helmetz's ear. "Thousand bucks for a lecture on the 'vaders!"

"Certainly. Tomorrow afternoon?"

"Now! I've a cab waiting. Come on."

"But ... but ..."

"We'll get you an audience. Hurry!" He turned to the mob. "Let us through! You can't hear the professor here. Come to Carnegie and he'll talk to you. Spread the word."

The word spread so well that Carnegie Hall was jammed by midnight, when the professor began to speak. By twelve-thirty, they'd rigged a loud-speaker system so the people outside could hear. By one o'clock in the morning the streets were jammed for blocks around.

There wasn't a sponsor on Earth with a million dollars to his name who wouldn't have given a million dollars to sponsor the broadcasting of that lecture—but it was not broadcast on the radio.

The line was busy.

"Questions?" asked Professor Helmetz.

A reporter in the front row made it first. "Professor," he asked, "have *all* direction-finding stations on Earth confirmed your statement as to the change this afternoon?"

"Yes, absolutely. At about noon, the directional indications began to grow weaker. At 2:47 o'clock, New York time, they ceased completely. Until then, the radio waves emanated from the sky, constantly changing direction with reference to the Earth's surface, but *constant* with reference to the point in the constellation Leo."

"What star in Leo?"

"No star. Merely a point in the sky coinciding exactly with the position of no visible star on the most minute charts. At 2:47 o'clock all direction finders went dead, but the signals persisted. They came from *all sides* equally. The invaders were here. There is no other conclusion to be drawn. Earth is now surrounded, completely blanketed, by radio waves which have *no point of origin*, which travel ceaselessly around the Earth in all directions, changing shape at will —which at the moment seems to be in imitation of the Earth-origin signals that attracted their attention, that brought them here."

"From nowhere? From just a point in space?"

"Why not, sir? They are creatures of *ether*, not of matter. Ether permeates space uniformly. They were, until they were attracted here, at a point in space not greater than twenty-three light-years away. Our first indication of their arrival—rather, the arrival of the first ones, if you want to put it that way—came with a repetition of Marconi's S-S-S transatlantic broadcast of forty-six years ago. Apparently that was the first Earth broadcast of sufficient power to send signals that they could perceive at that distance. They started for Earth then, presumably. It took twenty-three years for those waves to reach them and twenty-three years for them to reach us. The first to arrive had formed themselves, imitatively, to duplicate the shape, as it were, of the signals that attracted them. Later arrivals were in the form of other waves that they had met, or passed, or absorbed, on their way to Earth. There are now fragments of programs broadcast as recently as a few days ago ... uh ... wandering about the ether. Undoubtedly, also, there are fragments of the very last programs to be broadcast, but they have not yet been identified."

"Professor, can you *describe* one of the invaders?"

"No more than one can describe a radio wave. They *are* radio waves, in effect, although they emanate from no broadcasting station. They are a form of life dependent upon the movement of ether, as life as we know it is dependent upon the vibration of matter. Life is movement—or at least, life is contingent upon movement."

"They are different sizes?"

"Yes—in two senses of the word size. Radio waves are measured from crest to crest, which measurement is known as the wave length. Since the invaders cover the entire dials of our receiving sets, obviously they can—in imitation, undoubtedly, of the waves of ours that they have met—adjust themselves to any frequency, or crest-to-crest wave length.

"But that is only a crest-to-crest length. The actual length of a radio wave is much greater. If a broadcasting station sends out a program of one second's duration, the length of the wave carrying that program is one light-second, or 186,270 miles. A half-hour program is on a continuous wave, as it were, one-half light-hour long, and so on.

"On that basis, the individual ... uh ... invaders vary in length from a hundred thousand miles long—less than a second in duration—to about five million miles long—almost half a minute in duration. Each is in constant movement at the speed of light, and presumably that movement is now in a circle about the surface of the Earth. Each wave, as it were, extends many times, or many thousands of times, around the Earth."

"How can that be told?"

"By the length of the ... ah ... excerpts from various programs. None are under half a second in duration, none over half a minute."

"But why assume, Professor Helmetz, that these ... these waves are living things? Why not just inanimate waves?"

"An inanimate wave ... as you call it ... would follow certain laws. Just as inanimate matter follows certain laws. An animal can climb uphill, however, or run in circles, or ... uh ... climb a tree. A stone can do none of these unless impelled by some outside force. It is the same with these invaders. They are living things because they show volition, because they are not limited in direction of travel, because they can change their form—because they *retain their identity*; two signals never come together on the same radio or conflict with one another. They follow one another but do not come simultaneously. They do not blend or heterodyne as signals on the same wave length would ordinarily do. They follow laws and rules of their own. They are *not* merely radio waves."

"But, Professor, are they intelligent beings?"

Professor Helmetz took off his glasses and polished them thoughtfully. He said finally, "I doubt if we shall ever know. The intelligence of such beings, if any, would be on such a completely different plane from ours that there would be no common point from which we could start intercourse. We are material; they are immaterial. I do not think there can ever be common ground between us."

"But if they are intelligent at all, Professor—"

"Ants are intelligent, after a fashion. Even if one calls it instinct that enables them to do such marvelous things, still instinct is a form of intelligence. Yet we cannot communicate with ants; we shall be less likely to communicate with the invaders. The difference in type between ant intelligence and ours would be nothing to the difference in type between the intelligence of the invaders and our own. What *could* we have to say to one another?"

The professor must have had something there. Communication with the vaders—a clipped form, of course, of "invaders"—was never established.

Radio stocks stabilized on the Exchange. Until, a day after the midnight lecture, someone asked Dr. Helmetz the sixty-four-dollar question and the newspapers published his answer:

"Resume broadcasting? I don't know. Not until the invaders go away, and why should they? Unless, of course, radio communication is perfected on some other planet in some other Galaxy, and they're attracted there."

"And if they did go away—?"

"Oh, they'd be back when we started to broadcast again."

Radio stocks dropped to practically zero in an hour. There wasn't any frenzied scene on the Exchange, however; no frenzied selling, because there was no buying, frenzied or otherwise. No radio stocks exchanged hands.

Radio musicians took jobs in theaters, taverns, and the like. And failed completely to fulfill the increased demand for talent. With radio out, other forms of entertainment boomed.

Magazine sales boomed. Movies boomed. Vaudeville was coming back. Everything boomed except radio.

"One down," said George Bailey. The bartender asked what he meant.

"I dunno, Hank. I got a hunch."

"What kind of hunch?"

"I don't even know that. Shake me up one more of those, and I'll go home."

The electric shaker wouldn't work, and Hank had to shake it up by hand.

"Exercise; that's what you need," said George. "Take some of that fat off you."

Hank grunted and the ice tinkled merrily as he tilted the shaker to pour out the drink.

George Bailey drank it leisurely and strolled out into an April thundershower. He stood under the awning and watched for a taxi. An old man was standing in front of him.

"Some weather," George said.

The old man grinned at him. "You noticed it?"

"Huh? Noticed what?"

"Just watch a while, mister. Just watch a while."

The old man moved on. George stood there quite a while—for no cab went by empty—before he got it. His jaw dropped a trifle, and then he closed his mouth and went back into the tavern. He went into a phone booth and called Pete Mulvaney.

He got three wrong numbers and lost four nickels before he got Pete. Pete's voice said "Yeah?"

"George Bailey, Pete. Listen, the weather. Notice it?"

"Yes. What's it mean, you want to know. So do I. You tell me. I think it's—" A crackling sound on the wire blurred it out.

"Hey, Pete! You there?"

The sound of a violin. Pete Mulvaney didn't play the violin.

"Hey, Pete! What in—"

Pete's voice again. "Come on over, George. This isn't going to last long. Bring—" A buzzing noise and then a voice that was not Pete's said, "—come to Carnegie Hall. The best tunes of all come to Carnegie Hall. Yes, the best tunes of all come to Car—"

George slammed down the receiver.

He walked through the rain to Pete's place. On the way he bought a bottle of Scotch. Pete had started to tell him to bring something, and maybe, he figured, that was what it was.

It was.

They poured a drink apiece and lifted them. The lights flickered briefly, went out, and then on again.

"No lightning," said George. "No lightning and pretty soon no lighting. They're taking over the telephone. What do they do with lightning, though?"

"Eat it, maybe."

"No lightning," said George. "I can get by without a telephone, and candles and oil lamps aren't bad for lights, but I'm going to miss lightning. I *like* lightning."

Pete Mulvaney leaned back in his chair. He said, "Electric lights, electric toasters, electric hair curlers, vacuum cleaners. Electric power, and—automobiles and airplanes and Diesel-engined boats. George, do you know no gasoline engine can work without electricity?"

"Huh? For a starter, sure, but can't it be cranked by hand?"

"Yes, but the *spark*."

"Yes, the spark. Hey, how about those new rocket planes? Those, too?"

"Those, too."

"Movies?"

"Definitely, movies. You couldn't work a projector with an oil lamp. You need concentrated light for that. And sound tracks—well, that's electricity *per se*."

George Bailey shook his head slowly. "All right, scratch movies. Streetcars. Trucks, tanks, toasters—See what it means, Pete?"

Pete poured another drink. "It means we're going back to the original source of horsepower. Horses. If you want to invest, buy horses. Particularly mares; mares are going to be worth their weight in gold."

"Hey, though, there are steam engines. Locomotives."

Pete Mulvaney nodded. "The iron horse. We'll be back to it for the long hauls, and back to Dobbin for the short ones. Can you ride?"

George sipped his drink slowly. "Used to when I was a kid. Guess I can learn again. Say, it'll be fun. And say—"

"What?"

"Used to play the cornet when I was a kid. Think I'll get one and learn again. That'll be fun, too. And maybe I'll hole in somewhere and write that nov—Say, what about printing?"

"They printed books long before electricity. Take a while to readjust the printing industry, but there'll be books and magazines, all right."

George Bailey grinned and got up. He walked over to the window and looked out and down into the storm. A streetcar was stalled in the middle of the block outside. Behind him, the lights flickered again. An automobile stopped, then started more slowly, stopped again.

A neon light across the way suddenly went dark.

He looked up at the sky and sipped his drink.

"No lightning," he said. He was going to *miss* the lightning.

The change-over, for a wonder, went smoothly.

The government, having had experience of a multiplicity of divided authorities, created one board with practically unlimited authority, and under it three subsidiary boards. The main board, called the Economic Readjustment Bureau, had only seven members, and its job was to coordinate the efforts of the three subsidiary boards and to decide, quickly and without delay, any jurisdictional disputes among them.

First of the three subsidiary boards was the Transportation Bureau. It immediately took over, temporarily, the railroads. It ordered Diesel engines run on sidings and left there, organized use of the steam locomotives, and solved the problems of railroading sans telegraphy and electric signals. It dictated, then, what should be transported, food coming first, coal and fuel oil second, and essential manufactured articles in the order of their relative importance. Carload after carload of new radios, electric stoves, refrigerators, and such useless articles were dumped unceremoniously alongside the tracks, to be salvaged for scrap metal later.

All horses were declared wards of the government, graded according to capabilities, and put to work or to stud. Draft horses were used for only the most essential kinds of hauling. The breeding program was given the fullest possible emphasis; the bureau estimated that the equine population would double in two years, quadruple in three, and that within six or seven years there would be a horse in every garage in the country.

Farmers, deprived temporarily of their horses, and with their tractors rusting in the fields, were instructed how to use cattle for plowing and other work about the farm, including light hauling.

The second board, the Manpower Relocation Bureau, functioned just as one would deduce from its title. It handled unemployment benefits for the millions thrown temporarily out of work and helped relocate them—not too difficult a task, considering the tremendously increased demand for hand labor in many fields. In May of 1947, thirty-five million employables were out of work; in October, fifteen million; by May of 1948, five million. By 1949 the situation was completely in hand and competitive demand was already beginning to raise wages.

The third board had the most difficult job of the three. It was called the Factory Readjustment Bureau. It coped with the stupendous task of converting factories, filled with electrically operated machinery and, for the most part, tooled for the production of other electrically operated machinery, over to the production, without electricity, of essential nonelectrical articles.

The few available stationary steam engines worked twenty-four-hour shifts in those early days, and the first thing they were given to do was to run stampers and planers and millers turning out more stationary steam engines, of all sizes. These, in turn, were first put to work making still more steam engines. The number of steam engines grew by squares and cubes, as did the number of horses put to stud. The principle was the same. One might—and many did—refer to those early steam engines as stud horses. At any rate, there was no lack of metal for them. The factories were filled with nonconvertible machinery waiting to be melted down.

Only when steam engines—the basis of the new factory economy —were in full production were they assigned to running machinery for the manufacture of other articles: oil lamps, clothing, coal stoves, oil stoves, bathtubs, and bedsteads.

Not quite all the big factories were converted. For, while the con-version period went on, individual handicrafts sprang up in thousands of places. Little one- and two-man shops made and repaired furniture, shoes, candles, all sorts of things that *could* be made without complex machinery. At first these small shops made small fortunes because they had no competition from heavy indus-try. Later, they bought small steam engines to run small machines, and held their own, growing with the boom that came with a return to normal employment and buying power, increasing gradually in size until many of them rivaled the bigger factories in output and beat them in quality.

There *was* suffering, during the period of economic readjustment, but less than there had been during the great depression of the early 1930's. And the recovery was quicker.

The reason was obvious: In combating the depression, the govern-ment was working in the dark. They didn't know its cause—rather, they knew a thousand conflicting theories of its cause—and they didn't know the cure. They were hampered by the idea that the thing was temporary and would cure itself if left alone. Briefly and frankly, they didn't know what it was all about, and while they experimented, it snowballed.   −

But the situation that faced the country—and all other coun-tries—in 1947 was clear-cut and obvious. No more electricity. Re-adjust for steam and horsepower.

As simple and clear as that, and no ifs or ands or buts. And the whole people—except for the usual scattering of cranks—back of them.

By 1951—

It was a rainy day in April, and George Bailey was waiting under the sheltering roof of the little railroad station at Blakestown, Con-necticut, to see who might come in on the 3:14.

It chugged in at 3:25 and came to a panting stop: three coaches and a baggage car. The baggage-car door opened and a sack of mail was handed out and the door closed again. No luggage, so probably no passengers would—

Then at the sight of a tall, dark man swinging down from the platform of the rear coach, George Bailey let out a yip of delight. "Pete! Pete Mulvaney! What the devil—"

"Bailey, by all that's holy! What are you doing here?"

George was wringing his hand. "Me? I live here. Two years now. I bought the Blakestown *Weekly* in '49, for a song, and I run it—editor, reporter, and janitor. Got one printer to help me out with that end, and Maisie does the social items. She's—"

"Maisie? Maisie Hetterman?"

"Maisie Bailey now. We got married same time I bought the paper and moved here. What are you doing here, Pete?"

"Business. Just here overnight. See a man named Wilcox."

"Oh, Wilcox. Our local screwball—but don't get me wrong; he's a smart guy, all right. Well, you can see him tomorrow. You're coming home with me now for dinner and to stay overnight. Maisie'll be glad to see you. Come on, my buggy's over here."

"Sure. Finished whatever you were here for?"

"Yep, just to pick up the news on who came in on the train. And *you* came in, so here we go."

They got in the buggy, and George picked up the reins and said, "Giddap, Bessie," to the mare. Then, "What are you doing now, Pete?"

"Research. For a gas-supply company. Been working on a more efficient mantle, one that'll give more light and be less destructible. This fellow Wilcox wrote us he had something along that line; the company sent me up to look it over. If it's what he claims, I'll take him back to New York with me and let the company lawyers dicker with him."

"How's business, otherwise?"

"Great, George. *Gas;* that's the coming thing. Every new home's being piped for it, and plenty of the old ones. How about you?"

"We got it. Luckily we had one of the old linotypes that ran the metal pot off a gas burner, so it was already piped in. And our home is right over the office and print shop, so all we had to do was pipe it up a flight. Great stuff, gas. How's New York?"

"Fine, George. Down to its last million people, and stabilizing there. No crowding, and plenty of room for everybody. The *air* —why, it's better than Atlantic City, without gasoline fumes."

"Enough horses to go around yet?"

"Almost. But bicycling's the craze; the factories can't turn out enough to meet the demand. There's a cycling club in almost every block, and all the able-bodied cycle to and from work. Doing 'em good, too; a few more years, and the doctors will go on short rations."

"You got a bike?"

"Sure, a pre-vader one. Average five miles a day on it, and I eat like a horse."

George Bailey chuckled. "I'll have Maisie include some hay in the dinner. Well, here we are. Whoa, Bessie."

An upstairs window went up, and Maisie looked out and down. She called out, "Hi, Pete!"

"Extra plate, Maisie," George called. "We'll be up soon as I put the horse away and show Pete around downstairs."

He led Pete from the barn into the back door of the newspaper shop. "Our linotype!" he announced proudly, pointing.

"How's it work? Where's your steam engine?"

George grinned. "Doesn't work yet; we still handset the type. I could get only one steamer and had to use that on the press. But I've got one on order for the lino and coming up in a month or so. When we get it, Pop Jenkins, my printer, is going to put himself out of a job by teaching me to run it. With the linotype going, I can handle the whole thing myself."

"Kind of rough on Pop?"

George shook his head. "Pop eagerly awaits the day. He's sixty-nine and wants to retire. He's just staying on until I can do without him. Here's the press—a honey of a little Miehle; we do some job work on it, too. And this is the office, in front. Messy, but efficient."

Mulvaney looked around and grinned. "George, I believe you've found your niche. You were cut out for a small-town editor."

"Cut out for it? I'm crazy about it. I have more fun than everybody. Believe it or not, I work like a dog and like it. Come on upstairs."

On the stairs, Pete asked, "'And the novel you were going to write?"

"Half done, and it isn't bad. But it isn't the novel I was going to write; I was a cynic then. Now—"

"George, I think the waveries were your best friends."

"Waveries?"

"Lord, how long does it take slang to get from New York out to the sticks? The vaders, of course. Some professor who specializes in studying them described one as a wavery place in the ether, and 'wavery' stuck.... Hello there, Maisie, my girl. You look like a million."

They ate leisurely. Almost apologetically, George brought out beer, in cold bottles. "Sorry, Pete, haven't anything stronger to offer you. But I haven't been drinking lately. Guess—"

"*You* on the wagon, George?"

"Not on the wagon, exactly. Didn't swear off or anything, but haven't had a drink of strong liquor in almost a year. I don't know why, but—"

"I do," said Pete Mulvaney. "I know exactly why you don't—because I don't drink much either, for the same reason. We don't drink because we don't *have* to.... Say, isn't that a *radio* over there?"

George chuckled. "A souvenir. Wouldn't sell it for a fortune. Once in a while I like to look at it and think of the awful guff I used to sweat out for it. And then I go over and click the switch and nothing happens. Just silence. Silence is the most wonderful thing in the world sometimes, Pete. Of course, I couldn't do that if there was any juice, because I'd get vaders then. I suppose they're still doing business at the same old stand?"

"Yep, the Research Bureau checks daily. They try to get up current with a little generator run by a steam turbine. But no dice; the vaders suck it up as fast as it's generated."

"Suppose they'll ever go away?"

Mulvaney shrugged. "Helmetz thinks not. He thinks they prop-agate in proportion to the available electricity. Even if the development of radio broadcasting somewhere else in the Universe would attract them there, some would stay here—and multiply like flies the minute we tried to use electricity again. And meanwhile, they'll live on the static electricity in the air. What do you do evenings up here?"

"Do? Read, write, visit with one another, go to the amateur groups—Maisie's chairman of the Blakestown Players, and I play bit parts in it. With the movies out, everybody goes in for theatricals, and we've found some real talent. And there's the chess-and-checker club, and cycle trips and picnics. . . . There isn't time enough. Not to mention music. Everybody plays an instrument, or is trying to."

"You?"

"Sure, cornet. First cornet in the Silver Concert Band, with solo parts. And—Good heavens! Tonight's rehearsal, and we're giving a concert Sunday afternoon. I hate to desert you but—"

"Can't I come around and sit in? I've got my flute in the brief case here and—"

"*Flute?* We're short on flutes. Bring that around and Si Perkins, our director, will practically shanghai you into staying over for the concert Sunday—and it's only three days, so why not? And get it out now; we'll play a few old-timers to warm up. Hey, Maisie, skip those dishes and come on in to the piano!"

While Pete Mulvaney went to the guest room to get his flute from the brief case, George Bailey picked up his cornet from the top of the piano and blew a soft, plaintive little minor run on it. Clear as a bell; his lip was in good shape tonight.

And with the shining silver thing in his hand he wandered over to the window and stood looking out into the night. It was dusk, and the rain had stopped.

A high-stepping horse *clop-clopped* by, and the bell of a bicycle jangled. Somebody across the street was strumming a guitar and singing. He took a deep breath and let it out slowly.

The scent of spring was soft and sweet in the moist air.

Peace and dusk and distant rolling thunder. Thunder, but— "I wish," he said softly, "there was a bit of lightning. I *miss* the lightning."

The Portable Phonograph

Walter Van Tilburg Clark

The red sunset, with narrow, black cloud strips like threats across it, lay on the curved horizon of the prairie. The air was still and cold, and in it settled the mute darkness and greater cold of night. High in the air there was wind, for through the veil of the dusk the clouds could be seen gliding rapidly south and changing shapes. A queer sensation of torment, of two-sided, unpredictable nature, arose from the stillness of the earth air beneath the violence of the upper air. Out of the sunset, through the dead, matted grass and isolated weed stalks of the prairie, crept the narrow and deeply rutted remains of a road. In the road, in places, there were crusts of shallow, brittle ice. There were little islands of an old oiled pavement in the road too, but most of it was mud, now frozen rigid. The frozen mud still bore the toothed impress of great tanks, and a wanderer on the neighboring undulations might have stumbled, in this light, into large, partially filled-in and weed-grown cavities, their banks channelled and beginning to spread into badlands. These pits were such as might have been made by falling meteors, but they were not. They were the scars of gigantic bombs, their rawness already made a little natural by rain, seed, and time. Along the road, there were rakish remnants of fence. There was also, just visible, one portion of tangled and multiple barbed wire still erect, behind which was a shelving ditch with small caves, now very quiet and empty, at intervals in its back wall. Otherwise there was no structure or remnant of a structure visible over the dome of the darkling earth, but only, in sheltered hollows, the darker shadows of young trees trying again.

Under the wuthering arch of the high wind a V of wild geese fled south. The rush of their pinions sounded briefly, and the faint, plaintive notes of their expeditionary talk. Then they left a still greater vacancy. There was the smell and expectation of snow, as there is likely to be when the wild geese fly south. From the remote distance, towards the red sky, came faintly the protracted howl and quick yap-yap of a prairie wolf.

North of the road, perhaps a hundred yards, lay the parallel and deeply intrenched course of a small creek, lined with leafless alders and willows. The creek was already silent under ice. Into the bank above it was dug a sort of cell, with a single opening, like the mouth of a mine tunnel. Within the cell there was a little red of fire, which showed dully through the opening, like a reflection or a deception of the imagination. The light came from the chary burning of four blocks of poorly aged peat, which gave off a petty warmth and much acrid smoke. But the precious remnants of wood, old fence posts and timbers from the long-deserted dugouts, had to be saved for the real cold, for the time when a man's breath blew white, the moisture in his nostrils stiffened at once when he stepped out, and the expansive blizzards paraded for days over the vast open, swirling and settling and thickening, till the dawn of the cleared day when the sky was thin blue-green and the terrible cold, in which a man could not live for three hours unwarmed, lay over the uniformly drifted swell of the plain.

Around the smoldering peat, four men were seated cross-legged. Behind them, traversed by their shadows, was the earth bench, with two old and dirty army blankets, where the owner of the cell slept. In a niche in the opposite wall were a few tin utensils which caught the glint of the coals. The host was rewrapping in a piece of daubed burlap four fine, leather-bound books. He worked slowly and very carefully, and at last tied the bundle securely with a piece of grass-woven cord. The other three looked intently upon the process, as if a great significance lay in it. As the host tied the cord, he spoke. He was an old man, his long, matted beard and hair gray to nearly white. The shadows made his brows and cheekbones appear gnarled, his eyes and cheeks deeply sunken. His big hands, rough with frost and swollen by rheumatism, were awkward but gentle at their task. He was like a prehistoric priest performing a fateful ceremonial rite. Also his voice had in it a suitable quality of deep, reverent despair, yet perhaps at the moment, a sharpness of selfish satisfaction.

"When I perceived what was happening, " he said, "I told myself, 'It is the end. I cannot take much; I will take these.'

"Perhaps I was impractical," he continued. "But for myself, I do not regret, and what do we know of those who will come after us? We are the doddering remnant of a race of mechanical fools. I have saved what I love; the soul of what was good in us is here; perhaps the new ones will make a strong enough beginning not to fall behind when they become clever."

He rose with slow pain and placed the wrapped volumes in the niche with his utensils. The others watched him with the same ritualistic gaze.

"Shakespeare, the Bible, *Moby Dick, The Divine Comedy*," one of them said softly. "You might have done worse, much worse."

"You will have a little soul left until you die," said another harshly. "That is more than is true of us. My brain becomes thick, like my hands." He held the big, battered hands, with their black nails, in the glow to be seen.

"I want paper to write on," he said. "And there is none."

The fourth man said nothing. He sat in the shadow farthest from the fire, and sometimes his body jerked in its rags from the cold. Although he was still young, he was sick and coughed often. Writing implied a greater future than he now felt able to consider.

The old man seated himself laboriously, and reached out, groaning at the movement, to put another block of peat on the fire. With bowed heads and averted eyes, his three guests acknowledged his magnanimity.

"We thank you, Doctor Jenkins, for the reading," said the man who had named the books.

They seemed then to be waiting for something. Doctor Jenkins understood, but was loath to comply. In an ordinary moment he would have said nothing. But the words of *The Tempest*, which he had been reading, and the religious attention of the three made this an unusual occasion.

"You wish to hear the phonograph," he said grudgingly.

The two middle-aged men stared into the fire, unable to formulate and expose the enormity of their desire.

The young man, however, said anxiously, between suppressed coughs, "Oh, please," like an excited child.

The old man rose again in his difficult way, and went to the back of the cell. He returned and placed tenderly upon the packed floor, where the firelight might fall upon it, an old portable phonograph in a black case. He smoothed the top with his hand, and then opened it. The lovely green-felt-covered disk became visible.

"I have been using thorns as needles," he said. "But tonight, because we have a musician among us"—he bent his head to the young man, almost invisible in the shadow—"I will use a steel needle. There are only three left."

The two middle-aged men stared at him in speechless adoration. The one with the big hands, who wanted to write, moved his lips, but the whisper was not audible.

"Oh, don't!" cried the young man, as if he were hurt. "The thorns will do beautifully."

"No," the old man said. "I have become accustomed to the thorns, but they are not really good. For you, my young friend, we will have good music tonight."

"After all," he added generously, and beginning to wind the phonograph, which creaked, "they can't last forever."

"No, nor we," the man who needed to write said harshly. "The needle, by all means."

"Oh, thanks," said the young man. "Thanks," he said again in a low, excited voice, and then stifled his coughing with a bowed head.

"The records, though," said the old man when he had finished winding, "are a different matter. Already they are very worn. I do not play them more than once a week. One, once a week, that is what I allow myself.

"More than a week I cannot stand it; not to hear them," he apologized.

"No, how could you?" cried the young man. "And with them here like this."

"A man can stand anything," said the man who wanted to write, in his harsh, antagonistic voice.

"Please, the music," said the young man.

"Only the one," said the old man. "In the long run, we will remember more that way."

He had a dozen records with luxuriant gold and red seals. Even in that light the others could see that the threads of the records were becoming worn. Slowly he read out the titles and the tremendous dead names of the composers and the artists and the orchestras. The three worked upon the names in their minds, carefully. It was difficult to select from such a wealth what they would at once most like to remember. Finally, the man who wanted to write named Gershwin's "New York."

"Oh, no," cried the sick young man, and then could say nothing more because he had to cough. The others understood him, and the harsh man withdrew his selection and waited for the musician to choose.

The musician begged Doctor Jenkins to read the titles again, very slowly, so that he could remember the sounds. While they were read, he lay back against the wall, his eyes closed, his thin, horny hand pulling at his light beard, and listened to the voices and the orchestras and the single instruments in his mind.

When the reading was done he spoke despairingly. "I have forgotten," he complained; "I cannot hear them clearly.

"There are things missing," he explained.

"I know," said Doctor Jenkins. "I thought that I knew all of Shelley by heart. I should have brought Shelley."

"That's more soul than we can use," said the harsh man. "*Moby Dick* is better.

"By God, we can understand that," he emphasized.

The Doctor nodded.

"Still," said the man who had admired the books, "we need the absolute if we are to keep a grasp on anything.

"Anything but these sticks and peat clods and rabbit snares," he said bitterly.

"Shelley desired an ultimate absolute," said the harsh man. "It's too much," he said. "It's no good; no earthly good."

The musician selected a Debussy nocturne. The others considered and approved. They rose to their knees to watch the Doctor prepare for the playing, so that they appeared to be actually in an attitude of worship. The peat glow showed the thinness of their bearded faces, and the deep lines in them, and revealed the condition of their garments. The other two continued to kneel as the old man carefully lowered the needle onto the spinning disk, but the musician suddenly drew back against the wall again, with his knees up, and buried his face in his hands.

At the first notes of the piano the listeners were startled. They stared at each other. Even the musician lifted his head in amazement, but then quickly bowed it again, strainingly, as if he were suffering from a pain he might not be able to endure. They were all listening deeply, without movement. The wet, blue-green notes tinkled forth from the old machine, and were individual, delectable presences in the cell. The individual, delectable presences swept into a sudden tide of unbearably beautiful dissonance, and then continued fully the swelling and ebbing of that tide, the dissonant inpourings, and the resolutions, and the diminishments, and the little, quiet wavelets of interlude lapping between. Every sound was piercing and singularly sweet. In all the men except the musician, there occurred rapid sequences of tragically heightened recollection. He heard nothing but what was there. At the final, whispering disappearance, but moving quietly so that the others would not hear him and look at him, he let his head fall back in agony, as if it were drawn there by the hair, and clenched the fingers of one hand over his teeth. He sat that way while the others were silent, and until they began to breathe again normally. His drawn-up legs were trembling violently.

Quickly Doctor Jenkins lifted the needle off, to save it and not to spoil the recollection with scraping. When he had stopped the whirling of the sacred disk, he courteously left the phonograph open and by the fire, in sight.

The others, however, understood. The musician rose last, but then abruptly, and went quickly out at the door without saying anything. The others stopped at the door and gave their thanks in low voices. The Doctor nodded magnificently.

"Come again," he invited, "in a week. We will have the 'New York.' "

When the two had gone together, out towards the rimed road, he stood in the entrance, peering and listening. At first, there was only the resonant boom of the wind overhead, and then far over the dome of the dead, dark plain, the wolf cry lamenting. In the rifts of clouds the Doctor saw four stars flying. It impressed the

Doctor that one of them had just been obscured by the beginning of a flying cloud at the very moment he heard what he had been listening for, a sound of suppressed coughing. It was not near-by, however. He believed that down against the pale alders he could see the moving shadow.

With nervous hands he lowered the piece of canvas which served as his door, and pegged it at the bottom. Then quickly and quietly, looking at the piece of canvas frequently, he slipped the records into the case, snapped the lid shut, and carried the phonograph to his couch. There, pausing often to stare at the canvas and listen, he dug earth from the wall and disclosed a piece of board. Behind this there was a deep hole in the wall, into which he put the phonograph. After a moment's consideration, he went over and reached down his bundle of books and inserted it also. Then, guardedly, he once more sealed up the hole with the board and the earth. He also changed his blankets, and the grass-stuffed sack which served as a pillow, so that he could lie facing the entrance. After carefully placing two more blocks of peat upon the fire, he stood for a long time watching the stretched canvas, but it seemed to billow naturally with the first gusts of a lowering wind. At last he prayed, and got in under his blankets, and closed his smoke-smarting eyes. On the inside of the bed, next to the wall, he could feel with his hand the comfortable piece of lead pipe.

The Star

Arthur C. Clarke

It is three thousand light-years to the Vatican. Once I believed that space could have no power over Faith. Just as I believed that the heavens declared the glory of God's handiwork. Now I have seen that handiwork, and my faith is sorely troubled.

I stare at the crucifix that hangs on the cabin wall above the Mark VI computer, and for the first time in my life I wonder if it is no more than an empty symbol.

I have told no one yet, but the truth cannot be concealed. The data are there for anyone to read, recorded on the countless miles of magnetic tape and the thousands of photographs we are carrying back to Earth. Other scientists can interpret them as easily as I can—more easily, in all probability. I am not one who would condone that tampering with the Truth which often gave my Order a bad name in the olden days.

The crew is already sufficiently depressed, I wonder how they will take this ultimate irony. Few of them have any religious faith, yet they will not relish using this final weapon in their campaign against me—that private, good-natured but fundamentally serious war which lasted all the way from Earth. It amused them to have a Jesuit as a chief astrophysicist: Dr. Chandler, for instance, could never get over it (why are medical men such notorious atheists?). Sometimes he would meet me on the observation deck, where the lights are always low so that the stars shine with undiminished glory. He would come up to me in the gloom and stand staring out of the great oval port, while the heavens crawled slowly round us as the ship turned end over end with the residual spin we had never bothered to correct.

"Well, Father," he would say at last. "It goes on forever and forever, and perhaps *Something* made it. But how you can believe that Something has a special interest in us and our miserable little world—that just beats me." Then the argument would start, while the stars and nebulae would swing around us in silent, endless arcs beyond the flawlessly clear plastic of the observation port.

It was, I think, the apparent incongruity of my position which ... yes, *amused* ... the crew. In vain I would point to my three papers in the *Astrophysical Journal*, my five in the *Monthly Notices of the Royal Astronomical Society*. I would remind them that our Order has long been famous for its scientific works. We may be few now, but ever since the eighteenth century we have made contributions to astronomy and geophysics out of all proportions to our numbers.

Will my report on the Phoenix Nebula end our thousand years of history? It will end, I fear, much more than that.

I do not know who gave the Nebula its name, which seems to me a very bad one. If it contains a prophecy, it is one which cannot be verified for several thousand million years. Even the word nebula is misleading: this is a far smaller object than those stupendous clouds of mist—the stuff of unborn stars—which are scattered throughout the length of the Milky Way. On the cosmic scale, indeed, the Phoenix Nebula is a tiny thing—a tenuous shell of gas surrounding a single star.

Or what is left of a star...

The Rubens engraving of Loyola seems to mock me as it hangs there above the spectrophotometer tracings. What would *you*, Father, have made of this knowledge that has come into my keeping, so far from the little world that was all the universe you knew? Would your faith have risen to the challenge, as mine has failed to do?

You gaze into the distance, Father, but I have traveled a distance beyond any that you could have imagined when you founded our Order a thousand years ago. No other survey ship has been so far from Earth: we are at the very frontiers of the explored universe. We set out to reach the Phoenix Nebula, we succeeded, and we are homeward bound with our burden of knowledge. I wish I could lift that burden from my shoulders, but I call to you in vain across the centuries and the light-years that lie between us.

On the book you are holding the words are plain to read. AD MAIOREM DEI GLORIAM the message runs, but it is a message I can no longer believe. Would you still believe it, if you could see what we have found?

We knew, of course, what the Phoenix Nebula was. Every year, in *our* galaxy alone, more than a hundred stars explode, blazing for a few hours or days with thousands of times their normal brilliance before they sink back into death and obscurity. Such are the ordinary novae—the commonplace disasters of the universe. I have recorded the spectrograms and light-curves of dozens, since I started working at the lunar observatory.

But three or four times in every thousand years occurs something beside which even a nova pales into total insignificance.

When a star becomes a *supernova,* it may for a little while outshine all the massed suns of the galaxy. The Chinese astronomers watched this happen in 1054 A.D., not knowing what it was they saw. Five centuries later, in 1572, a supernova blazed in Cassiopeia so brilliantly that it was visible in the daylight sky. There have been three more in the thousand years that have passed since then.

Our mission was to visit the remnants of such a catastrophe, to reconstruct the events that led up to it, and, if possible, to learn its cause. We came slowly in through the concentric shells of gas that had been blasted out six thousand years before, yet were expanding still. They were immensely hot, radiating still with a fierce violet light, but far too tenuous to do us any damage. When the star had exploded, its outer layers had been driven upwards with such speed that they had escaped completely from its gravitational field. Now they formed a hollow shell large enough to engulf a thousand solar systems, and at its center burned the tiny, fantastic object which the star had now become—a white dwarf, smaller than the Earth yet weighing a million times as much.

The glowing gas shells were all around us, banishing the normal night of interstellar space. We were flying into the center of a cosmic bomb that had detonated millennia ago and whose incandescent fragments were still hurtling apart. The immense scale of the explosion, and the fact that the debris already covered a volume of space many billions of miles across, robbed the scene of any visible movement. It would take decades before the unaided eye could detect any motion in these tortured wisps and eddies of gas, yet the sense of turbulent expansion was overwhelming.

We had checked our primary drive hours before, and were drifting slowly towards the fierce little star ahead. Once it had been a sun like our own, but it had squandered in a few hours the energy that should have kept it shining for a million years. Now it was a shrunken miser, hoarding its resources as if trying to make amends for its prodigal youth.

No one seriously expected to find planets. If there had been any before the explosion, they would have been boiled into puffs of vapor, and their substance lost in the greater wreckage of the star itself. But we made the automatic search, as always when approaching an unknown sun, and presently we found a single small world circling the star at immense distance. It must have been the Pluto of this vanished solar system, orbiting on the frontiers of the night.

Too far from the central sun ever to have known life, its remoteness had saved it from the fate of all its lost companions.

The passing fires had seared its rocks and burnt away the mantle of frozen gas that must have covered it in the days before the disaster. We landed, and we found the Vault.

Its builders had made sure that we should. The monolithic marker that stood above the entrance was now a fused stump, but even the first long-range photographs told us that here was the work of intelligence. A little later we detected the continent-wide pattern of radioactivity that had been buried in the rock. Even if the pylon above the Vault had been destroyed, this would have remained, an immovable and all but eternal beacon calling to the stars. Our ship fell towards this gigantic bull's-eye like an arrow into its target.

The pylon must have been a mile high when it was built, but now it looked like a candle that had melted down into a puddle of wax. It took us a week to drill through the fused rock, since we did not have the proper tools for a task like this. We were astronomers, not archaeologists, but we could improvise. Our original program was forgotten: this lonely monument, reared at such labor at the greatest possible distance from the doomed sun, could have only one meaning. A civilization which knew it was about to die had made its last bid for immortality.

It will take us generations to examine all the treasures that were placed in the Vault. *They* had plenty of time to prepare, for their sun must have given its first warnings many years before the final detonation. Everything that they wished to preserve, all the fruits of their genius, they brought here to this distant world in the days before the end, hoping that some other race would find them and that they would not be utterly forgotten.

If only they had had a little more time! They could travel freely enough between the planets of their own sun, but they had not yet learned to cross the interstellar gulfs, and the nearest solar system was a hundred light-years away.

Even if they had not been so disturbingly human as their sculpture shows, we could not have helped admiring them and grieving for their fate. They left thousands of visual records and the machines for projecting them, together with elaborate pictorial instructions from which it will not be difficult to learn their written language. We have examined many of these records, and brought to life for the first time in six thousand years the warmth and beauty of a civilization which in many ways must have been superior to our own. Perhaps they only showed us the best, and one can hardly blame them. But their worlds were very lovely, and their cities were built with a grace that matches anything of ours. We have watched them at work and play, and listened to their musical speech sounding across the centuries. One scene is still before my eyes—a group of children on a beach of strange blue sand, playing in the waves as children play on Earth.

And sinking into the sea, still warm and friendly and life-giving, is the sun that will soon turn traitor and obliterate all this innocent happiness.

Perhaps if we had not been so far from home and so vulnerable to loneliness, we should not have been so deeply moved. Many of us had seen the ruins of ancient civilizations on other worlds, but they had never affected us so profoundly.

This tragedy was unique. It was one thing for a race to fail and die, as nations and cultures have done on Earth. But to be destroyed so completely in the full flower of its achievement, leaving no survivors—how could that be reconciled with the mercy of God?

My colleagues have asked me that, and I have given what answers I can. Perhaps you could have done better, Father Loyola, but I have found nothing in the *Exercitia Spiritualia* that helps me here. They were not an evil people: I do not know what gods they worshipped, if indeed they worshipped any. But I have looked back at them across the centuries, and have watched while the loveliness they used their last strength to preserve was brought forth again into the light of their shrunken sun.

I know the answers that my colleagues will give when they get back to Earth. They will say that the universe has no purpose and no plan, that since a hundred suns explode every year in our galaxy, at this very moment some race is dying in the depths of space. Whether that race had done good or evil during its lifetime will make no difference in the end: there is no divine justice, *for there is no God.*

Yet, of course, what we have seen proves nothing of the sort. Anyone who argues thus is being swayed by emotion, not logic. God has no need to justify His actions to man. He who built the universe can destroy it when He chooses. It is arrogance—it is perilously near blasphemy—for us to say what He may or may not do.

This I could have accepted, hard though it is to look upon whole worlds and peoples thrown into the furnace. But there comes a point when even the deepest faith must falter, and now, as I look at my calculations, I know I have reached that point at last.

We could not tell, before we reached the nebula, how long ago the explosion took place. Now, from the astronomical evidence and the record in the rocks of that one surviving planet, I have been able to date it very exactly. I know in what year the light of this colossal conflagration reached Earth. I know how brilliantly the supernova whose corpse now dwindles behind our speeding ship once shone in terrestrial skies. I know how it must have blazed low in the East before sunrise, like a beacon in that Oriental dawn.

There can be no reasonable doubt: the ancient mystery is solved at last. Yet—O God, there were so many stars you *could* have used.

What was the need to give these people to the fire, that the symbol of their passing might shine above Bethlehem?

Star Bright

Mark Clifton

Friday, June 11

At three years of age, a little girl shouldn't have enough function-ing intelligence to cut out and paste together a Moebius Strip.

Or, if she did it by accident, she surely shouldn't have enough reasoning ability to pick up one of her crayons and carefully trace the continuous line to prove it has only one surface.

And if by some strange coincidence she did, and it was still just an accident, how can I account for this generally active daughter of mine—and I do mean *active*—sitting for a solid half hour with her chin cupped in her hand, staring off into space, thinking with such concentration that it was almost painful to watch?

I was in my reading chair, going over some work. Star was sitting on the floor, in the circle of my light, with her blunt-nosed scissors and her scraps of paper.

Her long silence made me glance down at her as she was taping the two ends of the paper together. At that point I thought it was an accident that she had given a half twist to the paper strip before joining the circle. I smiled to myself as she picked it up in her chubby fingers.

"A little child forms the enigma of the ages," I mused.

But instead of throwing the strip aside, or tearing it apart as any other child would do, she carefully turned it over and around—studying it from all sides.

Then she picked up one of her crayons and began tracing the line. She did it as though she were substantiating a conclusion already reached!

It was a bitter confirmation for me. I had been refusing to face it for a long time, but I could ignore it no longer.

Star was a High I.Q.

For half an hour I watched her while she sat on the floor, one knee bent under her, her chin in her hand, unmoving. Her eyes were wide with wonderment, looking into the potentialities of the phenomenon she had found.

It had been a tough struggle, taking care of her since my wife's death. Now this added problem. If only she could have been normally dull, like other children!

I made up my mind while I watched her. If a child is afflicted, then let's face it, she's afflicted. A parent must teach her to compensate. At least she could be prepared for the bitterness I'd known. She could learn early to take it in stride.

I could use the measurements available, get the degree of intelligence, and in that way grasp the extent of my problem. A twenty-point jump in I.Q. creates an entirely different set of problems. The 140 child lives in a world nothing at all like that of the 100 child, and a world which the 120 child can but vaguely sense. The problems which vex and challenge the 160 pass over the 140 as a bird flies over a field mouse. I must not make the mistake of posing the problems of one if she is the other. I must know. In the meantime, I must treat it casually.

"That's called the Moebius Strip, Star," I interrupted her thoughts.

She came out of her reveries with a start. I didn't like the quick way her eyes sought mine—almost furtively, as though she had been caught doing something bad.

"Somebody already make it?" she disappointedly asked.

She knew what she had discovered! Something inside me spilled over with grief, and something else caught at me with dread.

I kept my voice casual. "A man by the name of Moebius. A long time ago. I'll tell you about him sometime when you're older."

"Now. While I'm little," she commanded, with a frown. "And don't tell. Read me."

What did she mean by that? Oh, she must be simply paraphrasing me at those times in the past when I've wanted the facts and not garbled generalizations. It could only be that!

"Okay, young lady." I lifted an eyebrow and glared at her in mock ferociousness, which usually sent her into gales of laughter. "I'll slow you down!"

She remained completely sober.

I turned to the subject in a physics book. It's not in simple language, by any means, and I read it as rapidly as I could speak. My thought was to make her admit she didn't understand it, so I could translate it into basic language.

Her reaction?

"You read too slow, Daddy," she complained. She was childishly irritable about it. "You say a word. Then I think a long time. Then you say another word."

I knew what she meant. I remember, when I was a child, my thoughts used to dart in and out among the slowly droning words of any adult. Whole patterns of universes would appear and disappear in those brief moments.

"So?" I asked.

"So," she mocked me impishly. "You teach me to read. Then I can think quick as I want."

"Quickly," I corrected in a weak voice. "The word is 'quickly,' an adverb."

She looked at me impatiently, as if she saw through this allegedly adult device to show up a youngster's ignorance. I felt like the dope!

September 1

A great deal has happened the past few months. I have tried a number of times to bring the conversation around to discuss Star's affliction with her. But she is amazingly adroit at heading me off, as though she already knows what I am trying to say and isn't concerned. Perhaps, in spite of her brilliance, she's too young to realize the hostility of the world toward intelligence.

Some of the visiting neighbors have been amused to see her sit on the floor with an encyclopedia as big as she is, rapidly turning the pages. Only Star and I know she is reading the pages as rapidly as she can turn them. I've brushed away the neighbors' comments with: "She likes to look at the pictures."

They talk to her in baby talk—and she answers in baby talk! How does she know enough to do that?

I have spent the months making an exhaustive record of her I.Q. measurements, aptitude speeds, reaction, tables, all the recommended paraphernalia for measuring something we know nothing about.

The tables are screwy, or Star is beyond all measurement.

All right, Pete Holmes, how are you going to pose those problems and combat them for her, when you have no conception of what they might be? But I must have a conception. I've got to be able to comprehend at least a little of what she may face. I simply couldn't stand by and do nothing.

Easy, though. Nobody knows better than you the futility of trying to compete out of your class. How many students, workers, and employers have tried to compete with you? You've watched them and pitied them, comparing them to a donkey trying to run the Kentucky Derby.

How does it feel to be in the place of the donkey, for a change? You've always blamed them for not realizing they shouldn't try to compete.

But this is my own daughter! I *must* understand.

October 1

Star is now four years old, and according to State Law her mind has now developed enough so that she may attend nursery school.

Again I tried to prepare her for what she might face. She listened through about two sentences and changed the subject. I can't tell about Star. Does she already know the answers? Or does she not even realize there is a problem?

I was in a sweat of worry when I took her to her first day at school yesterday morning. Last night I was sitting in my chair, reading. After she had put her dolls away, she went to the bookshelves and brought down a book of fairy tales.

That is another peculiarity of hers. She has an unmeasurably quick perception, yet she has all the normal reactions of a little girl. She likes her dolls, fairy stories, playing grownup. No, she's not a monster.

She brought the book of fairy tales over to me.

"Daddy, read me a story," she asked quite seriously.

I looked at her in amazement. "Since when? Go read your own story."

She lifted an eyebrow in imitation of my own characteristic gesture.

"Children of my age do not read," she instructed pedantically. "I can't learn to read until I am in the first grade. It is very hard to do and I am much too little."

She had found the answer to her affliction—conformity! She had already learned to conceal her intelligence. So many of us break our hearts before we learn that.

But you don't have to conceal it from me, Star! Not from me!

Oh, well, I could go along with the gag, if that was what she wanted.

"Did you like nursery school?" I asked the standard question.

"Oh, yes," she exclaimed enthusiastically. "It was fun."

"And what did you learn today, little girl?"

She played it straight back to me. "Not much. I tried to cut out paper dolls, but the scissors kept slipping." Was there an elfin deviltry back of her sober expression?

"Now, look," I cautioned, "don't overdo it. That's as bad as being too quick. The idea is that everybody has to be just about standard average. That's the only thing we will tolerate. It is expected that a little girl of four should know how to cut out paper dolls properly."

"Oh?" she questioned, and looked thoughtful. "I guess that's the hard part, isn't it, Daddy—to know how much you ought to know?"

"Yes, that's the hard part," I agreed fervently.

"But it's all right," she reassured me. "One of the Stupids showed me how to cut them out, so now that little girl likes me. She just took charge of me then and told the other kids they should like me too. So of course they did because she's leader. I think I did right, after all."

"Oh, no!" I breathed to myself. She knew how to manipulate other people already. Then my thought whirled around another concept. It was the first time she had verbally classified normal people as "Stupids," but it had slipped out so easily that I knew she'd been thinking to herself for a long time. Then my whirling thoughts hit a third implication.

"Yes, maybe it was the right thing," I conceded. "Where the little girl was concerned, that is. But don't forget you were being observed by a grownup teacher in the room. And she's smarter."

"You mean she's older, Daddy," Star corrected me.

"Smarter, too, maybe. You can't tell."

"I can," she sighed. "She's just older."

I think it was growing fear which made me defensive.

"That's good," I said emphatically. "That's very good. You can learn a lot from her then. It takes an awful lot of study to learn how to be stupid."

My own troublesome business life came to mind and I thought to myself, "I sometimes think I'll never learn it."

I swear I didn't say it aloud. But Star patted me consolingly and answered as though I'd spoken.

"That's because you're only fairly bright, Daddy. You're a Tween, and that's harder than being really bright."

"A Tween? What's a Tween?" I was bumbling to hide my confusion.

"That's what I mean, Daddy," she answered in exasperation. "You don't grasp quickly. An In Between, of course. The other people are Stupids, I'm a Bright, and you're a Tween. I made those names up when I was little."

Good God! Besides being unmeasurably bright, she's a telepath!

All right, Pete, there you are. On reasoning processes you might stand a chance—but not telepathy!

"Star," I said on impulse, "can you read people's minds?"

"Of course, Daddy," she answered, as if I'd asked a foolishly obvious question.

"Can you teach me?"

She looked at me impishly. "You're already learning it a little. But you're so slow! You see, you didn't even know you were learning."

Her voice took on a wistful note, a tone of loneliness.

"I wish—" she said, and paused.

"What do you wish?"

"You see what I mean, Daddy? You try, but you're slow."

All the same, I knew. I knew she was already longing for a companion whose mind could match her own.

A father is prepared to lose his daughter eventually, Star, but not so soon.

Not so soon . . .

June again

Some new people have moved in next door. Star says their name is Howell. Bill and Ruth Howell. They have a son, Robert, who looks maybe a year older than Star, who will soon be five.

Star seems to have taken up with Robert right away. He is a well-mannered boy and good company for Star.

I'm worried, though. Star had something to do with their moving in next door. I'm convinced of that. I'm also convinced, even from the little I've seen of him, that Robert is a Bright and a telepath.

Could it be that, failing to find quick accord with my mind, Star has reached out and out until she made contact with a telepath companion?

No, that's too fantastic. Even if it were so, how could she shape circumstances so she could bring Robert to live next door to her? The Howells came from another city. It just happened that the people who lived next door moved out and the house was put up for sale.

Just happened? How frequently do we find such abnormal Brights? What are the chances of one *just happening* to move in next door to another?

I know he is a telepath because, as I write this, I sense him reading it.

I even catch his thought: "Oh, pardon me, Mr. Holmes. I didn't intend to peek. Really I didn't."

Did I imagine that? Or is Star building a skill in my mind?

"It isn't nice to look into another person's mind unless you're asked, Robert," I thought back, rather severely. It was purely an experiment.

"I know it, Mr. Holmes. I apologize." He is in his bed in his house, across the driveway.

"No, Daddy, he really didn't mean to." And Star is in her bed in this house.

It is impossible to write how I feel. There comes a time when words are empty husks. But mixed with my expectant dread is a threat of gratitude for having been taught to be even stumblingly telepathic.

Saturday, August 11

I've thought of a gag. I haven't seen Jim Pietre in a month of Sundays, not since he was awarded that research fellowship with the museum. It will be good to pull him out of his hole, and this little piece of advertising junk Star dropped should be just the thing.

Strange about the gadget. The Awful Secret Talisman of the Mystic Junior G-Men, no doubt. Still, it doesn't have anything about crackles and pops printed on it. Merely an odd-looking coin, not even true round, bronze by the look of it. Crude. They must stamp them out by the million without ever changing a die.

But it is just the thing to send to Jim to get a rise out of him. He could always appreciate a good practical joke. Wonder how he'd feel to know he was only a Tween.

Monday, August 13

Sitting here at my study desk, I've been staring into space for an hour. I don't know what to think.

It was about noon today when Jim Pietre called the office on the phone.

"Now, look, Pete," he started out, "what kind of gag are you pulling?"

I chortled to myself and pulled the dead pan on him.

"What do you mean, boy?" I asked back into the phone. "Gag? What kind of gag? What are you talking about?"

"A coin. A coin." He was impatient. "You remember you sent me a coin in the mail?"

"Oh, yeah, that." I pretended to remember. "Look, you're an important research analyst on metals—too damned important to keep in touch with your old friends—so I thought I'd make a bid for your attention thataway."

"All right, give," he said in a low voice. "Where did you get it?" He was serious.

"Come off it, Jim. Are you practicing to be a stuffed shirt? I admit it's a rib. Something Star dropped the other day. A manufacturer's idea of kid advertising, no doubt."

"I'm in dead earnest, Peter," he answered. "It's no advertising gadget."

"It means something?"

In college Jim could take a practical joke and make six out of it.

"I don't know what it means. Where did Star get it?" He was being pretty crisp about it.

"Oh, I don't know," I said. I was getting a little fed up; the joke wasn't going according to plan. "Never asked her. You know how kids clutter up the place with their things. No father even tries to keep track of all the junk that can be bought with three boxtops and a dime."

"This was not bought with three boxtops and a dime," he spaced his words evenly. "This was not bought anywhere, for any price. In fact, if you want to be logical about it, this coin doesn't exist at all."

I laughed out loud. This was more like the old Jim.

"Okay, so you've turned the gag back on me. Let's call it quits. How about coming over to supper some night soon?"

"I'm coming over, my friend." He remained grim as he said it. "And I'm coming over tonight. As soon as you will be home. It's no gag I'm pulling. Can you get that through your stubborn head? You say you got it from Star, and of course I believe you. But it's no toy. It's the real thing." Then, as if in profound puzzlement, "Only it isn't."

A feeling of dread was settling upon me. Once you cried "Uncle" to Jim, he always let up.

"Suppose you tell me what you mean," I answered soberly.

"That's more like it, Pete. Here's what we know about the coin so far. It is apparently pre-Egyptian. It's hand-cast. It's made out of one of the lost bronzes. We fix it at around four thousand years old."

"That ought to be easy to solve," I argued. "Probably some coin collector is screaming all over the place for it. No doubt lost it and Star found it. Must be lots of old coins like that in museums and in private collections."

I was rationalizing more for my own benefit than for Jim. He would know all those things without my mentioning them. He waited until I had finished.

"Step two," he went on. "We've got one of the top coin men in the world here at the museum. As soon as I saw what the metal was, I took it to him. Now hold onto your chair, Pete. He says there is no coin like it in the world, either museum or private collection."

"You museum boys get beside yourselves at times. Come down to earth. Sometime, somewhere, some collector picked it up in some exotic place and kept it quiet. I don't have to tell you how some collectors are—sitting in a dark room, gloating over some worthless bauble, not telling a soul about it—"

"All right, wise guy," he interrupted. "Step three. That coin is at least four thousand years old *and it's also brand-new!* Let's hear you explain that away."

"New?" I asked weakly. "I don't get it."

"Old coins show wear. The edges get rounded with handling. The surface oxidizes. The molecular structure changes, crystalizes. This coin shows no wear, no oxidation, no molecular change. This coin might have been struck yesterday. *Where did Star get it?*"

"Hold it a minute," I pleaded.

I began to think back. Saturday morning. Star and Robert had been playing a game. Come to think of it, that was a peculiar game. Mighty peculiar.

Star would run into the house and stand in front of the ency-clopedia shelf. I could hear Robert counting loudly at the base tree outside in the backyard. She would stare at the encyclopedia for a moment.

Once I heard her mumble: "That's a good place."

Or maybe she merely thought it and I caught the thought. I'm doing that quite a bit of late.

Then she would run outside again. A moment later, Robert would run in and stand in front of the same shelf. Then he also would run outside again. There would be silence for several minutes. The silence would rupture with a burst of laughing and shouting. Soon, Star would come in again.

"How does he find me?" I heard her think once. "I can't reason it, and I can't ESP it out of him."

It was during one of their silences when Ruth called over to me.

"Hey, Pete! Do you know where the kids are? Time for their milk and cookies."

The Howells are awfully good to Star, bless 'em. I got up and went over to the window.

"I don't know, Ruth," I called back. "They were in and out only a few minutes ago."

"Well, I'm not worried," she said. She came through the kitchen door and stood on the back steps. "They know better than to cross the street by themselves. They're too little for that. So I guess they're over at Marily's. When they come back, tell 'em to come and get it."

"Okay, Ruth," I answered.

She opened the screen door again and went back into her kitchen. I left the window and returned to my work.

A little later, both the kids came running into the house. I managed to capture them long enough to tell them about the cookies and milk.

"Beat you there!" Robert shouted to Star.

There was a scuffle and they ran out the front door. I noticed then that Star had dropped the coin and I picked it up and sent it to Jim Pietre.

"Hello, Jim," I said into the phone. "Are you still there?"

"Yep, still waiting for an answer," he said.

"Jim, I think you'd better come over to the house right away. I'll leave my office now and meet you there. Can you get away?"

"Can I get away?" he exclaimed. "Boss says to trace this coin down and do nothing else. See you in fifteen minutes."

He hung up. Thoughtfully I replaced the receiver and went out to my car. I was pulling into my block from one arterial when I saw Jim's car pulling in from a block away. I stopped at the curb and waited for him. I didn't see the kids anywhere out front.

Jim climbed out of his car, and I never saw such an eager look of anticipation on a man's face before. I didn't realize I was showing my dread, but when he saw my face, he became serious.

"What is it, Pete? What on Earth is it?" he almost whispered.

"I don't know. At least I'm not sure. Come on inside the house."

We let ourselves in the front, and I took Jim into the study. It has a large window opening on the back garden, and the scene was very clear.

At first it was an innocent scene—so innocent and peaceful. Just three children in the backyard playing hide and seek. Marily, a neighbor's child, was stepping up to the base tree.

"Now look, you kids," she was saying. "You hide where I can find you or I won't play."

"But where can we go, Marily?" Robert was arguing loudly. Like all little boys, he seems to carry on his conversations at the top of his lungs. "There's the garage, and there's those trees and bushes. You have to look everywhere, Marily."

"And there's going to be other buildings and trees and bushes there afterward," Star called out with glee. "You gotta look behind them too."

"Yeah!" Robert took up the teasing refrain. "And there's been lots and lots of buildings and trees there before—especially trees. You gotta look behind them too."

Marily tossed her head petulantly. "I don't know what you're talking about, and I don't care. Just hide where I can find you, that's all."

She hid her face at the tree and started counting. If I had been alone, I would have been sure my eyesight had failed me, or that I was the victim of hallucinations. But Jim was standing there and saw it too.

Marily started counting, yet the other two didn't run away. Star reached out and took Robert's hand and they merely stood there. For an instant they seemed to shimmer and—*they disappeared without moving a step!*

Marily finished her counting and ran around to the few possible hiding places in the yard. When she couldn't find them, she started to blubber and pushed through the hedge to Ruth's back door.

"They runned away from me again," she whined through the screen at Ruth.

Jim and I stood staring out the window. I glanced at him. His face was set and pale, but probably no worse than my own.

We saw the instant shimmer again. Star, and then immediately Robert, materialized from the air and ran up to the tree, shouting, "Safe! Safe!"

Marily let out a bawl and ran home to her mother.

I called Star and Robert into the house. They came, still holding hands, a little shamefaced, a little defiant.

How to begin? What in hell could I say?

"It's not exactly fair," I told them. "Marily can't follow you there." I was shooting in the dark, but I had at least a glimmering to go by.

Star turned pale enough for the freckles on her little nose to stand out under her tan. Robert blushed and turned to her fiercely.

"I told you so, Star. I *told* you so! I said it wasn't sporting," he accused. He turned to me. "Marily can't play good hide-and-seek anyway. She's only a Stupid."

"Let's forget that for a minute, Robert." I turned to her. "Star, just where did you go?"

"Oh, it's nothing, Daddy." She spoke defensively, belittling the whole thing. "We just go a little ways when we play with her. She ought to be able to find us a little ways."

"That's evading the issue. *Where* do you go—and *how* do you go?"

Jim stepped forward and showed her the bronze coin I'd sent him.

"You see, Star," he said quietly, "we've found this."

"I shouldn't have to tell you my game." She was almost in tears. "You're both just Tweens. You couldn't understand." Then, struck with contrition, she turned to me. "Daddy, I've tried and tried to ESP you. Truly I did. But you don't ESP worth anything." She slipped her hand through Robert's arm. "Robert does it very nicely," she said primly, as though she were complimenting him on using his fork the right way. "He must be better than I am, because I don't know how he finds me."

"I'll tell you how I do it, Star," Robert exclaimed eagerly. It was as if he were trying to make amends now that grownups had caught on. "You don't use any imagination. I never saw anybody with so little imagination!"

"I do too have imagination," she countered loudly. "I thought up the game, didn't I? I told you how to do it, didn't I?"

"Yeah, yeah!" he shouted back. "But you always have to look at a book to ESP what's in it, so you leave an ESP smudge. I just go to the encyclopedia and ESP where you did—and I go to that place—and there you are. It's simple."

Star's mouth dropped open in consternation.

"I never thought of that," she said.

Jim and I stood there, letting the meaning of what they were saying penetrate slowly into our incredulous minds.

"Anyway," Robert was saying, "you haven't any imagination." He sank down cross-legged on the floor. "You can't teleport yourself to any place that's never been."

She went over to squat down beside him. "I can too! What about the Moon People? They haven't been yet."

He looked at her with childish disgust.

"Oh, Star, they have so been. You know that." He spread his hands out as though he were a baseball referee. "That time hasn't been yet for your daddy here, for instance, but it's already been for somebody like—well, say, like those things from Arcturus."

"Well, neither have you teleported yourself to some place that never was," Star was arguing back. "So there."

Waving Jim to one chair, I sank down into another. At least the arms of the chair felt solid beneath my hands.

"Now look, kids," I interrupted their evasive tactics, "let's start at the beginning. I gather you've figured a way to travel to places in the past or future."

"Well, of course, Daddy." Star shrugged the statement aside nonchalantly. "We just TP ourselves by ESP anywhere we want to go. It doesn't do any harm."

And these were the children who were too little to cross the street!

I have been through times of shock before. This was the same—somehow, the mind becomes too stunned to react beyond a point. One simply plows through the rest, the best he can, almost normally.

"Okay, okay," I said, and was surprised to hear the same tone I would have used over an argument about the biggest piece of cake. "I don't know whether it's harmful or not. I'll have to think it over. Right now, just tell me how you do it."

"It would be so much easier if I could ESP it to you," Star said doubtfully.

"Well, pretend I'm a Stupid and tell me in words."

"You remember the Moebius Strip?" she asked very slowly and carefully, starting with the first and most basic point in almost the way one explains to an ordinary child.

Yes, I remembered it. And I remembered how long ago it was that she had discovered it. Over a year, and her busy, brilliant mind had been exploring its possibilities ever since. And I thought she had forgotten it!

"That's where you join the ends of a strip of paper together with a half twist to make one surface," she went on, as though jogging my undependable, slow memory.

"Yes," I answered. "We all know the Moebius Strip."

Jim looked startled. I had never told him about the incident.

"Next you take a sheet and you give it a half twist and join the edge to itself all over to make a funny kind of holder."

"Klein's Bottle," Jim supplied.

She looked at him in relief.

"Oh, you know about that," she said. "That makes it easier. Well, then, the next step. You take a cube—" Her face clouded with doubt again, and she explained, "You can't do this with your hands. You've gotta ESP it done, because it's an imaginary cube anyway."

She looked at us questioningly. I nodded for her to continue.

"And you ESP the twisted cube all together the same way you did Klein's Bottle. Now if you do that big enough, all around you, so you're sort of half twisted in the middle, then you can TP yourself anywhere you want to go. And that's all there is to it," she finished hurriedly.

"Where have you gone?" I asked her quietly.

The technique of doing it would take some thinking. I knew enough physics to know that was the way the dimensions were built up. The line, the plane, the cube—Euclidian physics. The Moebius Strip, the Klein Bottle, the unnamed twisted cube— Einsteinian physics. Yes, it was possible.

"Oh, we've gone all over," Star answered vaguely. "The Romans and the Egyptians—places like that."

"You picked up a coin in one of those places?" Jim asked.

He was doing a good job of keeping his voice casual. I knew the excitement he must be feeling, the vision of the wealth of knowledge which must be opening before his eyes.

"I found it, Daddy," Star answered Jim's question. She was about to cry. "I found it in the dirt, and Robert was about to catch me. I forgot I had it when I went away from there so fast." She looked at me pleadingly. "I didn't mean to steal it, Daddy. I never stole anything, anywhere. And I was going to take it back and put it right where I found it. Truly I was. But I dropped it again, and then I ESP'd that you had it. I guess I was awful naughty."

I brushed my hand across my forehead.

"Let's skip the question of good and bad for a minute," I said, my head throbbing. "What about this business of going into the future?"

Robert spoke up, his eyes shining. "There isn't any future, Mr. Holmes. That's what I keep telling Star, but she can't reason—she's just a girl. It'll all pass. Everything is always past."

Jim stared at him, as though thunderstruck, and opened his mouth to protest. I shook my head warningly.

"Suppose you tell me about that, Robert," I said.

"Well," he began on a rising note, frowning, "it's kinda hard to explain at that. Star's a Bright and even she doesn't understand it exactly. But, you see, I'm older." He looked at her with superiority. Then, with a change of mood, he defended her. "But when she gets as old as I am, she'll understand it okay."

He patted her shoulder consolingly. He was all of six years old.

"You go back into the past. Back past Egypt and Atlantis. That's recent," he said with scorn. "And on back, and on back, and all of a sudden it's future."

"That isn't the way *I* did it." Star tossed her head contrarily. "I *reasoned* the future. I reasoned what would come next, and I went there, and then I reasoned again. And on and on. I can too reason."

"It's the same future," Robert told us dogmatically. "It has to be, because that's all that ever happened." He turned to Star. "The reason you never could find any Garden of Eden is because there wasn't any Adam and Eve." Then to me, "And man didn't come from the apes, either. Man started himself."

Jim almost strangled as he leaned forward, his face red and his eyes bulging.

"How?" he choked out.

Robert sent his gaze into the far distance.

"Well," he said, "a long time from now—you know what I mean, as a Stupid would think of Time-From-Now—men got into a mess. Quite a mess—

"There were some people in that time who figured out the same kind of traveling Star and I do. So when the world was about to blow up and form a new star, a lot of them teleported themselves back to when the Earth was young, and they started over again."

Jim just stared at Robert, unable to speak.

"I don't get it," I said.

"Not everybody could do it," Robert explained patiently. "Just a few Brights. But they enclosed a lot of other people and took them along." He became a little vague at this point. "I guess later on the Brights lost interest in the Stupids or something. Anyway, the Stupids sank down lower and lower and became like animals." He held his nose briefly. "They smelled worse. They worshiped the Brights as gods."

Robert looked at me and shrugged.

"I don't know all that happened. I've only been there a few times. It's not very interesting. Anyway," he finished, "the Brights finally disappeared."

"I'd sure like to know where they went," Star sighed. It was a lonely sigh. I helplessly took her hand and gave my attention back to Robert.

"I still don't quite understand," I said.

He grabbed up some scissors, a piece of cellophane tape, a sheet of paper. Quickly he cut a strip, gave it a half twist, and taped it together. Then rapidly, on the Moebius Strip, he wrote: "Cave men, This men, That men, Mu Men, Atlantis Men, Egyptians, History Men, Us Now Men, Atom Men, Moon Men, Planet Men, Star Men—"

"There," he said. "That's all the room there is on the strip. I've written clear around it. Right after Star Men comes Cave Men. It's all one thing, joined together. It isn't future, and it isn't past, either. It just plain *is*. Don't you see?"

"I'd sure like to know how the Brights got off the strip," Star said wistfully.

I had all I could take.

"Look, kids," I pleaded, "I don't know whether this game's dangerous or not. Maybe you'll wind up in a lion's mouth, or something."

"Oh, no, Daddy!" Star shrilled in glee. "We'd just TP ourselves right out of there."

"But fast," Robert chortled in agreement.

"Anyway, I've got to think it over," I said stubbornly. "I'm only a Tween, but, Star, I'm your daddy and you're just a little girl, so you have to mind me."

"I always mind you," she said virtuously.

"You do, eh?" I asked. "What about going off the block? Visiting the Greeks and Star Men isn't my idea of staying on the block."

"But you didn't say that, Daddy. You said not to cross the street. And I never did cross the street. Did we, Robert? Did we?"

"We didn't cross a single street, Mr. Holmes," he insisted.

"My God!" said Jim, and he went on trying to light a cigarette.

"All right, all *right!* No more leaving this time, then," I warned.

"Wait!" It was a cry of anguish from Jim. He broke the cigarette in sudden frustration and threw it in an ashtray. "The museum, Pete," he pleaded. "Think what it would mean. Pictures, specimens, voice recordings. And not only from historical places, but Star men, Pete. *Star men!* Wouldn't it be all right for them to go places they know are safe? I wouldn't ask them to take risks, but—"

"No, Jim," I said regretfully. "It's your museum, but this is my daughter."

"Sure," he breathed. "I guess I'd feel the same way."

I turned back to the youngsters.

"Star, Robert," I said to them both, "I want your promise that you will not leave this time, until I let you. Now I couldn't punish you if you broke your promise, because I couldn't follow you. But I want your promise on your word of honor you won't leave this time."

"We promise." They each held up a hand, as if swearing in court. "No more leaving this time."

I let the kids go back outside into the yard. Jim and I looked at one another for a long while, breathing hard enough to have been running.

"I'm sorry," I said at last.

"I know," he answered. "So am I. But I don't blame you. I simply forgot, for a moment, how much a daughter could mean to a man." He was silent, and then added, with the humorous quirk back at the corner of his lips, "I can just see myself reporting this interview to the museum."

"You don't intend to, do you?" I asked, alarmed.

"And get myself canned or laughed at? I'm not that stupid."

September 10

Am I actually getting it? I had a flash for an instant. I was concentrating on Caesar's triumphant march into Rome. For the briefest of instants, *there it was!* I was standing on the roadway, watching. But, most peculiar, it was still a picture; I was the only thing moving. And then, just as abruptly, I lost it.

Was it only a hallucination? Something brought about by intense concentration and wishful thinking?

Now let's see. You visualize a cube. Then you ESP it a half twist and seal the edges together—No, when it has the half twist there's only one surface. You seal that surface all around you . . .

Sometimes I think I have it. Sometimes I despair. If only I were a Bright instead of a Tween!

October 23

I don't see how I managed to make so much work of teleporting myself. It's the simplest thing in the world, no effort at all. Why, a child could do it! That sounds like a gag, considering that it was two children who showed me how, but I mean the whole thing is easy enough for even almost any kid to learn. The problem is understanding the steps . . . no, not understanding, because I can't say I do, but working out the steps in the process.

There's no danger, either. No wonder it felt like a still picture at first, for the speeding up is incredible. That bullet I got in the way of, for instance—I was able to go and meet it and walk along beside it while it traveled through the air. To the men who were dueling, I must have been no more than an instantaneous streak of movement.

That's why the youngsters laughed at the suggestion of danger. Even if they materialized right in the middle of an atomic blast, it is so slow by comparison that they could TP right out again before they got hurt. The blast can't travel any faster than the speed of light, you see, while there is no limit to the speed of thought.

But I still haven't given them permission to teleport themselves out of this time yet. I want to go over the ages pretty carefully before I do; I'm not taking any chances, even though I don't see how they could wind up in any trouble. Still, Robert claimed the Brights went from the future back into the beginning, which means they could be going through time and overtake any of the three of us, and one of them might be hostile . . .

I feel like a louse, not taking Jim's cameras, specimen boxes, and recorders along. But there's time for that. Plenty of time, once I get the feel of history without being encumbered by all that stuff to carry.

Speaking of time and history—what a rotten job historians have done! For instance:

George III of England was neither crazy nor a moron. He wasn't a particularly nice guy, I'll admit—I don't see how anybody could be with the amount of flattery I saw—but he was the victim of empire expansion and the ferment of the Industrial Revolution. So were all the other European rulers of the time, though. He certainly did better than Louis of France. At least George kept his job and his head.

On the other hand, John Wilkes Booth was definitely psychotic. He could have been cured if they'd had our methods of psychotherapy then, and Lincoln, of course, wouldn't have been assassinated. It was almost a compulsion to prevent the killing, but I didn't dare . . . God knows what effect it would have had on history. Strange thing, Lincoln looked less surprised than anybody else when he was shot, sad, yes, and hurt emotionally at least as much as physically, yet you'd swear he was expecting it.

Cheops was *plenty* worried about the number of slaves who died while the pyramid was being built. They weren't easy to replace. He gave them four hours off in the hottest part of the day, and I don't think any slaves in the country were fed or housed better.

I never found any signs of Atlantis or Lemuria, just tales of lands far off—a few hundred miles was a big distance then, remember—that had sunk beneath the sea. With the Ancients' exaggerated notion of geography, a big island was the same as a continent. Some islands did disappear, naturally, drowning a few thousand villagers and herdsmen. That must have been the source of the legends.

Columbus was a stubborn cuss. He was thinking of turning back when the sailors mutinied, which made him obstinate. I still can't see what was eating Genghis Khan and Alexander the Great—it would have been a big help to know the languages, because their big campaigns started off more like vacation or exploration trips. Helen of Troy was attractive enough, considering, but she was just an excuse to fight.

There were several attempts to federate the Indian tribes before the white man and the Five Nations, but going after wives and slaves ruined the movement every time. I think they could have kept America if they had been united and, it goes without saying, knew the deal they were going to get. At any rate, they might have traded for weapons and tools and industrialized the country somewhat in the way the Japanese did. I admit that's only speculation, but this would certainly have been a different world if they'd succeeded!

One day I'll put it all in a comprehensive and *corrected* history of mankind, *complete with photographs*, and then let the "experts" argue themselves into nervous breakdowns over it.

I didn't get very far into the future. Nowhere near the Star Men, or, for that matter, back to the beginning that Robert told us about. It's a matter of reasoning out the path and I'm not a Bright. I'll take Robert and Star along as guides, when and if.

What I did see of the future wasn't good, but it wasn't so bad, either. The real mess obviously doesn't happen until the Star Men show up very far ahead in history, if Robert is right, and I think he is. I can't guess what the trouble will be, but it must be something ghastly if they won't be able to get out of it even with the enormously advanced technology they'll have. Or maybe that's the answer. It's almost true of us now.

November, Friday 14

The Howells have gone for a weekend trip and left Robert in my care. He's a good kid and no trouble. He and Star have kept their promise, but they're up to something else. I can sense it and that feeling of expectant dread is back with me.

They've been secretive of late. I catch them concentrating intensely, sighing with vexation, and then breaking out into unexplained giggles.

"Remember your promise," I warned Star while Robert was in the room.

"We're not going to break it, Daddy," she answered seriously.

They both chorused, "No more leaving this time."

But they both broke into giggles!

I'll have to watch them. What good it would do, I don't know. They're up to something, yet how can I stop them? Shut them in their rooms? Tan their hides?

I wonder what someone else would recommend.

The kids are gone!

I've been waiting an hour for them. I know they wouldn't stay away so long if they could get back. There must be something they've run into. Bright as they are, they're still only children.

I have some clues. They promised me they wouldn't go out of this present time. With all her mischievousness, Star has never broken a promise to me—as her typically feminine mind interprets it, that is. So I know they are in our own time.

On several occasions Star has brought it up, wondering where the Old Ones, the Bright Ones, have gone—how they got off the Moebius Strip.

That's the clue. How can I get off the Moebius Strip and remain in the present?

A cube won't do it. There we have a mere journey along the single surface. We have a line, we have a plane, we have a cube. And then we have a supercube—a tesseract. That is the logical progression of mathematics. The Bright Ones must have pursued that line of reasoning.

Now I've got to do the same, but without the advantage of being a Bright. Still, it's not the same as expecting a normally intelligent person to produce a work of genius. (Genius by our standards, of course, which I suppose Robert and Star would classify as Tween.) Anyone with a pretty fair I.Q. and proper education and training can follow a genius' logic, provided the steps are there and especially if it has a practical application. What he can't do is initiate and complete that structure of logic. I don't have to, either—that was done for me by a pair of Brights and I "simply" have to apply their findings.

Now let's see if I can.

By reducing the present-past-future of man to a Moebius Strip, we have sheared away a dimension. It is a two-dimensional strip, because it has no depth. (Naturally it would be impossible for a Moebius Strip to have depth; it has only one surface.)

Reducing it to two dimensions makes it possible to travel anywhere you want to go on it via the third dimension. And you're in the third dimension when you enfold yourself in the twisted cube.

Let's go a step higher, into one more dimension. In short, the tesseract. To get the equivalent of a Moebius Strip with depth, you have to go into the fourth dimension, which, it seems to me, is the only way the Bright Ones could get off this closed cycle of past-present-future-past. They must have reasoned that one more notch up the dimensions was all they needed. It is equally obvious that Star and Robert have followed the same line of reasoning; they wouldn't break their promise not to leave the present—and getting off the Moebius Strip into *another* present would, in a sort of devious way, be keeping that promise.

I'm putting all this speculation down for you, Jim Pietre, knowing first that you're a Tween like myself, and second that you're sure to have been doing a lot of thinking about what happened after I sent you the coin Star dropped. I'm hoping you can explain all this to Bill and Ruth Howell—or enough, in any case, to let them understand the truth about their son Robert and my daughter Star, and where the children may have gone.

I'm leaving these notes where you will find them, when you and Bill and Ruth search the house and grounds for us. If you read this, it will be because I have failed in my search for the youngsters. There is also the possibility that I'll find them and that we won't be able to get back onto this Moebius Strip. Perhaps time has a different value there, or doesn't exist at all. What it's like off the Strip is anybody's guess.

Bill and Ruth: I wish I might give you hope that I will bring Robert back to you. But all I can do is wish. It may be no more than wishing upon a star—my Star.

I'm trying now to take six cubes and fold them in on one another so that every angle is a right angle.

It's not easy, but I can do it, using every bit of concentration I've learned from the kids. All right, I have the six cubes and I have every angle a right angle.

Now if, in the folding, I ESP the tesseract a half twist around myself and—

Hilifter

Gordon Dickson

It was locked—from the outside.

Not only that, but the mechanical latch handle that would override the button lock on the tiny tourist cabin aboard the *Star of the North* was hidden by the very bed on which Cully When sat crosslegged, like some sinewy mountain man out of Cully's own pioneering ancestry. Cully grinned at the image in the mirror which went with the washstand now hidden by the bed beneath him. He would not have risked such an expression as that grin if there had been anyone around to see him. The grin, he knew, gave too much of him away to viewers. It was the hard, unconquerable humor of a man dealing for high stakes.

Here, in the privacy of this locked cabin, it was also a tribute to the skill of the steward who had imprisoned him. A dour and cautious individual with a long Scottish face, and no doubt the greater part of his back wages reinvested in the very spaceship line he worked for. Or had Cully done something to give himself away? No. Cully shook his head. If that had been the case, the steward would have done more than just lock the cabin. It occurred to Cully that his face, at last, might be becoming known.

"I'm sorry, sir," the steward had said, as he opened the cabin's sliding door and saw the unmade bed. "Off-watch steward's missed making it up." He clucked reprovingly, "I'll fix it for you, sir."

"No hurry," said Cully. "I just want to hang my clothes; and I can do that later."

"Oh, no, sir." The lean, dour face of the other—as primitive in a different way as Cully's own—looked shocked. "Regulations. Passengers' gear to be stowed and bunk made up before overdrive."

"Well, I can't just stand here in the corridor," said Cully. "I want to get rid of the stuff and get a drink." And indeed the corridor was so narrow, they were like two vehicles on a mountain road. One would have to back up to some wider spot to let the other past.

154

"Have the sheets in a moment, sir," said the steward. "Just a moment, sir. If you wouldn't mind sitting up on the bed, sir?"

"All right," said Cully. "But hurry. I want to step up for a drink in the lounge."

He hopped up on to the bed, which filled the little cabin in its down position; and drew his legs up tailor-fashion to clear them out of the corridor.

"Excuse me, sir," said the steward, closed the door, and went off. As soon as he heard the button lock latch, Cully had realized what the man was up to. But an unsuspecting man would have waited at least several minutes before hammering on the locked door and calling for someone to let him out. Cully had been forced to sit digesting the matter in silence.

At the thought of it now, however, he grinned again. That steward was a regular prize package. Cully must remember to think up something appropriate for him, afterwards. At the moment, there were more pressing things to think of.

Cully looked in the mirror again and was relieved at the sight of himself without the betraying grin. The face that looked back at him at the moment was lean and angular. A little peroxide solution on his thick, straight brows, had taken the sharp appearance off his high cheekbones and given his pale blue eyes a faintly innocent expression. When he really wanted to fail to impress sharply discerning eyes, he also made it a point to chew gum.

The present situation, he considered now, did not call for that extra touch. If the steward was already even vaguely suspicious of him, he could not wait around for an ideal opportunity. He would have to get busy now, while they were still working the spaceship out of the solar system to a safe distance where the overdrive could be engaged without risking a mass-proximity explosion.

And this, since he was imprisoned so neatly in his own shoebox of a cabin, promised to be a problem right from the start.

He looked around the cabin. Unlike the salon cabins on the level overhead, where it was possible to pull down the bed and still have a tiny space to stand upright in—either beside the bed, in the case of single-bed cabins, or between them, in the case of doubles—in the tourist cabins once the bed was down, the room was completely divided into two spaces—the space above the bed and the space below. In the space above, with him, were the light and temperature and ventilation controls, controls to provide him with soft music or the latest adventure tape, food and drink dispensers and a host of other minor comforts.

There were also a phone and a signal button, both connected with the steward's office. Thoughtfully he tried both. There was, of course, no answer.

At that moment a red light flashed on the wall opposite him, and a voice came out of the grille that usually provided the soft music.

"We are about to maneuver. This is the Captain's Section, speak-ing. We are about to maneuver. Will all lounge passengers return to their cabins? Will all passengers remain in their cabins, and fasten seat belts. We are about to maneuver. This is the Captain's Sec-tion—"

Cully stopped listening. The steward would have known this announcement was coming. It meant that everybody but crew mem-bers would be in their cabins and crew members would be up top in control level at maneuver posts. And that meant nobody was likely to happen along to let Cully out. If Cully could get out of this cabin, however, those abandoned corridors could be a break for him.

However, as he looked about him now, Cully was rapidly revising downward his first cheerful assumption that he—who had gotten out of so many much more intentional prisons—would find this a relatively easy task. On the same principle that a pit with unclimb-able walls and too deep to jump up from and catch an edge is one of the most perfect traps designable—the tourist room held Cully. He was on top of the bed; and he needed to be below it to operate the latch handle.

First question: How impenetrable was the bed itself? Cully dug down through the covers, pried up the mattress, peered through the springs, and saw a blank panel of metal. Well, he had not really expected much in that direction. He put the mattress and covers back and examined what he had to work with above-bed.

There were all the control switches and buttons on the wall, but nothing among them promised him any aid. The walls were the same metal paneling as the base of the bed. Cully began to turn out his pockets in the hope of finding something in them that would inspire him. And he did indeed turn out a number of interesting items, including a folded piece of notepaper which he looked at rather soberly before laying it aside, unfolded, with a boy scout type of knife that just happened to have a set of lock picks among its other tools. The note would only take up valuable time at the moment, and—the lock being out of reach in the door—the lock picks were no good either.

There was nothing in what he produced to inspire him, however. Whistling a little mournfully, he began to make the next best use of his pile of property. He unscrewed the nib and cap of his long, gold fountain pen, took out the ink cartridge and laid the tube remaining aside. He removed his belt, and the buckle from the belt. The buckle, it appeared, clipped on to the fountain pen tube in somewhat the manner of a pistol grip. He reached in his mouth, removed a bridge covering from the second premolar to the second molar, and combined this with a small metal throwaway dispenser of the sort designed to contain antacid tablets. The two together had a remarkable resemblance to the magazine and miniaturized trigger assembly of a small handgun; and when he attached them to the buckle-fountain-pen-tube combination the resemblance became so marked as to be practically inarguable.

Cully made a few adjustments in this and looked around himself again. For the second time, his eye came to rest on the folded note, and, frowning at himself in the mirror, he did pick it up and unfold it. Inside it read: "O wae the pow'r the Giftie gie us" Love, Lucy. Well, thought Cully, that was about what you could expect from a starry-eyed girl with Scottish ancestors, and romantic notions about present-day conditions on Alderbaran IV and the other new worlds.

" . . . But if you have all that land on Asterope IV, why aren't you back there developing it?" she had asked him.

"The New Worlds are stifling to death," he had answered. But he saw then she did not believe him. To her, the New Worlds were still the romantic Frontier, as the Old Worlds Confederation newspapers capitalized it. She thought he had given up from lack of vision.

"You should try again . . ." she murmured. He gave up trying to make her understand. And then, when the cruise was over and their ship board acquaintance—that was all it was, really—ended on the Miami dock, he had felt her slip something in his pocket so lightly only someone as self-trained as he would have noticed it. Later he had found it to be this note—which he had kept now for too long.

He started to throw it away, changed his mind for the sixtieth time and put it back in his pocket. He turned back to the problem of getting out of the cabin. He looked it over, pulled a sheet from the bed and used its length to measure a few distances.

The bunk was pivoted near the point where the head of it entered the recess in the wall that concealed it in Up position. Up, the bunk was designed to fit with its foot next to the ceiling. Consequently, coming up, the foot would describe an arc—

About a second and a half later he had discovered that the arc of the foot, ascending, would leave just enough space in the opposite top angle between wall and ceiling so that if he could just manage to hang there, while releasing the safety latch at the foot of the bed, he might be able to get the bed up past him into the wall recess.

It was something which required the muscle and skill normally called for by so-called "chimney ascents" in mountain climbing—where the climber wedges himself between two opposing walls of rock. A rather wide chimney—since the room was a little more than four feet in width. But Cully had had some little experience in that line.

He tried it. A few seconds later, pressed against walls and ceiling, he reached down, managed to get the bed released, and had the satisfaction of seeing it fold up by him. Half a breath later he was free, out in the corridor of the Tourist Section.

The corridor was deserted and silent. All doors were closed. Cully closed his own thoughtfully behind him and went along the corridor to the more open space in the center of the ship. He looked up a steel ladder to the entrance of the Salon Section, where there would be another ladder to the Crew Section, and from there eventually to his objective—the Control level and the Captain's Section. Had the way up those ladders been open, it would have been simple. But level with the top of the ladder he saw the way to the Salon Section was closed off by a metal cover capable of withstanding fifteen pounds per square inch of pressure.

It had been closed, of course, as the other covers would have been, at the beginning of the maneuver period.

Cully considered it thoughtfully, his fingers caressing the pistol grip of the little handgun he had just put together. He would have preferred, naturally, that the covers be open and the way available to him without the need for fuss or muss. But the steward had effectively ruled out that possibility by reacting as and when he had. Cully turned away from the staircase, and frowned, picturing the layout of the ship, as he had committed it to memory five days ago.

There was an emergency hatch leading through the ceiling of the end tourist cabin to the end salon cabin overhead, at both extremes of the corridor. He turned and went down to the end cabin nearest him, and laid his finger quietly on the outside latch handle.

There was no sound from inside. He drew his put-together handgun from his belt; and, holding it in his left hand, calmly and without hesitation, opened the door and stepped inside.

He stopped abruptly. The bed in here was, of course, up in the wall, or he could never have entered. But the cabin's single occupant was asleep on the right-hand seat of the two seats that an upraised bed left exposed. The occupant was a small girl of about eight years old.

The slim golden barrel of the handgun had swung immediately to aim at the child's temple. For an automatic second, it hung poised there, Cully's finger half-pressing the trigger. But the little girl never stirred. In the silence, Cully heard the surge of his own blood in his ears and the faint crackle of the note in his shirt pocket. He lowered the gun and fumbled in the waistband of his pants, coming up with a child-sized anesthetic pellet. He slipped this into his gun above the regular load; aimed the gun, and fired. The child made a little uneasy movement all at once; and then lay still. Cully bent over her for a second, and heard the soft sound of her breathing. He straightened up. The pellet worked not through the blood stream, but immediately through a reaction of the nerves. In fifteen minutes the effect would be worn off, and the girl's sleep would be natural slumber again.

He turned away, stepped up on the opposite seat and laid his free hand on the latch handle of the emergency hatch overhead. A murmur of voices from above made him hesitate. He unscrewed the barrel of the handgun and put it in his ear with the other hollow end resting against the ceiling which was also the floor overhead. The voices came, faint and distorted, but understandable to his listening.

" . . . Hilifter," a female voice was saying.

"Oh, Patty!" another female voice answered. "He was just trying to scare you. You believe everything."

"How about that ship that got hilifted just six months ago? That ship going to one of the Pleiades, just like this one? The *Queen of Argyle*—"

"*Princess of Argyle*."

"Well, you know what I mean. Ships do get hilifted. Just as long as there're governments on the pioneer worlds that'll license them and no questions asked. And it could just as well happen to this ship. But you don't worry about it a bit."

"No, I don't."

"When hilifters take over a ship, they kill off everyone who can testify against them. None of the passengers or ship's officers from the *Princess of Argyle* was ever heard of again."

"Says who?"

"Oh, everybody knows that!"

Cully took the barrel from his ear and screwed it back onto his weapon. He glanced at the anesthetized child and thought of trying the other cabin with an emergency hatch. But the maneuver period would not last more than twenty minutes at the most and five of that must be gone already. He put the handgun between his teeth, jerked the latch to the overhead hatch, and pulled it down and open.

He put both hands on the edge of the hatch opening; and with one spring went upward into the salon cabin overhead.

He erupted into the open space between a pair of facing seats, each of which held a girl in her twenties. The one on his left was a rather plump, short, blond girl who was sitting curled up on her particular seat with a towel across her knees, an open bottle of pink nail polish on the towel, and the brush-cap to the bottle poised in her hand. The other was a tall, dark-haired, very pretty lass with a lap-desk pulled down from the wall and a handscriber on the desk where she was apparently writing a letter. For a moment both stared at him, and his gun; and then the blonde gave a muffled shriek, pulled the towel over her head and lay still, while the brunette, staring at Cully, went slowly pale.

"Jim!" she said.

"Sorry," said Cully. "The real name's Cully When. Sorry about this, too, Lucy." He held the gun casually, but it was pointed in her general direction. "I didn't have any choice."

A little of the color came back. Her eyes were as still as fragments of green bottle glass.

"No choice about what?" she said.

"To come through this way," said Cully. "Believe me, if I'd known you were here, I'd have picked any other way. But there wasn't any other way; and I didn't know."

"I see," she said, and looked at the gun in his hand. "Do you have to point that at me?"

"I'm afraid," said Cully, gently, "I do."

She did not smile.

"I'd still like to know what you're doing here," she said.

"I'm just passing through," said Cully. He gestured with the gun to the emergency hatch to the Crew Section, overhead. "As I say, I'm sorry it has to be through your cabin. But I didn't even know you were serious about emigrating."

"People usually judge other people by themselves," she said expressionlessly. "As it happened, I believed you." She looked at the gun again. "How many of you are there on board?"

"I'm afraid I can't tell you that," said Cully.

"No. You couldn't, could you?" Her eyes held steady on him. "You know, there's an old poem about a man like you. He rides by a farm maiden and she falls in love with him, just like that. But he makes her guess what he is; and she guesses ... oh, all sorts of honorable things, like soldier, or forester. But he tells her in the end he's just an outlaw, slinking through the wood."

Cully winced.

"Lucy—" he said. "Lucy—"

"Oh, that's all right," she said. "I should have known when you didn't call me or get in touch with me, after the boat docked." She glanced over at her friend, motionless under the towel. "You have the gun. What do you want us to do?"

"Just sit still," he said. "I'll go on up through here and be out of your way in a second. I'm afraid—" he reached over to the phone on the wall and pulled its cord loose. "You can buzz for the steward, still, after I'm gone," he said. "But he won't answer just a buzzer until after the maneuver period's over. And the stairway hatches are locked. Just sit tight and you'll be all right."

He tossed the phone aside and tucked the gun in the waistband.

"Excuse me," he said, stepping up on the seat beside her. She moved stiffly away from him. He unlatched the hatch overhead, pulled it down; and went up through it. When he glanced back down through it, he saw her face stiffly upturned to him.

He turned away and found himself in an equipment room. It was what he had expected from the ship's plans he had memorized before coming aboard. He went quickly out of the room and scouted the section.

As he had expected, there was no one at all upon this level. Weight and space on interstellar liners being at the premium that they were, even a steward like the one who had locked him in his cabin did double duty. In overdrive, no one but the navigating officer had to do much of anything. But in ordinary operation, there were posts for all ship's personnel, and all ship's personnel were at them up in the Captain's Section at Control.

The stair hatch to this top and final section of the ship, he found to be closed as the rest. This, of course, was routine. He had not expected this to be unlocked, though a few years back ships like this might have been that careless. There were emergency hatches from this level as well, of course, up to the final section. But it was no part of Cully's plan to come up in the middle of a Control Room or a Captain's Section filled with young, active, and almost certainly armed officers. The inside route was closed.

The outside route remained a possibility. Cully went down to the opposite end of the corridor and found the entry port closed, but sealed only by a standard lock. In an adjoining room there were outside suits. Cully spent a few minutes with his picks breaking the lock of the seal; and then went in to put on the suit that came closest to fitting his six-foot-two frame.

A minute later he stepped out onto the outside skin of the ship.

As he watched the outer door of the entry port closing ponderously in the silence of airless space behind him, he felt the usual inner coldness that came over him at times like this. He had a mild but very definite phobia about open space with its myriads of unchanging stars. He knew what caused it—several psychiatrists had told him it was nothing to worry about, but he could not quite accept their unconcern. He knew he was a very lonely individual, underneath it all; and subconsciously he guessed he equated space with the final extinction in which he expected one day to disappear and be forgotten forever. He could not really believe it was possible for someone like him to make a dent in such a universe.

It was symptomatic, he thought now, plodding along with the magnetic bootsoles of his suit clinging to the metal hull, that he had never had any success with women—like Lucy. A sort of bad luck seemed to put him always in the wrong position with anyone he stood a chance of loving. Inwardly, he was just as starry-eyed as Lucy, he admitted to himself, alone with the vastness of space and the stars, but he'd never had much success bringing it out in the open. Where she went all right, he seemed to go all wrong.

Well, he thought, that was life. She went her way and he would go his. And it was probably a good thing.

He looked ahead up the side of the ship, and saw the slight bulge of the observation window of the Navigator's Section. It was just a few more steps now.

Modern ships were sound insulated, thankfully, or the crew inside would have heard his dragging footsteps on the hull. He reached the window and peered in. The room he looked into was empty.

Beside the window was a small, emergency port for cleaning and repairs of the window. Clumsily, and with a good deal of effort, he got the lock-bolt holding it down, unscrewed, and let himself in. The space between outer and inner ports here was just enough to contain a space-suited man. He crouched in darkness after the outer port had closed behind him.

Incoming air screamed up to audibility. He cautiously cracked the interior door and looked into a room still empty of any crew members. He slipped inside and snapped the lock on the door before getting out of his suit.

As soon as he was out, he drew the handgun from his belt and cautiously opened the door he had previously locked. He looked out on a short corridor leading one way to the Control Room, and the other, if his memory of the memorized ship plans had not failed him, to the central room above the stairway hatch from below. Opening off this small circular space surrounding the hatch, would be another entrance directly to the Control Room, a door to the Captain's Quarters, and one to the Communications Room.

The corridor was deserted. He heard voices coming down it from the Control Room, and he slipped out the door that led instead to the space surrounding the stairway hatch. And checked abruptly.

The hatch was open. And it had not been open when he had checked it from the level below, ten minutes before.

For the first time he cocked an ear specifically to the kinds of voices coming from the Control Room. The acoustics of this part of the ship mangled all sense out of the words being said. But now that he listened, he had no trouble recognizing, among others, the voice of Lucy.

It occurred to him then with a kind of wonder at himself, that it would have been no feat for an active girl like herself to have followed him up through the open emergency hatch, and later mount the crew level stairs to the closed hatch there and pound on it until someone opened up.

He threw aside further caution and sprinted across to the doorway of the Captain's Quarters. The door was unlocked. He ducked inside and looked around him. It was empty. It occurred to him that Lucy and the rest of the ship's complement would probably still be expecting him to be below in the Crew's Section. He closed the door and looked about him, at the room he was in.

The room was more lounge than anything else, being the place where the captain of a spaceship did his entertaining. But there was a large and businesslike desk in one corner of the room, and in the wall opposite, was a locked, glassed-in case holding an assortment of rifles and handguns.

He was across the room in a moment and in a few savage seconds, had the lock to the case picked open. He reached in and took down a short-barreled, flaring-muzzled riot gun. He checked the chamber. It was filled with a full thousand-clip of the deadly steel darts. Holding this in one hand and his handgun in the other, he went back out the door and toward the other entrance to the Control Room—the entrance from the central room around the stairway hatch.

"... He wouldn't tell me if there were any others," Lucy was saying to a man in a captain's shoulder tabs, while eight other men, including the dour-faced steward who had locked Cully in his cabin, stood at their posts, but listening.

"There aren't any," said Cully, harshly. They all turned to him. He laid the handgun aside on a control table by the entrance to free his other hand, and lifted the heavy riot gun in both hands, covering them. "There's only me."

"What do you want?" said the man with the captain's tabs. His face was set, and a little pale. Cully ignored the question. He came into the room, circling to his right, so as to have a wall at his back.

"You're one man short," said Cully as he moved. "Where is he?"

"Off-shift steward's sleeping," said the steward who had locked Cully in his room.

"Move back," said Cully, picking up crew members from their stations at control boards around the room, and herding them before him back around the room's circular limit to the very entrance by which he had come in. "I don't believe you."

"Then I might as well tell you," said the captain, backing up now along with Lucy and the rest. "He's in Communications. We keep a steady contact with Solar Police right up until we go into overdrive. There are two of their ships pacing alongside us right now, lights off, a hundred miles each side of us."

"Tell me another," said Cully. "I don't believe that either." He was watching everybody in the room, but what he was most aware of were the eyes of Lucy, wide upon him. He spoke to her, harshly, "Why did you get into this?"

She was pale to the lips; and her eyes had a stunned look.

"I looked down and saw what you'd done to that child in the cabin below—" her voice broke off into a whisper. "Oh, Cully—"

He laughed mournfully.

"Stop there," he ordered. He had driven them back into a corner near the entrance he had come in. "I've got to have all of you together. Now, one of you is going to tell me where the other man is—and I'm going to pick you off, one at a time until somebody does."

"You're a fool," said the captain. A little of his color had come back. "You're all alone. You don't have a chance of controlling this ship by yourself. You know what happens to hilifters, don't you? It's not just a prison sentence. Give up now and we'll all put in a word for you. You might get off without mandatory execution."

"No thanks," said Cully. He gestured with the end of the riot gun. "We're going into overdrive. Start setting up the course as I give it to you."

"No," said the captain, looking hard at him.

"You're a brave man," said Cully. "But I'd like to point out something. I'm going to shoot you if you won't cooperate; and then I'm going to work down the line of your officers. Sooner or later somebody's going to preserve his life by doing what I tell him. So getting yourself killed isn't going to save the ship at all. It just means somebody with less courage than you lives. And you die."

There was a sharp, bitter intake of breath from the direction of Lucy. Cully kept his eyes on the captain.

"How about it?" Cully asked.

"No brush-pants of a Colonial," said the captain, slowly and deliberately, "is going to stand in my Control Room and tell me where to take my ship."

"Did the captain and officers of the *Princess of Argyle* ever come back?" said Cully, somewhat cryptically.

"It's nothing to me whether they came or stayed."

"I take it all back," said Cully. "You're too valuable to lose." The riot gun shifted to come to bear on the First Officer, a tall, thin, younger man whose hair was already receding at the temples. "But you aren't, friend. I'm not even going to tell you what I'm going to do. I'm just going to start counting; and when I decide to stop you've had it. One... two ..."

"Don't! Don't shoot!" The First Officer jumped across the few steps that separated him from the Main Computer Panel. "What's your course? What do you want me to set up—"

The captain began to curse the First Officer. He spoke slowly and distinctly and in a manner that completely ignored the presence of Lucy in the Control Room. He went right on as Cully gave the First Officer the course and the First Officer set it up. He stopped only, as—abruptly—the lights went out, and the ship overdrove.

When the lights came on again—it was a matter of only a fraction of a second of real time—the captain was at last silent. He seemed to have sagged in the brief interval of darkness and his face looked older.

And then, slamming through the tense silence of the room came the sound of the Contact Alarm Bell.

"Turn it on," said Cully. The First Officer stepped over and pushed a button below the room's communication screen. It cleared suddenly to show a man in a white jacket.

"We're alongside, Cully," he said, "we'll take over now. How're you fixed for casualties?"

"At the moment—" began Cully. But he got no further than that. Behind him, three hard, spaced words in a man's voice cut him off.

"Drop it, Hilifter!"

Cully did not move. He cocked his eyebrows a little sadly and grinned his untamable grin for the first time at the ship's officers, and Lucy and the figure in the screen. Then the grin went away.

"Friend," he said to the man hidden behind him. "Your business is running a spaceship. Mine is taking them away from people who run them. Right now you're figuring how to make me give up or shoot me down and this ship dodges back into overdrive, and you become a hero for saving it. But it isn't going to work that way."

He waited for a moment to hear if the off-watch steward behind him—or whoever the officer was—would answer. But there was only silence.

"You're behind me," said Cully. "But I can turn pretty fast. You may get me coming around, but unless you've got something like a small cannon, you're not going to stop me getting you at this short range, whether you've got me or not. Now, if you think I'm just talking, you better think again. For me, this is one of the risks of the trade."

He turned. As he did so he went for the floor; and heard the first shot go by his ear. As he hit the floor another shot hit the deck beside him and ricocheted into his side. But by that time he had the heavy riot gun aimed and he pressed the firing button. The stream of darts knocked the man backward out of the entrance to the Control Room to lie, a still and huddled shape, in the corridor outside.

Cully got to his feet, feeling the single dart in his side. The room was beginning to waver around him, but he felt that he could hold on for the necessary couple of minutes before the people from the ship moving in alongside could breach the lock and come aboard. His jacket was loose and would hide the bleeding underneath. None of those facing him could know he had been hit.

"All right, folks," he said, managing a grin. "It's all over but the shouting—" And then Lucy broke suddenly from the group and went running across the room toward the entrance through which Cully had come a moment or so earlier.

"Lucy—" he barked at her. And then he saw her stop and turn by the control table near the entrance, snatching up the little handgun he had left there. "Lucy, do you want to get shot?"

But she was bringing up the little handgun, held in the grip of both her hands and aiming it squarely at him. The tears were running down her face.

"It's better for you, Cully—" she was sobbing. "Better..."

He swung the riot gun to bear on her, but he saw she did not even see it.

"Lucy, I'll have to kill you!" he cried. But she no more heard him, apparently, than she saw the muzzle-on view of the riot gun in his hands. The wavering golden barrel in her grasp wobbled to bear on him.

"Oh, Cully!" she wept. "Cully—" And pulled the trigger.

"Oh, *hell!*" said Cully in despair. And let her shoot him down.

When he came back, things were fuzzy there at first. He heard the voice of the man in the white jacket, arguing with the voice of Lucy.

"Hallucination—" muttered Cully. The voices broke off.

"Oh, he said something!" cried the voice of Lucy.

"Cully?" said the man's voice. Cully felt a two-finger grip on his wrist in the area where his pulse should be—if, that was, he had a pulse. "How're you feeling?"

"Ship's Doctor?" muttered Cully, with great effort. "You got the *Star of the North?*"

"That's right. All under control. How do you feel?"

"Feel fine," mumbled Cully. The doctor laughed.

"Sure you do," said the doctor. "Nothing like being shot a couple of times and having a pellet and a dart removed to put a man in good shape."

"Not Lucy's fault—" muttered Cully. "Not understand." He made another great effort in the interests of explanation. "Stars'n eyes."

"Oh, what does he mean?" wept Lucy.

"He means," said the voice of the doctor harshly, "that you're just the sort of fine young idealist who makes the best sort of sucker for the sort of propaganda the Old World's Confederation dishes out."

"Oh, you'd say that!" flared Lucy's voice. "Of course, you'd say that!"

"Young lady," said the doctor, "how rich do you think our friend Cully, here, is?"

Cully heard her blow her nose, weakly.

"He's got millions, I suppose," she said, bitterly. "Hasn't he hilifted dozens of ships?"

"He's hilifted eight," said the doctor, dryly, "which, incidentally, puts him three ships ahead of any other contender for the title of hilifting champion around the populated stars. The mortality rate among single workers—and you can't get any more than a single 'lifter aboard Confederation ships nowadays—hits ninety percent with the third ship captured. But I doubt Cully's been able to save many millions on a salary of six hundred a month, and a bonus of one tenth of one percent of salvage value, at Colonial World rates."

There was a moment of profound silence.

"What do you mean?" said Lucy, in a voice that wavered a little.

"I'm trying," said the doctor, "for the sake of my patient—and perhaps for your own—to push aside what Cully calls those stars in your eyes and let a crack of surface daylight through."

"But why would he work for a salary—like that?" Disbelief was strong in her voice.

"Possibly," said the doctor, "just possibly because the picture of a bloodstained hilifter with a knife between his teeth, carousing in Colonial bars, shooting down Confederation officers for the fun of it, and dragging women passengers off by the hair, has very little to do with the real facts of a man like Cully."

"Smart girl," managed Cully. "S'little mixed up, s'all—" He managed to get his vision cleared a bit. The other two were standing facing each other, right beside his bed. The doctor had a slight flush above his cheekbones and looked angry. Lucy, Cully noted anxiously, was looking decidedly pale. "Mixed up—" Cully said again.

"Mixed up isn't the word for it," said the doctor angrily, without looking down at him. "She and all ninety-nine out of a hundred people on the Old Worlds." He went on to Lucy. "You met Cully Earthside. Evidently you liked him there. He didn't strike you as the scum of the stars, then.

"But all you have to do is hear him tagged with the name 'hilifter' and immediately your attitude changes."

Lucy swallowed.

"No," she said, in a small voice, "it didn't ... change."

"Then who do you think's wrong—you or Cully?" The doctor snorted. "If I have to give you reasons, what's the use? If you can't see things straight for yourself, who can help you? That's what's wrong with all the people back on the Old Worlds."

"I believe Cully," she said. "I just don't know why I should."

"Who has lots of raw materials—the raw materials to support trade—but hasn't any trade?" asked the doctor.

She frowned at him.

"Why . . . the New Worlds haven't any trade on their own," she said. "But they're too undeveloped yet, too young—"

"Young? There's three to five generations on most of them!"

"I mean they haven't got the industry, the commercial organization—" she faltered before the slightly satirical expression on the doctor's face. "All right, then, you tell me! If they've got everything they need for trade, why don't they? The Old Worlds did; why don't you?"

"In what?"

She stared at him.

"But the Confederation of the Old Worlds already has the ships for interworld trade. And they're glad to ship Colonial products. In fact they do," she said.

"So a load of miniaturized surgical power instruments made on Asterope in the Pleiades, has to be shipped to Earth and then shipped clear back out to its destination on Electra, also in the Pleiades. Only by the time they get there they've doubled or tripled in price, and the difference is in the pockets of Earth shippers."

She was silent.

"It seems to me," said the doctor, "that girl who was with you mentioned something about your coming from Boston, back in the United States on Earth. Didn't they have a tea party there once? Followed by a revolution? And didn't it all have something to do with the fact that England at that time would not allow its colonies to own and operate their own ships for trade—so that it all had to be funneled through England in English ships to the advantage of English merchants?"

"But why can't you build your own ships?" she said. Cully felt it was time he got in on the conversation. He cleared his throat, weakly.

"Hey—" he managed to say. They both looked at him, but he himself was looking only at Lucy.

"You see," he said, rolling over and struggling up on one elbow, "the thing is—"

"Lie down," said the doctor.

"Go jump out the air lock," said Cully. "The thing is, Honey, you can't build spaceships without a lot of expensive equipment and tools, and trained personnel. You need a spaceship-building industry. And you have to get the equipment, tools, and people from somewhere else to start with. You can't get 'em unless you can trade for 'em. And you can't trade freely without ships of your own, which the Confederation, by forcing us to ship through them, makes it impossible for us to have.

"So you see how it works out," said Cully. "It works out you've got to have shipping before you can build shipping. And if people on the outside refuse to let you have it by proper means, simply because they've got a good thing going and don't want to give it up—then some of us just have to break loose and go after it any way we can."

"Oh, Cully!"

Suddenly she was on her knees by the bed and her arms were around him.

"Of course the Confederation news services have been trying to keep up the illusion we're sort of half jungle-jims, half wild-west characters," said the doctor. "Once a person takes a good look at the situation on the New Worlds, though, with his eyes open—" He stopped. They were not listening.

"I might mention," he went on, a little more loudly, "while Cully here may not be exactly rich, he does have a rather impressive medal due him, and a commission as Brevet-Admiral in the upcoming New Worlds Space Force. The New Worlds Congress voted him both at their meeting just last week on Asterope, as soon as they'd finished drafting their Statement of Independence—"

But they were still not listening. It occurred to the doctor then that he had better uses for his time—here on this vessel where he had been Ship's Doctor ever since she first lifted into space—than to stand around talking to deaf ears.

He went out, closing the door of the sick bay on the former *Princess of Argyle* quietly behind him.

"Repent, Harlequin!" Said the Ticktockman

Harlan Ellison

There are always those who ask, what is it all about? For those who need to ask, for those who need points sharply made, who need to know "where it's at," this:

> The mass of men serve the state thus, not as men mainly, but as machines, with their bodies. They are the standing army, and the militia, jailors, constables, possee comitatus, etc. In most cases there is no free exercise whatever of the judgment or of the moral sense; but they put themselves on a level with wood and earth and stones; and wooden men can perhaps be manufactured that will serve the purpose as well. Such command no more respect than men of straw or a lump of dirt. They have the same sort of worth only as horses and dogs. Yet such as these even are commonly esteemed good citizens. Others—as most legislators, politicians, lawyers, ministers, and office-holders—serve the state chiefly with their heads; and, as they rarely make any moral distinctions, they are as likely to serve the Devil, without intending it, as God. A very few, as heroes, patriots, martyrs, reformers in the great sense, and *men*, serve the state with their consciences also, and so necessarily resist it for the most part; and they are commonly treated as enemies by it.*

That is the heart of it. Now begin in the middle, and later learn the beginning; the end will take care of itself.

But because it was the very world it was, the very world they had allowed it to *become*, for months his activities did not come

*From "Civil Disobedience" by Henry David Thoreau.

170

to the alarmed attention of The Ones Who Kept the Machine Functioning Smoothly, the ones who poured the very best butter over the cams and mainsprings of the culture. Not until it had become obvious that somehow, someway, he had become a notoriety, a celebrity, perhaps even a hero for (what Officialdom inescapably tagged) "an emotionally disturbed segment of the populace," did they turn it over to the Ticktockman and his legal machinery. But by then, because it was the very world it was, and they had no way to predict he would happen—possibly a strain of disease long-defunct, now, suddenly reborn in a system where immunity had been forgotten, had lapsed—he had been allowed to become too real. Now he had form and substance.

He had become a *personality*, something they had filtered out of the system many decades ago. But there it was, and there *he* was, a very definitely imposing personality. In certain circles—middle-class circles—it was thought disgusting. Vulgar ostentation. Anarchistic. Shameful. In others, there was only sniggering, those strata where thought is subjugated to form and ritual, niceties, proprieties. But down below, ah, down below, where the people always needed their saints and sinners, their bread and circuses, their heroes and villains, he was considered a Bolivar; a Napoleon; a Robin Hood; a Dick Bong (Ace of Aces); a Jesus; a Jomo Kenyatta.

And at the top—where, like socially attuned Shipwreck Kellys, every tremor and vibration threatens to dislodge the wealthy, powerful and titled from their flagpoles—he was considered a menace; a heretic; a rebel; a disgrace; a peril. He was known down the line, to the very heartmeat core, but the important reactions were high above and far below. At the very top, at the very bottom.

So his file was turned over, along with his time-card and his cardioplate, to the office of the Ticktockman.

The Ticktockman: very much over six feet tall, often silent, a soft purring man when things went timewise. The Ticktockman.

Even in the cubicles of the hierarchy, where fear was generated, seldom suffered, he was called the Ticktockman. But no one called him that to his mask.

You don't call a man a hated name, not when that man, behind his mask, is capable of revoking the minutes, the hours, the days and nights, the years of your life. He was called the Master Timekeeper to his mask. It was safer that way.

"This is *what* he is," said the Ticktockman with genuine softness, "but not *who* he is? This time-card I'm holding in my left hand has a name on it, but it is the name of *what* he is, not *who* he is. This cardioplate here in my right hand is also named, but not whom named, merely what named. Before I can exercise proper revocation I have to know who this what is."

To his staff, all the ferrets, all the loggers, all the finks, all the commex, even the mineez, he said, "Who is this Harlequin?"

He was not purring smoothly. Timewise, it was jangle.

However, it *was* the longest single speech they had ever heard him utter at one time, the staff, the ferrets, the loggers, the finks, the commex, but not the mineez, who usually weren't around to know, in any case. But even they scurried to find out—

Who is the Harlequin?

High above the third level of the city, he crouched on the humming aluminum-frame platform of the air-boat (foof! air-boat, indeed! swizzleskid is what it was, with a tow-rack jerry-rigged) and stared down at the neat Mondrian arrangement of the buildings.

Somewhere nearby, he could hear the metronomic left-right-left of the 2:47 P.M. shift, entering the Timkin roller-bearing plant in their sneakers. A minute later, precisely, he heard the softer right-left-right of the 5:00 A.M. formation going home.

An elfish grin spread across his tanned features, and his dimples appeared for a moment. Then, scratching at his thatch of auburn hair, he shrugged within his motley, as though girding himself for what came next, and threw the joystick forward, and bent into the wind as the air-boat dropped. He skimmed over a slidewalk, purposely dropping a few feet to crease the tassels of the ladies of fashion, and—inserting thumbs in large ears—he stuck out his tongue, rolled his eyes and went wugga-wugga-wugga. It was a minor diversion. One pedestrian skittered and tumbled, sending parcels everywhichway, another wet herself, a third keeled slantwise and the walk was stopped automatically by the servitors till she could be resuscitated. It was a minor diversion.

Then he swirled away on a vagrant breeze and was gone. Hi-ho.

As he rounded the cornice of the Time-Motion Study Building, he saw the shift, just boarding the slidewalk. With practiced motion and an absolute conservation of movement, they sidestepped up onto the slowstrip and (in a chorus line reminiscent of a Busby Berkeley film of the antediluvian 1930's) advanced across the strips ostrich-walking till they were lined up on the expresstrip.

Once more, in anticipation, the elfin grin spread, and there was a tooth missing back there on the left side. He dipped, skimmed, and swooped over them; and then, scrunching about on the air-boat, he released the holding pins that fastened shut the ends of the home-made pouring troughs that kept his cargo from dumping prematurely. And as he pulled the trough-pins, the air-boat slid over the factory workers and one hundred and fifty thousand dollars worth of jelly beans cascaded down on the expresstrip.

Jelly beans! Millions and billions of purples and yellows and greens and licorice and grape and raspberry and mint and round and smooth and crunchy outside and soft-mealy inside and sugary and bouncing jouncing tumbling clittering clattering skittering fell on the heads and shoulders and hardhats and carapaces of the Timkin workers, tinkling on the slidewalk and bouncing away and rolling about underfoot and filling the sky on their way down with all the colors of joy and childhood and holidays, coming down in a steady rain, a solid wash, a torrent of color and sweetness out of the sky from above, and entering a universe of sanity and metronomic order with quite-mad coocoo newness. Jelly beans!

The shift workers howled and laughed and were pelted, and broke ranks, and the jelly beans managed to work their way into the mechanism of the slidewalks; after which there was a hideous scraping as the sound of a million fingernails rasped down a quarter of a million blackboards, followed by a coughing and a sputtering, and then the slidewalks all stopped and everyone was dumped thisawayandthataway in a jackstraw tumble, and still laughing and popping little jelly-bean eggs of childish color into their mouths. It was a holiday, and a jollity, an absolute insanity, a giggle. But...

The shift was delayed seven minutes.

They did not get home for seven minutes.

The master schedule was thrown off by seven minutes.

Quotas were delayed by inoperative slidewalks for seven minutes.

He had tapped the first domino in the line, and one after another, like chik chik chik, the others had fallen.

The System had been seven minutes worth of disrupted. It was a tiny matter, one hardly worthy of note, but in a society where the single driving force was order and unity and promptness and clocklike precision and attention to the clock, reverence of the gods of the passage of time, it was a disaster of major importance.

So he was ordered to appear before the Ticktockman. It was broadcast across every channel of the communications web. He was ordered to be *there* at 7:00 dammit on time. And they waited, and they waited, but he didn't show up till almost ten-thirty, at which time he merely sang a little song about moonlight in a place no one had ever heard of, called Vermont, and vanished again. But they had all been waiting since seven, and it wrecked *hell* with their schedules. So the question remained: Who is the Harlequin?

But the *unasked* question (more important of the two) was: how did we get *in*to this position, where a laughing, irresponsible japer of jabberwocky and jive could disrupt our entire economic and cultural life with a hundred and fifty thousand dollars worth of jelly beans?

Jelly for God's sake beans! This is madness! Where did he get the money to buy a hundred and fifty thousand dollars worth of jelly beans? (They knew it would have cost that much, because they had a team of Situation Analysts pulled off another assignment, and rushed to the slidewalk scene to sweep up and count the candies, and produce findings, which disrupted *their* schedules and threw their entire branch at least a day behind.) Jelly beans! Jelly . . . *beans*? Now wait a second—a second accounted for—no one has manufactured jelly beans for over a hundred years. Where did he get jelly beans?

That's another good question. More than likely it will never be answered to your complete satisfaction. But then, how many questions ever are?

The middle you know. Here is the beginning. How it starts:

A desk pad. Day for day, and turn each day. 9:00—open the mail. 9:45—appointment with planning commission board. 10:30—discuss installation progress charts with J.L. 11:15—pray for rain. 12:00—lunch. *And so it goes.*

"I'm sorry, Miss Grant, but the time for interviews was set at 2:30, and it's almost five now. I'm sorry you're late, but those are the rules. You'll have to wait till next year to submit application for this college again." *And so it goes.*

The 10:10 local stops at Cresthaven, Galesville, Tonawanda Junction, Selby and Farnhurst, but not at Indiana City, except on Sunday. The 10:35 express stops at Galesville, Selby and Indiana City, except on Sundays & Holidays, at which time it stops at . . . *and so it goes.*

"I couldn't wait, Fred. I had to be at Pierre Cartain's by 3:00, and you said you'd meet me under the clock in the terminal at 2:45, and you weren't there, so I had to go on. You're always late, Fred. If you'd been there, we could have sewed it up together, but as it was, well, I took the order alone . . ." *And so it goes.*

Dear Mr. and Mrs. Atterley: in reference to your son Gerold's constant tardiness, I am afraid we will have to suspend him from school unless some more reliable method can be instituted guaranteeing he will arrive at his classes on time. Granted he is an exemplary student, and his marks are high, his constant flouting of the schedules of this school makes it impractical to maintain him in a system where the other children seem capable of getting where they are supposed to be on time *and so it goes.*

YOU CANNOT VOTE UNLESS YOU APPEAR AT 8:45 A.M.

"I don't care if the script is *good*, I need it Thursday!"

CHECK-OUT TIME IS 2:00 P.M.

"You got here late. The job's taken. Sorry."

YOUR SALARY HAS BEEN DOCKED FOR TWENTY MINUTES TIME LOST.

"God, what time is it, I've gotta run!"

And so it goes. And so it goes. And so it goes. And so it goes goes goes goes goes tick tock tick tock tick tock and one day we no longer let time serve us, we serve time and we are slaves of the schedule, worshippers of the sun's passing, bound into a life predicated on restrictions because the system will not function if we don't keep the schedule tight.

Until it becomes more than a minor inconvenience to be late. It becomes a sin. Then a crime. Then a crime punishable by this:

EFFECTIVE 15 JULY 2389, 12:00:00 midnight, the office of the Master Timekeeper will require all citizens to submit their time-cards and cardioplates for processing. In accordance with Statute 555-7-SGH-999 governing the revocation of time per capita, all cardioplates will be keyed to the individual holder and—

What they had done was devise a method of curtailing the amount of life a person could have. If he was ten minutes late, he lost ten minutes of his life. An hour was proportionately worth more revocation. If someone was consistently tardy, he might find himself, on a Sunday night, receiving a communique from the Master Timekeeper that his time had run out, and he would be "turned off" at high noon on Monday, please straighten your affairs, sir.

And so, by this simple scientific expedient (utilizing a scientific process held dearly secret by the Ticktockman's office) the system was maintained. It was the only expedient thing to do. It was, after all, patriotic. The schedules had to be met. After all, there *was* a war on!

But wasn't there always?

"Now that is really disgusting," the Harlequin said, when pretty Alice showed him the wanted poster. "Disgusting and *highly* improbable. After all, this isn't the days of desperadoes. A *wanted* poster!"

"You know," Alice noted, "you speak with a great deal of inflection."

"I'm sorry," said the Harlequin humbly.

"No need to be sorry. You're always saying 'I'm sorry.' You have such massive guilt, Everett, it's really very sad."

"I'm sorry," he repeated, then pursed his lips so the dimples appeared momentarily. He hadn't wanted to say that at all. "I have to go out again. I have to *do* something."

Alice slammed her coffee-bulb down on the counter. "Oh for God's *sake*, Everett, can't you stay home just *one* night! Must you always be out in that ghastly clown suit, running around *annoying* people?"

"I'm—" he stopped, and clapped the jester's hat onto his auburn thatch with a tiny tingling of bells. He rose, rinsed out his coffee-bulb at the tap, and put it into the drier for a moment. "I have to go."

She didn't answer. The faxbox was purring and she pulled a sheet out, read it, threw it toward him on the counter. "It's about you. Of course. You're ridiculous."

He read it quickly. It said the Ticktockman was trying to locate him. He didn't care, he was going out to be late again. At the door, dredging for an exit line, he hurled back petulantly, "Well, *you* speak with inflection, *too!*"

Alice rolled her pretty eyes heavenward. "You're ridiculous." The Harlequin stalked out, slamming the door, which sighed shut softly, and locked itself.

There was a gentle knock, and Alice got up with an exhalation of exasperated breath, and opened the door. He stood there. "I'll be back about ten-thirty, okay?"

She pulled a rueful face. "Why do you tell me that? Why? You *know* you'll be late! You *know* it! You're *always* late, so why do you tell me these dumb things?" She closed the door.

On the other side, the Harlequin nodded to himself. *She's right. She's always right. I'll be late. I'm always late. Why do I tell her these dumb things?*

He shrugged again, and went off to be late once more.

He had fired off the firecracker rockets that said: I will attend the 115th annual International Medical Association Invocation at 8:00 P.M. precisely. I do hope you will all be able to join me.

The words had burned in the sky, and of course the authorities were there, lying in wait for him. They assumed, naturally, that he would be late. He arrived twenty minutes early, while they were setting up the spiderwebs to trap and hold him, and blowing a large bullhorn, he frightened and unnerved them so that their own moisturized encirclement webs sucked closed, and they were hauled up, kicking and shrieking, high above the amphitheater's floor. The Harlequin laughed and laughed, and apologized profusely. The physicians, gathered in solemn conclave, roared with laughter, and accepted the Harlequin's apologies with exaggerated bowing and posturing, and a merry time was had by all, who thought the Harlequin was a regular foofaraw in fancy pants; all, that is, but the authorities, who had been sent out by the office of the Ticktockman, who hung there like so much dockside cargo, hauled up above the floor of the amphitheater in a most unseemly fashion.

(In another part of the same city where the Harlequin carried on his "activities," totally unrelated in every way to what concerns here, save that it illustrates the Ticktockman's power and import, a man named Marshall Delahanty received his turn-off notice from the Ticktockman's office. His wife received the notification from the gray-suited minee who delivered it, with the traditional "look of sorrow" plastered hideously across his face. She knew what it was, even without unsealing it. It was a billet-doux of immediate recognition to everyone these days. She gasped, and held it as though it were a glass slide tingled with botulism, and prayed it was not for her. Let it be for Marsh, she thought, brutally, realistically, or one of the kids, but not for me, please dear God, not for me. And then she opened it, and it *was* for Marsh, and she was at one and the same time horrified and relieved. The next trooper in the line had caught the bullet. "Marshall," she screamed, "Marshall! Termination, Marshall! OhmiGod, Marshall, whattl we do, whattl we do, Marshall, omigodmarshall . . ." and in their home that night was the sound of tearing paper and fear, and the stink of madness went up the flue and there was nothing, absolutely nothing they could do about it.

(But Marshall Delahanty tried to run. And early the next day, when turn-off time came, he was deep in the forest two hundred miles away, and the offices of the Ticktockman blanked his cardioplate, and Marshall Delahanty keeled over, running, and his heart stopped, and the blood dried up on its way to his brain, and he was dead that's all. One light went out on his sector map in the office of the Master Timekeeper, while notification was entered for fax reproduction, and Georgette Delahanty's name was entered on the dole rolls till she could re-marry. Which is the end of the footnote, and all the point that need be made, except don't laugh, because that is what would happen to the Harlequin if ever the Ticktockman found out his real name. It isn't funny.)

The shopping level of the city was thronged with the Thursday-colors of the buyers. Women in canary yellow chitons and men in pseudo-Tyrolean outfits that were jade and leather and fit very tightly, save for the balloon pants.

When the Harlequin appeared on the still-being-constructed shell of the new Efficiency Shopping Center, his bullhorn to his elfishly laughing lips, everyone pointed and stared. He berated them.

"Why let them order you about? Why let them tell you to hurry and scurry like ants or maggots? Take your time! Saunter a while! Enjoy the sunshine, enjoy the breeze, let life carry you at your own pace! Don't be slaves of time, it's a helluva way to die, slowly, by degrees . . . down with the Ticktockman!"

Who's the nut? most of the shoppers wanted to know. Who's the nut oh wow I'm gonna be late I gotta run . . .

And the construction gang on the Shopping Center received an urgent order from the office of the Master Timekeeper that the dangerous criminal known as the Harlequin was atop their spire, and their aid was urgently needed in apprehending him. The work crew said no, they would lose time on their construction schedule, but the Ticktockman managed to pull the proper threads of governmental webbing, and they were told to cease work and catch that nitwit up there on the spire with the bullhorn. So a dozen and more burly workers began climbing into their construction platforms, releasing the a-grav plates, and rising toward the Harlequin.

After the debacle (in which, through the Harlequin's attention to personal safety, no one was seriously injured), the workers tried to re-assemble and assault him again, but it was too late. He had vanished. It had attracted quite a crowd, however, and the shopping cycle was thrown off by hours, simply hours. The purchasing needs of the system were therefore falling behind, and so measures were taken to accelerate the cycle for the rest of the day, but it got bogged down and speeded up and they sold too many float-valves and not nearly enough wegglers, which meant that the popli ratio was off, which made it necessary to rush cases and cases of spoiling Smash-O to stores that usually needed a case only every three or four hours. The shipments were bollixed, the transshipments were misrouted, and in the end, even the swizzleskid industries felt it.

"Don't come back till you have him!" the Ticktockman said, very quietly, very sincerely, extremely dangerously.

They used dogs. They used probes. They used cardioplate cross-offs. They used teepers. They used bribery. They used stiktytes. They used intimidation. They used torment. They used torture. They used finks. They used cops. They used search & seizure. They used fallaron. They used betterment incentive. They used fingerprints. They used Bertillon. They used cunning. They used guile. They used treachery. They used Raoul Mitgong, but he didn't help much. They used applied physics. They used techniques of criminology.

And what the hell: they caught him.

After all, his name was Everett C. Marm, and he wasn't much to begin with, except a man who had no sense of time.

"Repent, Harlequin!" said the Ticktockman.

"Get stuffed!" the Harlequin replied, sneering.

"You've been late a total of sixty-three years, five months, three weeks, two days, twelve hours, forty-one minutes, fifty-nine seconds, point oh three six one one one microseconds. You've used up everything you can, and more. I'm going to turn you off."

"Scare someone else. I'd rather be dead than live in a dumb world with a bogey man like you."

"It's my job."

"You're full of it. You're a tyrant. You have no right to order people around and kill them if they show up late."

"You can't adjust. You can't fit in."

"Unstrap me and I'll fit my fist into your mouth."

"You're a non-conformist."

"That didn't used to be a felony."

"It is now. Live in the world around you."

"I hate it. It's a terrible world."

"Not everyone thinks so. Most people enjoy order."

"I don't, and most of the people I know don't."

"That's not true. How do you think we caught you?"

"I'm not interested."

"A girl named pretty Alice told us who you were."

"That's a lie."

"It's true. You unnerve her. She wants to belong, she wants to conform, I'm going to turn you off."

"Then do it already, and stop arguing with me."

"I'm not going to turn you off."

"You're an idiot!"

"Repent, Harlequin," said the Ticktockman.

"Get stuffed."

So they sent him to Coventry. And in Coventry they worked him over. It was just like what they did to Winston Smith in "1984," which was a book none of them knew about, but the techniques are really quite ancient, and so they did it to Everett C. Marm, and one day quite a long time later, the Harlequin appeared on the communications web, appearing elfish and dimpled and bright-eyed, and not at all brainwashed, and he said he had been wrong, that it was a good, a very good thing indeed, to belong, and be right on time hip-ho and away we go, and everyone stared up at him on the public screens that covered an entire city block, and they said to themselves, well, you see, he was just a nut after all, and if that's the way the system is run, then let's do it that way, because it doesn't pay to fight city hall, or in this case, the Ticktockman. So Everett C. Marm was destroyed, which was a loss, because of what Thoreau said earlier, but you can't make an omelette without breaking a few eggs, and in every revolution, a few die who shouldn't, but they have to, because that's the way it happens, and if you make only a little change, then it seems to be worthwhile. Or, to make the point lucidly:

"Uh, excuse me, sir, I, uh, don't know how to uh, to tell you this, but you were three minutes late. The schedule is a little, uh, bit off."

He grinned sheepishly.

"That's ridiculous!" murmured the Ticktockman behind his mask. "Check your watch." And then he went into his office, going mrmee, mrmee, mrmee, mrmee.

Cato the Martian

Howard Fast

They spoke only one language on Mars—which was one of the reasons why Earth languages fascinated them so. Mrs. Erdig had made the study of English her own hobby. English was rather popular, but lately more and more Martians were turning to Chinese; before that, it had been Russian. But Mrs. Erdig held that no other language had the variety of inflection, subtlety and meaning that English possessed.

For example, the word *righteousness*. She mentioned it to her husband tonight.

"I'm telling you, I just cannot understand it," she said. "I mean it eludes me just as I feel I can grasp it. And you know how inadequate one feels with an Earth word that is too elusive."

"I don't know how it is," Mr. Erdig replied absently. His own specialty among Earth languages was Latin—recorded only via the infrequent Vatican broadcasts—and this tells a good deal about what sort of Martian he was. Perhaps a thousand Martians specialized in Latin; certainly no more.

"Inadequate. It's obvious," his wife repeated.

"Oh? Why?"

"You know. I wish you wouldn't make yourself so obtuse. One expects to feel superior to those savages in there on the third planet. It's provoking to have a word in their language elude you."

"What word?" Mr. Erdig asked.

"You weren't listening at all. *Righteousness.*"

"Well, my own English is nothing to crow about, but I seem to remember what *right* means."

"And *righteous* means something else entirely, and it makes no sense whatsoever."

"Have you tried Lqynn's dictionary?" Mr. Erdig asked, his thoughts still wrapped around his own problems.

"Lqynn is a fool!"

180

"Of course, my dear. You might get through to Judge Grygly on the Intertator. He is considered an expert on English verbs."

"Oh, you don't even hear me," she cried in despair. "Even you would know that *righteous* is not a verb. I feel like I am talking to the wall."

Mr. Erdig sat up—or its equivalent, for his seven limbs were jointed very differently from a human's—and apologized to his wife. Actually he loved her and respected her. "Terribly sorry," he said. "Really, my dear. It's just that there are so many things these days. I get lost in my thoughts—and depressed too."

"I know. I know," she said with immediate tenderness. "There are so many things. I know how it all weighs on you."

"A burden I never asked for."

"I know," she nodded. "How well I know."

"Yes, there are Martians and Martians," Mr. Erdig sighed wearily. "I know some who schemed and bribed and used every trick in the book to get onto the Planetary Council. I didn't. I never wanted it, never thought of it."

"Of course," his wife agreed.

"I even thought of refusing—"

"How could you?" his wife agreed sympathetically. "How could you? No one has ever refused. We would have been pariahs. The children would never hold up their heads again. And it is an honor, darling—an honor second to none. You are a young man, two hundred and eighty years old, young and in your prime. I know what a burden it is. You must try to carry that burden as lightly as possible and not fight everything you don't agree with."

"Not what I don't agree with," Mr. Erdig said slowly but distinctly, "not at all. What is wrong."

"Can you be sure something is wrong?"

"This time. Yes, I am sure."

"Cato again, I suppose," Mrs. Erdig nodded.

"The old fool! Why don't they see through him! Why don't they see what a pompous idiot he is!"

"I suppose some do. But he appears to reflect the prevailing sentiment."

"Yes? Well, it seems to me," said Mr. Erdig, "that he created a good deal of what you call the prevailing sentiment. He rose to speak again yesterday, cleared his throat, and cried out, 'Earth must be destroyed!' Just as he has every session these past thirty years. And this time—mind you, my dear—this time he had the gall to repeat it in Latin: '*Earth esse delendam.*' Soon, he will believe that he *is* Cato."

"I think that is a great tribute to you," Mrs. Erdig told him calmly. "After all, you are the foremost Latin scholar on Mars. You were the first to call him Cato the Censor—and the name stuck.

Now everyone calls him Cato. I shouldn't be surprised if they have all forgotten his real name. You can be proud of your influence."

"That isn't the point at all," Mr. Erdig sighed.

"I only meant to cheer you a bit."

"I know, my dear. I shouldn't be annoyed with you. But the point is that each day they smile less and listen to him even more intently. I can remember quite well when he first began his campaign against Earth, the amused smiles, the clucking and shaking of heads. A good many of us were of the opinion that he was out of his mind, that he needed medical treatment. Then, bit by bit, the attitude changed. Now, they listen seriously—and they agree. Do you know that he plans to put it to a vote tomorrow?"

"Well, if he does, he does, and the Council will do what is right. So the best thing for you to do is to get a good night's sleep. Come along with me."

Mr. Erdig rose to follow her. They were in bed, when she said, "I do wish you had chosen English, my dear. Why should *righteous* be so utterly confusing?"

Most of the Planetary Council of Mars were already present when Mr. Erdig arrived and took his place. As he made his way among the other representatives, he could not fail to notice a certain coolness, a certain restraint in the greetings that followed him. Mrs. Erdig would have held that he was being over-sensitive and that he always had been too sensitive for his own peace of mind; but Mr. Erdig himself labored under no illusions. He prided himself upon his psychological awareness of the Council's mood. All things considered, he was already certain that today was Cato's day.

As he took his place, his friend, Mr. Kyegg, nodded and confirmed his gloomy view of things. "I see you are thinking along the same lines, Erdig," Mr. Kyegg said.

"Yes."

"Well—*que sera, sera*," Mr. Kyegg sighed. "What will be, will be. French. Language spoken by only a handful of people on the European Continent, but very elegant."

"I know that France is on the European Continent," Mr. Erdig observed stiffly.

"Of course. Well, old Fllari persuaded me to take lessons with him. Poor chap needs the money."

Mr. Erdig realized that his irritation with Kyegg was increasing, and without cause. Kyegg was a very decent fellow whom Mr. Erdig had known for better than two hundred years. It would be childish to allow a general state of irritation to separate him from any one of the narrowing circle he could still call his friends.

At moments of stress, like this one, Mr. Erdig would lie back in his seat and gaze at the Council ceiling. It had a soothing effect. Like most Martians, Mr. Erdig had a keen and well-developed sense of aesthetics, and he never tired of the beauties of Martian buildings and landscapes. Indeed, the creation of beauty and the appreciation of beauty were preoccupations of Martian society. Even Mr. Erdig would not have denied the Martian superiority in that direction.

The ceiling of the Council Chamber reproduced the Martian skies at night. Deep, velvety blue-purple, it was as full of stars as a tree in bloom is of blossoms. The silver starlight lit the Council Chamber.

"How beautiful and wise are the things we create and live with!" Mr. Erdig reflected. "How good to be a Martian!" He could afford pity for the poor devils of the third planet. Why couldn't others?

He awoke out of his reverie to the chimes that called the session to order. Now the seats were all filled.

"This is it," said Mr. Erdig's friend, Mr. Kyegg. "Not an empty seat in the house."

The minutes of the previous meeting were read.

"He'll recognize Cato first," Mr. Kyegg nodded.

"That doesn't take much foresight," Mr. Erdig replied sourly, pointing to Cato. Already Cato's arm (or limb or tentacle, depending on your point of view) was up.

The chairman bowed and recognized him.

Cato the Censor had concluded his speeches in the Roman Senate with the injunction that Carthage must be destroyed. Cato the Martian did him one better; he began and finished with the injunction that Earth must be destroyed.

"Earth must be destroyed," Cato the Martian began, and then paused for the ripple of applause to die down.

"Why do I go on, year after year, with what once seemed to so many to be a heartless and blood-thirsty plea? I assure you that the first time my lips formed that phrase, my heart was sick and my bowels turned over in disgust. I am a Martian like all of you; like all of you, I view murder as the ultimate evil, force as the mark of the beast.

"Think—all of you, think of what it cost me to create that phrase and to speak it for the first time in this chamber, so many years ago! Think of how you would have felt! Was it easy then—or any time in all the years since then? Is the role of a *patriot* ever easy? Yes, I use a word Earth taught us—*patriot*. A word most meaningful to us now."

"*Le patriotisme est le dernier refuge d'un gredin,*" Mr. Kyegg observed caustically. "French. A pithy language."

"English, as a matter of fact," Mr. Erdig corrected him. "*Patriotism is the last refuge of a scoundrel.* Samuel Johnson, I believe. Literary dean and wit in London, two centuries ago." Mr. Erdig felt unpleasant enough to put Mr. Kyegg in his place. "London," he went on, "largest city in England, which is an island a few miles from the European Continent."

"Oh, yes," Mr. Kyegg nodded weakly.

"—not only because I love Mars," Cato was saying, "but because I love the entire essence and meaning of life. It is almost half a century since we picked up the first radio signals from the planet Earth. We on Mars had never known the meaning of *war*; it took Earth to teach us that. We had never known what it meant to kill, destroy, to torture. Indeed, when we first began to analyze and understand the various languages of Earth, we doubted our own senses, our own analytical abilities. We heard, but at first we refused to believe what we heard. We refused to believe that there could be an entire race of intelligent beings whose existence was dedicated to assault, to murder and thievery and brutality beyond the imagination of Martians—"

"Never changes a word," muttered Mr. Erdig. "Same speech, over and over."

"He's learned to deliver it very well, don't you think?" Mr. Kyegg said.

"—we would not believe!" Cato cried. "Who could believe such things? We were a race of love and mercy. We tried to rationalize, to explain, to excuse—but when our receivers picked up the first television signals, well, we could no longer rationalize, explain or excuse. What our ears might have doubted, our eyes proved. What our sensibilities refused, fact forced upon us. I don't have to remind you or review what we saw in the course of fifteen Earth years of television transmission. Murder—murder—murder and violence! Murder and violent death to a point where one could only conclude that this is the dream, the being and the vision of Earth! Man against man, nation against nation, mother against child—and always violence and death—"

"He said he wasn't going to review it," Mr. Erdig murmured.

"It's rather nice to know every word of a speech," said Mr. Kyegg. "Then you don't have to listen with any attention."

But the members of the Council were listening with attention as Cato cried.

"And *war!* The word itself did not exist in our language until we heard it from Earth. War without end—large wars and small wars, until half of their world is a graveyard and their very atmosphere is soaked with hatred!"

"That's a rather nice turn of phrase for Cato, don't you think?" Mr. Kyegg asked his associate. Mr. Erdig did not even deign to answer.

"And then," Cato continued, his voice low and ominous now, "we watched them explode their first atom bomb. On their television, we watched this monstrous weapon exploded again and again as they poisoned their atmosphere and girded themselves for a new war. Ah, well do I remember how calm the philosophers were when this happened. 'Leave them alone,' said our philosophers, 'now they will destroy themselves.' Would they? By all that Mars means to every Martian, I will not put my faith in the philosophers!"

"He means you," said Mr. Kyegg to Mr. Erdig.

"Philosophers!" Cato repeated in contempt. "I know one of them well indeed. In derision, he dubbed me Cato—thinking to parade his Latin scholarship before me. Well, I accept the name. As Cato, I say, Earth must be destroyed! Not because of what Earth has done and continues to do to itself—I agree that is their affair—but because of what, as every Martian now knows, Earth will inevitably do to us. We watched them send up their first satellites; we did nothing as they sent their missiles probing into space; and now—now—as our astronomers confirm—they have sent an unmanned rocket to the moon!"

"That seals it," Mr. Erdig sighed.

"How long must we wait?" Cato cried. "Must all that we have made of our lovely planet be an atomic wasteland before we act? Are we to do nothing until the first Earth invaders land on Mars? Or do we destroy this blight as firmly and surely as we would wipe out some new and dreadful disease?

"I say that Earth must be destroyed! Not next month or next year, but now! Earth must be destroyed!"

Cato sat down, not as formerly to a small ripple of applause or to disapproving silence, but now to a storm of assent and approval.

"Silly of me to think of myself as a philosopher," Mr. Erdig reflected as he rose to speak, "but I suppose I am, in a very small way." And then he told the assembled Council members that he would not take too much of their time.

"I am one of those individuals," Mr. Erdig said, "who, even when they cannot hope to win an argument, get some small satisfaction out of placing their thoughts upon the record. That I do not agree with Cato, you know. I have said so emphatically and on many occasions; but this is the conclusion of a long debate, not the beginning of one.

"I never believed that I should live to see the day when this Council would agree that Earth should be destroyed. But that you are in agreement with Cato seems obvious. Let me only remind you of some of the things you propose to destroy.

"We Martians never paused to consider how fortunate we are in our longevity until we began to listen, as one might say, to Earth—and to watch Earth. We are all old enough to recall the years before the people of Earth discovered the secret of radio and television transmission. Were our lives as rich then as they are now?

"How much has changed in the mere two-score of Earth years that we have listened to them and watched them. Our ancient and beautiful Martian language has become all the richer for the inclusion of hundreds of Earth words. The languages of Earth have become the pastime and delight of millions of Martians. The games of Earth divert us and amuse us—to a point where baseball and tennis and golf seem native and proper among us. You all recall how dead and stagnant our art had become; the art of Earth brought it to life and gave us new forms, ideas and directions. Our libraries are filled with thousands of books on the subject of Earth, manners and customs and history, and due to their habit on Earth of reading books and verse over the radio, we now have available to us the literary treasures of Earth.

"Where in our lives is the influence of Earth not felt? Our architects have incorporated Earth styles and developments in their buildings. Our doctors have found techniques and methods on Earth that have saved lives here. The symphonies of Earth are heard in our concert halls and the songs of Earth fill the Martian air.

"I have suggested only some of an almost endless list of treasures Earth has given us. And this Earth you propose to destroy. Oh, I cannot refute Cato. He speaks the truth. Earth is still a mystery to us. We have never breathed the air of Earth or trod on the soil of Earth, or seen her mighty cities and green forests at first hand. We see only a shadow of the reality, and this shadow confuses us and frightens us. By Martian terms, Earth people are short-lived. From birth to death is only a moment. How have they done so much in such fragile moments of existence? We really don't know—we don't understand. We see them divided and filled with hate and fear and resentment; we watch them murder and destroy; and we are puzzled and confused. How can the same people who create so splendidly destroy so casually?

"But is destruction the answer to this problem? There are two and a half thousand million people on Earth, three times the number who inhabit Mars. Can we ever again sleep in peace, dream in peace, if we destroy them?"

Cato's answer to Mr. Erdig was very brief. "Can we ever again sleep in peace, dream in peace, if we don't?"

Then Mr. Erdig sat down and knew that it was over.

"It's not as if we were actually doing it ourselves," Mrs. Erdig said to her husband at home that evening.

"The same thing, my dear."

"But as you explain it, here are these two countries, as they call them, the Soviet Union and the United States of America—the two most powerful countries on Earth, armed to the teeth with heaven knows how many atom bombs and just waiting to leap at each other's throats. I know enough Earth history to realize that sooner or later they're bound to touch off a war—even if only through some accident."

"Perhaps."

"And all we will do," Mrs. Erdig said soothingly, "is to hasten that inevitable accident."

"Yes, we have come to that," Mr. Erdig nodded somberly. *"War* and *cruelty* and *injustice* are Earth words that we have learned —foreign words, nasty words. It would be utterly immoral for us to arm ourselves for war or even to contemplate war. But an accident is something else indeed. We will build a rocket and arm it with an atomic warhead and put it into space so that it will orbit Earth over their poles and come down and explode in the Arizona desert of the United States. At the worst, we destroy a few snakes and cows, so our hands are clean. Minutes after that atom bomb explodes, Earth will begin to destroy itself. Yet we have absolved ourselves—"

"I don't like to hear you talk like that, my dear," Mrs. Erdig protested. "I never heard any other Martian talk like that."

"I am not proud of being a Martian."

"Really!"

"It turns my stomach," said Mr. Erdig.

There was a trace of asperity in Mrs. Erdig's voice. "I don't see how you can be so sure that you are right and everyone else is wrong. Sometimes I feel that you disagree just for the pleasure of disagreeing—or of being disagreeable, if I must say it. It seems to me that every Martian should treasure our security and way of life above all else. And I can't see what is so terribly wrong about hastening something that is bound to happen sooner or later in any case. If Earth folk were deserving, it would be another matter entirely—"

Mr. Erdig was not listening. Long years of association had taught him that when his wife began this kind of tidal wave of argument and proof, it could go on for a very long time indeed. He closed off her sound and his thoughts ranged, as they did so often, across the green meadows and the white-capped blue seas of Earth. How often he had dreamed of that wilderness of tossing and restless water! How wonderful and terrible it must be! There were no seas on Mars, so even to visualize the oceans of Earth was not easy. But he could not think about the oceans of Earth and not think of the people of Earth, the mighty cities of Earth.

Suddenly, his heart constricted with a pang of knife-like grief. In the old, unspoken language of Earth, which he had come to cherish so much, he whispered,

"Magna civitas, magna solitudo—"

The rocket was built and fitted with an atomic warhead—no difficult task for the technology of Mars. In the churches (their equivalent, that is) of Mars, a prayer was said for the souls of the people of Earth, and then the rocket was launched.

The astronomers watched it and the mathematicians tracked it. In spite of its somber purpose and awful destiny, the Martians could not refrain from a flush of pride in the skill and efficiency of their scientists, for the rocket crossed over the North Pole of Earth and landed smack in the Arizona desert, not more than five miles away from the chosen target spot.

The air of Mars is thin and clear and millions of Martians have fine telescopes. Millions of them watched the atomic warhead burst and millions of them kept their telescopes trained to Earth, waiting to witness the holocaust of radiation and flame that would signal atomic war among the nations of earth.

They waited, but what they expected did not come. They were civilized beings, not at all blood-thirsty, but by now they were very much afraid; so some of them waited and watched until the Martian morning made the Martian skies blaze with burning red and violet.

Yet there was no war on Earth.

"I do wonder what could have gone wrong?" Mrs. Erdig said, looking up from the copy of *Vanity Fair*, which she was reading for the second time. She did not actually expect an answer, for her husband had become less and less communicative of late. She was rather surprised when he answered,

"Can't you guess?"

"I don't see why you should sound so superior. No one else can guess. Can you?"

Instead of answering her, he said, "I envy you your knowledge of English—if only to read novelists like Thackeray."

"It is amusing," Mrs. Erdig admitted, "but I never can quite get used to the nightmare of life on Earth."

"I didn't know you regarded it as a nightmare."

"How else could one regard it?"

"I suppose so," Mr. Erdig sighed. "Still—I would have liked to read Caesar's *Conquest of Gaul*. They have never broadcast it."

"Perhaps they will."

"No. No, they never will. No more broadcasts from Earth. No more television."

"Oh, well—if they don't start that war and wipe themselves out, they're bound to be broadcasting again."

"I wonder," Mr. Erdig said.

The second rocket from Mars exploded its warhead in the wastelands of Siberia. Once again, Martians watched for hours through their telescopes and waited. But Mr. Erdig did not watch. He seemed to have lost interest in the current obsession of Mars, and he devoted most of his time to the study of English, burying himself in his wife's novels and dictionaries and thesaurus. His progress, as his

wife told her neighbors, was absolutely amazing. He already knew
the language well enough to carry on a passable conversation.

When the Planetary Council of Mars met and took the decision
to aim a rocket at London, Mr. Erdig was not even present. He
remained at home and read a book—one of his wife's English tran-
scripts.

As with so many of her husband's recent habits, his truancy was
shocking to Mrs. Erdig, and she took it upon herself to lecture him
concerning his duties to Mars and Martians—and in particular, his
deplorable lack of patriotism. The word was very much in use upon
Mars these days.

"I have more important things to do," Mr. Erdig finally replied
to her insistence.

"Such as?"

"Reading this book, for instance."

"What book *are* you reading?"

"It's called *Huckleberry Finn*. Written by an American—Mark
Twain."

"It's a silly book. I couldn't make head or tail of it."

"Well—"

"And I don't see why it's important."

Mr. Erdig shook his head and went on reading.

And that night, when she turned on the Intertator, the Erdigs
learned, along with the rest of Mars, that a rocket had been launched
against the City of London....

After that, a whole month passed before the first atomic warhead,
launched from the Earth, exploded upon the surface of Mars. Other
warheads followed. And still, there was no war on the Planet Earth.

The Erdigs were fortunate, for they lived in a part of Mars that
had still not felt the monstrous, searing impact of a hydrogen bomb.
Thus, they were able to maintain at least a semblance of normal
life, and within this, Mr. Erdig clung to his habit of reading for
an hour or so before bedtime. As Mrs. Erdig had the Intertator on
almost constantly these days, he had retreated to the Martian equivalent of a man's den. He was sitting there on this particular evening
when Mrs. Erdig burst in and informed him that the first fleet of
manned space-rockets from Earth had just landed on Mars—the soldiers from Earth were proceeding to conquer Mars, and that there
was no opposition possible.

"Very interesting," Mr. Erdig agreed.

"Didn't you hear me?"

"I heard you, my dear," Mr. Erdig said.

"Soldiers—armed soldiers from Earth!"

"Yes, my dear." He went back to his book, and when Mrs. Erdig
saw that for the third time he was reading the nonsense called

Huckleberry Finn, she turned out of the room in despair. She was preparing to slam the door behind her, when Mr. Erdig said,

"Oh, my dear."

She turned back into the room. "Well—"

"You remember," Mr. Erdig said, just as if soldiers from Earth were not landing on Mars that very moment, "that a while back you were complaining that you couldn't make any sense out of an English word—*righteous?*"

"For heaven's sake!"

"Well, it seemed to puzzle you so—"

"Did you hear a word I said?"

"About the ships from Earth? Oh, yes—yes, of course. But here I was reading this book for the third time—it is a most remarkable book—and I came across that word, and it's not obscure at all. Not in the least. A righteous man is pure and wise and good and holy and just—above all, just. And equitable, you might say. Cato the Censor was such a man. Yes—and Cato the Martian, I do believe. Poor Cato—he was fried by one of those hydrogen bombs, wasn't he? A very righteous man—"

Sobbing hysterically, Mrs. Erdig fled from the room. Mr. Erdig sighed and returned to his novel.

Frances Harkins

Richard Goggin

Just think. In one week a new century. 2000 A.D. You know it's
real funny how a new year always brings her to my mind. I guess
most people have forgotten Frances Harkins. Oh, I've heard stories
about a few shrines in unlikely places, Massachusetts, Montana,
Alabama. You know how the rumors fly. But I've never seen one;
and if there are any, I guess the people who know aren't talking.
Excuse me, it's time for the 11 A.M. show and I don't want to miss
it.

There, that's over. Now I can settle down to writing this. Frances
was arrested on December 23, 1982. It seems like yesterday but you
know how it is with old ladies' memories. Frances and I worked
in the City Hall together for years. I've been retired for a long time
myself and I amuse myself writing things like this although I burn
them as fast as I write them. I don't know exactly why but it seems
to give me a sort of pleasure even though I do burn them. Although
there's nothing to be . . . to be afraid of.

My lands, when I think of it! The war with Russia had been over
for almost six months. Nobody ever thought it was going to stop.
It just seemed to go on and on and on. But one day they told us
to go to the television sets at 11 o'clock in the morning (our regular
11 A.M. program is in commemoration of that first show), and there
were the monsters surrendering. It was a good clear picture even
coming all the way from Yalta.

It seems funny to me now how anybody could have thought that
no one could rule the world. As if the world didn't need ruling.
As if we all aren't just children looking up to Old Mother Columbia.
Good night nurse, it was that simple. They just kept the war factories
going for two more years, and the army took care of passing them
around. In two years to the day they had a television set in every

191

home on the face of the earth. And then we all just listened. My, it was exciting!

But I was going to tell you about Frances. I might as well admit it: I always had my suspicions about that woman. Not that she wasn't all right in some ways. Everybody has some good in them, they say. But I'd seen her take eleven and sometimes twelve minutes on the coffee break in the morning. And one of the bosses who'd studied medicine told me no one, absolutely no one, had to go to the ladies' room as often as Frances went. Well, you know, where there's smoke, there's fire.

I can remember the day just as well. And I can remember Frances too. She wasn't any bigger than a minute. But spry, you know? Pert. And she did have the clearest, steadiest blue eyes I've ever seen on a human being.

I remember a long, long time ago when I was a young woman; and Frances and I had just gone to work in the Traffic Fines Bureau. That was the first time they ever asked us to sign anything about loyalty. It seems so silly now. As if there could be any question. Anyway I remember Frances questioning even that first one. I remember she went up to George Peters, our section head, and said, "Do you mean to say, Mr. Peters, that if I don't sign this thing, I'll be fired?"

Well . . . the rest of us just laughed. And Mr. Peters said, "I want all these in by 12 o'clock, you understand me, Miss Harkins?" You should have seen her. Both her cheeks got red as a beet. But she didn't say anything. Why should she? It was only ten to 12 then. Did it take her ten minutes to sign her name? Good night, I kind of pitied her in a way.

She signed it all right. By 12 o'clock too. And she signed all the rest of them too. That woman wasn't fooling me. She knew which side her bread was buttered on.

Well . . . the Russians surrendered in June, '82. My, it was nice to have it over. After living in terror so many years. A body could really think about relaxing. It was after that they declared this . . . what the dickens do you call the darn thing . . . Pex? Pax? Pax, that's it, Pax Americana. I don't know what it means but it sounds elegant, doesn't it? It was funny though. You'd expect people to be pleased and grateful that the war was over. But it wasn't like that. Everyone's temper seemed to get worse. It was the strangest thing. I actually remember one time I nearly snapped back at Mr. Peters himself.

Anyway, Frances came into the office one day and she looked real happy. I must say my heart warmed to her. She was that nice when she had her good days. She hadn't been sitting at her desk more than two minutes when Mr. Peters came down the aisle.

"Miss Harkins," he said, "if you can spare the time from your other numerous duties, we want you to do some work for us tonight." The people in authority used "we" all the time by '82. It really is very comfortable, like reading the editorial page.

"My dear Mr. Peters," says little Miss Harkins, "in case you haven't heard, the war is over."

Everybody just dropped what they were doing and stared at her. Like I said, we all were kind of jumpy those days, not jumpy exactly, but strange. After all, fifteen years is a long time. You won't believe it but every once in a while I caught myself wishing the war was going on again.

At first Mr. Peters acted as if he hadn't heard her. Then his voice got real low and horrible. "Exactly what difference do you think this makes, Miss Harkins?"

"If I weren't a lady," she says, "I'd tell you what to do with your night work."

We all expected Mr. Peters to lose his temper. At least I did. He just stood there looking at her for nearly a minute. Then he backed off a bit and straightened up. It was real dramatic. "I see," he said. "This makes it all much clearer. We're up against a really tough proposition this time." He looked around the office at all of us and then said, "Exactly how long have you worked for us, Miss Harkins, or whatever you call yourself?"

Frances stepped back from him. "Have you gone batty?" she said. "I've been here since '62, three years before the war started."

He nodded to himself. "It's the incredible patience and ingenuity that terrify you. Go into the next room," he told her. "I have something I wish to tell our people."

She looked frightened but I didn't know what of. We all wanted to hear what Mr. Peters was going to tell us. She looked all around the office at each one of us and then she turned and walked into the next room.

Mr. Peters went over to the door, waited a second, and then pulled it suddenly open. Frances was sitting at the other end of the room, looking out the window. Mr. Peters slammed the door and walked back to the center of the room.

"I have an official communique," he said. "A public announcement will be made tomorrow. But the scene you have just witnessed impels me to read it to you now." He took a Western Union message from his pocket, unfolded it, and read it to us:

GREETINGS TO THE LONG SUFFERING AND VICTORIOUS AMERICAN PEOPLE. YOU HAVE GALLANTLY BORNE A HERO'S BURDEN THROUGH THE DARK, TERRIBLE YEARS. HOWEVER, IT IS OUR GRIM DUTY TO PASS ON INFORMATION OF THE MOST URGENT NATURE TO YOU. WE HAVE BEEN RELIABLY INFORMED THAT THE PLANET SATURN HAS ONLY BEEN WAITING FOR THE WAR TO END BEFORE IT ATTACKS US. WE OF THE FREE WORLD MUST MEET THIS UNREASONING HATRED AND

AGGRESSION FACE TO FACE AND LOOK IT SQUARELY IN THE EYE. WITH
HOPE IN OUR HEARTS AND A FIRM BELIEF IN THE RIGHTEOUSNESS
OF OUR CAUSE, WE MUST ONCE AGAIN TURN TO GOD FOR ASSISTANCE
IN DESTROYING THIS NEW THREAT TO MANKIND. NIGHT IS FALLING
ALL OVER OUR WORLD. WE CALL UPON YOU IN THE NAME OF TRUTH
AND JUSTICE TO GIRD YOUR LOINS IN OUR COMMON DANGER.

Well... I guess you know everybody was horrified. But in a way
it was kind of a relief. It seemed so natural to see Mr. Peters standing
up there so stiff and military looking and everybody else frightened
and staring at each other.

"The rest of the communique is top secret," Mr. Peters said. "I
can only tell you that our best information points to the fact that
Saturnian spies have been living right amongst us." He paused.
"For years," he said. He paused again. "They may have been born
here."

Everybody just stood there. Finally old Mr. Johnson, who was
pretty deaf anyway, piped up from the rear corner by the multigraph
machines. "I didn't know they had proven any other planets had
people on them."

Mr. Peters didn't even reprimand him. "After all," he said simply,
"this is a communique." At least one or two of the rest of us snick-
ered at Mr. Johnson but not Mr. Peters. It's so good to know a man
who's really kind to old people.

"I don't want any of you," he said, and now he did glance sternly
at Mr. Johnson, "to mention this matter to the woman in the next
room. I will take care of that myself—at the proper time and with
the proper authorities."

I was nearly scared out of my wits. And I understood what he
meant about Frances all right. Little things about her came back
to me. Like the night we were going to the America Plus rally and
that dirty, shabby little man in the trench coat leered at us from
the alley, winked, and said, "You ladies wanna buy some dirty
stories about the truth?" I nearly died but Frances kind of giggled
and she bought a couple. She offered to show them to me but after
all there are some things a lady just doesn't do. It all began making
sense to me and you know, I was kind of sorry, because underneath
everything, you just couldn't help yourself liking her now and then.

The next day of course she was gone; and what a difference it
made in the office, having Mr. Peters smiling and everything.

It was only a couple of nights after that I was watching the 8
P.M. City show when they interrupted it to introduce someone
important.

The City of San Francisco is happy to bring you Dr. Ortho
Graham, the distinguished State of California psychiatrist

who has just completed the mental examination of the first inter-planetary spy apprehended in this area.

Dr. Graham just scared you stiff to look at him. He looked as if he knew anything, simply anything. He coughed apologetically like they all do and said, "Ah, now really, really, Bob [Bob was the announcer's first name, I guess], it wasn't much of anything. This... ah, thing, I rather imagine you'd call it, claims to be a woman named Frances Harkins...."

I nearly dropped my post-victory knitting. I knew it, I said to myself, I knew it all the time. Would you ever?

"... now, Bob, I don't want to baffle our good people with the scientific names of the various complexes and neuroses—upper-, lower-, and inter-planetary—that I discovered in this thing." He laughed a little and Bob laughed with him. "But I'm just going to tell them that it professed not to know one single solitary thing about Alfred Adler's power speculations."

Well... I thought Bob would split his sides. It was funny all right ... I guess. All the State and Federal psychiatrists say that this Dr. Adler was the only smart psychiatrist. But it's like Dr. Graham said, what I don't know about psychiatry would fill a book.

"Thank you, Dr. Ortho Graham," said Bob. "Folks," he said, "that was Dr. Ortho Graham who just completed the first mental examination of an inter-planetary spy. I guess I don't have to tell you people to watch your neighbor, do I? Remember. It's when they don't do anything that they are doing the most. And now... on with the show!"

He began playing the record to re-introduce us to the City of San Francisco show and I leaned back slowly and watched the exact center of the screen until I heard Bob's voice saying, "There we are. All comfortable and listening? We're all ready, aren't we?" And then we were in the middle of the City of San Francisco show again and was it ever good!

It couldn't have been more than two or three nights after that when I was sitting in my apartment and the doorbell rang. I nearly jumped out of my skin. It's bad enough in the daytime but at night it's just awful. And when I opened the door, there she was.

"Well, don't stare at me," she said. "I'm no ghost. It's me, Frances."

I let her in. It was just that underneath everything and in spite of everything, I... I wanted to. "But you can't stay here, Frances," I told her. "You can't. I heard about you on the television. Oh, Frances, why did you have to pick me? Good night, I know you're my friend and everything but...."

"Look," she said, "just say the word and I'll get right out of here."

"No, no," I whispered, "sit down. Sit down, Frances. I'll fix some tea."

"Thanks. They've been hunting me all over the City. I simply had to get someplace to think a moment."

"Did you escape, Frances?" This made me more suspicious than ever because you just don't escape. Everybody knows that.

"I escaped," she said. "About two hours ago. I think they expect me to make for one of the bridges."

"Frances. Are you really from Saturn?"

"For pete's sake, you've known me for years. Do I look like I came from another planet?"

"No," I said cautiously. But then I remembered. "How can I be sure? How do we know what Saturnians look like? All we know is that they're after us. How can I be sure? How do we know what Saturnians look like? All we know . . ."

She didn't say anything until I stopped. Then she said, "Thanks, thanks for letting me in. The tea tasted good."

"What are you going to do, Frances? You'll never get out of town. Why don't you go back and give yourself up?"

She looked at me a long time I remember before she answered me. Then she seemed to make up her mind about something. "I'm going out on the beach," she said, "and work my way down the coast. It shouldn't be too hard if I take my time about it."

I'm going to write this down quickly before I forget the word again. She'd trusted me. Trusted. There, after all these years. Why, it just seems like yesterday that I used it all the time. Excuse me a moment while I start a little fire for this page.

I remember waiting after she'd left for the impulses toward the police to come. I screamed and tossed all night but in the morning they were less strong and I decided to take a chance on myself outside the house. And in a few days I got so I could walk past a police station without even jerking. I still remember that feeling. We used to call it something that began with a p. Prow? No. Principle? No. Whatever was that? Proud. That's it. That's the good one. Proud. But of what? Of whom? I get confused. I'm a very old lady and I hate remembering unpleasant things, I just remembered. You'll have to excuse me tonight. I feel sick . . . real sick . . . and lonely.

Well . . . here I am, back again and fresh as a daisy. What was I writing? Oh, yes, about Frances. She didn't get away, of course. They caught her on the beach and brought her back for the investigations. Nobody knew what went on. The investigations had been secret for years. Naturally none of us was allowed inside the Hall of Justice Building.

It only took two weeks and then the announcement of the television trial came out in all the papers. They don't use the newspapers except for things like public announcements. Stuff you can't copy down from the television. It's funny about the newspapers. You'd think you'd miss them. But you don't. What you miss are the voices talking to you and the pictures moving.

They gave us the whole day off for it. This was the first time they actually declared a public holiday for a trial like this and everybody was just as excited as anything. We all hustled home and got in a good night's sleep. You couldn't have kept us away from our television sets with a team of wild horses.

I can see it just like it was yesterday. And besides I took down real verbatim notes of the whole thing. Naturally it was all military. Oh, they looked so fine in their uniforms. The Opera House was just littered with flags, our flags. And such a spirit of unanimity. I'll never forget it.

Frances wore some kind of simple black dress and she'd drawn her long, blonde hair straight back. The Opera House is so big; and the cameras make everything look so big; and the crowd was cheering so much. She looked very tiny standing there in the witness box.

The Defense Attorney was a scream. We all knew he was pretending of course but they know it makes life more exciting if they let us pretend. Well... this Defense Attorney must have come straight out of a TV workshop. He was that good. Gestures, tears, everything. I'm telling you, if anybody was on the street, they could have heard the audience all the way out to the beach. What a character! Even the judge laughed a couple of times.

I remember her standing up straight, gripping the rail of the box with both hands while the Prosecuting Attorney from the Judge Advocate General's Office made his charges. She kept looking straight into his eyes and I guess the lighting in the Opera House must have been bothering him or something because he turned away quite frequently. I'll never forget one part of the questioning, the one where she was supposed to break down and confess. Wait a minute, I've got it here among my notes somewhere. Where the dickens? Oh, here it is!

PROSECUTING ATTORNEY: ... now, come, you mean to stand there and tell us you don't owe your allegiance to another planet?

FRANCES: Of course not.

PROSECUTING ATTORNEY: I suppose the next thing you're going to tell us is that you love this World?

FRANCES: I don't love you. I'll tell you that.

JUDGE: The defendant will refrain from injecting personal opinion into the testimony.

PROSECUTING ATTORNEY: Do you deny repeatedly provoking a certain Mr. Peters, your immediate and lawful superior?

FRANCES: No. That is ...

PROSECUTING ATTORNEY: That's enough. Thank you. An excellent example of what our good Dr. Adler would have called a true slip of the tongue.

FRANCES: I was just going to say that isn't all I wanted to do to him.

PROSECUTING ATTORNEY: Ladies and gentlemen of the TV audience, you have just heard from the prisoner's own lips an expression of the arrogant brutality for which Saturn is infamous.

FRANCES: Is this your idea of justice?

PROSECUTING ATTORNEY: I wish to call the Court's attention to the sly, twisted fashion in which the defendant attempts to slander this Court.

JUDGE: Thank you, counsel. It will be in the defendant's interest to remember that she is on trial for her life.

FRANCES: I . . .

PROSECUTING ATTORNEY: I do not think I have any further questions for the defendant. I feel confident that the prosecution has established beyond any reasonable doubt the existence of a foreign mentality, alien and hateful to any standards of justice and truth in our USA World.

FRANCES: I . . .

JUDGE: Are you or are you not guilty of the charges brought against you?

FRANCES: I confess. . . . [*There was a tremendous hubbub in the Opera House, flashlight bulbs popping, people shouting, with the brightest spotlights and direct air currents playing on our Flags.*]

PROSECUTING ATTORNEY: Kindly move the last four cameras in closer. That's it. Thank you.

FRANCES: I disagree with you.

PROSECUTING ATTORNEY: Really? Please proceed with your confession.

FRANCES: That's it.

PROSECUTING ATTORNEY: Your Honor, never in 30 years of legal practice have I listened to more contemptuous treatment of a Court than that of this prisoner. I call upon you to preserve this Court's dignity.

JUDGE: I agree with counsel completely. In the light of the evidence and in a sincere conviction of my duty as a human being and citizen of this USA World, I do sentence the defendant to death for . . .

You could have heard a pin drop. The cameras swept all around the Opera House slowly and every single person was on the edge of their seats. And then he did it . . .

Everybody else can say all they want to, and I've talked this over with a lot of people. None of them will admit he did it but I was listening and looking just as hard as I could and I heard him. And

I saw the grimace he made when he covered it up. I may be an old lady and a little crazy to be sitting here writing stuff like this down on paper but I heard him. They can call on their old Dr. Adler or whoever they want to.

He was speaking right directly into the middle microphone on the Opera House stage and he said, "... for disagree—" Well... it seemed as if everybody in the Opera House just caught their breath. But he recovered right away, and said, "for seeking the violent overthrow of this USA World."

I suppose I should be scared out of my wits looking at that awful word after all these years. *Disagree,* he said. Right out. And him a judge and all.

I heard him, I tell you. With my own ears. My own ears! What am I saying? My own... my own... well, I did. They *are* my own ears. I don't care if I'm crazy or not. Because I remember two things. I did let her in and I didn't go to the police. And I'm old now and it doesn't seem to matter so much so I'm just going to write it all down again and hide the papers in the apartment; and I'm *not* going to burn them; and maybe someone... sometime....

A Discovery in the Woods

Graham Greene

The village lay among the great red rocks about a thousand feet up and five miles from the sea, which was reached by a path that wound along the contours of the hills. No one in Pete's village had ever travelled further, though Pete's father had once, while fishing, encountered men from another small village beyond the headland, which stabbed the sea twenty miles to the east. The children, when they didn't accompany their fathers to the shingled cove in which the boats lay, would climb up higher for their games—of "Old Noh" and "Ware that Cloud"—below the red rocks that dominated their home. Low scrub a few hundred feet up gave place to woodland: trees clung to the rock-face like climbers caught in an impossible situation, and among the trees were the bushes of blackberry, the biggest fruits always sheltered from the sun. In the right season the berries formed a tasty sharp dessert to the invariable diet of fish. It was, taking it all in all, a sparse and simple yet a happy life.

Pete's mother was a little under five feet tall; she had a squint and she was inclined to stumble when she walked, but her movements to Pete seemed at their most uncertain the height of human grace, and when she told him stories, as she often did on the fifth day of the week, her stammer had for him the magical effect of music. There was one word in particular "t-t-t-tree" which fascinated him. "What is it?" he would ask, and she would try to explain. "You mean an oak?" "A t-tree is not an oak. But an oak is a t-t-tree, and so is a b-birch." "But a birch is quite different from an oak. Anyone can tell they are not the same, even a long way off, like a dog and a cat." "A dog and a c-cat are both animals." She had from some past generation inherited this ability to generalise, of which he and his father were quite incapable.

Not that he was a stupid child unable to learn from experience. He could even with some difficulty look back into the past for four winters, but the furthest time he could remember was very like a sea-fog, which the wind may disperse for a moment from a rock or a group of trees, but it closes down again. His mother claimed that he was seven years old, but his father said that he was nine and that after one more winter he would be old enough to join the crew of the boat which his father shared with a relation (everybody in the village was in some way related). Perhaps his mother had deliberately distorted his age to postpone the time when he would have to go fishing with the men. It was not only the question of danger—though every winter brought a mortal casualty along with it, so that the size of the village hardly increased more than a colony of ants; it was also the fact that he was the only child. (There were two sets of parents in the village, the Torts and the Foxes,who had more than one child, and the Torts had triplets.) When the time came for Pete to join his father, his mother would have to depend on other people's children for blackberries in the autumn, or just go without, and there was nothing she loved better than blackberries with a splash of goat's milk.

So this, he believed, was to be the last autumn on land, and he was not much concerned about it. Perhaps his father was in the right about his age, for he had become aware that his position as leader of a special gang was now too incontestable: his muscles felt the need of strengthening against an opponent greater than himself. His gang consisted this October of four children, to three of whom he had allotted numbers, for this made his commands sound more abrupt and discipline so much the easier. The fourth member was a seven-year-old girl called Liz, unwillingly introduced for reasons of utility.

They met among the ruins at the edge of the village. The ruins had always been there, and at night the children, if not the adults too, believed them to be haunted by giants. Pete's mother, who was far superior in knowledge to all the other women in the village, nobody knew why, said that her grandmother had spoken of a great catastrophe which thousands of years ago had involved a man called Noh—perhaps it was a thunderbolt from the sky, a huge wave (it would have needed a wave at least a thousand feet high to have extinguished this village), or maybe a plague, so some of the legends went, that had killed the inhabitants and left these ruins to the slow destruction of time. Whether the giants were the phantoms of the slayers or of the slain the children were never quite clear.

The blackberries this particular autumn were nearly over and in any case the bushes that grew within a mile of the village—which was called Bottom, perhaps because it lay at the foot of the red rocks —had been stripped bone-bare. When the gang had gathered at the rendezvous Pete made a revolutionary proposal—that they should enter a new territory in search of fruit.

Number One said disapprovingly, "We've never done that before." He was in all ways a conservative child. He had small deep-sunk eyes like holes in stone made by the dropping of water, and there was practically no hair on his head and that gave him the air of a shrivelled old man.

"We'll get into trouble," Liz said, "if we do."

"Nobody need know," Pete said, "so long as we take the oath."

The village by long custom claimed that the land belonging to it extended in a semi-circle three miles deep from the last cottage—even though the last cottage was a ruin of which only the foundations remained. Of the sea too they reckoned to own the water for a larger, more ill-defined area that extended some twelve miles out to sea. This claim, on the occasion when they encountered the boats from beyond the headland, nearly caused a conflict. It was Pete's father who made peace by pointing towards the clouds which had begun to mass over the horizon, one cloud in particular of enormous black menace, so that both parties turned in agreement towards the land, and the fishermen from the village beyond the headland never sailed again so far from their home. (Fishing was always done in grey overcast weather or in fine blue clear weather, or even during moonless nights, when the stars were sufficiently obscured; it was only when the shape of the clouds could be discerned that by general consent fishing stopped.)

"But suppose we meet someone?" Number Two asked.

"How could we?" Pete said.

"There must be a reason," Liz said, "why they don't want us to go."

"There's no reason," Pete said, "except the law."

"Oh, if it's only the law," Number Three said, and he kicked a stone to show how little he thought of the law.

"Who does the land belong to?" Liz asked.

"To nobody," Pete said. "There's no one there at all."

All the same nobody has rights," Number One said sententiously, looking inwards, with his watery sunk eyes.

"You are right there," Pete said. "Nobody has."

"But I didn't mean what you mean," Number One replied.

"You think there are blackberries there, further up?" Number Two asked. He was a reasonable child who only wanted to be assured that a risk was worthwhile.

"There are bushes all the way up through the woods," Pete said.

"How do you know?"

"It stands to reason."

It seemed odd to him that day how reluctant they were to take his advice. Why should the blackberry-bushes abruptly stop their growth on the border of their own territory? Blackberries were not created for the special use of Bottom. Pete said, "Don't you want to pick them one time more before the winter comes?" and they hung their heads, as though they were seeking a reply in the red earth where the ants made roads from stone to stone. At last Number One said, "Nobody's been there before," as if that was the worst thing he could think of to say.

"All the better blackberries," Pete replied.

Number Two said after consideration, "The wood looks deeper up there and blackberries like the shade."

Number Three yawned. "Who cares about blackberries anyway? There's other things to do than pick. It's new ground, isn't it? Let's go and see. Who knows...?"

"Who knows?" Liz repeated in a frightened way and looked first at Pete and then at Number Three as though it were possible that perhaps *they* might.

"Hold up your hands and vote," Pete said. He shot his own arm commandingly up and Number Three was only a second behind. After a little hesitation Number Two followed suit; then, seeing that there was a majority anyway for going further, Liz raised a cautious hand but with a backward glance at Number One. "So you're for home?" Pete said to Number One with scorn and relief.

"He'll have to take the oath anyway," Number Three said, "or else..."

"I don't have to take the oath if I'm going home."

"Of course you have to or else you'll tell."

"What do I care about your silly oath? It doesn't mean a thing. I can take it and tell just the same."

There was a silence: the other three looked at Pete. The whole foundation of their mutual trust seemed to be endangered. No one had ever suggested breaking the oath before. At last Number Three said, "Let's bash him."

"No," Pete said. Violence, he knew, was not the answer. Number One would run home just the same and tell everything. The whole blackberry-picking would be spoilt by the thought of the punishment to come.

"Oh hell," Number Two said. "Let's forget the blackberries and play Old Noh."

Liz, like the girl she was, began to weep. "I want to pick blackberries."

But Pete had been given time to reach his decision. He said, "He's going to take the oath and he's going to pick blackberries too. Tie his hands."

Number One tried to escape, but Number Two tripped him up. Liz bound his wrists with her hair-ribbon, pulling a hard knot which only she knew—it was for such special skills as this that she had gained her entry into the gang. Number One sat on a chunk of ruin and sneered at them. "How do I pick blackberries with my hands tied?"

"You were greedy and ate them all. You brought none home. They'll find the stains all over your clothes."

"Oh, he'll get such a beating," Liz said with admiration. "I bet they'll beat him bare."

"Four against one."

"Now you are going to take the oath," Pete said. He broke off two twigs and held them in the shape of a cross. Each of the other three members of the gang gathered saliva in the mouth and smeared the four ends of the cross. Then Pete thrust the sticky points of wood between the lips of Number One. Words were unnecessary: the same thought came inevitably to the mind of everyone with the act: "Strike me dead if I tell." After they had dealt forcibly with Number One each followed the same ritual. (Not one of them knew the origin of the oath; it had passed down through generations of such gangs. Once Pete, and perhaps all the others at one time or another had done the same in the darkness of bed, tried to explain to himself the ceremony of the oath: in sharing the spittle maybe they were sharing each other's lives, like mixing blood, and the act was solemnised upon a cross because for some reason a cross always signified shameful death.)

"Who's got a bit of string?" Pete said.

They tied the string to Liz's hair-ribbon and jerked Number One to his feet. Number Two pulled the string and Number Three pushed from behind. Pete led the way, upwards and into the wood, while Liz trailed alone behind; she couldn't move quickly because she had very bandy legs. Now that he realised there was nothing to be done about it, Number One made little trouble; he contented himself with an occasional sneer and lagged enough to keep the cord stretched tight, so that their march was delayed, and nearly two hours passed before they came to the edge of the known territory, emerging from the woods of Bottom on to the edge of a shallow ravine. On the other side the rocks rose again in exactly the same way, with the birch-trees lodged in every crevice up to the sky-line, to which no one from the village of Bottom had ever climbed; in all the interstices of roots and rocks the blackberries grew. From where they stood they could imagine they saw a blue haze like autumn smoke from the great luscious untouched fruit dangling in the shade.

2

All the same they hesitated a while before they started going down; it was as though Number One retained a certain malevolent influence and they had bound themselves to it by the cord. He squatted on the ground and sneered up at them. "You see you don't dare..."

"Dare what?" Pete asked, trying to brush his words away before any doubts could settle on Two or Three or Liz and sap the uncertain power he still possessed.

"Those blackberries don't belong to us," One said.

"Then who do they belong to?" Pete asked him, noting how Number Two looked at Number One as though he expected an answer.

Three said with scorn, "Finding's keepiNg," and kicked a stone down into the ravine.

"They belong to the next village. You know that as well as I do."

"And where's the next village?" Pete asked.

"Somewhere."

"For all you know there isn't another village."

"There must be. It's common sense. We can't be the only ones—we and Two Rivers." That was what they called the village which lay beyond the headland.

"But how do you *know*?" Pete said. His thoughts took wing. "Perhaps we *are* the only ones. Perhaps we could climb up there and go on for ever and ever. Perhaps the world's empty." He could feel that Number Two and Liz were half-way with him—as for Number Three he was a hopeless case; he cared for nothing. But all the same, if he had to choose his successor, he would prefer Number Three's care-for-nothing character than the elderly inherited rules of Number One or the unadventurous reliability of Number Two.

Number One said, "You are just crazy," and spat down into the ravine. "We couldn't be the only ones alive. It's common sense."

"Why not?" Pete said. "Who knows?"

"Perhaps the blackberries are poisoned," Liz said. "Perhaps we'll get the gripes. Perhaps there's savages there. Perhaps there's giants."

"I'll believe in giants when I see them," Pete said. He knew how shallow her fear was; she only wanted to be reassured by someone stronger.

"You talk a lot," Number One said, "but you can't even organise. Why didn't you tell us to bring baskets if we were going to pick things?"

"We don't need baskets. We've got Liz's skirt."

"And it's Liz who'll be thrashed when her skirt's all stained."

"Not if it's full of blackberries she won't. Tie up your skirt, Liz."

Liz tied it up, making it into a pannier in front, with a knot behind just above the opening of her small plump buttocks. The boys watched her with interest to see how she fixed it. "They'll all fall out," Number One said. "You ought to have taken the whole thing off an' made a sack."

"How could I climb holding a sack? You don't know a thing, Number One. I can fix this easy." She squatted on the ground with a bare buttock on each heel and tied and retied the knot till she was quite satisfied that it was firm.

"So now we go down," Number Three said.

"Not till I give the order. Number One, I'll release you if you promise to give no trouble."

"I'll give plenty of trouble."

"Number Two and Three, you take charge of Number One. You're the rear-guard, see. If we have to retreat in a hurry, you just leave the prisoner behind. Liz and I go ahead to reconnoitre."

"Why Liz?" Number Three said. "What good's a girl?"

"In case we have to use a spy. Girl spies are always best. Anyway they wouldn't bash a girl."

"Pa does," Liz said, twitching her buttocks.

"But I want to be in the van," Three said.

"We don't know which is the van yet. They may be watching us now while we talk. They may be luring us on, and then they'll attack in the rear."

"You're afraid," Number One said. "Fainty goose! Fainty goose!"

"I'm not afraid, but I'm boss, I'm responsible for the gang. Listen all of you, in case of danger we give one short whistle. Stay where you are. Don't move. Don't breathe. Two short whistles mean abandon the prisoner and retreat double-quick. One long whistle means treasure discovered, all well, come as quick as you can. Everybody got that clear?"

"Yah," said Number Two. "But suppose we're just lost?"

"Stay where you are and wait for a whistle."

"Suppose *he* whistles—to confuse?" Number Two asked, digging at Number One with his toe.

"If he does gag him. Gag him hard, so his teeth squeak."

Pete went to the edge of the plateau and gazed down, to choose his path through the scrub; the rocks descended some thirty feet. Liz stood close behind him and held the edge of his shirt. "Who are *They?*" she whispered.

"Strangers."

"You don't believe in giants?"

"No."

"When I think of giants, I shiver—here," and she laid her hand on the little bare mount of Venus below her panniered skirt.

Pete said, "We'll start down there between those clumps of gorse. Be careful. The stones are loose and we don't want to make any noise at all." He turned back to the others, who watched him with admiration, envy and hate (that was Number One). "Wait till you

see us start climbing up the other side and then you come on down."
He looked at the sky. "The invasion began at noon," he announced
with the precision of an historian recording an event in the past
which had altered the shape of the world.

3

"We could whistle now," Liz suggested. They were half-way up
the slope of the ravine by this time, out of breath from the scramble.
She put a blackberry in her mouth and added, "They're sweet. Sweet-
er than ours. Shall I start picking?" Her thighs and bottom were
scratched with briars and smeared with blood the colour of blackberry juice.

Pete said, "Why, I've seen better than these in our territory. Liz,
don't you notice, not one of them's been picked. No one's ever come
here. These ones are nothing to what we'll find later. They've been
growing for years and years and years—why, I wouldn't be surprised
if we came on a whole forest of them with bushes as high as trees
and berries as big as apples. We'll leave the little ones for the others
if they want to pick them. You and I will climb up higher and find
real treasure." As he spoke he could hear the scrape of the others'
shoes and the roll of a loose stone, but they could see nothing
because the bushes grew so thick around the trees. "Come on. If
we find treasure first, it's ours."

"I wish it was real treasure, not just blackberries."

"It might be real treasure. No one's ever explored here before
us."

"Giants?" Liz asked him with a shiver.

"Those are stories they tell children. Like Old Noh and his ship.
There never were giants."

"Not Noh?"

"What a baby you are."

They climbed up and up among the birches and bushes, and the
sound of the others diminished below them. There was a different
smell here: hot and moist and metallic, far away from the salt of
the sea. Then the trees and bushes thinned and they were at the
summit of the hills. When they looked backwards, Bottom was hidden by the ridge between, but through the trees they could see
a line of blue as though the sea had been lifted up almost to their
level by some gigantic convulsion. They turned nervously away from
it and stared into the unknown land ahead.

4

"It's a house," Liz said. "It's a huge house."

"It can't be. You've never seen a house that size—or that shape,"
but he knew that Liz was right. This had been made by men and

not by nature. It was something in which people had once lived.

"A house for giants," Liz said fearfully.

Pete lay on his stomach and peered over the edge of the ravine. A hundred feet down among the red rocks lay a long structure glinting here and there among the bushes and moss which overgrew it—it stretched beyond their sight, trees climbed along its sides, trees had seeded on the roof, and up the length of two enormous chimneys ivy twined and flowering plants with trumpet-mouths. There was no smoke, no sign of any occupant; only the birds, perhaps disturbed by their voices, called warnings among the trees, and a colony of starlings rose from one of the chimneys and dispersed.

"Let's go back," Liz whispered.

"We can't now," Pete said. "Don't be afraid. It's only another ruin. What's wrong with ruins? We've always played in them."

"It's scary. It's not like the ruins at Bottom."

"Bottom's not the world," Pete said. It was the expression of a profound belief he shared with no one else.

The huge structure was tilted at an angle, so that they could almost see down one of the enormous chimneys, which gaped like a hole in the world. "I'm going down to look," Pete said, "but I'll spy out the land first."

"Shall I whistle?"

"Not yet. Stay where you are in case the others come."

He moved with caution along the ridge. Behind him the strange thing—not built of stone or wood—extended a hundred yards or more, sometimes hidden, sometimes obscured by trees, but in the direction he now took the cliff was bare of vegetation, and he was able to peer down at the great wall of the house, not straight but oddly curved, like the belly of a fish or... He stood still for a moment, looking hard at it: the curve was the enormous magnification of something that was familiar to him. He went thoughtfully on, pondering on the old legend which had been the subject of their games. Nearly a hundred yards further he stopped again. It was as though at this point some enormous hand had taken the house and split it in two. He could look down between the two portions and see the house exposed floor by floor—there must be five, six, seven of them, with nothing stirring inside, except where the bushes had found a lodging and a wing flickered. He could imagine the great halls receding into the dark, and he thought how all the inhabitants of Bottom could have lived in a single room on a single floor and still have found space for their animals and their gear. How many thousand people, he wondered, had once lived in this enormous house? He hadn't realised the world contained so many.

When the house was broken—how?—one portion had been flung upwards at an angle, and only fifty yards from where he stood he could see where the end of it penetrated the ridge, so that if he wished to explore further he had only to drop a few yards to find himself upon the roof. There trees grew again and made an easy descent. He had no excuse to stay, and suddenly aware of loneliness and ignorance and the mystery of the great house he put his fingers to his mouth and gave one long whistle to summon all the others.

5

They were overawed too, and if Number One had not so jeered at them, perhaps they would have decided to go home with the secret of the house locked in their minds with a dream of one day returning. But when Number One said, "Softies, Fainties..." and shot his spittle down towards the house, Number Three broke silence. "What are we waiting for?" Then Pete had to act, if he was to guard his leadership. Scrambling from branch to branch of a tree that grew from a plateau of rock below the ridge, he got within six feet of the roof and dropped. He landed on his knees upon a surface cold and smooth as an eggshell. The four children looked down at him and waited.

The slope of the roof was such that he had to slide cautiously downwards on his bottom. At the end of the descent there was another house which had been built upon the roof, and he realised from where he sat that the whole structure was not one house but a succession of houses built one over the other, and above the topmost house loomed the tip of the enormous chimney. Remembering how the whole thing had been torn apart, he was careful not to slide too fast for fear that he should plunge into the gap between. None of the others had followed him; he was alone.

Ahead of him was a great arch of some unknown material, and below the arch a red rock rose and split it in two. This was like a victory for the mountains; however hard the material men had used in making the house, the mountains remained the stronger. He came to rest with his feet against a rock and looked down into the wide gap where the rock had come up and split the houses; the gap was many yards across; it was bridged by a fallen tree, and although he could see but a little way down, he had the same sense which he had received above that he was looking into something as deep as the sea. Why was it he half expected to see fishes moving there?

With his hand pressed on the needle of red rock he stood upright and, looking up, was startled to see two unwinking eyes regarding him from a few feet away. Then as he moved again he saw that they belonged to a squirrel, the colour of the rock: it turned without hurry or fear, lifted a plumy tail and neatly evacuated before it leapt into the hall ahead of him.

The hall—it was indeed a hall, he realised, making his way towards it astride the fallen tree, and yet the first impression he had was of a forest, with the trees regularly spaced as in a plantation made by men. It was possible to walk there on a level, though the ground was hummocked with red rock which here and there had burst through the hard paving. The trees were not trees at all but pillars of wood, which still showed in patches a smooth surface, but pitted for most of their length with worm-holes and draped with ivy that climbed to the roof fifty feet up to escape through a great tear in the ceiling. There was a smell of vegetation and damp, and all down the hall were dozens of small green tumuli like woodland-graves.

He kicked one of the mounds with a foot and it disintegrated immediately below the thick damp moss that covered it. Gingerly he thrust his hand into the soggy greenery and pulled out a strut of rotting wood. He moved on and tried again a long curved hump of green which stood more than breast-high—not like a common grave—and this time he stubbed his toes and winced with the pain. The greenery had taken no root here, but had spread from tumulus to hump across the floor, and he was able to pluck away without difficulty the leaves and tendrils. Underneath lay a stone slab in many beautiful colours, green and rose-pink and red the colour of blood. He moved around it, cleaning the surface as he went, and here at last he came on real treasure. For a moment he did not realise what purpose those half-translucent objects could have served; they stood in rows behind a smashed panel, most broken into green rubble, but a few intact, except for the discoloration of age. It was from their shape he realised that they must once have been drinking pots, made of a material quite different from the rough clay to which he was accustomed. Scattered on the floor below were hundreds of hard round objects stamped with the image of a human head like those his grandparents had dug up in the ruins of Bottom—objects useless except that with their help it was possible to draw a perfect circle and they could be used as forfeits, in place of pebbles, in the game of "Ware that Cloud." They were more interesting than pebbles. They had dignity and rareness which belonged to all old things made by man—there was so little to be seen in the world older than an old man. He was tempted momentarily to keep the discovery to himself, but what purpose would they serve if they were not employed? A forfeit was of no value kept secret in a hole, so, putting his fingers to his mouth, he blew the long whistle again.

While waiting for the others to join him, he sat on the stone slab deep in thought and pondered all he had seen, especially that great wall like a fish's belly. The whole huge house, it seemed to him, was like a monstrous fish thrown up among the rocks to die, but what a fish and what a wave to carry it so high.

The children came sliding down the roof, Number One still in tow between them; they gave little cries of excitement and delight; they were quite forgetful of their fear, as though it were the season of snow. Then they picked themselves up by the red rock, as he had done, straddled the fallen tree, and hobbled across the vast space of the hall, like insects caught under a cup.

"There's treasure for you," Pete said with pride and he was glad to see them surprised into silence at the spectacle; even Number One forgot to sneer, and the cord by which they held him trailed neglected on the ground. At last Number Two said, "Coo! It's better than blackberries."

"Put the forfeits into Liz's skirt. We'll divide them later."

"Does Number One get any?" Liz asked.

"There's enough for all," Pete said. "Let him go." It seemed the moment for generosity, and in any case they needed all their hands. While they were gathering up the forfeits he went to one of the great gaps in the wall that must once have been windows, covered perhaps like the windows of Bottom with straw mats at night, and leant far out. The hills rose and fell, a brown and choppy sea; there was no sign of a village anywhere, not even of a ruin. Below him the great black wall curved out of sight; the place where it touched the ground was hidden by the tops of trees that grew in the valley below. He remembered the old legend, and the game they played among the ruins of Bottom. "Noh built a boat. What kind of a boat? A boat for all the beasts and Brigit too. What kind of beasts? Big beasts like bears and beavers and Brigit too . . ."

Something went twang with a high musical sound and then there was a sigh which faded into silence. He turned and saw that Number Three was busy at yet another mound—the second biggest mound in the hall. He had unearthed a long box full of the oblongs they called dominoes, but every time he touched a piece a sound came, each a little different, and when he touched one a second time it remained silent. Number Two, in the hope of further treasure, groped in the mound and found only rusty wires which scratched his hands. No more sounds were to be coaxed out of the box, and no one ever discovered why at the beginning it seemed to sing to them.

6

Had they ever experienced a longer day even at the height of mid-summer? The sun, of course, stayed longer on the high plateau, and they could not tell how far night was already encroaching on the woods and valleys below them. There were two long narrow passages in the house down which they raced, tripping sometimes on the broken floor—Liz kept to the rear, unable to run fast for fear of spilling the forfeits from her skirt. The passages were lined with rooms, each one large enough to contain a family from Bottom, with strange tarnished twisted fixtures of which the purpose remained a mystery. There was another great hall, this one without pillars, which had a great square sunk in the floor lined with coloured stone; it shelved upwards, so that at one end it was ten feet deep and at the other so shallow that they could drop down to the drift of dead leaves and the scraps of twigs blown there by winter winds, and everywhere the droppings of birds like splashes of soiled snow.

At the end of yet a third hall they came, all of them, to a halt, for there in front of them, in bits and pieces, were five children staring back, a half-face, a head cut in two as though by a butcher's hatchet, a knee severed from a foot. They stared at the strangers and one of them defiantly raised a fist—it was Number Three. At once one of the strange flat children lifted his fist in reply. Battle was about to be joined; it was a relief in this empty world to find real enemies to fight, so they advanced slowly like suspicious cats, Liz, a little in the rear, and there on the other side was another girl with skirts drawn up in the same fashion as hers to hold the same forfeits, with a similar little crack under the mount below the belly, but her face obscured with a green rash, one eye missing. The strangers moved their legs and arms, and yet remained flat against the wall, and suddenly they were touching nose to nose, and there was nothing there at all but the cold smooth wall. They backed away and approached and backed away: this was something not one of them could understand. So without saying anything to each other, in a private awe, they moved away to where steps led down to the floor below; there they hesitated again, listening and peering, their voices twittering against the unbroken silence, but they were afraid of the darkness, where the side of the mountain cut off all light, so they ran away and screamed defiantly down the long passages, where the late sun slanted in, until they came to rest at last in a group on the great stairs which led upwards into brighter daylight where the enormous chimneys stood.

"Let's go home," Number One said. "If we don't go, soon it will be dark."

"Who's a Faintie now?" Number Three said.

"It's only a house. It's a big house, but it's only a house."

Pete said, "It's not a house," and they all turned and looked their questions at him.

"What do you mean, not a house?" Number Two asked.

"It's a boat," Pete said.

"You are crazy. Whoever saw a boat as big as this?"

"Whoever saw a house as big as this?" Liz asked.

"What's a boat doing on top of a mountain? Why would a boat have chimneys? What would a boat have forfeits for? When did a boat have rooms and passages?" They threw their sharp objections at him, like handfuls of gravel to sting him into sense.

"It's Noh's boat," Pete said.

"You're nuts," Number One said. "Noh's a game. There was never anyone called Noh."

"How can we tell? Maybe he did live hundreds of years ago. And if he had all the beasts with him, what could he do without lots of cages? Perhaps those aren't rooms along the passage there; perhaps they are cages."

"And that hole in the floor?" Liz asked. "What's that for?"

"I've been thinking about it. It might be a tank for water. Don't you see, he'd have to have somewhere to keep the water-rats and the tadpoles."

"I don't believe it," Number One said. "How would a boat get up here?"

"How would a house as big as this get up here? You know the story. It floated here, and then the waters went down again and left it."

"Then Bottom was at the bottom of the sea once?" Liz asked. Her mouth fell open and she scratched her buttocks stung with briars and scraped with rock and smeared with bird-droppings.

"Bottom didn't exist then. It was all so long ago . . ."

"He might be right," Number Two said. Number Three made no comment: he began to mount the stairs towards the roof, and Pete followed quickly and overtook him. The sun lay flat across the tops of the hills which looked like waves, and in all the world there seemed to be nobody but themselves. The great chimney high above shot out a shadow like a wide black road. They stood silent, awed by its size and power, where it tilted towards the cliff above them. Then Number Three said, "Do you really believe it?"

"I think so."

"What about all our other games? 'Ware that Cloud.' "

"It may have been the cloud which frightened Noh."

"But where did everybody go? There aren't any corpses."

"There wouldn't be. Remember the game. When the water went down, they all climbed off the boat two by two."

"Except the water-rats. The water went down too quickly and one of them was stranded. We ought to find *his* corpse."

"It was hundreds of years ago. The ants would have eaten him."

"Not the bones, they couldn't eat those."

"I'll tell you something I saw—in those cages. I didn't say anything to the others because Liz would have been scared."

"What did you see?"

"I saw snakes."

"No!"

"Yes, I did. And they're all turned to stone. They curled along the floor, and I kicked one and it was hard like one of those stone fish they found above Bottom."

"Well," Number Three said, "that seems to prove it," and they were silent again, weighed down by the magnitude of their discovery. Above their heads, between them and the great chimney, rose yet another house in this nest of houses, and a ladder went up to it from a spot close to where they stood. On the front of the house twenty feet up was a meaningless design in tarnished yellow. Pete memorised the shape, to draw it later in the dust for his father who would never, he knew, believe their story, who would think they had dug the forfeits—their only proof—up in the ruins at the edge of Bottom. The design was like this:

"Perhaps that's where Noh lived," Number Three whispered, gazing at the design as if it contained a clue to the time of legends, and without another word they both began to climb the ladder, just as the other children came on to the roof below them.

"Where are you going?" Liz called, but they didn't bother to answer her. The thick yellow rust came off on their hands as they climbed and climbed.

The other children came chattering up the stairs and then they saw the man too and were silent.

"Noh," Pete said.

"A giant," Liz said.

He was a white clean skeleton, and his skull had rolled on to the shoulder-bone and rested there as though it had been laid on a shelf. All round him lay forfeits brighter and thicker than the forfeits in the hall, and the leaves had drifted against the skeleton, so that they had the impression that he was lying stretched in sleep in a green field. A shred of faded blue material, which the birds had somehow neglected to take at nesting-time, still lay, as though for modesty, across the loins, but when Liz took it up in her fingers it crumbled away to a little powder. Number Three paced the length of the skeleton. He said, "He was nearly six feet tall."

"So there *were* giants," Liz said.

"And they played forfeits," Number Two said, as though that reassured him of their human nature.

"Moon ought to see him," Number One said; "that would take him down a peg." Moon was the tallest man ever known in Bottom, but he was more than a foot shorter than this length of white bone. They stood around the skeleton with eyes lowered as though they were ashamed of something.

At last Number Two said suddenly, "It's late. I'm going home," and he made his hop-and-skip way to the ladder, and after a moment's hesitation Number One and Number Three limped after him. A forfeit went crunch under a foot. No one had picked these forfeits up, nor any other of the strange objects which lay gleaming among the leaves. Nothing here was treasure-trove; everything belonged to the dead giant.

At the top of the ladder Pete turned to see what Liz was up to. She sat squatting on the thigh-bones of the skeleton, her naked buttocks rocking to and fro as though in the act of possession. When he went back to her he found that she was weeping.

"What is it, Liz?" he asked.

She leant forward towards the gaping mouth. "He's beautiful," she said, "he's so beautiful. And he's a giant. Why aren't there giants now?" She began to keen over him like a little old woman at a funeral. "He's six feet tall," she cried, exaggerating a little, "and he has beautiful straight legs. No one has straight legs in Bottom. Why aren't there giants now? Look at his lovely mouth with all the teeth. Who has teeth like that in Bottom?"

"*You* are pretty, Liz," Pete said, shuffling around in front of her, trying in vain to straighten his own spine like the skeleton's, beseeching her to notice him, feeling jealousy for those straight white bones upon the floor and for the first time a sensation of love for the little bandy-legged creature bucketing to and fro.

"Why aren't there any giants now?" she repeated for the third time, with her tears falling among the bird-droppings. He went sadly to the window and looked out. Below him the red rock split the floor, and up the long slope of the roof he could see the three children scrambling towards the cliff; awkward, with short uneven limbs, they moved like little crabs. He looked down at his own stunted and uneven legs and heard her begin to keen again for a whole world lost.

"He's six feet tall and he has beautiful straight legs."

Earth's Holocaust

Nathaniel Hawthorne

Once upon a time—but whether in the time past or time to come is a matter of little or no moment—this wide world had become so overburdened with an accumulation of wornout trumpery that the inhabitants determined to rid themselves of it by a general bonfire. The site fixed upon at the representation of the insurance companies, and as being as central a spot as any other on the globe, was one of the broadest prairies of the West, where no human habitation would be endangered by the flames, and where a vast assemblage of spectators might commodiously admire the show. Having a taste for sights of this kind, and imagining, likewise, that the illumination of the bonfire might reveal some profundity of moral truth heretofore hidden in mist or darkness, I made it convenient to journey thither and be present. At my arrival, although the heap of condemned rubbish was as yet comparatively small, the torch had already been applied. Amid that boundless plain, in the dusk of the evening, like a far off star alone in the firmament, there was merely visible one tremulous gleam, whence none could have anticipated so fierce a blaze as was destined to ensue. With every moment, however, there came foot travellers, women holding up their aprons, men on horseback, wheelbarrows, lumbering baggage wagons, and other vehicles, great and small, and from far and near laden with articles that were judged fit for nothing but to be burned.

"What materials have been used to kindle the flame?" inquired I of a by-stander; for I was desirous of knowing the whole process of the affair from beginning to end.

The person whom I addressed was a grave man, fifty years old or thereabout, who had evidently come thither as a looker on. He struck me immediately as having weighed for himself the true value of life and its circumstances, and therefore as feeling little personal interest in whatever judgment the world might form of them. Before answering my question, he looked me in the face by the kindling light of the fire.

"Oh, some very dry combustibles," replied he, "and extremely suitable to the purpose—no other, in fact, than yesterday's newspapers, last month's magazines, and last year's withered leaves. Here now comes some antiquated trash that will take fire like a handful of shavings."

As he spoke some rough-looking men advanced to the verge of the bonfire, and threw in, as it appeared, all the rubbish of the herald's office—the blazonry of coat armor, the crests and devices of illustrious families, pedigrees that extended back, like lines of light, into the mist of the dark ages, together with stars, garters, and embroidered collars, each of which, as paltry a bawble as it might appear to the uninstructed eye, had once possessed vast significance, and was still, in truth, reckoned among the most precious of moral or material facts by the worshippers of the gorgeous past. Mingled with this confused heap, which was tossed into the flames by armfuls at once, were innumerable badges of knighthood, comprising those of all the European sovereignties, and Napoleon's decoration of the Legion of Honor, the ribbons of which were entangled with those of the ancient order of St. Louis. There, too, were the medals of our own society of Cincinnati, by means of which, as history tells us, an order of hereditary knights came near being constituted out of the king quellers of the revolution. And besides, there were the patents of nobility of German counts and barons, Spanish grandees, and English peers, from the worm-eaten instruments signed by William the Conqueror down to the brand new parchment of the latest lord who has received his honors from the fair hand of Victoria.

At sight of the dense volumes of smoke, mingled with vivid jets of flame, that gushed and eddied forth from this immense pile of earthly distinctions, the multitude of plebeian spectators set up a joyous shout, and clapped their hands with an emphasis that made the welkin echo. That was their moment of triumph, achieved, after long ages, over creatures of the same clay and the same spiritual infirmities, who had dared to assume the privileges due only to Heaven's better workmanship. But now there rushed towards the blazing heap a grayhaired man, of stately presence, wearing a coat, from the breast of which a star, or other badge of rank, seemed to have been forcibly wrenched away. He had not the tokens of intellectual power in his face; but still there was the demeanor, the habitual and almost native dignity, of one who had been born to the idea of his own social superiority, and had never felt it questioned till that moment.

"People," cried he, gazing at the ruin of what was dearest to his eyes with grief and wonder, but nevertheless with a degree of

stateliness—"people, what have you done? This fire is consuming
all that marked your advance from barbarism, or that could have
prevented your relapse thither. We, the men of the privileged orders,
were those who kept alive from age to age the old chivalrous spirit;
the gentle and generous thought; the higher, the purer, the more
refined and delicate life. With the nobles, too, you cast off the poet,
the painter, the sculptor—all the beautiful arts; for we were their
patrons, and created the atmosphere in which they flourish. In abol-
ishing the majestic distinctions of rank, society loses not only its
grace, but its steadfastness—"

More he would doubtless have spoken; but here there arose an
outcry, sportive, contemptuous, and indignant, that altogether
drowned the appeal of the fallen nobleman, insomuch that, casting
one look of despair at his own half-burned pedigree, he shrunk
back into the crowd, glad to shelter himself under his new-found
insignificance.

"Let him thank his stars that we have not flung him into the
same fire!" shouted a rude figure, spurning the embers with his
foot. "And henceforth let no man dare to show a piece of musty
parchment as his warrant for lording it over his fellows. If he have
strength of arm, well and good; it is one species of superiority. If
he have wit, wisdom, courage, force of character, let these attributes
do for him what they may; but from this day forward no mortal
must hope for place and consideration by reckoning up the mouldy
bones of his ancestors. That nonsense is done away."

"And in good time," remarked the grave observer by my side,
in a low voice, however, "if no worse nonsense comes in its place;
but, at all events, this species of nonsense has fairly lived out its
life."

There was little space to muse or moralize over the embers of
this time-honored rubbish; for, before it was half burned out, there
came another multitude from beyond the sea, bearing the purple
robes of royalty, and the crowns, globes, and sceptres of emperors
and kings. All these had been condemned as useless bawbles,
playthings at best, fit only for the infancy of the world or rods to
govern and chastise it in its nonage, but with which universal manhood at its full-grown stature could no longer brook to be insulted.
Into such contempt had these regal insignia now fallen that the
gilded crown and tinselled robes of the player king from Drury Lane
Theatre had been thrown in among the rest, doubtless as a mockery
of his brother monarchs on the great stage of the world. It was a
strange sight to discern the crown jewels of England glowing and
flashing in the midst of the fire. Some of them had been delivered
down from the time of the Saxon princes; others were purchased
with vast revenues, or perchance ravished from the dead brows of

the native potentates of Hindostan; and the whole now blazed with a dazzling lustre, as if a star had fallen in that spot and been shattered into fragments. The splendor of the ruined monarchy had no reflection save in those inestimable precious stones. But enough on this subject. It were but tedious to describe how the Emperor of Austria's mantle was converted to tinder, and how the posts and pillars of the French throne became a heap of coals, which it was impossible to distinguish from those of any other wood. Let me add, however, that I noticed one of the exiled Poles stirring up the bonfire with the Czar of Russia's sceptre, which he afterwards flung into the flames.

"The smell of singed garments is quite intolerable here," observed my new acquaintance, as the breeze enveloped us in the smoke of a royal wardrobe. "Let us get to windward and see what they are doing on the other side of the bonfire."

We accordingly passed around, and were just in time to witness the arrival of a vast procession of Washingtonians—as the votaries of temperance call themselves nowadays—accompanied by thousands of the Irish disciples of Father Mathew, with that great apostle at their head. They brought a rich contribution to the bonfire—being nothing less than all the hogsheads and barrels of liquor in the world, which they rolled before them across the prairie.

"Now, my children," cried Father Mathew, when they reached the verge of the fire, "one shove more, and the work is done. And now let us stand off and see Satan deal with his own liquor."

Accordingly, having placed their wooden vessels within reach of the flames, the procession stood off at a safe distance, and soon beheld them burst into a blaze that reached the clouds and threatened to set the sky itself on fire. And well it might; for here was the whole world's stock of spirituous liquors, which, instead of kindling a frenzied light in the eyes of individual topers as of yore, soared upwards with a bewildering gleam that startled all mankind. It was the aggregate of that fierce fire which would otherwise have scorched the hearts of millions. Meantime numberless bottles of precious wine were flung into the blaze, which lapped up the contents as if it loved them, and grew, like other drunkards, the merrier and fiercer for what it quaffed. Never again will the insatiable thirst of the fire fiend be so pampered. Here were the treasures of famous bon vivants—liquors that had been tossed on ocean, and mellowed in the sun, and hoarded long in the recesses of the earth—the pale, the gold, the ruddy juice of whatever vineyards were most delicate—the entire vintage of Tokay—all mingling in one stream with the vile fluids of the common pothouse, and contributing to heighten the selfsame blaze. And while it rose in a gigantic spire that seemed to wave against the arch of the firmament and combine itself with the light of stars, the multitude gave a shout as if the broad earth were exulting in its deliverance from the curse of ages.

But the joy was not universal. Many deemed that human life would be gloomier than ever when that brief illumination should sink down. While the reformers were at work, I overheard muttered expostulations from several respectable gentlemen with red noses and wearing gouty shoes; and a ragged worthy, whose face looked like a hearth where the fire is burned out, now expressed his discontent more openly and boldly.

"What is this world good for," said the last toper, "now that we can never be jolly any more? What is to comfort the poor man in sorrow and perplexity? How is he to keep his heart warm against the cold winds of this cheerless earth? And what do you propose to give him in exchange for the solace that you take away? How are old friends to sit together by the fireside without a cheerful glass between them? A plague upon your reformation! It is a sad world, a cold world, a selfish world, a low world, not worth an honest fellow's living in, now that good fellowship is gone forever!"

This harangue excited great mirth among the bystanders; but, preposterous as was the sentiment, I could not help commiserating the forlorn condition of the last toper, whose boon companions had dwindled away from his side, leaving the poor fellow without a soul to countenance him in sipping his liquor, nor indeed any liquor to sip. Not that this was quite the true state of the case; for I had observed him at a critical moment filch a bottle of fourth-proof brandy that fell beside the bonfire and hide it in his pocket.

The spirituous and fermented liquors being thus disposed of, the zeal of the reformers next induced them to replenish the fire with all the boxes of tea and bags of coffee in the world. And now came the planters of Virginia, bringing their crops and tobacco. These, being cast upon the heap of inutility, aggregated it to the size of a mountain, and incensed the atmosphere with such potent fragrance that methought we should never draw pure breath again. The present sacrifice seemed to startle the lovers of the weed more than any that they had hitherto witnessed.

"Well, they've put my pipe out," said an old gentleman flinging it into the flames in a pet. "What is this world coming to? Everything rich and racy—all the spice of life—is to be condemned as useless. Now that they have kindled the bonfire, if these nonsensical reformers would fling themselves into it, all would be well enough!"

"Be patient," responded a stanch conservative; "it will come to that in the end. They will first fling us in, and finally themselves."

From the general and systematic measures of reform I now turned to consider the individual contributions to this memorable bonfire. In many instances these were of a very amusing character. One poor fellow threw in his empty purse, and another a bundle of counterfeit on insolvable bank notes. Fashionable ladies threw in their last season's bonnets, together with heaps of ribbons, yellow lace, and much other half-worn milliner's ware, all of which proved even more evanescent in the fire than it had been in the fashion. A multitude of lovers of both sexes—discarded maids or bachelors and couples mutually weary of one another—tossed in bundles of perfumed letters and enamored sonnets. A hack politician, being deprived of bread by the loss of office, threw in his teeth, which happened to be false ones. The Rev. Sydney Smith—having voyaged across the Atlantic for that sole purpose—came up to the bonfire with a bitter grin and threw in certain repudiated bonds, fortified though they were with the broad seal of a sovereign state. A little boy of five years old, in the premature manliness of the present epoch, threw in his playthings; a college graduate his diploma; an apothecary, ruined by the spread of homoeopathy, his whole stock of drugs and medicines; a physician his library; a parson his old sermons; and a fine gentleman of the old school his code of manners, which he had formerly written down for the benefit of the next generation. A widow, resolving on a second marriage, slyly threw in her dead husband's miniature. A young man, jilted by his mistress, would willingly have flung his own desperate heart into the flames, but could find no means to wrench it out of his bosom. An American author, whose works were neglected by the public, threw his pen and paper into the bonfire, and betook himself to some less discouraging occupation. It somewhat startled me to overhear a number of ladies, highly respectable in appearance, proposing to fling their gowns and petticoats into the flames, and assume the garb, together with the manners, duties, offices, and responsibilities, of the opposite sex.

What favor was accorded to this scheme I am unable to say, my attention being suddenly drawn to a poor, deceived, and half-delirious girl, who, exclaiming that she was the most worthless thing alive or dead, attempted to cast herself into the fire amid all that wrecked and broken trumpery of the world. A good man, however, ran to her rescue.

"Patience, my poor girl!" said he, as he drew her back from the fierce embrace of the destroying angel. "Be patient, and abide Heaven's will. So long as you possess a living soul, all may be restored to its first freshness. These things of matter and creations of human fantasy are fit for nothing but to be burned when once they have had their day; but your day is eternity!"

"Yes," said the wretched girl, whose frenzy seemed now to have sunk down into deep despondency—"yes and the sunshine is blotted out of it!"

It was now rumored among the spectators that all the weapons and munitions of war were to be thrown into the bonfire, with the exception of the world's stock of gunpowder, which, as the safest mode of disposing of it, had already been drowned in the sea. This intelligence seemed to awaken great diversity of opinion. The hopeful philanthropist esteemed it a token that the millennium was already come; while persons of another stamp, in whose view mankind was a breed of bulldogs, prophesied that all the old stoutness, fervor, nobleness, generosity, and magnanimity of the race would disappear—these qualities, as they affirmed, requiring blood for their nourishment. They comforted themselves, however, in the belief that the proposed abolition of war was impracticable for any length of time together.

Be that as it might, numberless great guns, whose thunder had long been the voice of battle—the artillery of the Armada, the battering trains of Marlborough, and the adverse cannon of Napoleon and Wellington—were trundled into the midst of the fire. By the continual addition of dry combustibles, it had now waxed so intense that neither brass nor iron could withstand it. It was wonderful to behold how these terrible instruments of slaughter melted away like playthings of wax. Then the armies of the earth wheeled around the mighty furnace, with their military music playing triumphant marches, and flung in their muskets and swords. The standard-bearers, likewise, cast one look upward at their banners, all tattered with shot holes and inscribed with the names of victorious fields; and, giving them a last flourish on the breeze, they lowered them into the flame, which snatched them upward in its rush towards the clouds. This ceremony being over, the world was left without a single weapon in its hands, except possibly a few old king's arms and rusty swords and other trophies of the Revolution in some of our state armories. And now the drums were beaten and the trumpets brayed all together, as a prelude to the proclamation of universal and eternal peace and the announcement that glory was no longer to be won by blood, but that it would henceforth be the contention of the human race to work out the greatest mutual good, and that beneficence, in the future annals of the earth, would claim the praise of valor. The blessed tidings were accordingly promulgated, and caused infinite rejoicings among those who had stood aghast at the horror and absurdity of war.

But I saw a grim smile pass over the seared visage of a stately old commander—by his warworn figure and rich military dress, he might have been one of Napoleon's famous marshals—who, with the rest of the world's soldiery, had just flung away the sword that had been familiar to his right hand for half a century.

"Ay! ay!" grumbled he. "Let them proclaim what they please; but, in the end, we shall find that all this foolery has only made more work for the armorers and cannon founders."

"Why, sir," exclaimed I, in astonishment, "do you imagine that the human race will ever so far return on the steps of its past madness as to weld another sword or cast another cannon?"

"There will be no need," observed, with a sneer, one who neither felt benevolence nor had faith in it. "When Cain wished to slay his brother, he was at no loss for a weapon."

"We shall see," replied the veteran commander. "If I am mistaken, so much the better; but in my opinion, without pretending to philosophize about the matter, the necessity of war lies far deeper than these honest gentlemen suppose. What! is there a field for all the petty disputes of individuals? and shall there be no great law court for the settlement of national difficulties? The battle field is the only court where such suits can be tried."

"You forget, general," rejoined I, "that, in this advanced stage of civilization, Reason and Philanthropy combined will constitute just such a tribunal as is requisite."

"Ah, I had forgotten that, indeed!" said the old warrior, as he limped away.

The fire was now to be replenished with materials that had hitherto been considered of even greater importance to the well being of society than the warlike munitions which we had already seen consumed. A body of reformers had travelled all over the earth in quest of the machinery by which the different nations were accustomed to inflict the punishment of death. A shudder passed through the multitude as these ghastly emblems were dragged forward. Even the flames seemed at first to shrink away, displaying the shape and murderous contrivance of each in a full blaze of light, which of itself was sufficient to convince mankind of the long and deadly error error of human law. Those old implements of cruelty; those horrible monsters of mechanism; those inventions which seemed to demand something worse than man's natural heart to contrive, and which had lurked in the dusky nooks of ancient prisons, the subject of terror-stricken legend—were now brought forth to view. Headsmen's axes, with the rust of noble and royal blood upon them, and a vast collection of halters that had choked the breath of plebeian victims, were thrown in together. A shout greeted the arrival of the guillotine, which was thrust forward on the same wheels that had borne it from one to another of the blood-stained streets of Paris. But the loudest roar of applause went up, telling the distant sky of the triumph of the earth's redemption, when the gallows made its appearance. An ill-looking fellow, however, rushed forward, and, putting himself in the path of the reformers, bellowed hoarsely, and fought with brute fury to stay their progress.

It was little matter of surprise, perhaps, that the executioner should thus do his best to vindicate and uphold the machinery by which he himself had his livelihood and worthier individuals their death; but it deserved special note that men of a far different sphere—even of that consecrated class in whose guardianship the world is apt to trust its benevolence—were found to take the hangman's view of the question.

"Stay, my brethren!" cried one of them. "You are misled by a false philanthropy; you know not what you do. The gallows is a Heaven-ordained instrument. Bear it back, then, reverently, and set it up in its old place, else the world will fall to speedy ruin and desolation!"

"Onward! onward!" shouted a leader in the reform. "Into the flames with the accursed instrument of man's blood policy! How can human law inculcate benevolence and love while it persists in setting up the gallows as its chief symbol? One heave more, good friends, and the world will be redeemed from its greatest error."

A thousand hands, that nevertheless loathed the touch, now lent their assistance, and thrust the ominous burden far, far into the centre of the raging furnace. There its fatal and abhorred image was beheld, first black, then a red coal, then ashes.

"That was well done!" exclaimed I.

"Yes, it was well done," replied, but with less enthusiasm than I expected, the thoughtful observer who was still at my side; "well done, if the world be good enough for the measure. Death, however, is an idea that cannot easily be dispensed with in any condition between the primal innocence and that other purity and perfection which perchance we are destined to attain after travelling round the full circle: but, at all events, it is well that the experiment should now be tried."

"Too cold! too cold!" impatiently exclaimed the young and ardent leader in this triumph. "Let the heart have its voice here as well as the intellect. And as for ripeness, and as for progress, let mankind always do the highest, kindest, noblest thing that, at any given period, it has attained the perception of; and surely that thing cannot be wrong nor wrongly timed."

I know not whether it were the excitement of the scene, or whether the good people around the bonfire were really growing more enlightened every instant; but they now proceeded to measures in the full length of which I was hardly prepared to keep them company. For instance, some threw their marriage certificates into the flames, and declared themselves candidates for a higher, holier, and more comprehensive union that that which had subsisted from the birth of time under the form of the connubial tie. Others hastened to the vaults of banks and to the coffers of the rich—all of which were open to the first comer on this fated occasion—and brought entire bales of paper money to enliven the blaze, and tons of coin to be melted down by its intensity. Henceforth, they said, universal benevolence, uncoined and exhaustless, was to be the golden currency of the world. At this intelligence the bankers and speculators in the stocks grew pale, and a pickpocket, who had reaped a rich harvest among the crowd, fell down in a deadly fainting fit. A few men of business burned their daybooks and ledgers, the notes and

obligations of their creditors, and all other evidences of debts due
to themselves; while perhaps a somewhat larger number satisfied
their zeal for reform with the sacrifice of any uncomfortable recollection of their own indebtment. There was then a cry that the period
was arrived when the title deeds of landed property should be given
to the flames, and the whole soil of the earth revert to the public,
from whom it had been wrongfully abstracted and most unequally
distributed among individuals. Another party demanded that all
written constitutions, set forms of government, legislative acts,
statute books, and everything else on which human invention had
endeavored to stamp its arbitrary laws, should at once be destroyed,
leaving the consummated world as free as the man first created.

Whether any ultimate action was taken with regard to these propositions is beyond my knowledge; for, just then, some matters were
in progress that concerned my sympathies more nearly.

"See! see! What heaps of books and pamphlets!" cried a fellow,
who did not seem to be a lover of literature. "Now we shall have
a glorious blaze!"

"That's just the thing!" said a modern philosopher. "Now we shall
get rid of the weight of dead men's thought, which has hitherto
pressed so heavily on the living intellect that it has been incompetent
to any effectual self-exertion. Well done, my lads! Into the fire with
them! Now you are enlightening the world indeed!"

"But what is to become of the trade?" cried a frantic bookseller.

"Oh, by all means, let them accompany their merchandise," coolly
observed an author. "It will be a noble funeral pile!"

The truth was, that the human race had now reached a stage of
progress so far beyond what the wisest and wittiest men of former
ages had ever dreamed of that it would have been a manifest absurdity to allow the earth to be any longer encumbered with their poor
achievements in the literary line. Accordingly a thorough and searching investigation had swept the booksellers' shops, hawkers' stands,
public, and private libraries, and even the little book-shelf by the
country fireside, and had brought the world's entire mass of printed
paper, bound or in sheets, to swell the already mountain bulk of
our illustrious bonfire. Thick, heavy folios, containing the labors
of lexicographers, commentators, and encyclopedists, were flung in,
and falling among the embers with a leaden thump, smouldered
away to ashes like rotten wood. The small, richly gilt French tomes
of the last age, with the hundred volumes of Voltaire among them,
went off in a brilliant shower of sparkles and little jets of flame;
while the current literature of the same nation burned red and blue,
and threw an infernal light over the visages of the spectators, converting them all to the aspect of party-colored fiends. A collection
of German stories emitted a scent of brimstone. The English standard
authors made excellent fuel, generally exhibiting the properties of

sound oak logs. Milton's works, in particular, sent up a powerful blaze, gradually reddening into a coal, which promised to endure longer than almost any other material of the pile. From Shakespeare there gushed a flame of such marvellous splendor that men shaded their eyes as against the sun's meridian glory; nor even when the works of his own elucidators were flung upon him did he cease to flash forth a dazzling radiance from beneath the ponderous heap. It is my belief that he is blazing as fervidly as ever.

"Could a poet but light a lamp at that glorious flame," remarked I, "he might then consume the midnight oil to some good purpose."

"That is the very thing which modern poets have been too apt to do, or at least to attempt," answered a critic. "The chief benefit to be expected from this conflagration of past literature undoubtedly is, that writers will henceforth be compelled to light their lamps at the sun or stars."

"If they can reach so high," said I; "but that task requires a giant, who may afterwards distribute the light among inferior men. It is not every one that can steal the fire from heaven like Prometheus; but, when once he had done the deed, a thousand hearths were kindled by it."

It amazed me much to observe how indefinite was the proportion between the physical mass of any given author and the property of brilliant and long-continued combustion. For instance, there was not a quarto volume of the last century—nor, indeed, of the present—that could compete in that particular with a child's little gilt-covered book, containing Mother Goose's Melodies. The Life and Death of Tom Thumb outlasted the biography of Marlborough. An epic, indeed a dozen of them, was converted to white ashes before the single sheet of an old ballad was half consumed. In more than one case, too, when volumes of applauded verse proved incapable of anything better than a stifling smoke, an unregarded ditty of some nameless bard—perchance in the corner of a newspaper—soared up among the stars with a flame as brilliant as their own. Speaking of the properties of flame, methought Shelley's poetry emitted a purer light than almost any other productions of his day, contrasting beautifully with the fitful and lurid gleams and gushes of black vapor that flashed and eddied from the volumes of Lord Byron. As for Tom Moore, some of his songs diffused an odor like a burning pastil.

I felt particular interest in watching the combustion of American authors, and scrupulously noted by my watch the precise number of moments that changed most of them from shabbily-printed books to indistinguishable ashes. It would be invidious, however, if not perilous, to betray these awful secrets; so that I shall content myself with observing that it was not invariably the writer most frequent in the public mouth that made the most splendid appearance in the bonfire. I especially remember that a great deal of excellent inflammability was exhibited in a thin volume of poems by Ellery Channing; although, to speak the truth, there were certain portions that hissed and spluttered in a very disagreeable fashion. A curious phenomenon occurred in reference to several writers, native as well as foreign. Their books, though of highly respectable figure, instead of bursting into a blaze, or even smouldering out their substance in smoke, suddenly melted away in a manner that proved them to be ice.

If it be no lack of modesty to mention my own works, it must here be confessed that I looked for them with fatherly interest, but in vain. Too probably they were changed to vapor by the first action of the heat; at best, I can only hope that, in their quiet way, they contributed a glimmering spark or two to the splendor of the evening.

"Alas! and woe is me!" thus bemoaned himself a heavy-looking gentleman in green spectacles. "The world is utterly ruined, and there is nothing to live for any longer. The business of my life is snatched from me. Not a volume to be had for love or money!"

"This," remarked the sedate observer beside me, "is a bookworm —one of those men who are born to gnaw dead thoughts. His clothes, you see, are covered with the dust of libraries. He has no inward fountain of ideas; and, in good earnest, now that the old stock is abolished, I do not see what is to become of the poor fellow. Have you no word of comfort for him?"

"My dear sir," said I to the desperate bookworm, "is not Nature better than a book? Is not the human heart deeper than any system of philosophy? Is not life replete with more instruction than past observers have found it possible to write down in maxims? Be of good cheer. The great book of Time is still spread wide open before us; and, if we read it aright, it will be to us a volume of eternal truth."

"Oh, my books, my books, my precious printed books!" reiterated the forlorn bookworm. "My only reality was a bound volume; and now they will not leave me even a shadowy pamphlet!"

In fact, the last remnant of the literature of all the ages was now descending upon the blazing heap in the shape of a cloud of pamphlets from the press of the New World. These likewise were consumed in the twinkling of an eye, leaving the earth, for the first time since the days of Cadmus, free from the plague of letters—an enviable field for the authors of the next generation.

"Well, and does anything remain to be done?" inquired I somewhat anxiously. "Unless we set fire to the earth itself, and then leap boldly off into infinite space, I know not that we can carry reform to any farther point."

"You are vastly mistaken, my good friend," said the observer. "Believe me, the fire will not be allowed to settle down without the addition of fuel that will startle many persons who have lent a willing hand thus far."

Nevertheless there appeared to be a relaxation of effort for a little time, during which, probably, the leaders of the movement were considering what should be done next. In the interval, a philosopher threw his theory into the flames—a sacrifice which, by those who knew how to estimate it, was pronounced the most remarkable that had yet been made. The combustion, however, was by no means brilliant. Some indefatigable people, scorning to take a moment's ease, now employed themselves in collecting all the withered leaves and fallen boughs of the forest, and thereby recruited the bonfire to a greater height than ever. But this was mere by-play.

"Here comes the fresh fuel that I spoke of," said my companion.

To my astonishment, the persons who now advanced into the vacant space around the mountain fire bore surplices and other priestly garments, mitres, crosiers, and a confusion of Popish and Protestant emblems, with which it seemed their purpose to consummate the great act of faith. Crosses from the spires of old cathedrals were cast upon the heap with as little remorse as if the reverence of centuries, passing in long array beneath the lofty towers, had not looked up to them as the holiest of symbols. The font in which infants were consecrated to God, the sacramental vessels whence piety received the hallowed draught, were given to the same destruction. Perhaps it most nearly touched my heart to see among these devoted relics fragments of the humble communion tables and undecorated pulpits which I recognized as having been torn from the meeting-houses of New England. Those simple edifices might have been permitted to retain all of sacred embellishment that their Puritan founders had bestowed, even though the mighty structure of St. Peter's had sent its spoils to the fire of this terrible sacrifice. Yet I felt that these were but the externals of religion, and might most safely be relinquished by spirits that best knew their deep significance.

"All is well," said I, cheerfully. "The woodpaths shall be the aisles of our cathedral—the firmament itself shall be its ceiling. What needs an earthly roof between the Deity and his worshippers? Our faith can well afford to lose all the drapery that even the holiest men have thrown around it, and be only the more sublime in its simplicity."

"True," said my companion; "but will they pause here?"

The doubt implied in his question was well founded. In the general destruction of books already described, a holy volume, that stood apart from the catalogue of human literature, and yet, in one sense, was at its head, had been spared. But the Titan of innovation—angel or fiend, double in his nature, and capable of deeds befitting both characters—at first shaking down only the old and rotten shapes of things, had now, as it appeared, laid his terrible hand upon the main pillars which supported the whole edifice of our moral and spiritual state. The inhabitants of the earth had grown too enlightened to define their faith within a form of words, or to limit the spiritual by any analogy to our material existence. Truths which the heavens trembled at were now but a fable of the world's infancy. Therefore, as the final sacrifice of human error, what else remained to be thrown upon the embers of that awful pile except the book which, though a celestial revelation to past ages, was but a voice from a lower sphere as regarded the present race of man? It was done! Upon the blazing heap of falsehood and wornout truth—things that the earth had never needed, or had ceased to need, or had grown childishly weary of—fell the ponderous church Bible, the great old volume that had lain so long on the cushion of the pulpit, and whence the pastor's solemn voice had given holy utterance on so many a Sabbath day. There, likewise, fell the family Bible, which the long-buried patriarch had read to his children—in prosperity or sorrow, by the fireside and in the summer shade of trees—and had bequeathed downward as the heirloom of generations. There fell the bosom Bible, the little volume that had been the soul's friend of some sorely-tried child of dust, who thence took courage, whether his trial were for life or death, steadfastly confronting both in the strong assurance of immortality.

All these were flung into the fierce and riotous blaze; and then a mighty wind came roaring across the plain with a desolate howl, as if it were the angry lamentation of the earth for the loss of heaven's sunshine; and it shook the gigantic pyramid of flame and scattered the cinders of half-consumed abominations around upon the spectators.

"This is terrible!" said I, feeling that my cheek grew pale, and seeing a like change in the visages about me.

"Be of good courage yet," answered the man with whom I had so often spoken. He continued to gaze steadily at the spectacle with a singular calmness, as if it concerned him merely as an observer. "Be of good courage, nor yet exult too much; for there is far less both of good and evil in the effect of this bonfire than the world might be willing to believe."

"How can that be?" exclaimed I, impatiently. "Has it not consumed everything? Has it not swallowed up or melted down every human or divine appendage of our mortal state that had substance enough to be acted on by fire? Will there be anything left us tomorrow morning better or worse than a heap of embers and ashes?"

"Assuredly there will," said my grave friend. "Come hither tomorrow morning, or whenever the combustible portion of the pile

shall be quite burned out, and you will find among the ashes everything really valuable that you have seen cast into the flames. Trust
me, the world of to-morrow will again enrich itself with the gold
and diamonds which have been cast off by the world of to-day.
Not a truth is destroyed nor buried so deep among the ashes but
it will be raked up at last."

This was a strange assurance. Yet I felt inclined to credit it, the
more especially as I beheld among the wallowing flames a copy of
the Holy Scriptures, the pages of which, instead of being blackened
into tinder, only assumed a more dazzling whiteness as the finger
marks of human imperfection were purified away. Certain marginal
notes and commentaries, it is true, yielded to the intensity of the
fiery test, but without detriment to the smallest syllable that had
flamed from the pen of inspiration.

"Yes; there is the proof of what you say," answered I, turning
to the observer; "but if only what is evil can feel the action of the
fire, then, surely, the conflagration has been of inestimable utility.
Yet, if I understand aright, you intimate a doubt whether the world's
expectation of benefit would be realized by it."

"Listen to the talk of these worthies," said he, pointing to a group
in front of the blazing pile; "possibly they may teach you something
useful without intending it."

The persons whom he indicated consisted of that brutal and most
earthy figure who had stood forth so furiously in defence of the
gallows—the hangman, in short—together with the last thief and
the last murderer, all three of whom were clustered about the last
toper. The latter was liberally passing the brandy bottle, which he
had rescued from the general destruction of wines and spirits. This
little convivial party seemed at the lowest pitch of despondency,
as considering that the purified world must needs be utterly unlike
the sphere that they had hitherto known, and therefore but a strange
and desolate abode for gentlemen of their kidney.

"The best counsel for all of us is," remarked the hangman, "that,
as soon as we have finished the last drop of liquor, I help you,
my three friends, to a comfortable end upon the nearest tree, and
then hang myself on the same bough. This is no world for us any
longer."

"Poh, poh, my good fellows!" said a dark-complexioned personage, who now joined the group—his complexion was indeed fearfully dark, and his eyes glowed with a redder light than that of
the bonfire; "be not so cast down, my dear friends; you shall see
good days yet. There's one thing that these wiseacres have forgotten
to throw into the fire, and without which all the rest of the conflagration is just nothing at all; yes, though they had burned the earth
itself to a cinder."

"And what may that be?" eagerly demanded the last murderer.

"What but the human heart itself?" said the dark-visaged stranger, with a portentous grin. "And, unless they hit upon some method of purifying that foul cavern, forth from it will reissue all the shapes of wrong and misery—the same old shapes or worse ones—which they have taken such a vast deal of trouble to consume to ashes. I have stood by this livelong night and laughed in my sleeve at the whole business. Oh, take my word for it, it will be the old world yet!"

This brief conversation supplied me with a theme for lengthened thought. How sad a truth, if true it were, that man's agelong endeavor for perfection had served only to render him the mockery of the evil principle, from the fatal circumstance of an error at the very root of the matter! The heart, the heart—there was the little yet boundless sphere wherein existed the original wrong of which the crime and misery of this outward world were merely types. Purify that inward sphere, and the many shapes of evil that haunt the outward, and which now seem almost our only realities, will turn to shadowy phantoms and vanish of their own accord; but if we go no deeper than the intellect, and strive, with merely that feeble instrument, to discern and rectify what is wrong, our whole accomplishment will be a dream, so unsubstantial that it matters little whether the bonfire, which I have so faithfully described, were what we choose to call a real event and a flame that would scorch the finger, or only a phosphoric radiance and a parable of my own brain.

The Green Hills of Earth

Robert A. Heinlein

This is the story of Rhysling, the Blind Singer of the Spaceways—but not the official version. You sang his words in school:

> I pray for one last landing
> On the globe that gave me birth;
> Let me rest my eyes on the fleecy skies
> And the cool, green hills of Earth.

Or perhaps you sang in French, or German. Or it might have been Esperanto, while Terra's rainbow banner rippled over your head.

The language does not matter—it was certainly an *Earth* tongue. No one has ever translated *"Green Hills"* into the lisping Venerian speech; no Martian ever croaked and whispered it in the dry corridors. This is ours. We of Earth have exported everything from Hollywood crawlies to synthetic radioactives, but this belongs solely to Terra, and to her sons and daughters wherever they may be.

We have all heard many stories of Rhysling. You may even be one of the many who have sought degrees, or acclaim, by scholarly evaluations of his published works—*Songs of the Spaceways, The Grand Canal, and other Poems, High and Far,* and *"UP SHIP!"*

Nevertheless, although you have sung his songs and read his verses, in school and out your whole life, it is at least an even money bet—unless you are a spaceman yourself—that you have never even heard of most of Rhysling's unpublished songs, such items as *Since the Pusher Met My Cousin, That Red-Headed Venusburg Gal, Keep Your Pants On, Skipper,* or *A Space Suit Built for Two.*

Nor can we quote them in a family magazine.

Rhysling's reputation was protected by a careful literary executor and by the happy chance that he was never interviewed. *Songs of the Spaceways* appeared the week he died; when it became a best seller, the publicity stories about him were pieced together from what people remembered about him plus the highly colored handouts from his publishers.

The resulting traditional picture of Rhysling is about as authentic as George Washington's hatchet or King Alfred's cakes.

In truth you would not have wanted him in your parlor; he was not socially acceptable. He had a permanent case of sun itch, which he scratched continually, adding nothing to his negligible beauty.

Van der Voort's portrait of him for the Harriman Centennial edition of his works shows a figure of high tragedy, a solemn mouth, sightless eyes concealed by a black silk bandage. He was never solemn! His mouth was always open, singing, grinning, drinking, or eating. The bandage was any rag, usually dirty. After he lost his sight he became less and less neat about his person.

"Noisy" Rhysling was a jetman, second class, with eyes as good as yours, when he signed on for a loop trip to the Jovian asteroids in the R. S. *Goshawk*. The crew signed releases for everything in those days; a Lloyd's associate would have laughed in your face at the notion of insuring a spaceman. The Space Precautionary Act had never been heard of, and the Company was responsible only for wages, if and when. Half the ships that went further than Luna City never came back. Spacemen did not care; by preference they signed for shares, and any one of them would have bet you that he could jump from the 200th floor of Harriman Tower and ground safely, if you offered him three to two and allowed him rubber heels for the landing.

Jetmen were the most carefree of the lot and the meanest. Compared with them the masters, the radarmen, and the astrogators (there were no supers or stewards in those days) were gentle vegetarians. Jetmen knew too much. The others trusted the skill of the Captain to get them down safely; jetmen knew that skill was useless against the blind and fitful devils chained inside their rocket motors.

The *Goshawk* was the first of Harriman's ships to be converted from chemical fuel to atomic power-piles—or rather the first that did not blow up. Rhysling knew her well; she was an old tub that had plied the Luna City run, Supra-New York Space Station to Leyport and back, before she was converted for deep space. He had worked the Luna run in her and had been along on the first deep space trip, Drywater on Mars—and back, to everyone's surprise.

He should have made chief engineer by the time he signed for the Jovian loop trip, but, after the Drywater pioneer trip, he had been fired, blacklisted, and grounded at Luna City for having spent his time writing a chorus and several verses at a time when he should have been watching his gauges. The song was the infamous *The*

Skipper is a Father to his Crew, with the uproariously unprintable final couplet.

The blacklist did not bother him. He won an accordion from a Chinese barkeep in Luna City by cheating at one-thumb and thereafter kept going by singing to the miners for drinks and tips until the rapid attrition in spacemen caused the Company agent there to give him another chance. He kept his nose clean on the Luna run for a year or two, got back into deep space, helped give Venusburg its original ripe reputation, strolled the banks of the Grand Canal when a second colony was established at the ancient Martian capital, and froze his toes and ears on the second trip to Titan.

Things moved fast in those days. Once the power-pile drive was accepted the number of ships that put out from the Luna-Terra system was limited only by the availability of crews. Jetmen were scarce; the shielding was cut to a minimum to save weight and few married men cared to risk possible exposure to radioactivity. Rhysling did not want to be a father, so jobs were always open to him during the golden days of the claiming boom. He crossed and recrossed the system, singing the doggerel that boiled up in his head and chording it out on his accordion.

The master of the *Goshawk* knew him; Captain Hicks had been astrogator on Rhysling's first trip in her. "Welcome home, Noisy," Hicks had greeted him. "Are you sober, or shall I sign the book for you?"

"You can't get drunk on the bug juice they sell here, Skipper." He signed and went below, lugging his accordion.

Ten minutes later he was back. "Captain," he stated darkly, "that number two jet ain't fit. The cadmium dampers are warped."

"Why tell me? Tell the Chief."

"I did, but he says they will do. He's wrong."

The Captain gestured at the book. "Scratch out your name and scram. We raise ship in thirty minutes."

Rhysling looked at him, shrugged, and went below again.

It is a long climb to the Jovian planetoids; a Hawk-class clunker had to blast for three watches before going into free flight. Rhysling had the second watch. Damping was done by hand then, with a multiplying vernier and a danger gauge. When the gauge showed red, he tried to correct it—no luck.

Jetmen don't wait; that's why they are jetmen. He slapped the emergency discover and fished at the hot stuff with the tongs. The lights went out, he went right ahead. A jetman has to know his power room the way your tongue knows the inside of your mouth.

He sneaked a quick look over the top of the lead baffle when the lights went out. The blue radioactive glow did not help him any; he jerked his head back and went on fishing by touch.

When he was done he called over the tube, "Number two jet out. And for crissake get me some light down here!"

There was light—the emergency circuit—but not for him. The blue radioactive glow was the last thing his optic nerve ever responded to.

II

As Time and Space come bending back to shape this star-
        specked scene,
The tranquil tears of tragic joy still spread their silver
        sheen;
Along the Grand Canal still soar the fragile Towers of
        Truth;
Their fairy grace defends this place of Beauty, calm and
        couth.

Bone-tired the race that raised the Towers, forgotten are
        their lores;
Long gone the gods who shed the tears that lap these
        crystal shores.
Slow beats the time-worn heart of Mars beneath this icy
        sky;
The thin air whispers voicelessly that all who live must
        die—

Yet still the lacy Spires of Truth sing Beauty's madrigal
And she herself will ever dwell along the Grand Canal!

from THE GRAND CANAL, by permission of
Lux Transcriptions, Ltd., London and Luna City

On the swing back they set Rhysling down on Mars at Drywater; the boys passed the hat and the skipper kicked in a half month's pay. That was all—*finish*—just another space bum who had not had the good fortune to finish it off when his luck ran out. He holed up with the prospectors and archeologists at How-Far? for a month or so, and could probably have stayed forever in exchange for his songs and his accordion playing. But spacemen die if they stay in one place; he hooked a crawler over to Drywater again and thence to Marsopolis.

The capital was well into its boom; the processing plants lined the Grand Canal on both sides and roiled the ancient waters with the filth of the run-off. This was before the Tri-Planet Treaty forbade disturbing cultural relics for commerce; half the slender, fairylike towers had been torn down, and others were disfigured to adapt them as pressurized buildings for Earthmen.

Now Rhysling had never seen any of these changes and no one described them to him; when he "saw" Marsopolis again, he visualized it as it had been, before it was rationalized for trade. His memory was good. He stood on the riparian esplanade where the ancient great of Mars had taken their ease and saw its beauty spreading out before his blinded eyes—ice blue plain of water unmoved by tide, untouched by breeze, and reflecting serenely the sharp, bright stars of the Martian sky, and beyond the water the lacy buttresses and flying towers of an architecture too delicate for our rumbling, heavy planet.

The result was *Grand Canal.*

The subtle change in his orientation which enabled him to see beauty at Marsopolis where beauty was not now began to affect his whole life. All women became beautiful to him. He knew them by their voices and fitted their appearances to the sounds. It is a mean spirit indeed who will speak to a blind man other than in gentle friendliness; scolds who had given their husbands no peace sweetened their voices to Rhysling.

It populated his world with beautiful women and gracious men. *Dark Star Passing, Berenice's Hair, Death Song of a Wood's Colt,* and his other love songs of the wanderers, the womenless men of space, were the direct result of the fact that his conceptions were unsullied by tawdry truths. It mellowed his approach, changed his doggerel to verse, and sometimes even to poetry.

He had plenty of time to think now, time to get all the lovely words just so, and to worry a verse until it sang true in his head. The monotonous beat of *Jet Song*—

> When the field is clear, the reports all seen,
> When the lock sighs shut, when the lights wink green,
> When the check-off's done, when it's time to pray,
> When the Captain nods, when she blasts away—
>
> Hear the jets!
> Hear them snarl at your back
> When you're stretched on the rack;
> Feel your ribs clamp your chest,
> Feel your neck grind its rest.
> Feel the pain in your ship,
> Feel her strain in their grip.
> Feel her rise! Feel her drive!
> Straining steel, come alive,
> On her jets!

—came to him not while he himself was a jetman but later while he was hitchhiking from Mars to Venus and sitting out a watch with an old shipmate.

At Venusburg he sang his new songs and some of the old, in the bars. Someone would start a hat around for him; it would come back with a minstrel's usual take doubled or tripled in recognition of the gallant spirit behind the bandaged eyes.

It was an easy life. Any space port was his home and any ship his private carriage. No skipper cared to refuse to lift the extra mass of blind Rhysling and his squeeze box; he shuttled from Venusburg to Leyport to Drywater to New Shanghai, or back again, as the whim took him.

He never went closer to Earth than Supra-New York Space Station. Even when signing the contract for *Songs of the Spaceways* he made his mark in a cabin-class liner somewhere between Luna City and Ganymede. Horowitz, the original publisher, was aboard for a second honeymoon and heard Rhysling sing at a ship's party. Horowitz knew a good thing for the publishing trade when he heard it; the entire contents of *Songs* were sung directly into the tape in the communications room of the ship before he let Rhysling out of his sight. The next three volumes were squeezed out of Rhysling at Venusburg, where Horowitz had sent an agent to keep him liquored up until he had sung all he could remember.

UP SHIP! is not certainly authentic Rhysling throughout. Much of it is Rhysling's, no doubt, and *Jet Song* is unquestionably his, but most of the verses were collected after his death from people who had known him during his wanderings.

The Green Hills of Earth grew through twenty years. The earliest form we know about was composed before Rhysling was blinded, during a drinking bout with some of the indentured men on Venus. The verses were concerned mostly with the things the labor clients intended to do back on Earth if and when they ever managed to pay their bounties and thereby be allowed to go home. Some of the stanzas were vulgar, some were not, but the chorus was recognizably that of *Green Hills*.

We know exactly where the final form of *Green Hills* came from, and when.

There was a ship in at Venus Ellis Isle which was scheduled for the direct jump from there to Great Lakes, Illinois. She was the old *Falcon*, youngest of the Hawk class and the first ship to apply the Harriman Trust's new policy of extrafare express service between Earth cities and any colony with scheduled stops.

Rhysling decided to ride her back to Earth. Perhaps his own song had gotten under his skin—or perhaps he just hankered to see his native Ozarks one more time.

The Company no longer permitted deadheads; Rhysling knew this but it never occurred to him that the ruling might apply to him. He was getting old, for a spaceman, and just a little matter of fact about his privileges. Not senile—he simply knew that he was one of the landmarks in space, along with Halley's Comet, the Rings, and Brewster's Ridge. He walked in the crew's port, went below, and made himself at home in the first empty acceleration couch.

The Captain found him there while making a last minute tour of his ship. "What are you doing here?" he demanded.

"Dragging it back to Earth, Captain," Rhysling needed no eyes to see a skipper's four stripes.

"You can't drag in this ship; you know the rules. Shake a leg and get out of here. We raise ship at once." The Captain was young; he had come up after Rhysling's active time, but Rhysling knew the type—five years at Harriman Hall with only cadet practice trips instead of solid, deep space experience. The two men did not touch in background nor spirit; space was changing.

"Now, Captain, you wouldn't begrudge an old man a trip home."

The officer hesitated—several of the crew had stopped to listen. "I can't do it. 'Space Precautionary Act, Clause Six: No one shall enter space save as a licensed member of a crew of a chartered vessel, or as a paying passenger of such a vessel under such regulations as may be issued pursuant to this act.' Up you get and out you go."

Rhysling lolled back, his hands under his head. "If I've got to go, I'm damned if I'll walk. Carry me."

The Captain bit his lip and said, "Master-at-Arms! Have this man removed."

The ship's policeman fixed his eyes on the overhead struts. "Can't rightly do it, Captain. I've sprained my shoulder." The other crew members, present a moment before, had faded into the bulkhead paint.

"Well, get a working party!"

"Aye, aye, sir." He, too, went away.

Rhysling spoke again. "Now look, Skipper—let's not have any hard feelings about this. You've got an out to carry me if you want to—the 'Distressed Spaceman' clause."

" 'Distressed Spaceman,' my eye! You're no distressed spaceman; you're a space-lawyer. I know who you are; you've been bumming around the system for years. Well, you won't do it in my ship. That clause was intended to succor men who had missed their ships, not to let a man drag free all over space."

"Well, now, Captain, can you properly say I haven't missed my ship? I've never been back home since my last trip as a signed-on crew member. The law says I can have a trip back."

"But that was years ago. You've used up your chance."

"Have I now? The clause doesn't say a word about how soon a man has to take his trip back; it just says he's got it coming to him. Go look it up, Skipper. If I'm wrong, I'll not only walk out on my two legs, I'll beg your humble pardon in front of your crew. Go on—look it up. Be a sport."

Rhysling could feel the man's glare, but he turned and stomped out of the compartment. Rhysling knew that he had used his blindness to place the Captain in an impossible position, but this did not embarrass Rhysling—he rather enjoyed it.

Ten minutes later the siren sounded, he heard the orders on the bull horn for Up-Stations. When the soft sighing of the locks and the slight pressure change in his ears let him know that take-off was imminent he got up and shuffled down to the power room, as he wanted to be near the jets when they blasted off. He needed no one to guide him in any ship of the Hawk class.

Trouble started during the first watch. Rhysling had been lounging in the inspector's chair, fiddling with the keys of his accordion and trying out a new version of *Green Hills.*

> Let me breathe unrationed air again
> Where there's no lack nor dearth

"And something, something, something 'Earth' "—it would not come out right. He tried again.

> Let the sweet fresh breezes heal me
> As they rove around the girth
> Of our lovely mother planet,
> Of the cool, green hills of Earth.

That was better, he thought. "How do you like that, Archie?" he asked over the muted roar.

"Pretty good. Give out with the whole thing." Archie Macdougal, Chief Jetman, was an old friend, both spaceside and in bars; he had been an apprentice under Rhysling many years and millions of miles back.

Rhysling obliged, then said, "You youngsters have got it soft. Everything automatic. When I was twisting her tail you had to stay awake."

"You still have to stay awake." They fell to talking shop and Macdougal showed him the direct response damping rig which had replaced the manual vernier control which Rhysling had used. Rhysling felt out the controls and asked questions until he was familiar with the new installation. It was his conceit that he was still a jetman and that his present occupation as a troubadour was simply an expedient during one of the fusses with the Company that any man could get into.

"I see you still have the old hand damping plates installed," he remarked, his agile fingers flitting over the equipment.

"All except the links. I unshipped them because they obscure the dials."

"You ought to have them shipped. You might need them."

"Oh, I don't know. I think—" Rhysling never did find out what Macdougal thought for it was at that moment the trouble tore loose. Macdougal caught it square, a blast of radioactivity that burned him down where he stood.

Rhysling sensed what had happened. Automatic reflexes of old habit came out. He slapped the discover and rang the alarm to the control room simultaneously. Then he remembered the unshipped links. He had to grope until he found them, while trying to keep as low as he could to get maximum benefit from the baffles. Nothing but the links bothered him as to location. The place was as light to him as any place could be; he knew every spot, every control, the way he knew the keys of his accordion.

"Power room! Power room! What's the alarm?"

"Stay out!" Rhysling shouted. "The place is 'hot.' " He could feel it on his face and in his bones, like desert sunshine.

The links he got into place, after cursing someone, anyone, for having failed to pack the wrench he needed. Then he commenced trying to reduce the trouble by hand. It was a long job and ticklish. Presently he decided that the jet would have to be spilled, pile and all.

First he reported. "Control!"

"Control aye aye!"

"Spilling jet three—emergency."

"Is this Macdougal?"

"Macdougal is dead. This is Rhysling, on watch. Stand by to record."

There was no answer; dumbfounded the Skipper may have been, but he could not interfere in a power room emergency. He had the ship to consider, and the passengers and crew. The doors had to stay closed.

The Captain must have been still more surprised at what Rhysling sent for record. It was:

> We rot in the molds of Venus,
> We retch at her tainted breath.
> Foul are her flooded jungles,
> Crawling with unclean death.

Rhysling went on cataloguing the Solar System as he worked, "—harsh bright soil of Luna—," "—Saturn's rainbow rings—," "—the frozen night of Titan—," all the while opening and spilling the jet and fishing it clean. He finished with an alternate chorus—

> We've tried each spinning space mote
> And reckoned its true worth:

Take us back again to the homes of men
On the cool, green hills of Earth.

—then, almost absentmindedly remembered to tack on his revised first verse:

The arching sky is calling
Spacemen back to their trade.
All hands! Stand by! Free falling!
And the lights below us fade.
Out ride the sons of Terra,
Far drives the thundering jet,
Up leaps the race of Earthmen,
Out, far, and onward yet—

The ship was safe now and ready to limp home shy one jet. As for himself, Rhysling was not so sure. That "sunburn" seemed sharp, he thought. He was unable to see the bright, rosy fog in which he worked but he knew it was there. He went on with the business of flushing the air out through the outer valve, repeating it several times to permit the level of radioaction to drop to something a man might stand under suitable armor. While he did this he sent one more chorus, the last bit of authentic Rhysling that ever could be:

We pray for one last landing
On the globe that gave us birth;
Let us rest our eyes on fleecy skies
And the cool, green hills of Earth.

As Easy as A.B.C.

Rudyard Kipling

The A.B.C., that semi-elected, semi-nominated body of a few score persons, controls the Planet. Transportation is Civilisation, our motto runs. Theoretically we do what we please, so long as we do not interfere with the traffic and all it implies. Practically, the A.B.C. confirms or annuls all international arrangements, and, to judge from its last report, finds our tolerant, humorous, lazy little Planet only too ready to shift the whole burden of public administration on its shoulders.

"With the Night Mail."*

Isn't it almost time that our Planet took some interest in the proceedings of the Aërial Board of Control? One knows that easy communications nowadays, and lack of privacy in the past, have killed all curiosity among mankind, but as the Board's Official Reporter I am bound to tell my tale.

At 9:30 A.M., August 26, A.D. 2065, the Board, sitting in London, was informed by De Forest that the District of Northern Illinois had riotously cut itself out of all systems and would remain disconnected till the Board should take over and administer it direct.

Every Northern Illinois freight and passenger tower was, he reported, out of action; all District main, local, and guiding lights had been extinguished; all General Communications were dumb, and through traffic had been diverted. No reason had been given, but he gathered unofficially from the Mayor of Chicago that the District complained of "Crowd-making and invasion of privacy."

As a matter of fact, it is of no importance whether Northern Illinois stay in or out of planetary circuit; as a matter of policy, any complaint of invasion of privacy needs immediate investigation, lest worse follow.

*In *Actions and Reactions*, by Rudyard Kipling.

By 9:45 A.M. De Forest, Dragomiroff (Russia), Takahira (Japan), and Pirolo (Italy) were empowered to visit Illinois and "to take such steps as might be necessary for the resumption of traffic and *all that that implies.*" By 10 A.M. the Hall was empty, and the four Members and I were aboard what Pirolo insisted on calling "my leetle godchild"—that is to say, the new *Victor Pirolo.* Our Planet prefers to know Victor Pirolo as a gentle, grey-haired enthusiast who spends his time near Foggia, inventing or creating new breeds of Spanish-Italian olive-trees; but there is another side to his nature—the manufacture of quaint inventions, of which the *Victor Pirolo* is, perhaps, not the least surprising. She and a few score sister-craft of the same type embody his latest ideas. But she is not comfortable. An A.B.C. boat does not take the air with the level-keeled lift of a liner, but shoots up rocket-fashion like the "aeroplane" of our ancestors, and makes her height at top-speed from the first. That is why I found myself sitting suddenly on the large lap of Eustace Arnott, who commands the A.B.C. Fleet. One knows vaguely that there is such a thing as a Fleet somewhere on the Planet, and that, theoretically, it exists for the purposes of what used to be known as "war." Only a week before, while visiting a glacier sanatorium behind Gothaven, I had seen some squadrons making false auroras far to the north while they manoeuvred round the Pole; but, naturally, it had never occurred to me that the things could be used in earnest.

Said Arnott to De Forest as I staggered to a seat on the chart-room divan: "We're tremendously grateful to 'em in Illinois. We've never had a chance of exercising all the Fleet together. I've turned in a General Call, and I expect we'll have at least two hundred keels aloft this evening."

"Well aloft?" De Forest asked.

"Of course, sir. Out of sight till they're called for."

Arnott laughed as he lolled over the transparent chart-table where the map of the summer-blue Atlantic slid along, degree by degree, in exact answer to our progress. Our dial already showed 320 m.p.h. and we were two thousand feet above the uppermost traffic lines.

"Now, where is this Illinois District of yours?" said Dragomiroff. "One travels so much, one sees so little. Oh, I remember! It is in North America."

De Forest, whose business it is to know the out districts, told us that it lay at the foot of Lake Michigan, on a road to nowhere in particular, was about half an hour's run from end to end, and, except in one corner, as flat as the sea. Like most flat countries nowadays, it was heavily guarded against invasion of privacy by forced timber—fifty-foot spruce and tamarack, grown in five years. The population was close on two millions, largely migratory between Florida and California, with a backbone of small farms (they call a thousand acres a farm in Illinois) whose owners come into Chicago for amusements and society during the winter. They were, he said, noticeably kind, quiet folk, but a little exacting, as all flat countries must be, in their notions of privacy. There had, for instance, been no printed news-sheet in Illinois for twenty-seven years. Chicago argued that engines for printed news sooner or later developed into engines for invasion of privacy, which in turn might bring the old terror of Crowds and blackmail back to the Planet. So news-sheets were not.

"And that's Illinois," De Forest concluded. "You see, in the Old Days, she was in the forefront of what they used to call 'progress,' and Chicago—"

"Chicago?" said Takahira. "That's the little place where there is Salati's Statue of the Nigger in Flames? A fine bit of old work."

"When did you see it?" asked De Forest quickly. "They only unveil it once a year."

"I know. At Thanksgiving. It was then," said Takahira, with a shudder. "And they sang MacDonough's Song, too."

"Whew!" De Forest whistled. "I did not know that! I wish you'd told me before. MacDonough's Song may have had its uses when it was composed, but it was an infernal legacy for any man to leave behind."

"It's protective instinct, my dear fellows," said Pirolo, rolling a cigarette. "The Planet, she has had her dose of popular government. She suffers from inherited agoraphobia. She has no—ah—use for Crowds."

Dragomiroff leaned forward to give him a light. "Certainly," said the white-bearded Russian, "the Planet has taken all precautions against Crowds for the past hundred years. What is our total population today? Six hundred million, we hope; five hundred, we think; but—but if next year's census shows more than four hundred and fifty, I myself will eat all the extra little babies. We have cut the birth-rate out—right out! For a long time we have said to Almighty God, 'Thank You, Sir, but we do not much like Your game of life, so we will not play.'"

"Anyhow," said Arnott defiantly, "men live a century apiece on the average now."

"Oh, that is quite well! I am rich—you are rich—we are all rich and happy because we are so few and we live so long. Only I think Almighty God He will remember what the Planet was like in the time of Crowds and the Plague. Perhaps He will send us nerves. Eh, Pirolo?"

The Italian blinked into space. "Perhaps," he said, "He has sent them already. Anyhow, you cannot argue with the Planet. She does not forget the Old Days, and—what can you do?"

"For sure we can't remake the world." De Forest glanced at the map flowing smoothly across the table from west to east. "We ought to be over our ground by nine tonight. There won't be much sleep afterwards."

On which hint we dispersed, and I slept till Takahira waked me for dinner. Our ancestors thought nine hours' sleep ample for their little lives. We, living thirty years longer, feel ourselves defrauded with less than eleven out of the twenty-four.

By ten o'clock we were over Lake Michigan. The west shore was lightless, except for a dull ground-glare at Chicago, and a single traffic-directing light—its leading beam pointing north—at Waukegan on our starboard bow. None of the Lake villages gave any sign of life; and inland, westward, so far as we could see, blackness lay unbroken on the level earth. We swooped down and skimmed low across the dark, throwing calls county by county, Now and again we picked up the faint glimmer of a house-light, or heard the rasp and rend of a cultivator being played across the fields, but Northern Illinois as a whole was one inky, apparently uninhabited, waste of high, forced woods. Only our illuminated map, with its little pointer switching from county to county as we wheeled and twisted, gave us any idea of our position. Our calls, urgent, pleading, coaxing or commanding, through the General Communicator brought no answer. Illinois strictly maintained her own privacy in the timber which she grew for that purpose.

"Oh, this is absurd!" said De Forest. "We're like an owl trying to work a wheat-field. Is this Bureau Creek? Let's land, Arnott, and get hold of someone."

We brushed over a belt of forced woodland—fifteen-year-old maple sixty feet high—grounded on a private meadowdock, none too big, where we moored to our own grapnels, and hurried out through the warm dark night towards a light in a verandah. As we neared the garden gate I could have sworn we had stepped knee-deep in quicksand, for we could scarcely drag our feet against the prickling currents that clogged them. After five paces we stopped, wiping our foreheads, as hopelessly stuck on dry smooth turf as so many cows in a bog.

"Pest!" cried Pirolo angrily. "We are ground-circuited. And it is my own system of ground-circuits too! I know the pull."

"Good evening," said a girl's voice from the verandah. "Oh, I'm sorry! We've locked up. Wait a minute."

We heard the click of a switch, and almost fell forward as the currents round our knees were withdrawn.

The girl laughed, and laid aside her knitting. An old-fashioned Controller stood at her elbow, which she reversed from time to time, and we could hear the snort and clank of the obedient cultivator half a mile away, behind the guardian woods.

"Come in and sit down," she said. "I'm only playing a plough. Dad's gone to Chicago to—Ah! Then it was *your* call I heard just now!"

She had caught sight of Arnott's Board uniform, leaped to the switch, and turned it full on.

We were checked, gasping, waist-deep in current this time, three yards from the verandah.

"We only want to know what's the matter with Illinois," said De Forest placidly.

"Then hadn't you better go to Chicago and find out?" she answered. "There's nothing wrong here. We own ourselves."

"How can we go anywhere if you won't loose us?" De Forest went on, while Arnott scowled. Admirals of Fleets are still quite human when their dignity is touched.

"Stop a minute—you don't know how funny you look!" She put her hands on her hips and laughed mercilessly.

"Don't worry about that," said Arnott, and whistled. A voice answered from the *Victor Pirolo* in the meadow.

"Only a single-fuse ground-circuit!" Arnott called. "Sort it out gently, please."

We heard the ping of a breaking lamp; a fuse blew out somewhere in the verandah roof, frightening a nestful of birds. The ground-circuit was open. We stooped and rubbed our tingling ankles.

"How rude—how very rude of you!" the maiden cried.

"Sorry, but we haven't time to look funny," said Arnott. "We've got to go to Chicago; and if I were you, young lady, I'd go into the cellars for the next two hours, and take mother with me."

Off he strode, with us at his heels, muttering indignantly, till the humour of the thing struck and doubled him up with laughter at the foot of the gangway ladder.

"The Board hasn't shown what you might call a fat spark on this occasion," said De Forest, wiping his eyes. "I hope *I* didn't look as big a fool as you did, Arnott! Hullo! What on earth is that? Dad coming home from Chicago?"

There was a rattle and a rush, and a five-plough cultivator, blades in air like so many teeth, trundled itself at us round the edge of the timber, fuming and sparking furiously.

"Jump!" said Arnott, as we bundled ourselves through the none-too-wide door. "Never mind about shutting it. Up!"

The *Victor Pirolo* lifted like a bubble, and the vicious machine shot just underneath us, clawing high as it passed.

"There's a nice little spit-kitten for you!" said Arnott, dusting his knees. "We ask her a civil question. First she circuits us and then she plays a cultivator at us!"

"And then we fly," said Dragomiroff. "If I were forty years more young, I would go back and kiss her. Ho! Ho!"

"I," said Pirolo, "would smack her! My pet ship has been chased by a dirty plough; a—how do you say?—agricultural implement."

"Oh, that is Illinois all over," said De Forest. "They don't content themselves with talking about privacy. They arrange to have it. And now, where's your alleged Fleet, Arnott? We must assert ourselves against this wench."

Arnott pointed to the black heavens.

"Waiting on—up there," said he. "Shall I give them the whole installation, sir?"

"Oh, I don't think the young lady is quite worth that," said De Forest. "Get over Chicago, and perhaps we'll see something."

In a few minutes we were hanging at two thousand feet over an oblong block of incandescence in the centre of the little town.

"That looks like the old City Hall. Yes, there's Salati's Statue in front of it," said Takahira. "But what on earth are they doing to the place? I thought they used it for a market nowadays! Drop a little, please."

We could hear the sputter and crackle of road-surfacing machines —the cheap Western type which fuse stone and rubbish into lava-like ribbed glass for their rough country roads. Three or four surfacers worked on each side of a square of ruins. The brick and stone wreckage crumbled, slid forward, and presently spread out into white-hot pools of sticky slag, which the leveling-rods smoothed more or less flat. Already a third of the big block had been so treated, and was cooling to dull red before our astonished eyes.

"It is the Old Market," said De Forest. "Well, there's nothing to prevent Illinois from making a road through a market. It doesn't interfere with traffic, that I can see."

"Hsh!" said Arnott, gripping me by the shoulder. "Listen! They're singing. Why on earth are they singing?"

We dropped again till we could see the black fringe of people at the edge of that glowing square.

At first they only roared against the roar of the surfacers and level-lers. Then the words came up clearly—the words of the Forbidden Song that all men knew, and none let pass their lips—poor Pat MacDonough's Song, made in the days of the Crowds and the Plague—every silly word of it loaded to sparking-point with the Planet's inherited memories of horror, panic, fear and cruelty. And Chicago—innocent, contented little Chicago—was singing it aloud to the infernal tune that carried riot, pestilence and lunacy round our Planet a few generations ago!

> Once there was The People—Terror gave it birth;
> Once there was The People, and it made a Hell of Earth!

(Then the stamp and pause):

> Earth arose and crushed it. Listen, O ye slain!
> Once there was The People—it shall never be again!

The levellers thrust in savagely against the ruins as the song renewed itself again, again and again, louder than the crash of the melting walls.

De Forest frowned.

"I don't like that," he said. "They've broken back to the Old Days! They'll be killing somebody soon. I think we'd better divert 'em, Arnott."

"Ay, ay, sir." Arnott's hand went to his cap, and we heard the hull of the *Victor Pirolo* ring to the command: "Lamps! Both watches stand by! Lamps! Lamps! Lamps!"

"Keep still!" Takahira whispered to me. "Blinkers, please, quartermaster."

"It's all right—all right!" said Pirolo from behind, and to my horror slipped over my head some sort of rubber helmet that locked with a snap. I could feel thick colloid bosses before my eyes, but I stood in absolute darkness.

"To save the sight," he explained, and pushed me on to the chartroom divan. "You will see in a minute."

As he spoke I became aware of a thin thread of almost intolerable light, let down from heaven at an immense distance—one vertical hairsbreadth of frozen lightning.

"Those are our flanking ships," said Arnott at my elbow. "That one is over Galena. Look south—that other one's over Keithburg. Vincennes is behind us, and north yonder is Winthrop Woods. The Fleet's in position, sir"—this to De Forest. "As soon as you give the word."

"Ah no! No!" cried Dragomiroff at my side. I could feel the old man tremble. "I do not know all that you can do, but be kind! I ask you to be a little kind to them below! This is horrible—horrible!"

> When a Woman kills a Chicken,
> Dynasties and Empires sicken,

Takahira quoted. "It is too late to be gentle now."

"Then take off my helmet! Take off my helmet!" Dragomiroff began hysterically.

Pirolo must have put his arm round him.

"Hush," he said, "I am here. It is all right, Ivan, my dear fellow."

"I'll just send our little girl in Bureau County a warning," said Arnott. "She don't deserve it, but we'll allow her a minute or two to take mamma to the cellar."

In the utter hush that followed the growling spark after Arnott had linked up his Service Communicator with the invisible Fleet, we heard MacDonough's Song from the city beneath us grow fainter as we rose to position. Then I clapped my hand before my mask lenses, for it was as though the floor of heaven had been riddled and all the inconceivable blaze of suns in the making was poured through the manholes.

"You needn't count," said Arnott. I had had no thought of such a thing. "There are two hundred and fifty keels up there, five miles apart. Full power, please, for another twelve seconds."

The firmament, as far as eye could reach, stood on pillars of white fire. One fell on the glowing square at Chicago, and turned it black.

"Oh! Oh! Oh! Can men be allowed to do such things?" Dragomiroff cried, and fell across our knees.

"Glass of water, please," said Takahira to a helmeted shape that leaped forward. "He is a little faint."

The lights switched off, and the darkness stunned like an avalanche. We could hear Dragomiroff's teeth on the glass edge.

Pirolo was comforting him.

"All right, all ra-ight," he repeated. "Come and lie down. Come below and take off your mask. I give you my word, old friend, it is all right. They are my siege-lights. Little Victor Pirolo's leetle lights. You know *me!* I do not hurt people."

"Pardon!" Dragomiroff moaned. "I have never seen Death. I have never seen the Board take action. Shall we go down and burn them alive, or is that already done?"

"Oh, hush," said Pirolo, and I think he rocked him in his arms.

"Do we repeat, sir?" Arnott asked De Forest.

"Give 'em a minute's break," De Forest replied. "They may need it."

We waited a minute, and then MacDonough's Song, broken but defiant, rose from undefeated Chicago.

"They seem fond of that tune," said De Forest. "I should let 'em have it, Arnott."

"Very good, sir," said Arnott, and felt his way to the Communicator keys.

No lights broke forth, but the hollow of the skies made herself the mouth for one note that touched the raw fibre of the brain. Men hear such sounds in delirium, advancing like tides from horizons beyond the ruled foreshores of space.

"That's our pitch-pipe," said Arnott. "We may be a bit ragged. I've never conducted two hundred and fifty performers before." He pulled out the couplers, and struck a full chord on the Service Communicators.

The beams of light leaped down again, and danced, solemnly and awfully, a stilt-dance, sweeping thirty or forty miles left and right at each stiff-legged kick, while the darkness delivered itself—there is no scale to measure against that utterance—of the tune to which

they kept time. Certain notes—one learned to expect them with terror—cut through one's marrow, but, after three minutes, thought
and emotion passed in indescribable agony.

We saw, we heard, but I think we were in some sort swooning.
The two hundred and fifty beams shifted, re-formed, straddled and
split, narrowed, widened, rippled in ribbons, broke into a thousand
white-hot parallel lines, melted and revolved in interwoven rings
like old-fashioned engine-turning, flung up to the zenith, made as
if to descend and renew the torment, halted at the last instant,
twizzled insanely round the horizon, and vanished, to bring back
for the hundredth time darkness more shattering than their instantly
renewed light over all Illinois. Then the tune and lights ceased
together, and we heard one single devastating wail that shook all
the horizon as a rubbed wet finger shakes the rim of a bowl.

"Ah, that is my new siren," said Pirolo. "You can break an iceberg
in half, if you find the proper pitch. They will whistle by squadrons
now. It is the wind through pierced shutters in the bows."

I had collapsed beside Dragomiroff, broken and snivelling feebly,
because I had been delivered before my time to all the terrors of
Judgment Day, and the Archangels of the Resurrection were hailing
me naked across the Universe to the sound of the music of the
spheres.

Then I saw De Forest smacking Arnott's helmet with his open
hand. The wailing died down in a long shriek as a black shadow
swooped past us, and returned to her place above the lower clouds.

"I hate to interrupt a specialist when he's enjoying himself," said
De Forest. "But, as a matter of fact, all Illinois has been asking us
to stop for these last fifteen seconds."

"What a pity." Arnott slipped off his mask. "I wanted you to
hear us really hum. Our lower C can lift street-paving."

"It is Hell—Hell!" cried Dragomiroff, and sobbed aloud.

Arnott looked away as he answered:

"It's a few thousand volts ahead of the old shoot-'em-and-sink-'em
game, but I should scarcely call it *that*. What shall I tell the Fleet,
sir?"

"Tell 'em we're very pleased and impressed. I don't think they
need wait any longer. There isn't a spark left down there." De Forest
pointed. "They'll be deaf and blind."

"Oh, I think not, sir. The demonstration lasted less than ten
minutes."

"Marvellous!" Takahira sighed. "I should have said it was half
a night. Now, shall we go down and pick up the pieces?"

"But first a small drink," said Pirolo. "The Board must not arrive
weeping at its own works."

"I am an old fool—an old fool!" Dragomiroff began piteously. "I did not know what would happen. It is all new to me. We reason with them in Little Russia."

Chicago North landing-tower was unlighted, and Arnott worked his ship into the clips by her own lights. As soon as these broke out we heard groanings of horror and appeal from many people below.

"All right," shouted Arnott into the darkness. "We aren't beginning again!" We descended by the stairs, to find ourselves knee-deep in a grovelling crowd, some crying that they were blind, others beseeching us not to make any more noises, but the greater part writhing face downward, their hands or their caps before their eyes.

It was Pirolo who came to our rescue. He climbed the side of a surfacing-machine, and there, gesticulating as though they could see, made oration to those afflicted people of Illinois.

"You stchewpids!" he began. "There is nothing to fuss for. Of course, your eyes will smart and be red tomorrow. You will look as if you and your wives had drunk too much, but in a little while you will see again as well as before. I tell you this, and I—*I* am Pirolo. Victor Pirolo!"

The Crowd with one accord shuddered, for many legends attach to Victor Pirolo of Foggia, deep in the secrets of God.

"Pirolo?" An unsteady voice lifted itself. "Then tell us was there anything except light in those lights of yours just now?"

The question was repeated from every corner of the darkness. Pirolo laughed.

"No!" he thundered. (Why have small men such large voices?) "I give you my word and the Board's word that there was nothing except light—just light! You stchewpids! Your birth-rate is too low already as it is. Some day I must invent something to send it up, but send it down—never!"

"Is that true?—We thought—somebody said—"

One could feel the tension relax all round.

"You *too* big fools," Pirolo cried. "You could have sent us a call and we would have told you."

"Send you a call!" a deep voice shouted. "I wish you had been at our end of the wire."

"I'm glad I wasn't," said De Forest. "It was bad enough from behind the lamps. Never mind! It's over now. Is there any one here I can talk business with? I'm De Forest—for the Board."

"You might begin with me, for one—I'm Mayor," the bass voice replied.

A big man rose unsteadily from the street, and staggered towards us where we sat on the broad turf-edging, in front of the garden fences.

"I ought to be the first on my feet. Am I?" said he.

"Yes," said De Forest, and steadied him as he dropped down beside us.

"Hello, Andy. Is that you?" a voice called.

"Excuse me," said the Mayor; "that sounds like my Chief of Police, Bluthner!"

"Bluthner it is; and here's Mulligan and Keefe—on their feet."

"Bring 'em up please, Blut. We're supposed to be the Four in charge of this hamlet. What we say, goes. And, De Forest, what do you say?"

"Nothing—yet," De Forest answered, as we made room for the panting, reeling men. *"You've* cut out of system. Well?"

"Tell the steward to send down drinks, please," Arnott whispered to an orderly at his side.

"Good!" said the Mayor, smacking his dry lips. "Now I suppose we can take it, De Forest, that henceforward the Board will administer us direct?"

"Not if the Board can avoid it," De Forest laughed. "The A.B.C. is responsible for the planetary traffic only."

"And all that that implies." The big Four who ran Chicago chanted their Magna Charta like children at school.

"Well, get on," said De Forest wearily. "What is your silly trouble anyway?"

"Too much dam' Democracy," said the Mayor, laying his hand on De Forest's knee.

"So? I thought Illinois had had her dose of that."

"She has. That's why. Blut, what did you do with our prisoners last night?"

"Locked 'em in the water-tower to prevent the women killing 'em," the Chief of Police replied. "I'm too blind to move just yet, but—"

"Arnott, send some of your people, please, and fetch 'em along," said De Forest.

"They're triple-circuited," the Mayor called. "You'll have to blow out three fuses." He turned to De Forest, his large outline just visible in the paling darkness. "I hate to throw any more work on the Board. I'm an administrator myself, but we've had a little fuss with our Serviles. What? In a big city there's bound to be a few men and women who can't live without listening to themselves, and who prefer drinking out of pipes they don't own both ends of. They inhabit flats and hotels all the year round. They say it saves 'em trouble. Anyway, it gives 'em more time to make trouble for their neighbours. We call 'em Serviles locally. And they are apt to be tuberculous."

"Just so!" said the man called Mulligan. "Transportation is Civilisation. Democracy is Disease. I've proved it by the blood-test, every time."

"Mulligan's our Health Officer, and a one-idea man," said the Mayor, laughing. "But it's true that most Serviles haven't much control. They *will* talk; and when people take to talking as a business, anything may arrive—mayn't it, De Forest?"

"Anything—except the facts of the case," said De Forest, laughing.

"I'll give you those in a minute," said the Mayor. "Our Serviles got to talking—first in their houses and then on the streets, telling men and women how to manage their own affairs. (You can't teach a Servile not to finger his neighbour's soul.) That's invasion of privacy, of course, but in Chicago we'll suffer anything sooner than make Crowds. Nobody took much notice, and so I let 'em alone. My fault! I was warned there would be trouble, but there hasn't been a Crowd or murder in Illinois for nineteen years."

"Twenty-two," said his Chief of Police.

"Likely. Anyway, we'd forgot such things. So, from talking in the houses and on the streets, our Serviles go to calling a meeting at the Old Market yonder." He nodded across the square where the wrecked buildings heaved up grey in the dawn-glimmer behind the square-cased statue of The Negro in Flames. "There's nothing to prevent any one calling meetings except that it's against human nature to stand in a Crowd, besides being bad for the health. I ought to have known by the way our men and women attended that first meeting that trouble was brewing. There were as many as a thousand in the market-place, touching each other. Touching! Then the Serviles turned in all tongue-switches and talked, and we—"

"What did they talk about?" said Takahira.

"First, how badly things were managed in the city. That pleased us Four—we were on the platform—because we hoped to catch one or two good men for City work. You know how rare executive capacity is. Even if we didn't it's—it's refreshing to find anyone interested enough in our job to damn our eyes. You don't know what it means to work, year in, year out, without a spark of difference with a living soul."

"Oh, don't we!" said De Forest. "There are times on the Board when we'd give our positions if any one would kick us out and take hold of things themselves."

"But they won't," said the Mayor ruefully. "I assure you, sir, we Four have done things in Chicago, in the hope of rousing people, that would have discredited Nero. But what do they say? 'Very good, Andy. Have it your own way. Anything's better than a Crowd. I'll go back to my land.' You *can't* do anything with folk who can go where they please, and don't want anything on God's earth except their own way. There isn't a kick or a kicker left on the Planet."

"Then I suppose that little shed yonder fell down by itself?" said De Forest. We could see the bare and still smoking ruins, and hear the slag-pools crackle as they hardened and set.

"Oh, that's only amusement. 'Tell you later. As I was saying, our Serviles held the meeting, and pretty soon we had to ground-circuit the platform to save 'em from being killed. And that didn't make our people any more pacific."

"How d'you mean?" I ventured to ask.

"If you've ever been ground-circuited," said the Mayor, "you'll know it don't improve any man's temper to be held up straining against nothing. No, sir! Eight or nine hundred folk kept pawing and buzzing like flies in treacle for two hours, while a pack of perfectly safe Serviles invades their mental and spiritual privacy, may be amusing to watch, but they are not pleasant to handle afterwards."

Pirolo chuckled.

"Our folk own themselves. They were of opinion things were going too far and too fiery. I warned the Serviles; but they're born house-dwellers. Unless a fact hits 'em on the head they cannot see it. Would you believe me, they went on to talk of what they called 'popular government'? They did! They wanted us to go back to the old Voodoo-business of voting with papers and wooden boxes, and word-drunk people and printed formulas, and news-sheets! They said they practised it among themselves about what they'd have to eat in their flats and hotels. Yes, sir! They stood up behind Bluthner's doubled ground-circuits, and they said that, in this present year of grace, *to* self-owning men and women, *on* that very spot! Then they finished"—he lowered his voice cautiously—"by talking about 'The People.' And then Bluthner he had to sit up all night in charge of the circuits because he couldn't trust his men to keep 'em shut."

"It was trying 'em too high," the Chief of Police broke in. "But we couldn't hold the Crowd ground-circuited for ever. I gathered in all the Serviles on charge of Crowd-making, and put 'em in the water-tower, and then I let things cut loose. I had to! The District lit like a sparked gas-tank!"

"The news was out over seven degrees of country," the Mayor continued; "and when once it's a question of invasion of privacy, good-bye to right and reason in Illinois! They began turning out traffic-lights and locking up landing-towers on Thursday night. Friday, they stopped all traffic and asked for the Board to take over. Then they wanted to clean Chicago off the side of the Lake and rebuild elsewhere—just for a souvenir of 'The People' that the Serviles talked about. I suggested that they should slag the Old Market where the meeting was held, while I turned in a call to you all on the Board. That kept 'em quiet till you came along. And—and now *you* can take hold of the situation."

" 'Any chance of their quieting down?" De Forest asked.

"You can try," said the Mayor.

De Forest raised his voice in the face of the reviving Crowd that had edged in towards us. Day was come.

"Don't you think this business can be arranged?" he began. But there was a roar of angry voices:

"We've finished with Crowds! We aren't going back to the Old Days! Take us over! Take the Serviles away! Administer direct or we'll kill 'em! Down with The People!"

An attempt was made to begin MacDonough's Song. It got no further than the first line, for the *Victor Pirolo* sent down a warning drone on one stopped horn. A wrecked sidewall of the Old Market tottered and fell inwards on the slag-pools. None spoke or moved till the last of the dust had settled down again, turning the steel case of Salati's Statue ashy grey.

"You see you'll just *have* to take us over," the Mayor whispered.

De Forest shrugged his shoulders.

"You talk as if executive capacity could be snatched out of the air like so much horse-power. Can't you manage yourselves on any terms?" he said.

"We can, if you say so. It will only cost those few lives to begin with."

The Mayor pointed across the square, where Arnott's men guided a stumbling group of ten or twelve men and women to the lake-front and halted them under the Statue.

"Now I think," said Takahira under his breath, "there will be trouble."

The mass in front of us growled like beasts.

At that moment the sun rose clear, and revealed the blinking assembly to itself. As soon as it realised that it was a Crowd we saw the shiver of horror and mutual repulsion shoot across it precisely as the steely flaws shot across the Lake outside. Nothing was said, and, being half blind, of course it moved slowly. Yet in less than fifteen minutes most of that vast multitude—three thousand at the lowest count—melted away like frost on south eaves. The remnant stretched themselves on the grass, where a Crowd feels and looks less like a Crowd.

"These mean business," the Mayor whispered to Takahira. "There are a goodish few women there who've borne children. I don't like it."

The morning draught off the Lake stirred the trees round us with promise of a hot day; the sun reflected itself dazzlingly on the canister-shaped covering of Salati's Statue; cocks crew in the gardens, and we could hear gate-latches clicking in the distance as people stumblingly resought their homes.

"I'm afraid there won't be any morning deliveries," said De Forest. "We rather upset things in the country last night."

"That makes no odds," the Mayor returned. "We're all provisioned for six months. *We* take no chances."

Nor, when you come to think of it, does any one else. It must be three-quarters of a generation since any house or city faced a food shortage. Yet is there house or city on the Planet today that has not half a year's provisions laid in? We are like the shipwrecked seamen in the old books, who, having once nearly starved to death, ever afterwards hide away bits of food and biscuit. Truly we trust no Crowds, nor system based on Crowds!

De Forest waited till the last footstep had died away. Meantime the prisoners at the base of the Statue shuffled, posed, and fidgeted, with the shamelessness of quite little children. None of them were more than six feet high, and many of them were as grey-haired as the ravaged, harassed heads of old pictures. They huddled together in actual touch, while the Crowd, spaced at large intervals, looked at them with congested eyes.

Suddenly a man among them began to talk. The Mayor had not in the least exaggerated. It appeared that our Planet lay sunk in slavery beneath the heel of the Aërial Board of Control. The orator urged us to arise in our might, burst our prison doors and break our fetters (all his metaphors, by the way, were of the most mediaeval). Next he demanded that every matter of daily life, including most of the physical functions, should be submitted for decision at any time of the week, month, or year to, I gathered, anybody who happened to be passing by or residing within a certain radius, and that everybody should forthwith abandon his concerns to settle the matter, first by Crowd-making, next by talking to the Crowds made, and lastly by describing crosses on pieces of paper, which rubbish should later be counted with certain mystic ceremonies and oaths. Out of this amazing play, he assured us, would automatically arise a higher, nobler, and kinder world, based—he demonstrated this with the awful lucidity of the insane—based on the sanctity of the Crowd and the villainy of the single person. In conclusion, he called loudly upon God to testify to his personal merits and integrity. When the flow ceased, I turned bewildered to Takahira, who was nodding solemnly.

"Quite correct," said he. "It is all in the old books. He has left nothing out, not even the war-talk."

"But I don't see how this stuff can upset a child, much less a district," I replied.

"Ah, you are too young," said Dragomiroff. "For another thing, you are not a mamma. Please look at the mammas."

Ten or fifteen women who remained had separated themselves from the silent men, and were drawing in towards the prisoners. It reminded one of the stealthy encircling, before the rush in at the quarry, of wolves round musk-oxen in the North. The prisoners saw, and drew together more closely. The Mayor covered his face with his hands for an instant. De Forest, bareheaded, stepped forward between the prisoners and the slowly, stiffly moving line.

"That's all very interesting," he said to the dry-lipped orator. "But the point seems that you've been making Crowds and invading privacy."

A woman stepped forward, and would have spoken, but there was a quick assenting murmur from the men, who realised that De Forest was trying to pull the situation down to ground-line.

"Yes! Yes!" they cried. "We cut out because they made Crowds and invaded privacy! Stick to that! Keep on that switch! Lift the Serviles out of this! The Board's in charge! Hsh!"

"Yes, the Board's in charge," said De Forest. "I'll take formal evidence of Crowd-making if you like, but the Members of the Board can testify to it. Will that do?"

The women had closed in another pace, with hands that clenched and unclenched at their sides.

"Good! Good enough!" the men cried. "We're content. Only take them away quickly."

"Come along up!" said De Forest to the captives. "Breakfast is quite ready."

It appeared, however, that they did not wish to go. They intended to remain in Chicago and make Crowds. They pointed out that De Forest's proposal was gross invasion of privacy.

"My dear fellow," said Pirolo to the most voluble of the leaders, "you hurry, or your Crowd that can't be wrong will kill you!"

"But that would be murder," answered the believer in Crowds; and there was a roar of laughter from all sides that seemed to show the crisis had broken.

A woman stepped forward from the line of women, laughing, I protest, as merrily as any of the company. One hand, of course, shaded her eyes, the other was at her throat.

"Oh, they needn't be afraid of being killed!" she called.

"Not in the least," said De Forest. "But don't you think that, now the Board's in charge, you might go home while we get these people away?"

"I shall be home long before that. It—it has been rather a trying day."

She stood up to her full height, dwarfing even De Forest's six-foot-eight, and smiled, with eyes closed against the fierce light.

"Yes, rather," said De Forest. "I'm afraid you feel the glare a little. We'll have the ship down."

He motioned to the *Pirolo* to drop between us and the sun, and at the same time to loop-circuit the prisoners, who were a trifle unsteady. We saw them stiffen to the current where they stood. The woman's voice went on, sweet and deep and unshaken:

"I don't suppose you men realise how much this—this sort of thing means to a woman. I've borne three. We women don't want our children given to Crowds. It must be an inherited instinct. Crowds make trouble. They bring back the Old Days. Hate, fear, blackmail, publicity, 'The People'—*That! That! That!*" She pointed to the Statue, and the Crowd growled once more.

"Yes, if they are allowed to go on," said De Forest. "But this little affair—"

"It means so much to us women that this—this little affair should never happen again. Of course, never's a big word, but one feels so strongly that it is important to stop Crowds at the very beginning. Those creatures"—she pointed with her left hand at the prisoners swaying like seaweed in a tideway as the circuit pulled them—"those people have friends and wives and children in the city and elsewhere. One doesn't want anything done to *them*, you know. It's terrible to force a human being out of fifty or sixty years of good life. I'm only forty myself. *I* know. But, at the same time, one feels that an example should be made, because no price is too heavy to pay if—if these people and *all that they imply* can be put an end to. Do you quite understand, or would you be kind enough to tell your men to take the casing off the Statue? It's worth looking at."

"I understand perfectly. But I don't think anybody here wants to see the Statue on an empty stomach. Excuse me one moment." De Forest called up to the ship, "A flying loop ready on the port side, if you please." Then to the woman he said with some crispness, "You might leave us a little discretion in the matter."

"Oh, of course, Thank you for being so patient. I know my arguments are silly, but—" She half turned away and went on in a changed voice, "Perhaps this will help you to decide."

She threw out her right arm with a knife in it. Before the blade could be returned to her throat or her bosom it was twitched from her grip, sparked as it flew out of the shadow of the ship above, and fell flashing in the sunshine at the foot of the Statue fifty yards away. The outflung arm was arrested, rigid as a bar for an instant, till the releasing circuit permitted her to bring it slowly to her side. The other women shrank back silent among the men.

Pirolo rubbed his hands, and Takahira nodded.

"That was clever of you, De Forest," said he.

"What a glorious pose!" Dragomiroff murmured, for the frightened woman was on the edge of tears.

"Why did you stop me? I would have done it!" she cried.

"I have no doubt you would," said De Forest. "But we can't waste a life like yours on these people. I hope the arrest didn't sprain your wrist; it's so hard to regulate a flying loop. But I think you are quite right about those persons' women and children. We'll take them all away with us if you promise not to do anything stupid to yourself."

"I promise—I promise." She controlled herself with an effort. "But it is so important to us women. We know what it means; and I thought if you saw I was in earnest—"

"I saw you were, and you've gained your point. I shall take all your Serviles away with me at once. The Mayor will make lists of their friends and families in the city and the District, and he'll ship them after us this afternoon."

"Sure," said the Mayor, rising to his feet. "Keefe, if you can see, hadn't you better finish levelling off the Old Market? It don't look sightly the way it is now, and we shan't use it for Crowds any more."

"I think you had better wipe out that Statue as well, Mr. Mayor," said De Forest. "I don't question its merits as a work of art, but I believe it's a shade morbid."

"Certainly, sir. Oh, Keefe! Slag the Nigger before you go on to fuse the Market. I'll get to the Communicators and tell the District that the Board is in charge. Are you making any special appointments, sir?"

"None. We haven't men to waste on these backwoods. Carry on as before, but under the Board. Arnott, run your Serviles aboard, please. Ground ship and pass them through the bilge-doors. We'll wait till we've finished with this work of art."

The prisoners trailed past him, talking fluently, but unable to gesticulate in the drag of the current. Then the surfacers rolled up, two on each side of the Statue. With one accord the spectators looked elsewhere, but there was no need. Keefe turned on full power, and the thing simply melted within its case. All I saw was a surge of white-hot metal pouring over the plinth, a glimpse of Salati's inscription, "To the Eternal Memory of the Justice of the People," ere the stone base itself cracked and powdered into finest lime. The crowd cheered.

"Thank you," said De Forest; "but we want our breakfasts, and I expect you do too. Good-bye, Mr. Mayor! Delighted to see you at any time, but I hope I shan't have to, officially, for the next thirty years. Good-bye, madam. Yes. We're all given to nerves nowadays. I suffer from them myself. Good-bye, gentlemen all! You're under the tyrannous heel of the Board from this moment, but if ever you feel like breaking your fetters you've only to let us know. This is no treat to us. Good luck!"

We embarked amid shouts, and did not check our lift till they had dwindled into whispers. Then De Forest flung himself on the chart-room divan and mopped his forehead.

"I don't mind men," he panted, "but women are the devil!"

"Still the devil," said Pirolo cheerfully. "That one would have suicided."

"I know it. That was why I signalled for the flying loop to be clapped on her. I owe you an apology for that, Arnott. I hadn't time to catch your eye, and you were busy with our caitiffs. By the way, who actually answered my signal? It was a smart piece of work."

"Ilroy," said Arnott; "but he overloaded the wave. It may be pretty gallery-work to knock a knife out of a lady's hand, but didn't you notice how she rubbed 'em? He scorched her fingers. Slovenly, I call it."

"Far be it from me to interfere with Fleet discipline, but don't be too hard on the boy. If that woman had killed herself they would have killed every Servile and everything related to a Servile throughout the District by nightfall."

"That was what she was playing for," Takahira said. "And with our Fleet gone we could have done nothing to hold them."

"I may be ass enough to walk into a ground-circuit," said Arnott, "but I don't dismiss my Fleet till I'm reasonably sure that trouble is over. They're in position still, and I intend to keep 'em there till the Serviles are shipped out of the District. That last little Crowd meant murder, my friends."

"Nerves! All nerves!" said Pirolo. "You cannot argue with agoraphobia."

"And it is not as if they had seen much dead—or *is* it?" said Takahira.

"In all my ninety years I have never seen Death." Dragomiroff spoke as one who would excuse himself. "Perhaps that was why—last night—"

Then it came out as we sat over breakfast, that, with the exception of Arnott and Pirolo, none of us had ever seen a corpse, or knew in what manner the spirit passes.

"We're a nice lot to flap about governing the Planet," De Forest laughed. "I confess, now it's all over, that my main fear was I mightn't be able to pull it off without losing a life."

"I thought of that too," said Arnott; "but there's no death reported, and I've inquired everywhere. What are we supposed to do with our passengers? I've fed 'em."

"We're between two switches," De Forest drawled. "If we drop them in any place that isn't under the Board the natives will make their presence an excuse for cutting out, same as Illinois did, and forcing the Board to take over. If we drop them in any place under the Board's control they'll be killed as soon as our backs are turned."

"If you say so," said Pirolo thoughtfully, " I can guarantee that they will become extinct in process of time, quite happily. What is their birth-rate now?"

"Go down and ask 'em," said De Forest.

"I think they might become nervous and tear me to bits," the philosopher of Foggia replied.

"Not really! Well?"

"Open the bilge-doors," said Takahira with a downward jerk of the thumb.

"Scarcely—after all the trouble we've taken to save 'em," said De Forest.

"Try London," Arnott suggested. "You could turn Satan himself loose there, and they'd only ask him to dinner."

"Good man! You've given me an idea. Vincent! Oh, Vincent!" He threw the General Communicator open so that we could all hear, and in a few minutes the chart-room filled with the rich, fruity voice of Leopold Vincent, who has purveyed all London her choicest amusements for the last thirty years. We answered with expectant grins, as though we were actually in the stalls of, say, the Combination on a first night.

"We've picked up something in your line," De Forest began.

"That's good, dear man. If it's old enough. There's nothing to beat the old things for business purposes. Have you seen *London, Chatham, and Dover* at Earl's Court? No? I thought I missed you there. Immense! I've had the real steam locomotive engines built from the old designs and the iron rails cast specially by hand. Cloth cushions in the carriages, too! Immense! And paper railway tickets. And Polly Milton."

"Polly Milton back again!" said Arnott rapturously. "Book me two stalls for tomorrow night. What's she singing now, bless her?"

"The old songs. Nothing comes up to the old touch. Listen to this, dear men." Vincent carolled with flourishes:

> Oh, cruel lamps of London,
> If tears your light could drown,
> Your victims' eyes would weep them,
> Oh, lights of London Town!

"Then they weep."

"You see?" Pirolo waved his hands at us. "The old world always weeped when it saw Crowds together. It did not know why, but it weeped. We know why, but we do not weep, except when we pay to be made to by fat, wicked old Vincent."

"Old, yourself!" Vincent laughed. "I'm a public benefactor, I keep the world soft and united."

"And I'm De Forest of the Board," said De Forest acidly, "trying to get a little business done. As I was saying, I've picked up a few people in Chicago."

"I cut out. Chicago is—"

"Do listen! They're perfectly unique."

"Do they build houses of baked mudblocks while you wait—eh? That's an old contact."

"They're an untouched primitive community, with all the old ideas."

"Sewing-machines and maypole-dances? Cooking on coal-gas stoves, lighting pipes with matches, and driving horses? Gerolstein tried that last year. An absolute blow-out!"

De Forest plugged him wrathfully, and poured out the story of our doings for the last twenty-four hours on the top-note.

"And they do it *all* in public," he concluded. "You can't stop 'em. The more public, the better they are pleased. They'll talk for hours—like you! Now you can come in again!"

"Do you really mean they know how to vote?" said Vincent. "Can they act it?"

"Act? It's their life to 'em! And you never saw such faces! Scarred like volcanoes. Envy, hatred, and malice in plain sight. Wonderfully flexible voices. They weep, too."

"Aloud? In public?"

"I guarantee. Not a spark of shame or reticence in the entire installation. It's the chance of your career."

"D'you say you've brought their voting props along—those papers and ballot-box things?"

"No, confound you! I'm not a luggage-lifter. Apply direct to the Mayor of Chicago. He'll forward you everything. Well?"

"Wait a minute. Did Chicago want to kill 'em? That 'ud look well on the Communicators."

"Yes! They were only rescued with difficulty from a howling mob—if you know what that is."

"But I don't," answered the Great Vincent simply.

"Well then, they'll tell you themselves. They can make speeches hours long."

"How many are there?"

"By the time we ship 'em all over they'll be perhaps a hundred, counting children. An old world in miniature. Can't you see it?"

"M-yes; but I've got to pay for it if it's a blow-out, dear man."

"They can sing the old war songs in the streets. They can get word-drunk, and make Crowds, and invade privacy in the genuine old-fashioned way; and they'll do the voting trick as often as you ask 'em a question."

"Too good!" said Vincent.

"You unbelieving Jew! I've got a dozen head aboard here. I'll put you through direct. Sample 'em yourself."

He lifted the switch and we listened. Our passengers on the lower deck at once, but not less than five at a time, explained themselves to Vincent. They had been taken from the bosom of their families, stripped of their possessions, given food without finger-bowls, and cast into captivity in anoisome dungeon.

"But look here," said Arnott aghast; "they're saying what isn't true. My lower deck isn't noisome, and I saw to the finger-bowls myself."

"My people talk like that sometimes in Little Russia," said Dragomiroff. "We reason with them. We never kill. No!"

"But it's not true," Arnott insisted. "What can you do with people who don't tell facts? They're mad!"

"Hsh!" said Pirolo, his hand to his ear. "It is such a little time since all the Planet told lies."

We heard Vincent silkily sympathetic. Would they, he asked, repeat their assertions in public—before a vast public? Only let Vincent give them a chance, and the Planet, they vowed, should ring with their wrongs. Their aim in life—two women and a man explained it together—was to reform the world. Oddly enough, this also had been Vincent's life-dream. He offered them an arena in which to explain, and by their living example to raise the Planet to loftier levels. He was eloquent on the moral uplift of a simple, old-world life presented in its entirety to a deboshed civilisation.

Could they—would they—for three months certain, devote themselves under his auspices, as missionaries, to the elevation of mankind at a place called Earl's Court, which he said, with some truth, was one of the intellectual centres of the Planet? They thanked him, and demanded (we could hear his chuckle of delight) time to discuss and to vote on the matter. The vote, solemnly managed by counting heads—one head, one vote—was favourable. His offer, therefore, was accepted, and they moved a vote of thanks to him in two speeches—one by what they called the "proposer" and the other by the "seconder."

Vincent threw over to us, his voice shaking with gratitude:

"I've got 'em! Did you hear those speeches? That's Nature, dear men. Art can't teach *that*. And they voted as easily as lying. I've never had a troupe of natural liars before. Bless you, dear men! Remember, you're on my free lists for ever, anywhere—all of you. Oh, Gerolstein will be sick—sick!"

"Then you think they'll do?" said De Forest.

"Do? The Little Village'll go crazy! I'll knock up a series of old-world plays for 'em. Their voices will make you laugh and cry. My God, dear men, where *do* you suppose they picked up all their misery from, on this sweet earth? I'll have a pageant of the world's beginnings, and Mosenthal shall do the music. I'll—"

"Go and knock up a village for 'em by tonight. We'll meet you at No. 15 West Landing Tower," said De Forest. "Remember the rest will be coming along tomorrow."

"Let 'em all come!" said Vincent. "You don't know how hard it is nowadays even for me, to find something that really gets under the public's damned iridium-plated hide. But I've got it at last. Good-bye!"

"Well," said De Forest when we had finished laughing, "if anyone understood corruption in London I might have played off Vincent against Gerolstein, and sold my captives at enormous prices. As it is, I shall have to be their legal adviser tonight when the contracts are signed. And they won't exactly press any commission on me, either."

"Meantime," said Takahira, "we cannot, of course, confine members of Leopold Vincent's last-engaged company. Chairs for the ladies, please, Arnott."

"Then I go to bed," said De Forest. "I can't face any more women!" And he vanished.

When our passengers were released and given another meal (finger-bowls came first this time) they told us what they thought of us and the Board; and, like Vincent, we all marvelled how they had contrived to extract and secrete so much bitter poison and unrest out of the good life God gives us. They raged, they stormed, they palpitated, flushed and exhausted their poor, torn nerves, panted themselves into silence, and renewed the senseless, shameless attacks.

"But can't you understand," said Pirolo pathetically to a shrieking woman, "that if we'd left you in Chicago you'd have been killed?"

"No, we shouldn't. You were bound to save us from being murdered."

"Then we should have had to kill a lot of other people."

"That doesn't matter. We were preaching the Truth. You can't stop us. We shall go on preaching in London; and *then* you'll see!"

"You can see now," said Pirolo, and opened a lower shutter.

We were closing on the Little Village, with her three million people spread out at ease inside her ring of girdling Main-Traffic lights —those eight fixed beams at Chatham, Tonbridge, Redhill, Dorking, Woking, St. Albans, Chipping Ongar, and Southend.

Leopold Vincent's new company looked, with small pale faces, at the silence, the size, and the separated houses.

Then some began to weep aloud, shamelessly—always without shame.

MacDonough's Song

Whether the State can loose and bind
  In Heaven as well as on Earth:
If it be wiser to kill mankind
  Before or after the birth—

These are matters of high concern
   Where State-kept schoolmen are;
But Holy State (we have lived to learn)
   Endeth in Holy War.

Whether The People be led by the Lord,
   Or lured by the loudest throat:
If it be quicker to die by the sword
   Or cheaper to die by vote—
These are the things we have dealt with once,
   (And they will not rise from their grave)
For Holy People, however it runs,
   Endeth in wholly Slave.

Whatsoever, for any cause,
   Seeketh to take or give.
Power above or beyond the Laws,
   Suffer it not to live!
Holy State or Holy King—
   Or Holy People's Will—
Have no truck with the senseless thing.
   Order the guns and kill!
     Saying—after—me:—

Once there was The People—Terror gave it birth;
Once there was The People and it made a Hell of Earth.
Earth arose and crushed it. Listen, O ye slain!
Once there was The People—it shall never be again!

Invasion from Mars

Howard Koch

The radio-script version of H. G. Wells's famous novel, The War of the Worlds; *freely adapted by Howard Koch and presented by Orson Welles and his Mercury Theatre on the Air over the Columbia Broadcasting System, October 30, 1938.*

NARRATOR: We know now that in the early years of the twentieth century this world was being watched closely by intelligences greater than man's and yet as mortal as his own. We know now that as human beings busied themselves about their various concerns they were scrutinized and studied, perhaps almost as narrowly as a man with a microscope might scrutinize the transient creatures that swarm and multiply in a drop of water. With infinite complacence people went to and fro over the Earth about their little affairs, serene in the assurance of their dominion over this small, spinning fragment of solar driftwood which by chance or design man has inherited out of the dark mystery of Time and Space. Yet across an immense ethereal gulf, minds that are to our minds as ours are to the beasts in the jungle, intellects vast, cool, and unsympathetic, regarded this Earth with envious eyes and slowly and surely drew their plans against us. In the thirty-ninth year of the twentieth century came the great disillusionment.

It was near the end of October. Business was better. The war scare was over. More men were back at work. Sales were picking up. On this particular evening, October 30, the Crossley service estimated that thirty-two million people were listening in on radios.

ANNOUNCER CUE: ... for the next twenty-four hours not much change in temperature. A slight atmospheric disturbance of undetermined origin is reported over Nova Scotia, causing a low-pressure area to move down rather rapidly over the northeastern states, bringing a forecast of rain, accompanied by winds of light gale force.

Maximum temperature 66; minimum 48. This weather report comes to you from the Government Weather Bureau.

ANNOUNCER TWO: We now take you to the Meridian Room in the Hotel Park Plaza in downtown New York, where you will be entertained by the music of Ramon Raquello and his orchestra.

(Spanish theme song . . . Fades)

ANNOUNCER THREE: Good evening, ladies and gentlemen. From the Meridian Room in the Park Plaza in New York City, we bring you the music of Ramon Raquello and his orchestra. With a touch of the Spanish, Ramon Raquello leads off with "La Cumparsita."

(Piece starts playing)

ANNOUNCER TWO: Ladies and gentlemen, we interrupt our program of dance music to bring you a special bulletin from the Intercontinental Radio News. At twenty minutes before eight, central time, Professor Farrell of the Mount Jennings Observatory, Chicago, Illinois, reports observing several explosions of incandescent gas, occurring at regular intervals on the planet Mars.

The spectroscope indicates the gas to be hydrogen and moving toward the Earth with enormous velocity. Professor Pierson of the observatory at Princeton confirms Farrell's observation, and describes the phenomenon as (quote) like a jet of blue flame shot from a gun (unquote). We now return you to the music of Ramon Raquello, playing for you in the Meridian Room of the Park Plaza Hotel, situated in downtown New York.

(Music plays for a few moments until piece ends . . . Sound of applause)

Now a tune that never loses favor, the ever popular "Star Dust." Ramon Raquello and his orchestra . . .

(Music)

ANNOUNCER TWO: Ladies and gentlemen, following on the news given in our bulletin a moment ago, the Government Meteorological Bureau has requested the large observatories of the country to keep an astronomical watch on any other disturbances occurring on the planet Mars. Due to the unusual nature of this occurrence, we have arranged an interview with the noted astronomer, Professor Pierson, who will give us his views on this event. In a few moments we will take you to the Princeton Observatory at Princeton, New Jersey. We return you until then to the music of Ramon Raquello and his orchestra.

(Music)

ANNOUNCER TWO: We are ready now to take you to the Princeton Observatory at Princeton, where Carl Phillips, our commentator, will interview Professor Richard Pierson, famous astronomer. We take you now to Princeton, New Jersey.

(Echo chamber)

PHILLIPS: Good evening, ladies and gentlemen. This is Carl Phillips, speaking to you from the observatory at Princeton. I am standing in a large semicircular room, pitch-black except for an oblong split in the ceiling. Through this opening I can see a sprinkling of stars that cast a kind of frosty glow over the intricate mechanism of the huge telescope. The ticking sound you hear is the vibration of the clockwork. Professor Pierson stands directly above me on a small platform, peering through the giant lens. I ask you to be patient, ladies and gentlemen, during any delay that may arise during our interview. Besides his ceaseless watch of the heavens, Professor Pierson may be interrupted by telephone or other communications. During this period he is in constant touch with the astronomical centers of the world—Professor, may I begin our questions?

PIERSON: At any time, Mr. Phillips.

PHILLIPS: Professor, would you please tell our radio audience exactly what you see as you observe the planet Mars through your telescope?

PIERSON: Nothing unusual at the moment, Mr. Phillips. A red disk swimming in a blue sea. Transverse stripes across the disk. Quite distinct now because Mars happens to be at the point nearest the earth—in opposition, as we call it.

PHILLIPS: In your opinion, what do these transverse stripes signify, Professor Pierson?

PIERSON: Not canals, I can assure you, Mr. Phillips, although that's the popular conjecture of those who imagine Mars to be inhabited. From a scientific viewpoint the stripes are merely the result of atmospheric conditions peculiar to the planet.

PHILLIPS: Then you're quite convinced as a scientist that living intelligence as we know it does not exist on Mars?

PIERSON: I should say the chances against it are a thousand to one.

PHILLIPS: And yet, how do you account for these gas eruptions occurring on the surface of the planet at regular intervals?

PIERSON: Mr. Phillips, I cannot account for it.

PHILLIPS: By the way, Professor, for the benefit of our listeners, how far is Mars from the Earth?

PIERSON: Approximately forty million miles.

PHILLIPS: Well, that seems a safe enough distance— Just a moment, ladies and gentlemen, someone has just handed Professor Pierson a message. While he reads it, let me remind you we are speaking to you from the observatory in Princeton, New Jersey, where we are interviewing the world-famous astronomer, Professor Pierson.... One moment, please. Professor Pierson has passed me a message which he has just received. Professor, may I read the message to the listening audience?

PIERSON: Certainly, Mr. Phillips.

PHILLIPS: Ladies and gentlemen, I shall read you a wire addressed to Professor Pierson from Dr. Gray of the National History Museum, New York. "9:15 P.M. Eastern standard time. Seismograph registered shock of almost earthquake intensity occurring within a radius of twenty miles of Princeton. Please investigate. Signed, Lloyd Gray, Chief of Astronomical Division." Professor Pierson, could this occurrence possibly have something to do with the disturbances observed on the planet Mars?

PIERSON: Hardly, Mr. Phillips. This is probably a meteorite of unusual size, and its arrival at this particular time is merely a coincidence. However, we shall conduct a search, as soon as daylight permits.

PHILLIPS: Thank you, Professor. Ladies and gentlemen, for the past ten minutes we've been speaking to you from the observatory at Princeton, bringing you a special interview with Professor Pierson, noted astronomer. This is Carl Phillips speaking. We now return you to our New York studio.

(Fade in piano playing)

ANNOUNCER TWO: Ladies and gentlemen, here is the latest bulletin from the Intercontinental Radio News. Toronto, Canada: Professor Morse of Macmillan University reports observing a total of three explosions on the planet Mars, between the hours of 7:45 P.M. and 9:20 P.M., Eastern standard time. This confirms earlier reports received from American observatories. Now, nearer home, comes a special announcement from Trenton, New Jersey. It is reported that at 8:50 P.M. a huge, flaming object, believed to be a meteorite, fell on a farm in the neighborhood of Grovers Mill, New Jersey, twenty-two miles from Trenton. The flash in the sky was visible within a radius of several hundred miles and the noise of the impact was heard as far north as Elizabeth.

We have dispatched a special mobile unit to the scene, and will have our commentator, Mr. Phillips, give you a word description as soon as he can reach there from Princeton. In the meantime, we take you to the Hotel Martinet in Brooklyn, where Bobby Millette and his orchestra are offering a program of dance music.

(Swing band for 20 seconds ... Then cut)

ANNOUNCER TWO: We take you now to Grovers Mill, New Jersey.

(Crowd noises ... Police sirens)

PHILLIPS: Ladies and gentlemen, this is Carl Phillips again, at the Wilmuth farm, Grovers Mill, New Jersey. Professor Pierson and myself made the eleven miles from Princeton in ten minutes. Well,

I—I hardly know where to begin, to paint for you a word picture of the strange scene before my eyes, like something out of a modern *Arabian Nights*. Well, I just got here. I haven't had a chance to look around yet. I guess that's it. Yes, I guess that's the—thing, directly in front of me, half buried in a vast pit. Must have struck with terrific force. The ground is covered with splinters of a tree it must have struck on its way down. What I can see of the—object itself doesn't look very much like a meteor, at least not the meteors I've seen. It looks more like a huge cylinder. It has a diameter of—what would you say, Professor Pierson?

PIERSON (*off*): About thirty yards.

PHILLIPS: About thirty yards— The metal on the sheath is—well, I've never seen anything like it. The color is sort of yellowish-white. Curious spectators now are pressing close to the object in spite of the efforts of the police to keep them back. They're getting in front of my line of vision. Would you mind standing on one side, please?

POLICEMAN: One side, there, one side.

PHILLIPS: While the policemen are pushing the crowd back, here's Mr. Wilmuth, owner of the farm here. He may have some interesting facts to add. Mr. Wilmuth, would you please tell the radio audience as much as you remember of this rather unusual visitor that dropped in your back yard? Step closer, please. Ladies and gentlemen, this is Mr. Wilmuth.

WILMUTH: I was listenin' to the radio—

PHILLIPS: Closer and louder, please.

WILMUTH: Pardon me!

PHILLIPS: Louder, please, and closer.

WILMUTH: Yes, sir—while I was listening to the radio and kinda drowsin', that Professor fellow was talkin' about Mars, so I was half dozin' and half—

PHILLIPS: Yes, yes, Mr. Wilmuth. And then what happened?

WILMUTH: As I was sayin', I was listenin' to the radio kinda half-ways—

PHILLIPS: Yes, Mr. Wilmuth, and then you saw something?

WILMUTH: Not first off. I heard something.

PHILLIPS: And what did you hear?

WILMUTH: A hissing sound. Like this: sssssssss—kinda like a Fourt' of July rocket.

PHILLIPS: Then what?

WILMUTH: Turned my head out the window and would have swore I was to sleep and dreamin'.

PHILLIPS: Yes?

WILMUTH: I seen a kinda greenish streak and then zingo! Somethin' smacked the ground. Knocked me clear out of my chair!

PHILLIPS: Well, were you frightened, Mr. Wilmuth?

WILMUTH: Well, I—I ain't quite sure. I reckon I—I was kinda riled.

PHILLIPS: Thank you, Mr. Wilmuth. Thank you.

WILMUTH: Want me to tell you some more?

PHILLIPS: No—that's quite all right, that's plenty—Ladies and gentlemen, you've just heard Mr. Wilmuth, owner of the farm where this thing has fallen. I wish I could convey the atmosphere—the background of this—fantastic scene. Hundreds of cars are parked in a field in back of us. Police are trying to rope off the roadway leading into the farm. But it's no use. They're breaking right through. Their headlights throw an enormous spot on the pit where the object's half buried. Some of the more daring souls are venturing near the edge. Their silhouettes stand out against the metal sheen.

(Faint humming sound)

One man wants to touch the thing—he's having an argument with a policeman. The policeman wins— Now, ladies and gentlemen, there's something I haven't mentioned in all this excitement, but it's becoming more distinct. Perhaps you've caught it already on your radio. Listen *(Long pause)* . . . Do you hear it? It's a curious humming sound that seems to come from inside the object. I'll move the microphone nearer. Here. *(Pause)* Now we're not more than twenty-five feet away. Can you hear it now? Oh, Professor Pierson!

PIERSON: Yes, Mr. Phillips?

PHILLIPS: Can you tell us the meaning of that scraping noise inside the thing?

PIERSON: Possibly the unequal cooling of its surface.

PHILLIPS: Do you still think it's a meteor, Professor?

PIERSON: I don't know what to think. The metal casing is definitely extraterrestrial—not found on this Earth. Friction with the Earth's atmosphere usually tears holes in a meteorite. This thing is smooth and, as you can see, of cylindrical shape.

PHILLIPS: Just a minute! Something's happening! Ladies and gentlemen, this is terrific! This end of the thing is beginning to flake off! The top is beginning to rotate like a screw! The thing must be hollow!

VOICES: She's a-movin'!

Look, the darn thing's unscrewing!

Keep back, there! Keep back, I tell you.

Maybe there's men in it trying to escape!

It's red-hot, they'll burn to a cinder!

Keep back there! Keep those idiots back!

(Suddenly the clanking sound of a huge piece of falling metal)

VOICES: She's off! The top's loose!

Look out there! Stand back!

PHILLIPS: Ladies and gentlemen, this is the most terrifying thing I have ever witnessed— Wait a minute! Someone's crawling out of the hollow top. Someone or—something. I can see peering out of that black hole two luminous disks—are they eyes? It might be a face. It might be—

(*Shout of awe from the crowd*)

Good heavens, something's wriggling out of the shadow like a gray snake. Now it's another one, and another. They look like tentacles to me. There, I can see the thing's body. It's large as a bear and glistens like wet leather. But that face. It—it's indescribable. I can hardly force myself to keep looking at it. The eyes are black and gleam like a serpent. The mouth is V-shaped with saliva dripping from its rimless lips that seem to quiver and pulsate. The monster or whatever it is can hardly move. It seems weighed down by—possibly gravity or something. The thing's raising up. The crowd falls back. They've seen enough. This is the most extraordinary experience. I can't find words—I'm pulling this microphone with me as I talk. I'll have to stop the description until I've taken a new position. Hold on, will you please, I'll be back in a minute.

(*Fade into piano*)

ANNOUNCER TWO: We are bringing you an eyewitness account of what's happening on the Wilmuth farm, Grovers Mill, New Jersey.

(*More piano*)

We now return you to Carl Phillips at Grovers Mill.

PHILLIPS: Ladies and gentlemen (Am I on?)—ladies and gentlemen, here I am, back of a stone wall that adjoins Mr. Wilmuth's garden. From here I get a sweep of the whole scene. I'll give you every detail as long as I can talk. As long as I can see. More State Police have arrived. They're drawing up a cordon in front of the pit, about thirty of them. No need to push the crowd back now. They're willing to keep their distance. The captain is conferring with someone. We can't quite see who. Oh, yes, I believe it's Professor Pierson. Yes, it is. Now they've parted. The professor moves around one side, studying the object, while the captain and two policemen advance with something in their hands. I can see it now. It's a white handkerchief tied to a pole—a flag of truce. If those creatures know what that means—what anything means!... *Wait!* Something's happening!

(*Hissing sound followed by a humming that increases in intensity*)

A humped shape is rising out of the pit. I can make out a small beam of light against a mirror. What's that? There's a jet of flame springing from that mirror, and it leaps right at the advancing men. It strikes them head on! Good Lord, they're turning into flame!

(*Screams and unearthly shrieks*)

Now the whole field's caught fire. (*Explosion*) The woods—the barns—the gas tanks of automobiles—it's spreading everywhere. It's coming this way. About twenty yards to my right—

(*Crash of microphone . . . Then dead silence . . .*)

ANNOUNCER TWO: Ladies and gentlemen, due to circumstances beyond our control, we are unable to continue the broadcast from Grovers Mill. Evidently there's some difficulty with our field transmission. However, we will return to that point at the earliest opportunity. In the meantime, we have a late bulletin from San Diego, California. Professor Indellkoffer, speaking at a dinner of the California Astronomical Society, expressed the opinion that the explosions on Mars are undoubtedly nothing more than severe volcanic disturbances on the surface of the planet. We continue now with our piano interlude.

(*Piano . . . Then cut*)

Ladies and gentlemen, I have just been handed a message that came in from Grovers Mill by telephone. Just a moment. At least forty people, including six State Troopers, lie dead in a field east of the village of Grovers Mill, their bodies burned and distorted beyond all possible recognition. The next voice you hear will be that of Brigadier General Montgomery Smith, commander of the State Militia at Trenton, New Jersey.

SMITH: I have been requested by the Governor of New Jersey to place the counties of Mercer and Middlesex as far west as Princeton, and east to Jamesburg, under martial law. No one will be permitted to enter this area except by special pass issued by state or military authorities. Four companies of State Militia are proceeding from Trenton to Grovers Mill and will aid in the evacuation of homes within the range of military operations. Thank you.

ANNOUNCER: You have just been listening to General Montgomery Smith, commanding the State Militia at Trenton. In the meantime, further details of the catastrophe at Grovers Mill are coming in. The strange creatures, after unleashing their deadly assault, crawled back in their pit and made no attempt to prevent the efforts of the firemen to recover the bodies and extinguish the fire. Combined fire departments of Mercer County are fighting the flames, which menace the entire countryside.

We have been unable to establish any contact with our mobile unit at Grovers Mill, but we hope to be able to return you there at the earliest possible moment. In the meantime we take you—uh, just one moment please.

(*Long pause . . . Whisper*)

Ladies and gentlemen, I have just been informed that we have finally established communication with an eyewitness of the tragedy. Professor Pierson has been located at a farmhouse near Grovers Mill, where he has established an emergency observation post. As a scientist, he will give you his explanation of the calamity. The next voice you hear will be that of Professor Pierson, brought to you by direct wire. Professor Pierson.

PIERSON: Of the creatures in the rocket cylinder at Grovers Mill, I can give you no authoritative information—either as to their nature, their origin, or their purposes here on Earth. Of their destructive instrument I might venture some conjectural explanation. For want of a better term, I shall refer to the mysterious weapon as a heat-ray. It's all too evident that these creatures have scientific knowledge far in advance of our own. It is my guess that in some way they are able to generate an intense heat in a chamber of practically absolute nonconductivity. This intense heat they project in a parallel beam against any object they choose, by means of a polished parabolic mirror of unknown composition, much as the mirror of a lighthouse projects a beam of light. That is my conjecture of the origin of the heat-ray.

ANNOUNCER TWO: Thank you, Professor Pierson. Ladies and gentlemen, here is a bulletin from Trenton. It is a brief statement informing us that the charred body of Carl Phillips, the radio commentator, has been identified in a Trenton hospital. Now here's another bulletin from Washington, D.C.

Office of the director of the National Red Cross reports ten units of Red Cross emergency workers have been assigned to the headquarters of the State Militia stationed outside of Grovers Mill, New Jersey. Here's a bulletin from State Police, Princeton Junction: The fires at Grovers Mill and vicinity now under control. Scouts report all quiet in the pit, and no sign of life appearing from the mouth of the cylinder. And now, ladies and gentlemen, we have a special statement from Mr. Harry McDonald, vice-president in charge of operations.

MC DONALD: We have received a request from the militia at Trenton to place at their disposal our entire broadcasting facilities. In view of the gravity of the situation, and believing that radio has a definite responsibility to serve in the public interest at all times, we are turning over our facilities 5o the State Militia at Trenton.

ANNOUNCER: We take you now to the field headquarters of the State Militia near Grovers Mill, New Jersey.

CAPTAIN: This is Captain Lansing of the Signal Corps, attached to the State Militia now engaged in military operations in the vicinity of Grovers Mill. Situation arising from the reported presence of certain individuals of unidentified nature is now under complete control.

The cylindrical object which lies in a pit directly below our position is surrounded on all sides by eight battalions of infantry, without heavy fieldpieces, but adequately armed with rifles and machine guns. All cause for alarm, if such cause ever existed, is now entirely unjustified. The things, whatever they are, do not even venture to poke their heads above the pit. I can see their hiding place plainly in the glare of the searchlights here. With all their reported resources, these creatures can scarcely stand up against heavy machine-gun fire. Anyway, it's an interesting outing for the troops. I can make out their khaki uniforms, crossing back and forth in front of the lights. It looks almost like a real war. There appears to be some slight smoke in the woods bordering the Millstone River. Probably fire started by campers. Well, we ought to see some action soon. One of the companies is deploying on the left flank. A quick thrust and it will all be over. Now wait a minute! I see something on top of the cylinder. No, it's nothing but a shadow. Now the troops are on the edge of the Wilmuth farm. Seven thousand armed men closing in on an old metal tube. Wait, that wasn't a shadow! It's something moving—solid metal—kind of a shieldlike affair rising up out of the cylinder— It's going higher and higher. Why, it's standing on legs—actually rearing up on a sort of metal framework. Now it's reaching above the trees and the searchlights are on it! Hold on!

(Silence)

ANNOUNCER TWO: Ladies and gentlemen, I have a grave announcement to make. Incredible as it may seem, both the observations of science and the evidence of our eyes lead to the inescapable assumption that those strange beings who landed in the Jersey farmlands tonight are the vanguard of an invading army from the planet Mars. The battle which took place tonight at Grovers Mill has ended in one of the most startling defeats ever suffered by an army in modern times; seven thousand men armed with rifles and machine guns pitted against a single fighting machine of the invaders from Mars. One hundred and twenty known survivors. The rest strewn over the battle area from Grovers Mill to Plainsboro, crushed and trampled to death under the metal feet of the monster, or burned to cinders by its heat-ray. The monster is now in control of the middle section of New Jersey and has effectively cut the state through its center. Communication lines are down from Pennsylvania to the Atlantic Ocean. Railroad tracks are torn, and service from New York to Philadelphia discontinued except routing some of the trains through Allentown and Phoenixville. Highways to the north, south, and west are clogged with frantic human traffic. Police and Army reserves are unable to control the mad flight. By morning the fugitives will have swelled Philadelphia, Camden, and Trenton, it is estimated, to twice their normal population.

At this time martial law prevails throughout New Jersey and eastern Pennsylvania. We take you now to Washington for a special broadcast on the National Emergency.... The Secretary of the Interior—

SECRETARY: Citizens of the nation: I shall not try to conceal the gravity of the situation that confronts the country, nor the concern of your government in protecting the lives and property of its people. However, I wish to impress upon you—private citizens and public officials, all of you—the urgent need of calm and resourceful action. Fortunately, this formidable enemy is still confined to a comparatively small area, and we may place our faith in the military forces to keep them there. In the meantime, placing our faith in God, we must continue the performance of our duties each and every one of us, so that we may confront this destructive adversary with a nation united, courageous, and consecrated to the preservation of human supremacy on this Earth. I thank you.

ANNOUNCER: You have just heard the Secretary of the Interior speaking from Washington. Bulletins too numerous to read are piling up in the studio here. We are informed that the central portion of New Jersey is blacked out from radio communication due to the effect of the heat-ray upon power lines and electrical equipment. Here is a special bulletin from New York. Cables received from English, French, German scientific bodies offering assistance. Astronomers report continued gas outbursts at regular intervals on planet Mars. Majority voice opinion that enemy will be reinforced by additional rocket machines. Attempts made to locate Professor Pierson of Princeton, who has observed Martians at close range. It is feared he was lost in recent battle. Langham Field, Virginia: Scouting planes report three Martian machines visible above treetops, moving north toward Somerville with population fleeing ahead of them. Heat-ray not in use; although advancing at express-train speed, invaders pick their way carefully. The seem to be making conscious effort to avoid destruction of cities and countryside. However, they stop to uproot power lines, bridges, and railroad tracks. Their apparent objective is to crush resistance, paralyze communication, and disorganize human society.

Here is a bulletin from Basking Ridge, New Jersey: Coon hunters have stumbled on a second cylinder similar to the first embedded in the great swamp twenty miles south of Morristown. U.S. Army fieldpieces are proceeding from Newark to blow up second invading unit before cylinder can be opened and the fighting machine rigged. They are taking up position in the foothills of Watchung Mountains. Another bulletin from Langham Field, Virginia: Scouting planes report enemy machines now, three in number, increasing speed

northward, kicking over houses and trees in their evident haste to
form a conjunction with their allies south of Morristown. Machines
also sighted by telephone operator east of Middlesex within ten miles
of Plainfield. Here's a bulletin from Winston Field, Long Island: Fleet
of army bombers carrying heavy explosives flying north in pursuit
of enemy. Scouting planes act as guides. They keep speeding enemy
in sight. Just a moment please. Ladies and gentlemen, we've run
special wires to the artillery line in adjacent villages to give you
direct reports in the zone of the advancing enemy. First we take
you to the battery of the twenty-second Field Artillery, located in
the Watchung Mountains.

OFFICER: Range—thirty-two meters.
GUNNER: Thirty-two meters.
OFFICER: Projection, thirty-nine degrees.
GUNNER: Thirty-nine degrees.
OFFICER: Fire!

(Boom of heavy gun ... Pause)

OBSERVER: One hundred and forty yards to the right, sir.
OFFICER: Shift range—thirty-one meters.
GUNNER: Thirty-one meters.
OFFICER: Projection—thirty-seven degrees.
GUNNER: Thirty-seven degrees.
OFFICER: Fire!

(Boom of heavy gun ... Pause)

OBSERVER: A hit, sir! We got the tripod of one of them. They've
stopped. The others are trying to repair it.
OFFICER: Quick, get the range! Shift fifty thirty meters.
GUNNER: Thirty meters.
OFFICER: Projection—twenty-seven degrees.
GUNNER: Twenty-seven degrees.
OFFICER: Fire!

(Boom of heavy gun ... Pause)

OBSERVER: Can't see the shell land, sir. They're letting off a smoke.
OFFICER: What is it?
OBSERVER: A black smoke, sir. Moving this way. Lying close to
the ground. It's moving fast.
OFFICER: Put on gas masks. *(Pause)* Get ready to fire. Shift to
twenty-four meters.
GUNNER: Twenty-four meters.
OFFICER: Projection, twenty-four degrees.
GUNNER: Twenty-four degrees.
OFFICER: Fire! *(Boom)*
OBSERVER: I still can't see, sir. The smoke's coming nearer.

OFFICER: Get the range. (*Coughs*)
OBSERVER: Twenty-three meters. (*Coughs*)
OFFICER: Twenty-three meters. (*Cough*)
OBSERVER: Projection—twenty-two degrees. (*Coughing*)
OFFICER: Twenty-two degrees. (*Fade in coughing*)

(*Fading in . . . sound of airplane motor*)

COMMANDER: Army bombing plane, V-8-43 off Bayonne, New Jersey, Lieutenant Voght, commanding eight bombers. Reporting to Commander Fairfax, Langham Field— This is Voght, reporting to Commander Fairfax, Langham Field— Enemy tripod machines now in sight. Reinforced by three machines from the Morristown cylinder. Six altogether. One machine partially crippled. Believed hit by shell from Army gun in Watchung Mountains. Guns now appear silent. A heavy black fog hanging close to the Earth—of extreme density, nature unknown. No sign of heat-ray. Enemy now turns east, crossing Passaic River into the Jersey marshes. Another straddles the Pulaski Skyway. Evident objective is New York City. They're pushing down a high-tension power station. The machines are close together now, and we're ready to attack. Planes circling, ready to strike. A thousand yards and we'll be over the first—eight hundred yards . . . six hundred . . . four hundred . . . two hundred . . . There they go! The giant arm raised— Green flash! They're spraying us with flame! Two thousand feet. Engines are giving out. No chance to release bombs. Only one thing left—drop on them, plane and all. We're diving on the first one. Now the engine's gone! Eight—

OPERATOR ONE: This is Bayonne, New Jersey, calling Langham Field— This is Bayonne, New Jersey, calling Langham Field— Come in, please— Come in, please—

OPERATOR TWO: This is Langham Field—go ahead—

OPERATOR ONE: Eight Army bombers engagement with enemy tripod machines over Jersey flats. Engines incapacitated by heat-ray. All crashed. One enemy machine destroyed. Enemy now discharging heavy black smoke in direction of—

OPERATOR THREE: This is Newark, New Jersey— This is Newark, New Jersey— Warning! Poisonous black smoke pouring in from Jersey marshes. Reaches South Street. Gas masks useless. Urge population to move into open spaces—automobiles use routes 7, 23, 24—avoid congested areas. Smoke now spreading over Raymond Boulevard—

OPERATOR FOUR: 2X2L—calling CQ—2X2L—calling CQ—2X2L calling 8X3R—

OPERATOR FIVE: This is 8X3R—coming back at 2X2L.

OPERATOR FOUR: How's reception? How's the reception? K, please. Where are you, 8X3R? What's the matter? Where are you?

(Bells ringing over city, gradually diminishing)

ANNOUNCER: I'm speaking from the roof of Broadcasting Building, New York City. The bells you hear are ringing to warn the people to evacuate the city as the Martians approach. Estimated in last two hours three million people have moved out along the roads to the north, Hutchison River Parkway still kept open for motor traffic. Avoid bridges to Long Island—hopelessly jammed. All communication with Jersey shore closed ten minutes ago. No more defenses. Our army wiped out—artillery, Air Force, everything wiped out. This may be the last broadcast. We'll stay here to the end. People are holding service below us—in the cathedral.

(Voices singing hymn)

Now I look down the harbor. All manner of boats, overloaded with fleeing population, pulling out from docks.

(Sound of boat whistles)

Streets are all jammed. Noise in crowds like New Year's Eve in city. Wait a minute— Enemy now in sight above the Palisades. Five great machines. First one is crossing river. I can see it from here, wading the Hudson like a man wading through a brook— A bulletin's handed me—Martian cylinders are falling all over the country. One outside Buffalo, one in Chicago, St. Louis—seems to be timed and spaced— Now the first machine reaches the shore. He stands watching, looking over the city. His steel, cowlish head is even with the skyscrapers. He waits for the others. They rise like a line of new towers on the city's west side— Now they're lifting their metal hands. This is the end now. Smoke comes out—black smoke, drifting over the city. People in the streets see it now. They're running toward the East River—thousands of them, dropping in like rats. Now the smoke's spreading faster. It's reached Times Square. People are trying to run away from it, but it's no use. They're falling like flies. Now the smoke's crossing Sixth Avenue—Fifth Avenue—a . . . a hundred yards away— it's fifty feet—

OPERATOR FOUR: 2X2L calling CQ—2X2L calling CQ—2X2L calling CQ— New York— Isn't there anyone on the air? Isn't there anyone on the air? Isn't there anyone— 2X2L—

II

PIERSON: As I set down these notes on paper, I'm obsessed by the thought that I may be the last living man on Earth. I have been hiding in this empty house near Grovers Mill—a small island of daylight cut off by the black smoke from the rest of the world. All that happened before the arrival of these monstrous creatures in the world now seems part of another life—a life that has no continuity with the present, furtive existence of the lonely derelict who pencils these words on the back of some astronomical notes bearing the signature of Richard Pierson. I look down at my blackened hands, my torn shoes, my tattered clothes, and I try to connect them with a professor who lives at Princeton and who, on the night of October 30, glimpsed through his telescope an orange splash of light on a distant planet. My wife, my colleagues, my students, my books, my observatory, my—my world—where are they? Did they ever exist? Am I Richard Pierson? What day is it? Do days exist without calendars? Does time pass when there are no human hands left to wind the clocks? In writing down my daily life I tell myself I shall preserve human history between the dark covers of this little book that was meant to record the movements of the stars. But to write I must live, and to live I must eat— I find moldy bread in the kitchen, and an orange not too spoiled to swallow. I keep watch at the window. From time to time I catch sight of a Martian above the black smoke.

The smoke still holds the house in its black coil—but at length there is a hissing sound and suddenly I see a Martian mounted on his machine, spraying the air with a jet of steam, as if to dissipate the smoke. I watch in a corner as his huge metal legs nearly brush against the house. Exhausted by terror, I fall asleep.

It's morning. It's morning. Sun streams in the window. The black cloud of gas has lifted, and the scorched meadows to the north look as though a black snowstorm had passed over them. I venture from the house. I make my way to a road. No traffic. Here and there a wrecked car, baggage overturned, a blackened skeleton. I push on north. For some reason I feel safer trailing these monsters than running away from them. And I keep a careful watch. I have seen the Martians feed. Should one of their machines appear over the top of trees, I am ready to fling myself flat on the earth. I come to a chestnut tree. October, chestnuts are ripe. I fill my pockets. I must keep alive. Two days I wander in a vague northerly direction through a desolate world. Finally I notice a living creature—a small red squirrel in a beech tree. I stare at him and wonder. He stares back at me. I believe at that moment the animal and I shared the same emotion—the joy of finding another living being— I push on north. I find dead cows in a blackish field. Beyond, the charred ruins of a dairy. The silo remains standing guard over the wasteland like a lighthouse deserted by the sea. Astride the silo perches a weathercock. The arrow points north.

Next day I came to a city vaguely familiar in its contours, yet its buildings strangely dwarfed and leveled off as if a giant had sliced off its highest towers with a capricious sweep of his hand. I reached the outskirts. I found Newark, undemolished, but humbled by some whim of the advancing Martians. Presently, with an odd feeling of being watched, I caught sight of something crouching in a doorway. I made a step toward it, and it rose up and became a man—a man, armed with a large knife.

STRANGER: Stop— Where did you come from?

PIERSON: I come from—many places. A long time ago from Princeton.

STRANGER: Princeton, huh? That's near Grovers Mill!

PIERSON: Yes.

STRANGER: Grovers Mill— (*Laughs as at a great joke*) There's no food here. This is my country—all this end of town down to the river. There's only food for one— Which way are you going?

PIERSON: I don't know. I guess I'm looking for—for people.

STRANGER: (*nervously*) What was that? Did you hear something just then?

PIERSON: No. Only a bird—a live bird!

STRANGER: You get to know that birds have shadows these days— Say, we're in the open here. Let's crawl into this doorway and talk.

PIERSON: Have you seen any Martians?

STRANGER: They've gone over to New York. At night the sky is alive with their lights. Just as if people were still living. By daylight you can't see them. Five days ago a couple of them carried something big across the flats from the airport. I believe they're learning how to fly.

PIERSON: Fly!

STRANGER: Yeah, fly.

PIERSON: Then it's all over with humanity. Stranger, there's still you and I. Two of us left.

STRANGER: They got themselves in solid; they wrecked the greatest country in the world. Those green stars, they're probably falling somewhere every night. They've only lost one machine. There isn't anything to do. We're done. We're licked.

PIERSON: Where were you? You're in uniform.

STRANGER: What's left of it. I was in the militia—National Guard. That's good! Wasn't any war any more than there's war between men and ants.

PIERSON: And we're eatable ants. I found that out. What will they do to us?

STRANGER: I've thought it all out. Right now we're caught as we're wanted. The Martian only has to go a few miles to get a crowd on the run. But they won't keep doing that. They'll begin catching us systematic like—keeping the best and storing us in cages and things. They haven't begun on us yet!

PIERSON: Not begun!

STRANGER: Not begun. All that's happened so far is because we don't have sense enough to keep quiet—bothering them with guns and such stuff and losing our heads and rushing off in crowds. Now instead of our rushing around blind, we've got to fix ourselves up according to the way things are now. Cities, nations, civilization, progress—

PIERSON: But if that's so, what is there to live for?

STRANGER: There won't be any more concerts for a million years or so, and no nice little dinners at restaurants. If it's amusement you're after, I guess the game's up.

PIERSON: And what is there left?

STRANGER: Life—that's what! I want to live. And so do you! We're not going to be exterminated. And I don't mean to be caught, either, and tamed, and fattened, and bred like an ox.

PIERSON: What are you going to do?

STRANGER: I'm going on—right under their feet. I gotta plan. We men, as men, are finished. We don't know enough. We gotta learn plenty before we've got a chance. And we've got to live and keep free while we learn. See? I've thought it all out, see.

PIERSON: Tell me the rest.

STRANGER: Well, it isn't all of us that are made for wild beasts, and that's what it's got to be. That's why I watched you. All these little office workers that used to live in these houses—they'd be no good. They haven't any stuff to 'em. They just used to run off to work. I've seen hundreds of 'em, running wild to catch their commuters' train in the morning for fear that they'd get canned if they didn't; running back at night afraid they won't be in time for dinner. Lives insured and a little invested in case of accidents. And on Sundays, worried about the hereafter. The Martians will be a godsend for these guys. Nice roomy cages, good food, careful breeding, no worries. After a week or so chasing about the fields on empty stomachs, they'll come and be glad to be caught.

PIERSON: You've thought it all out, haven't you?

STRANGER: Sure. You bet I have! And that isn't all. These Martians will make pets of some of them, train 'em to do tricks. Who knows? Get sentimental over the pet boy who grew up and had to be killed. And some, maybe, they'll train to hunt us.

PIERSON: No, that's impossible. No human being—

STRANGER: Yes, they will. There's men who'll do it, gladly. If one of them ever comes after me—

PIERSON: In the meantime, you and I and others like us—where are we to live when the Martians own the Earth?

STRANGER: I've got it all figured out. We'll live underground. I've been thinking about the sewers. Under New York are miles and miles of 'em. The main ones are big enough for anybody. Then there's cellars, vaults, underground storerooms, railway tunnels, subways. You begin to see, eh? And we'll get a bunch of strong men together. No weak ones, that rubbish, out.

PIERSON: As you meant me to go?

STRANGER: Well, I gave you a chance, didn't I?

PIERSON: We won't quarrel about that. Go on.

STRANGER: And we've got to make safe places for us to stay in, see, and get all the books we can—science books. That's where men like you come in, see? We'll raid the museums, we'll even spy on the Martians. It may be not so much we have to learn before—just imagine this: Four of five of their own fighting machines suddenly start off—heat-rays right and left and not a Martian in 'em. Not a Martian in 'em! See? But men—men who have learned the way how. It may even be in our time. Gee! Imagine having one of them lovely things with its heat-ray wide and free! We'd turn it on Martians, we'd turn it on men. We'd bring everybody down to their knees.

PIERSON: That's your plan?

STRANGER: You and me and a few more of us, we'd own the world.

PIERSON: I see.

STRANGER: Say, what's the matter? Where are you going?

PIERSON: Not to *your* world. Good-by, stranger.... After parting with the artilleryman, I came at last to the Holland Tunnel. I entered that silent tube anxious to know the fate of the great city on the other side of the Hudson. Cautiously I came out of the tunnel and made my way up Canal Street.

I reached Fourteenth Street, and there again were black powder and several bodies, and an evil, ominous smell from the gratings of the cellars of some of the houses. I wandered up through the Thirties and Forties; I stood alone on Times Square. I caught sight of a lean dog running down Seventh Avenue with a piece of dark-brown meat in his jaws, and a pack of starving mongrels at his heels. He made a wide circle around me, as though he feared I might prove a fresh competitor. I walked up Broadway in the direction of that strange powder—past silent shop windows, displaying their mute wares to empty sidewalks—past the Capitol Theater, silent, dark—past a shooting-gallery, where a row of empty guns faced an arrested line of wooden ducks. Near Columbus Circle I noticed models of 1939 motorcars in the showrooms facing empty streets. From over the top of the General Motors Building I watched a flock of black birds circling in the sky. I hurried on. Suddenly, I caught sight of the hood of a Martian machine, standing somewhere in Central Park, gleaming in the late afternoon sun. An insane idea! I rushed recklessly across Columbus Circle and into the Park. I climbed a small hill above the pond at Sixtieth Street. From there I could see, standing in a silent row along the Mall, nineteen of those great metal Titans, their cowls empty, their steel arms hanging listlessly by their sides. I looked in vain for the monsters that inhabit those machines.

Suddenly, my eyes were attracted to the immense flock of black birds that hovered directly below me. They circled to the ground, and there before my eyes, stark and silent, lay the Martians, with the hungry birds pecking and tearing brown shreds of flesh from their dead bodies. Later, when their bodies were examined in laboratories, it was found that they were killed by the putrefactive and disease bacteria against which their systems were unprepared —slain, after all Man's defenses had failed, by the humblest thing that God in His wisdom has put upon this Earth.

Before the cylinder fell, there was a general persuasion that through all the deep of space no life existed beyond the petty surface of our minute sphere. Now we see farther. Dim and wonderful is the vision I have conjured up in my mind of life spreading slowly from this little seedbed of the Solar System throughout the inanimate vastness of sidereal space. But that is a remote dream. It may be that the destruction of the Martians is only a reprieve. To them, and not to us, is the future ordained, perhaps.

Strange it now seems to sit in my peaceful study at Princeton writing down this last chapter of the record begun at a deserted farm in Grovers Mill. Strange to see from my window the university spires dim and blue through an April haze. Strange to watch children playing in the streets. Strange to see young people strolling on the green, where the new spring grass heals the last black scars of a bruised Earth. Strange to watch the sightseers enter the museum where the disassembled parts of a Martian machine are kept on public view. Strange when I recall the time when I first saw it, bright and clean-cut, hard and silent, under the dawn of that last great day.

The Altar at Midnight

C. M. Kornbluth

He had quite a rum blossom on him for a kid, I thought at first. But when he moved closer to the light by the cash register to ask the bartender for a match or something, I saw it wasn't that. Not just the nose. Broken veins on his cheeks, too, and the funny eyes. He must have seen me look, because he slid back away from the light.

The bartender shook my bottle of ale in front of me like a Swiss bell ringer so it foamed inside the green glass.

"You ready for another, sir?" he asked.

I shook my head. Down the bar, he tried it on the kid—he was drinking scotch and water or something like that—and found out he could push him around. He sold him three scotch and waters in ten minutes.

When he tried for number four, the kid had his courage up and said, "I'll tell *you* when I'm ready for another, Jack." But there wasn't any trouble.

It was almost nine and the place began to fill up. The manager, a real hood type, stationed himself by the door to screen out the high school kids and give the big hello to conventioneers. The girls came hurrying in, too, with their little make up cases and their fancy hair piled up and their frozen faces with the perfect mouths drawn on them. One of them stopped to say something to the manager, some excuse about something, and he said: "That's aw ri'; get inna dressing room."

A three-piece band behind the drapes at the back of the stage began to make warm-up noises and there were two bartenders keeping busy. Mostly it was beer—a midweek crowd. I finished my ale and had to wait a couple of minutes before I could get another bottle. The bar filled up from the end near the stage because all the cus-

tomers wanted a good, close look at the strippers for their fifty-cent
bottles of beer. But I noticed that nobody sat down next to the kid,
or, if anybody did, he didn't stay long—you go out for some fun
and the bartender pushes you around and nobody wants to sit next
to you. I picked up my bottle and glass and went down on the
stool to his left.

He turned to me right away and said: "What kind of a place is
this, anyway?" The broken veins were all over his face, little ones,
but so many, so close, that they made his face look something like
marbled rubber. The funny look in his eyes was it—the trick contact
lenses. But I tried not to stare and not to look away.

"It's okay," I said. "It's a good show if you don't mind a lot of
noise from—"

He stuck a cigarette into his mouth and poked the pack at me.
"I'm a spacer," he said, interrupting.

I took one of his cigarettes and said, "Oh."

He snapped a lighter for the cigarettes and said, "Venus."

I was noticing that his pack of cigarettes on the bar had some
kind of yellow sticker instead of the blue tax stamp.

"Ain't that a crock?" he asked. "You can't smoke and they give
you lighters for a souvenir. But it's a good lighter. On Mars last
week, they gave us all some cheap pen-and-pencil sets."

"You get something every trip, hah?" I took a good, long drink
of ale and he finished his scotch and water.

"Shoot. You call a trip a 'shoot.' "

One of the girls was working her way down the bar. She was
going to slide onto the empty stool at his right and give him the
business, but she looked at him first and decided not to. She curled
around me and asked if I'd buy her a li'l ole drink. I said no and
she moved on to the next. I could kind of feel the young fellow
quivering. When I looked at him, he stood up. I followed him out
of the dump. The manager grinned without thinking and said,
"G'night, boys," to us.

The kid stopped in the street and said to me: "You don't have
to follow me around, Pappy." He sounded like one wrong word
and I would get socked in the teeth.

"Take it easy. I know a place where they won't spit in your eye."

He pulled himself together and made a joke of it. "This I have
to see," he said. "Near here?"

"A few blocks."

We started walking. It was a nice night.

"I don't know this city at all," he said. "I'm from Covington,
Kentucky. You do your drinking at home there. We don't have places
like this." He meant the whole Skid Row area.

"It's not so bad," I said. "I spend a lot of time here."

"Is that a fact? I mean, down home a man your age would likely
have a wife and children."

"I do. The hell with them."

He laughed like a real youngster and I figured he couldn't even be twenty-five. He didn't have any trouble with the broken curbstones in spite of his scotch and waters. I asked him about it.

"Sense of balance," he said. "You have to be tops for balance to be a spacer—you spend so much time outside in a suit. People don't know how much. Punctures. And you aren't worth a damn if you lose your point."

"What's that mean?"

"Oh. Well, it's hard to describe. When you're outside and you lose your point, it means you're all mixed up, you don't know which way the can—that's the ship—which way the can is. It's having all that room around you. But if you have a good balance, you feel a little tugging to the ship, or maybe you just *know* which way the ship is without feeling it. Then you have your point and you can get the work done."

"There must be a lot that's hard to describe."

He thought that might be a crack and he clammed up on me.

"You call this Gandytown," I said after a while. "It's where the stove-up old railroad men hang out. This is the place."

It was the second week of the month, before everybody's pension check was all gone. Oswiak's was jumping. The Grandsons of the Pioneers were on the juke singing the *Man from Mars Yodel* and old Paddy Shea was jigging in the middle of the floor. He had a full seidel of beer in his right hand and his empty left sleeve was flapping.

The kid balked at the screen door. "Too damn bright," he said.

I shrugged and went on in and he followed. We sat down at a table. At Oswiak's you can drink at the bar if you want to, but none of the regulars do.

Paddy jigged over and said: "Welcome home, Doc." He's a Liverpool Irishman; they talk like Scots, some say, but they sound almost like Brooklyn to me.

"Hello, Paddy. I brought somebody uglier than you. Now what do you say?"

Paddy jigged around the kid in a half-circle with his sleeve flapping and then flopped into a chair when the record stopped. He took a big drink from the seidel and said: "Can he do this?" Paddy stretched his face into an awful grin that showed his teeth. He had three of them. The kid laughed and asked me: "What the hell did you drag me into here for?"

"Paddy says he'll buy drinks for the house the day anybody uglier than he is comes in."

Oswiak's wife waddled over for the order and the kid asked us what we'd have. I figured I could start drinking, so it was three double scotches.

After the second round, Paddy started blowing about how they took his arm off without any anesthetics except a bottle of gin because the red-ball freight he was tangled up in couldn't wait.

That brought some of the other old gimps over to the table with their stories.

Blackie Bauer had been sitting in a boxcar with his legs sticking through the door when the train started with a jerk. Wham, the door closed. Everybody laughed at Blackie for being that dumb in the first place, and he got mad.

Sam Fireman has palsy. This week he was claiming he used to be a watchmaker before he began to shake. The week before, he'd said he was a brain surgeon. A woman I didn't know, a real old Boxcar Bertha, dragged herself over and began some kind of story about how her sister married a Greek, but she passed out before we found out what happened.

Somebody wanted to know what was wrong with the kid's face—Bauer, I think it was, after he came back to the table.

"Compression and decompression," the kid said. "You're all the time climbing into your suit and out of your suit. Inboard air's thin to start with. You get a few red lines—that's these ruptured blood vessels—and you say the hell with the money; all you'll make is just one more trip. But, God, it's a lot of money for anybody my age! You keep saying that until you can't be anything but a spacer. The eyes are hard-radiation scars."

"You like dot all ofer?" asked Oswiak's wife politely.

"All over, ma'am," the kid told her in a miserable voice. "But I'm going to quit before I get a Bowman head."

"I don't care," said Maggie Rorty. "I think he's cute."

"Compared with—" Paddy began, but I kicked him under the table.

We sang for a while, and then we told gags and recited limericks for a while, and I noticed that the kid and Maggie had wandered into the back room—the one with the latch on the door.

Oswiak's wife asked me, very puzzled: "Doc, w'y dey do dot flyink by planyets?"

"It's the damn govermint," Sam Fireman said.

"Why not?" I said. "They got the Bowman Drive, why the hell shouldn't they use it? Serves 'em right." I had a double scotch and added, "Twenty years of it and they found out a few things they didn't know. Red lines are only one of them. Twenty years more, maybe they'll find out a few more things they didn't know. Maybe by the time there's a bathtub in every American home and an alcoholism clinic in every American town, they'll find out a whole *lot* of things they didn't know. And every American boy will be a pop-eyed, blood-raddled wreck, like our friend here, from riding the Bowman Drive."

"It's the damn govermint," Sam Fireman repeated.

"And what the hell did you mean by that remark about alcoholism?" Paddy said, real sore. "Personally, I can take it or leave it alone."

So we got to talking about that and everybody there turned out to be people who could take it or leave it alone.

It was maybe midnight when the kid showed at the table again, looking kind of dazed. I was drunker than I ought to be by midnight, so I said I was going for a walk. He tagged along and we wound up on a bench at Screwball Square. The soapboxers were still going strong. Like I said, it was a nice night. After a while, a pot-bellied old auntie who didn't give a damn about the face sat down and tried to talk the kid into going to see some etchings. The kid didn't get it and I led him over to hear the soapboxers before there was trouble.

One of the orators was a mush-mouthed evangelist. "And oh, my friends," he said, "when I looked through the porthole of the space ship and beheld the wonder of the firmament—"

"You're a stinkin' Yankee liar!" the kid yelled at him. "You say one damn more word about can shootin' and I'll ram your space ship down your lyin' throat! Wheah's your red lines if you're such a hot spacer?"

The crowd didn't know what he was talking about, but "wheah's your red lines" sounded good to them, so they heckled mush-mouth off his box with it.

I got the kid to a bench. The liquor was working in him all of a sudden. He simmered down after a while and asked: "Doc, should I've given Miz Rorty some money? I asked her afterward and she said she'd admire to have something to remember me by, so I gave her my lighter. She seem' to be real pleased with it. But I was wondering if maybe I embarrassed her by asking her right out. Like I tol' you, back in Covington, Kentucky, we don't have places like that. Or maybe we did and I just didn't know about them. But what do you think I should've done about Miz Rorty?"

"Just what you did," I told him. "If they want money, they ask you for it first. Where you staying?"

"YMCA," he said, almost asleep. "Back in Covington, Kentucky, I was a member of the Y and I kept up my membership. They have to let me in because I'm a member. Spacers have all kinds of trouble, Doc. Woman trouble. Hotel trouble. Fam'ly trouble. Religious trouble. I was raised a Southern Baptist, but wheah's Heaven, anyway? I ask' Doctor Chitwood las' time home before the red lines got so thick—Doc, you aren't a minister of the Gospel, are you? I hope I di'n' say anything to offend you."

"No offense, son," I said. "No offense."

I walked him to the avenue and waited for a fleet cab. It was almost five minutes. The independents that roll drunks dent the fenders of fleet cabs if they show up in Skid Row and then the fleet drivers have to make reports on their own time to the company. It keeps them away. But I got one and dumped the kid in.

"The Y hotel," I told the driver. "Here's five. Help him in when you get there."

When I walked through Screwball Square again, some college kids were yelling "wheah's your red lines" at old Charlie, the last of the Wobblies.

Old Charlie kept roaring, "The hell with your bread lines! I'm talking about atomic bombs. *Right—up—there!*" And he pointed at the Moon.

It was a nice night, but the liquor was dying in me.

There was a joint around the corner, so I went in and had a drink to carry me to the club; I had a bottle there. I got into the first cab that came.

"Athletic Club," I said.

"Inna dawghouse, harh?" the driver said, and he gave me a big personality smile.

I didn't say anything and he started the car.

He was right, of course. I was in everybody's doghouse. Some day I'd scare hell out of Tom and Lise by going home and showing them what their daddy looked like.

Down at the Institute, I was in the doghouse.

"Oh, dear," everybody at the Institute said to everybody, "I'm sure I don't know what ails the man. A lovely wife and two lovely grown children and she had to tell him 'either you go or I go.' And *drinking!* And this is rather subtle, but it's a well-known fact that neurotics seek out low company to compensate for their guilt feelings. The *places* he frequents. Doctor Francis Bowman, the man who made space flight a reality. The man who put the Bomb Base on the Moon! Really, I'm sure I don't know what ails him."

The hell with them all.

Continued on Next Rock

R. A. Lafferty

Up in the Big Lime country there is an upthrust, a chimney rock that is half fallen against a newer hill. It is formed of what is sometimes called Dawson Sandstone and is interlaced with tough shell. It was formed during the glacial and recent ages in the bottomlands of Crow Creek and Green River when these streams (at least five times) were mighty rivers.

The chimney rock is only a little older than mankind, only a little younger than grass. Its formation had been upthrust and then eroded away again, all but such harder parts as itself and other chimneys and blocks.

A party of five persons came to this place where the chimney rock had fallen against a newer hill. The people of the party did not care about the deep limestone below: they were not geologists. They *did* care about the newer hill (it was man-made) and they did care a little about the rock chimney; they were archeologists.

Here was time heaped up, bulging out in casing and accumulation, and not in line sequence. And here also was striated and banded time, grown tall, and then shattered and broken.

The five party members came to the site early in the afternoon, bringing the working trailer down a dry creek bed. They unloaded many things and made a camp there. It wasn't really necessary to make a camp on the ground. There was a good motel two miles away on the highway; there was a road along the ridge above. They could have lived in comfort and made the trip to the site in five minutes every morning. Terrence Burdock, however, believed that one could not get the feel of a digging unless he lived on the ground with it day and night.

The five persons were Terrence Burdock, his wife Ethyl, Robert Derby, and Howard Steinleser: four beautiful and balanced people.

And Magdalen Mobley, who was neither beautiful nor balanced. But she was electric; she was special. They roughed around in the formations a little after they had made camp and while there was still light. All of them had seen the formations before and had guessed that there was promise in them.

"That peculiar fluting in the broken chimney is almost like a core sample," Terrence said, "and it differs from the rest of it. It's like a lightning bolt through the whole length. It's already exposed for us. I believe we will remove the chimney entirely. It covers the perfect access for the slash in the mound, and it is the mound in which we are really interested. But we'll study the chimney first. It is so available for study."

"Oh, I can tell you everything that's in the chimney," Magdalen said crossly. "I can tell you everything that's in the mound too."

"I wonder why we take the trouble to dig if you already know what we will find," Ethyl sounded archly.

"I wonder too," Magdalen grumbled. "But we will need the evidence and the artifacts to show. You can't get appropriations without evidence and artifacts. Robert, go kill that deer in the brush about forty yards northeast of the chimney. We may as well have deer meat if we're living primitive."

"This isn't deer season," Robert Derby objected. "And there isn't any deer there. Or, if there is, it's down in the draw where you couldn't see it. And if there's one there, it's probably a doe."

"No, Robert, it is a two-year-old buck and a very big one. Of course it's in the draw where I can't see it. Forty yards northeast of the chimney would have to be in the draw. If I could see it, the rest of you could see it too. Now go kill it! Are you a man or a *mus microtus*? Howard, cut poles and set up a tripod to string and dress the deer on."

"You had better try the thing, Robert," Ethyl Burdock said, "or we'll have no peace this evening."

Robert Derby took a carbine and went northeastward of the chimney, descending into the draw at forty yards. There was the high ping of the carbine shot. And after some moments, Robert returned with a curious grin.

"You didn't miss him, Robert, you killed him," Magdalen called loudly. "You got him with a good shot through the throat and up into the brain when he tossed his head high like they do. Why didn't you bring him? Go back and get him!"

"Get him? I couldn't even lift the thing. Terrence and Howard, come with me and we'll lash it to a pole and get it here somehow."

"Oh Robert, you're out of your beautiful mind," Magdalen chided. "It only weighs a hundred and ninety pounds. Oh, I'll get it."

Magdalen Mobley went and got the big buck. She brought it back, carrying it listlessly across her shoulders and getting herself bloodied, stopping sometimes to examine rocks and kick them with her foot, coming on easily with her load. It looked as if it might weigh two hundred and fifty pounds; but if Magdalen said it weighed a hundred and ninety, that is what it weighed.

Howard Steinleser had cut poles and made a tripod. He knew better than not to. They strung the buck up, skinned it off, ripped up its belly, drew it, and worked it over in an almost professional manner.

"Cook it, Ethyl," Magdalen said.

Later, as they sat on the ground around the fire and it had turned dark, Ethyl brought the buck's brains to Magdalen, messy and not half cooked, believing that she was playing an evil trick. And Magdalen ate them avidly. They were her due. She had discovered the buck.

If you wonder how Magdalen knew what invisible things were where, so did the other members of the party always wonder.

"It bedevils me sometimes why I am the only one to notice the analogy between historical geology and depth psychology," Terrence Burdock mused as they grew lightly profound around the campfire. "The isostatic principle applies to the mind and the under-mind as well as it does to the surface and undersurface of the earth. The mind has its erosions and weatherings going on along with its deposits and accumulations. It also has its upthrusts and its stresses. It floats on a similar magma. In extreme cases it has its volcanic eruptions and its mountain building."

"And it has its glaciations," Ethyl Burdock said, and perhaps she was looking at her husband in the dark.

"The mind has its hard sandstone, sometimes transmuted to quartz, or half transmuted into flint, from the drifting and floating sand of daily events. It has its shale from the old mud of daily ineptitudes and inertias. It has limestone out of its more vivid experiences, for lime is the remnant of what was once animate: and this limestone may be true marble if it is the deposit of rich enough emotion, or even travertine if it has bubbled sufficiently through agonized and evocative rivers of the under-mind. The mind has its sulphur and its gemstones—" Terrence bubbled on sufficiently, and Magdalen cut him off.

"Say simply that we have rocks in our heads," she said. "But they're random rocks, I tell you, and the same ones keep coming back. It *isn't* the same with us as it is with the earth. The world gets new rocks all the time. But it's the same people who keep turning up, and the same minds. Damn, one of the samest of them just turned up again! I wish he'd leave me alone. The answer is still no."

Very often Magdalen said things that made no sense. Ethyl Burdock assured herself that neither her husband, nor Robert, nor

Howard, had slipped over to Magdalen in the dark. Ethyl was jealous of the chunky and surly girl.

"I am hoping that this will be as rich as Spiro Mound," Howard Steinleser hoped. "It could be, you know. I'm told that there was never a less prepossessing site than that, or a trickier one. I wish we had someone who had dug at Spiro."

"Oh, he dug at Spiro," Magdalen said with contempt.

"He? Who?" Terrence Burdock asked. "No one of us was at Spiro. Magdalen, you weren't even born yet when that mound was opened. What could you know about it?"

"Yeah, I remember him at Spiro," Magdalen said, "always turning up his own things and pointing them out."

"*Were* you at Spiro?" Terrence suddenly asked a piece of the darkness. For some time, they had all been vaguely aware that there were six, and not five, persons around the fire.

"Yeah, I was at Spiro," the man said. "I dig there. I dig at a lot of the digs. I dig real well, and I always know when we come to something that will be important. You give me a job."

"Who are you?" Terrence asked him. The man was pretty visible now. The flame of the fire seemed to lean toward him as if he compelled it.

"Oh, I'm just a rich old poor man who keeps following and hoping and asking. There is *one* who is worth it all forever, so I solicit that one forever. And sometimes I am other things. Two hours ago I was the deer in the draw. It is an odd thing to munch one's own flesh." And the man was munching a joint of the deer, unasked.

"Him and his damn cheap poetry!" Magdalen cried angrily.

"What's your name?" Terrence asked him.

"Manypenny. Anteros Manypenny is my name forever."

"What are you?"

"Oh, just Indian. Shawnee, Choc, Creek, Anadarko, Caddo and pre-Caddo. Lots of things."

"How could anyone be pre-Caddo?"

"Like me. I am."

"Is Anteros a Creek name?"

"No. Greek. Man, I am a going Jessie, I am one digging man! I show you tomorrow."

Man, he was one digging man! He showed them tomorrow. With a short-handled rose hoe he began the gash in the bottom of the mound, working too swiftly to be believed.

"He will smash anything that is there. He will not know what he comes to," Ethyl Burdock complained.

"Woman, I will *not* smash whatever is there," Anteros said. "You can hide a wren's egg in one cubic meter of sand. I will move all the sand in one minute. I will uncover the egg wherever it is. And I will not crack the egg. I sense these things. I come now to a small pot of the proto-Plano period. It is broken, of course, but I do not break it. It is in six pieces and they will fit together perfectly. I tell you this beforehand. Now I reveal it."

And Anteros revealed it. There was something wrong about it even before he uncovered it. But it was surely a find, and perhaps it *was* of the proto-Plano period. The six shards came out. They were roughly cleaned and set. It was apparent that they would fit wonderfully.

"Why, it is perfect!" Ethyl exclaimed.

"It is too perfect," Howard Steinleser protested. "It was a turned pot, and who had turned pots in America without the potter's wheel? But the glyphs pressed into it do correspond to proto-Plano glyphs. It is fishy." Steinleser was in a twitchy humor today and his face was livid.

"Yes, it is the ripple and the spinosity, the fish-glyph," Anteros pointed out. "And the sun-sign is riding upon it. It is a fish-god."

"It's fishy in another way," Steinleser insisted. "Nobody finds a thing like that in the first sixty seconds of a dig. And there *could not be* such a pot. I wouldn't believe it was proto-Plano unless points were found in the exact site with it."

"Oh here," Anteros said. "One can smell the very shape of the flint points already. Two large points, one small one. Surely you get the whiff of them already? Four more hoe cuts and I come to them."

Four more hoe cuts, and Anteros *did* come to them. He uncovered two large points and one small one, spearheads and arrowhead. Lanceolate they were, with ribbon flaking. They were late Folsom, or they were proto-Plano; they were what you will.

"This cannot be," Steinleser groaned. "They're the missing chips, the transition pieces. They fill the missing place too well. I won't believe it. I'd hardly believe it if mastodon bones were found on the same level here."

"In a moment," said Anteros, beginning to use the hoe again. "Hey, those old beasts *did smell funny!* An elephant isn't in it with them. And a lot of it still clings to their bones. Will a sixth thoracic bone do? I'm pretty sure that's what it is. I don't know where the rest of the animal is. Probably somebody gnawed the thoracic here. Nine hoe cuts, and then very careful."

Nine hoe cuts—and then Anteros, using a mason's trowel, unearthed the old gnawed bone very carefully. Yes, Howard said almost angrily, it was a sixth thoracic of a mastodon. Robert Derby said it was a fifth or a sixth; it is not easy to tell.

"Leave the digging for a while, Anteros," Steinleser said. "I want to record and photograph and take a few measurements here."

Terrence Burdock and Magdalen Mobley were working at the bottom of the chimney rock, at the bottom of the fluting that ran the whole height of it like a core sample.

"Get Anteros over here and see what he can uncover in sixty seconds," Terrence offered.

"Oh, him! He'll just uncover some of his own things."

"What do you mean, his own things? Nobody could have made an intrusion here. It's hard sandstone."

"And harder flint here," Magdalen said. "I might have known it. Pass the damned thing up. I know just about what it says anyhow."

"What it says? What do you mean? But it is marked! And it's large and dressed rough. Who'd carve in flint?"

"Somebody real stubborn, just like flint," Magdalen said. "All right then, let's have it out. Anteros! Get this out in one piece. And do it without shattering it or tumbling the whole thing down on us. He can do it, you know, Terrence. He can do things like that."

"What do you know about his doings, Magdalen? You never saw or heard about the poor man till last night."

"Oh well. I know that it'll turn out to be the same damned stuff."

Anteros did get it out without shattering it or bringing down the chimney column. A cleft with a digging bar, three sticks of the stuff and a cap, and he touched the leads to the battery when he was almost on top of the charge. The blast, it sounded as if the whole sky were falling down on them, and some of those sky-blocks were quite large stones. The ancients wondered why fallen pieces of the sky should always be dark rock-stuff and never sky-blue clear stuff. The answer is that it is only pieces of the night sky that ever fall, even though they may sometimes be most of the daytime in falling, such is the distance. And the blast that Anteros set off did bring down rocky hunks of the night sky even though it was broad daylight. They brought down darker rocks than any of which the chimney was composed.

Still, it was a small blast. The chimney tottered but did not collapse. It settled back uneasily on its base. And the flint rock was out in the clear.

"A thousand spearheads and arrowheads could be shattered and chipped out of that hunk," Terrence marveled. "That flint block would have been a primitive fortune for a primitive man."

"I had several such fortunes," Anteros said dully, "and this one I preserved and dedicated."

They had all gathered around it.

"Oh, the poor man!" Ethyl suddenly exclaimed. But she was not looking at any of the men. She was looking at the stone.

"I wish he'd get off that kick," Magdalen sputtered angrily. "I don't care *how* rich he is. I can pick up better stuff than him in the alleys."

"What are the women chirping about?" Terrence asked. "But those do look like true glyphs. Almost like Aztec, are they not, Steinleser?"

"Nahuat-Tanoan, cousins-german to the Aztec, or should I say cousins-yaqui?"

"Call it anything, but can you read it?"

"Probably. Give me eight or ten hours on it and I should come up with a contingent reading of many of the glyphs. We can hardly expect a rational rendering of the message, however. All Nahuat-Tanoan translations so far have been gibberish."

"And remember, Terrence, that Steinleser is a slow reader," Magdalen said spitefully. "And he isn't very good at interpreting *other* signs either."

Steinleser was sullen and silent. How had his face come to bear those deep livid claw-marks today?

They moved a lot of rock and rubble that morning, took quite a few pictures, wrote up bulky notes. There were constant finds as the divided party worked up the shag-slash in the mound and the core-flute of the chimney. There were no more really startling discoveries; no more turned pots of the proto-Plano period; how could there be? There were no more predicted and perfect points of the late Folsom, but there were broken and unpredictable points. No other mastodon thoracic was found, but bones were uncovered of *bison latifrons*, of dire wolf, of coyote, of man. There were some anomalies in the relationships of the things discovered, but it was not as fishy as it had been in the early morning, not as fishy as when Anteros had announced and then dug out the shards of the pot, the three points, the mastodon bone. The things now were as authentic as they were expected, and yet their very profusion had still the smell of a small fish.

And that Anteros was one digging man. He moved the sand, he moved the stone, he missed nothing. And at noon he disappeared.

An hour later he reappeared in a glossy station wagon, coming out of a thicketed ravine where no one would have expected a way. He had been to town. He brought a variety of cold cuts, cheeses, relishes, and pastries, a couple cases of cold beer, and some V.O.

"I thought you were a poor man, Anteros," Terrence chided.

"I told you that I was a rich old poor man. I have nine thousand acres of grassland, I have three thousand head of cattle, I have alfalfa land and clover land and corn land and hay-grazer land—"

"Oh, knock it off!" Magdalen snapped.

They ate, they rested, they worked the afternoon. Magdalen worked as swiftly and solidly as did Anteros. She was young, she was stocky, she was light-burned-dark. She was not at all beautiful. (Ethyl was.) She could have any man there any time she wanted to. (Ethyl couldn't.) She was Magdalen, the often unpleasant, the mostly casual, the suddenly intense one. She was the tension of the party, the string of the bow.

"Anteros!" she called sharply just at sundown.

"The turtle?" he asked. "The turtle that is under the ledge out of the current where the backwater curls in reverse? But he is fat and happy and he has never harmed anything except for food or fun. I know you do not want me to get that turtle."

"I do! There's eighteen pounds of him. He's fat. He'll be good. Only eighty yards, where the bank crumbles down to Green River, under the lower ledge that's shale that looks like slate, two feet deep—"

"I know where he is. I will go get the fat turtle," Anteros said. "I myself am the fat turtle. I am the Green River." He went to get it.

"Oh that damned poetry of his!" Magdalen spat when he was gone.

Anteros brought back the fat turtle. He looked as if he'd weigh twenty-five pounds; but if Magdalen said he weighed eighteen pounds, then it was eighteen.

"Start cooking, Ethyl," Magdalen said. Magdalen was a mere undergraduate girl permitted on the digging by sheer good fortune. The others of the party were all archeologists of moment. Magdalen had no right to give orders to anyone, except her born right.

"I don't know how to cook a turtle," Ethyl complained.

"Anteros will show you how."

"The late evening smell of newly exposed excavation!" Terrence Burdock burbled as they lounged around the campfire a little later, full of turtle and V.O. and feeling rakishly wise. "The exposed age can be guessed by the very timbre of the smell, I believe."

"Timbre of the smell! What is your nose wired up to?" from Magdalen.

And, indeed, there was something time-evocative about the smell of the diggings; cool, at the same time musty and musky, ripe with old stratified water and compressed death. Stratified time.

"It helps if you already know what the exposed age is," said Howard Steinleser. "Here there is an anomaly. The chimney sometimes acts as if it were younger than the mound. The chimney cannot be young enough to include written rock, but it is."

"Archeology is made up entirely of anomalies," said Terrence, "rearranged to make them fit in a fluky pattern. There'd be no system to it otherwise."

"Every science is made up entirely of anomalies rearranged to fit," said Robert Derby. "Have you unriddled the glyph-stone, Howard?"

"Yes, pretty well. Better than I expected. Charles August can verify it, of course, when we get it back to the university. It is a non-royal, non-tribal, non-warfare, non-hunt declaration. It does not come under any of the usual radical signs, any of the categories. It can only be categorized as uncategorized or personal. The translation will be rough."

"Rocky is the word," said Magdalen.

"On with it, Howard," Ethyl cried.

" 'You are the freedom of wild pigs in the sour-grass, and the nobility of badgers. You are the brightness of serpents and the soaring of vultures. You are passion of mesquite bushes on fire with lightning. You are serenity of toads.' "

"You've got to admit he's got a different line," said Ethyl. "Your own love notes were less acrid, Terrence."

"What kind of thing is it, Steinleser?" Terrence questioned. "It must have a category."

"I believe Ethyl is right. It's a love poem. 'You are the water in rock cisterns and the secret spiders in that water. You are the dead coyote lying half in the stream, and you are the old entrapped dreams of the coyote's brains oozing liquid through the broken eyesocket. You are the happy ravening flies about that broken socket.' "

"Oh, hold it, Steinleser," Robert Derby cried. "You can't have gotten all that from scratches on flint. What is 'entrapped dreams' in Nahuat-Tanoan glyph-writing?"

"The solid-person sign next to the hollow-person sign, both enclosed in the night sign—that has always been interpreted as the dream glyph. And here the dream glyph is enclosed in the glyph of the deadfall trap. Yes, I believe it means entrapped dreams. To continue: 'You are the cornworm in the dark heart of the corn, the naked small bird in the nest. You are the pustules on the sick rabbit, devouring life and flesh and turning it into your own serum. You are stars compressed into charcoal. But you cannot give, you cannot take. Once again you will be broken at the foot of the cliff, and the word will remain unsaid in your swollen and purpled tongue.' "

"A love poem, perhaps, but with a difference," said Robert Derby.

"I never was able to go his stuff, and I tried, I really tried," Magdalen moaned.

"Here is the change of person-subject shown by the canted-eye glyph linked with the self-glyph," Steinleser explained. "It is now a first-person talk. 'I own ten thousand back-loads of corn. I own gold and beans and nine buffalo horns full of watermelon seeds. I own the loincloth that the sun wore on his fourth journey across the sky. Only three loincloths in the world are older and more valued than this. I cry out to you in a big voice like the hammering of herons' (that sound-verb particle is badly translated, the hammer being not a modern pounding hammer but a rock angling, chipping hammer) 'and the belching of buffalos. My love is sinewy as entwined snakes, it is steadfast as the sloth, it is like a feathered arrow shot into your abdomen—such is my love. Why is my love unrequited?' "

"I challenge you, Steinleser," Terrence Burdock cut in. "What is the glyph for 'unrequited'?"

"The glyph of the extended hand—with all the fingers bent backwards. It goes on, 'I roar to you. Do not throw yourself down. You believe you are on the hanging sky bridge, but you are on the terminal cliff. I grovel before you. I am no more than dog-droppings.' "

"You'll notice he said that and not me," Magdalen burst out. There was always a fundamental incoherence about Magdalen.

"Ah—continue, Steinleser," said Terrence. "The girl is daft, or she dreams out loud."

"That is all of the inscription, Terrence, except for a final glyph which I don't understand. Glyph-writing takes a lot of room. That's all the stone would hold."

"What is the glyph that you don't understand, Howard?"

"It's the spear-thrower glyph entwined with the time glyph. It sometimes means 'flung forward or beyond.' But what does it mean here?"

"It means 'continued,' dummy, 'continued,' " Magdalen said. "Do not fear. There'll be more stones."

"I think it's beautiful," said Ethyl Burdock, "in its own context, of course."

"Then why don't you take him on, Ethyl, in his own context, of course?" Magdalen asked. "Myself, I don't care how many back-loads of corn he owns. I've had it."

"Take whom on, dear?" Ethyl asked. "Howard Steinleser can interpret the stones, but who can interpret our Magdalen?"

"Oh, I can read her like a rock," Terrence Burdock smiled. But he couldn't.

But it had fastened on them. It was all about them and through them: the brightness of serpents and the serenity of toads, the secret spiders in the water, the entrapped dreams oozing through the broken eyesocket, the pustules of the sick rabbit, the belching of buffalo, and the arrow shot into the abdomen. And around it all was the night smell of flint and turned earth and chuckling streams, the mustiness, and the special muskiness which bears the name Nobility of Badgers.

They talked archeology and myth talk. Then it was steep night, and the morning of the third day.

Oh, the sample digging went well. This was already a richer mound than Spiro, though the gash in it was but a small promise of things to come. And the curious twin of the mound, the broken chimney, confirmed and confounded and contradicted. There was time gone wrong in the chimney, or at least in the curious fluted core of it; the rest of it was normal enough, and sterile enough.

Anteros worked that day with a soft sullenness, and Magdalen brooded with a sort of lightning about her.

"Beads, glass beads!" Terrence Burdock exploded angrily. "All right! Who is the hoaxer in our midst? I will not tolerate this at all." Terrence had been angry of face all day. He was clawed deeply, as Steinleser had been the day before, and he was sour on the world.

"There have been glass-bead caches before, Terrence, hundreds of them," Robert Derby said softly.

"There have been hoaxes before, hundreds of them," Terrence howled. "These have 'Hong Kong Contemporary' written all over them, damned cheap glass beads sold by the pound. They have no business in a stratum of around the year seven hundred. All right, who is guilty?"

"I don't believe that any one of us is guilty, Terrence," Ethyl put in mildly. "They are found four feet in from the slant surface of the mound. Why, we've cut through three hundred years of vegetable loam to get to them, and certainly the surface was eroded beyond that."

"We are scientists," said Steinleser. "We find these. Others have found such. Let us consider the improbabilities of it."

It was noon, so they ate and rested and considered the improbabilities. Anteros had brought them a great joint of white pork, and they made sandwiches and drank beer and ate pickles.

"You know," said Robert Derby, "that beyond the rank impossibility of glass beads found so many times where they *could not be found*, there is a real mystery about *all* early Indian beads, whether of bone, stone, or antler. There are millions and millions of these fine beads with pierced holes finer than any piercer ever found. There are residues, there are centers of every other Indian industry, and there is evolution of every other tool. Why have there been these millions of pierced beads, and never one piercer? There was no technique to make so fine a piercer. How were they done?"

Magdalen giggled. "Bead-spitter," she said.

"Bead-spitter! You're out of your fuzzy mind," Terrence erupted. "That's the silliest and least sophisticated of all Indian legends."

"But it *is* the legend," said Robert Derby, "the legend of more than thirty separate tribes. The Carib Indians of Cuba said that they got their beads from Bead-spitters. The Indians of Panama told Balboa the same thing. The Indians of the pueblos told the same story to Coronado. Every Indian community had an Indian who was its Bead-spitter. There are Creek and Alabama and Koasati stories of Bead-spitter; see Swanton's collections. And his stories were taken down within living memory.

"More than that, when European trade-beads were first

introduced, there is one account of an Indian receiving some and saying, 'I will take some to Bead-spitter. If he sees them, he can spit them too.' And that Bead-spitter did then spit them by the bushel. There was never any other Indian account of the origin of their beads. *All* were spit by a Bead-spitter."

"Really, this is very unreal," Ethyl said. Really it was.

"Hog hokey! A Bead-spitter of around the year seven hundred could not spit future beads, he could not spit cheap Hong Kong glass beads of the present time!" Terrence was very angry.

"Pardon me, yes sir, he could," said Anteros. "A Bead-spitter can spit future beads, if he faces North when he spits. That has always been known."

Terrence was angry, he fumed and poisoned the day for them, and the claw marks on his face stood out livid purple. He was angrier yet when he said that the curious dark capping rock on top of the chimney was dangerous, that it would fall and kill someone; and Anteros said that there was no such capping rock on the chimney, that Terrence's eyes were deceiving him, that Terrence should go sit in the shade and rest.

And Terrence became excessively angry when he discovered that Magdalen was trying to hide something that she had discovered in the fluted core of the chimney. It was a large and heavy shale-stone, too heavy even for Magdalen's puzzling strength. She had dragged it out of the chimney flute, tumbled it down to the bottom, and was trying to cover it with rocks and scarp.

"Robert, mark the extraction point!" Terrence called loudly. "It's quite plain yet. Magdalen, stop that! Whatever it is, it must be examined now."

"Oh, it's just more of the damned same thing! I wish he'd let me alone. With his kind of money he can get plenty girls. Besides, it's private, Terrence. You don't have any business reading it."

"You are hysterical, Magdalen, and you may have to leave the digging site."

"I wish I could leave. I can't. I wish I could love. I can't. Why isn't it enough that I die?"

"Howard, spend the afternoon on this," Terrence ordered. "It has writing of a sort on it. If it's what I think it is, it scares me. It's too recent to be in any eroded chimney rock formation, Howard, and it comes from far below the top. Read it."

"A few hours on it and I may come up with something. I never saw anything like it either. What did you think it was, Terrence?"

"What do you think I think it is? It's much later than the other, and that one was impossible. I'll not be the one to confess myself crazy first."

Howard Steinleser went to work on the incised stone; and two hours before sundown they brought him another one, a gray soapstone block from higher up. Whatever this was covered with, it was not at all the same thing that covered the shale-stone.

And elsewhere things went well, too well. The old fishiness was back on it. No series of finds could be so perfect, no petrification could be so well ordered.

"Robert," Magdalen called down to Robert Derby just at sunset, "in the high meadow above the shore, about four hundred yards down, just past the old fence line—"

"—there is a badger hole, Magdalen. Now you have me doing it, seeing invisible things at a distance. And if I take a carbine and stroll down there quietly, the badger will stick his head out just as I get there (I being strongly downwind of him), and I'll blam him between the eyes. He'll be a big one, fifty pounds."

"Thirty. Bring him, Robert. You're showing a little understanding at last."

"But, Magdalen, badger is rampant meat. It's seldom eaten."

"May not the condemned girl have what she wishes for her last meal? Go get it, Robert."

Robert went, The voice of the little carbine was barely heard at that distance. Soon, Robert brought back the dead badger.

"Cook it, Ethyl," Magdalen ordered.

"Yes, I know. And if I don't know how, Anteros will show me." But Anteros was gone. Robert found him on a sundown knoll with his shoulders hunched. The odd man was sobbing silently and his face seemed to be made out of dull pumice stone. But he came back to aid Ethyl in preparing the badger.

"If the first of today's stones scared you, the second should have lifted the hair right off your head, Terrence," Howard Steinleser said.

"It does, it does. All the stones are too recent to be in a chimney formation, but this last one is an insult. It isn't two hundred years old, but there's a thousand years of strata above it. What time is deposited there?"

They had eaten rampant badger meat and drunk inferior whisky (which Anteros, who had given it to them, didn't know was inferior), and the muskiness was both inside them and around them. The campfire sometimes spit angrily with small explosions, and its glare reached high when it did so. By one such leaping glare, Terrence Burdock saw that the curious dark capping rock was once more on the top of the chimney. He thought he had seen it there in the daytime; but it had not been there after he had sat in the shade and rested, and it had absolutely not been there when he climbed the chimney itself to be sure.

"Let's have the second chapter and then the third, Howard," Ethyl said. "It's neater that way."

"Yes. Well, the second chapter (the first and lowest and apparently the earliest rock we came on today) is written in a language that no one ever saw written before; and yet it's no great trouble to read it. Even Terrence guessed what it was and it scared him. It is Anadarko-Caddo hand-talk graven in stone. It is what is called the sign language of the Plains Indians copied down in formalized pictograms. And it *has* to be very recent, within the last three hundred years. Hand-talk was fragmentary at the first coming of the Spanish, and well developed at the first coming of the French. It was an explosive development, as such things go, worked out within a hundred years. This rock has to be younger than its *situs*, but it was absolutely found in place."

"Read it, Howard, read it," Robert Derby called. Robert was feeling fine and the rest of them were gloomy tonight.

" 'I own three hundred ponies,' Steinleser read the rock out of his memory. 'I own two days' ride north and east and south, and one day's ride west. I give you all. I blast out with a big voice like fire in tall trees, like the explosion of crowning pine trees. I cry like closing-in wolves, like the high voice of the lion, like the hoarse scream of torn dew on crazy-weed in the morning. You are the swift crooked wings of the night-hawk, the dainty feet of the skunk, you are the juice of the sour squash. Why can you not take or give? I am the humpbacked bull of the high plains, I am the river itself and the stagnant pools left by the river, I am the raw earth and the rocks. Come to me, but do not come so violently as to destroy yourself.'

"Ah, that was the text of the first rock of the day, the Anadarko-Caddo hand-talk graven in stone. And final pictograms which I don't understand: a shot-arrow sign, and a boulder beyond."

" 'Continued on next rock,' of course," said Robert Derby. "Well, why *wasn't* hand-talk ever written down? The signs are simple and easily stylized and they were understood by many different tribes. It would have been natural to write it."

"Alphabetical writing was in the region *before* hand-talk was well developed," Terrence Burdock said. "In fact, it was the coming of the Spanish that gave the impetus to hand-talk. It was really developed for communication between Spanish and Indian, not between Indian and Indian. And yet, I believe hand-talk *was* written down once; it was the beginning of the Chinese pictographs. And there also it had its beginning as communication between differing peoples. Depend on it, if all mankind had always been of a single language, there would never have been any written language developed at all. Writing always began as a bridge, and there had to be some chasm for it to bridge."

"We have one to bridge here," said Steinleser. "That whole chimney is full of rotten smoke. The highest part of it should be older than the lowest part of the mound, since the mound was built on a base eroded away from the chimney formation. But in many ways they seem to be contemporary. We must all be under a spell here. We've worked two days on this, parts of three days, and the total impossibility of the situation hasn't struck us yet.

"The old Nahuatlan glyphs for Time are the chimney glyphs. Present time is a lower part of a chimney and fire burning at the base. Past time is black smoke from a chimney, and future time is white smoke from a chimney. There was a signature glyph running through our yesterday's stone which I didn't and don't understand. It seemed to indicate something coming down out of the chimney rather than going up it."

"It really doesn't look much like a chimney," Magdalen said.

"And a maiden doesn't look much like dew on crazy-weed in the morning, Magdalen," Robert Derby said, "but we recognize these identities."

They talked a while about the impossibility of the whole business.

"There are scales on our eyes," Steinleser said. "The fluted core of the chimney is wrong. I'm not even sure the rest of the chimney is right."

"No, it isn't," said Robert Derby. "We can identify most of the strata of the chimney with known periods of the river and stream. I was above and below today. There is one stretch where the sandstone was not eroded at all, where it stands three hundred yards back from the shifted river and is overlaid with a hundred years of loam and sod. There are other sections where the stone is cut away variously. We can tell when most of the chimney was laid down, we can find its correspondences up to a few hundred years ago. But when were the top ten feet of it down? There were no correspondences anywhere to that. The centuries represented by the strata of the top of the chimney, people, those centuries haven't happened yet."

"And when was the dark capping rock on top of it all formed—?" Terrence began. "Ah, I'm out of my mind. It isn't there. I'm demented."

"No more than the rest of us," said Steinleser. "I saw it too, I thought, today. And then I didn't see it again."

"The rock-writing, it's like an old novel that I only half remember," said Ethyl.

"Oh, that's what it is, yes," Magdalen murmured.

"But I don't remember what happened to the girl in it."

"I remember what happened to her, Ethyl," Magdalen said.

"Give us the third chapter, Howard," Ethyl asked. "I want to see how it comes out."

"First you should all have whisky for those colds," Anteros suggested humbly.

"But none of us have colds," Ethyl objected.

"You take your own medical advice, Ethyl, and I'll take mine," Terrence said. "I will have whisky. My cold is not rheum but fear-chill."

They all had whisky. They talked a while, and some of them dozed.

"It's late, Howard," Ethyl said after a while. "Let's have the next chapter. Is it the last chapter? Then we'll sleep. We have honest digging to do tomorrow."

"Our third stone, our second stone of the day just past, is another and even later form of writing, and it has never been seen in stone before. It is Kiowa picture writing. The Kiowas did their out-turning spiral writing on buffalo skins dressed almost as fine as vellum. In its more sophisticated form (and this is a copy of that) it is quite late. The Kiowa picture writing probably did not arrive at its excellence until influenced by white artists."

"How late, Steinleser?" Robert Derby asked.

"Not more than a hundred and fifty years old. But I have never seen it copied in stone before. It simply isn't stone-styled. There's a lot of things around here lately that I haven't seen before.

"Well then, to the text, or should I say the pictography? 'You fear the earth, you fear rough ground and rocks, you fear moister earth and rotting flesh, you fear the flesh itself, all flesh is rotting flesh. If you love not rotting flesh, you love not at all. You believe the bridge hanging in the sky, the bridge hung by tendrils and woody vines that diminish as they go up and up till they are no thicker than hairs. There is no sky-bridge, you cannot go upon it. Did you believe that the roots of love grow upside down? They come out of deep earth that is old flesh and brains and hearts and entrails, that is old buffalo bowels and snakes' pizzles, that is black blood and rot and moaning underground. This is old and worn-out and bloody time, and the roots of love grow out of its gore.' "

"You seem to give remarkably detailed translations of the simple spiral pictures, Steinleser, but I begin to get in the mood of it," Terrence said.

"Ah, perhaps I cheat a little," said Steinleser.

"You lie a lot," Magdalen challenged.

"No I do not. There is some basis for every phrase I've used. It goes on: 'I own twenty-two trade rifles. I own ponies. I own Mexico silver, eight-bit pieces. I am rich in all ways. I give all to you. I cry out with big voice like a bear full of mad-weed, like a bullfrog in love, like a stallion rearing against a puma. It is the earth that calls you. I am the earth, woollier than wolves and rougher than rocks. I am the bog earth that sucks you in. You cannot give, you cannot take, you cannot love, you think there is something else, you think there is a sky-bridge you may loiter on without crashing

down. I am bristled-boar earth, there is no other. You will come
to me in the morning. You will come to me easy and with grace.
Or you will come to me reluctant and you be shattered in every
bone and member of you. You be broken by our encounter. You
be shattered as by a lightning bolt striking up from the earth. I
am the red calf which is in the writings. I am the rotting red earth.
Live in the morning or die in the morning, but remember that love
in death is better than no love at all.' "

"Oh brother! Nobody gets that stuff from such kid pictures, Steinleser," Robert Derby moaned.

"Ah well, that's the end of the spiral picture. And a Kiowa spiral
pictograph ends with either an in-sweep or an out-sweep line. This
ends with an out-sweep, which means—"

" 'Continued on next rock,' that's what it means," Terrence cried
roughly.

"You won't find the next rocks," Magdalen said. "They're hidden,
and most of the time they're not there yet, but they will go on and
on. But for all that, you'll read it in the rocks tomorrow morning.
I want it to be over with. Oh, I don't know what I want!"

"I believe I know what you want tonight, Magdalen," Robert
Derby said.

But he didn't.

The talk trailed off, the fire burned down, they went to their sleeping sacks.

Then it was long jagged night, and the morning of the fourth
day. But wait! In Nahuat-Tanoan legend, the world ends on the
fourth morning. All the lives we lived or thought we lived had been
but dreams of third night. The loincloth that the sun wore on the
fourth day's journey was not so valuable as one has made out. It
was worn for no more than an hour or so.

And, in fact, there was something terminal about fourth morning.
Anteros had disappeared. Magdalen had disappeared. The chimney
rock looked greatly diminished in its bulk (something had gone out
of it) and much crazier in its broken height. The sun had come
up a garish gray-orange color through fog. The signature-glyph of
the first stone dominated the ambient. It was as if something were
coming down from the chimney. a horrifying smoke; but it was
only noisome morning fog.

No it wasn't. There was something else coming down from the
chimney, or from the hidden sky: pebbles, stones, indescribable
bits of foul oozings, the less fastidious pieces of the sky; a light
nightmare rain had begun to fall there; the chimney was apparently
beginning to crumble.

"It's the damnedest thing I ever heard about," Robert Derby
growled. "Do you think that Magdalen really went off with

Anteros?'' Derby was bitter and fumatory this morning and his face was badly clawed.

"Who is Magdalen? Who is Anteros?'' Ethyl Burdock asked.

Terrence Burdock was hooting from high on the mound. "All come up,'' he called. "Here is a find that will make it all worthwhile. We'll have to photo and sketch and measure and record and witness. It's the finest basalt head I've ever seen, man-sized, and I suspect that there's a man-sized body attached to it. We'll soon clean it and clear it. Gah! What a weird fellow he was!''

But Howard Steinleser was studying a brightly colored something that he held in his two hands.

"What is it, Howard? What are you doing?'' Derby demanded.

"Ah, I believe this is the next stone in sequence. The writing is alphabetical but deformed, there is an element missing. I believe it is in modern English, and I will solve the deformity and see it true in a minute. The text of it seems to be—''

Rocks and stones were coming down from the chimney, and fog, amnesic and wit-stealing fog.

"Steinleser, are you all right?'' Robert Derby asked with compassion. "That isn't a stone that you hold in your hand.''

"It isn't a stone. I thought it was. What is it then?''

"It is the fruit of the Osage orange tree, the American Meraceous. It isn't a stone, Howard.'' And the thing was a tough, woody, wrinkled mock-orange, as big as a small melon.

"You have to admit that the wrinkles look a little bit like writing, Robert.''

"Yes, they look a little like writing, Howard. Let us go up where Terrence is bawling for us. You've read too many stones. And it isn't safe here.''

"Why go up, Robert? The other thing is coming down.''

It was the bristled-boar earth reaching up with a rumble. It was a lightning bolt struck upward out of the earth, and it got its prey. There was explosion and roar. The dark capping rock was jerked from the top of the chimney and slammed with terrible force to the earth, shattering with a great shock. And something else that had been on that capping rock. And the whole chimney collapsed about them.

She was broken by the encounter. She was shattered in every bone and member of her. And she was dead.

"Who—who is she?'' Howard Steinleser stuttered.

"Oh God! Magdalen, of course!'' Robert Derby cried.

"I remember her a little bit. Didn't understand her. She put out like an evoking moth but she wouldn't be had. Near clawed the face off me the other night when I misunderstood the signals. She believed there was a sky-bridge. It's in a lot of the mythologies. But there isn't one, you know. Oh well."

"The girl is dead! Damnation! What are you doing grubbing in those stones?"

"Maybe she isn't dead in them yet, Robert. I'm going to read what's here before something happens to them. This capping rock that fell and broke, it's impossible of course. It's a stratum that hasn't been laid down yet. I always did want to read the future and I may never get another chance."

"You fool! The girl's dead! Does nobody care? Terrence, stop bellowing about your find. Come down. The girl's dead."

"Come up, Robert and Howard," Terrence insisted. "Leave that broken stuff down there. It's worthless. But nobody ever saw anything like this."

"Do come up, men," Ethyl sang. "Oh, it's a wonderful piece! I never saw anything like it in my life."

"Ethyl, is the whole morning mad?" Robert Derby demanded as he came up to her. "She's dead. Don't you really remember her? Don't you remember Magdalen?"

"I'm not sure. Is she the girl down there? Isn't she the same girl who's been hanging around here a couple days? She shouldn't have been playing on that high rock. I'm sorry she's dead. But just look what we're uncovering here!"

"Terrence. Don't *you* remember Magdalen?"

"The girl down there? She's a little bit like the girl that clawed the hell out of me the other night. Next time someone goes to town they might mention to the sheriff that there's a dead girl here. Robert, did you ever see a face like this one? And it digs away to reveal the shoulders. I believe there's a whole man-sized figure here. Wonderful, wonderful!"

"Terrence, you're off your head. Well, do you remember Anteros?"

"Certainly, the twin of Eros, but nobody ever made much of the symbol of unsuccessful love. Thunder! That's the name for him! It fits him perfectly. We'll call him Anteros."

Well, it *was* Anteros, lifelike in basalt stone. His face was contorted. He was sobbing soundlessly and frozenly and his shoulders were hunched with emotion. The carving was fascinating in its miserable passion, his stony love unrequited. Perhaps he was more impressive now than he would be when he was cleaned. He was earth, he was earth itself. Whatever period the carving belonged to, it was outstanding in its power.

"The live Anteros, Terrence. Don't you remember our digging man, Anteros Manypenny?"

"Sure. He didn't show up for work this morning, did he? Tell him he's fired."

"Magdalen is dead! She was one of us! Dammit, she was the main one of us!" Robert Derby cried. Terrence and Ethyl Burdock were earless to his outburst. They were busy uncovering the rest of the carving.

And down below, Howard Steinleser was studying dark broken rocks before they would disappear, studying a stratum that hadn't been laid down yet, reading a foggy future.

An Eel by the Tail

Allen Lang

The strip-teaser materialized in the first-period physics class at Terre Haute's Technical High School.

It all happened just because Mr. Tedder was fresh out of college and anxious to make good in his first teaching job. He'd been given Physics II, a tough class for a new teacher. His pupils, a set of hardened II-A boys, were sure of themselves, and so were the few girls in the class. It was with hopes of shaking that assurance that Mr. Tedder had spent a month of after-school hours studying an article on Ziegler's Effect. He also hoped, but with less faith than wistfulness, that a demonstration of Ziegler's Effect might shock his class into staying awake. Above all, Mr. Tedder felt that his Junior boys might be considerably edified by an electrical phenomenon that was not yet understood by the best physical theorists of three planets.

Mr. Tedder wanted to give his class a good show. So, with more feeling for dramatic effect than for scientific good sense, he'd wound the three solenoids with heavy, insulated silver wire rather than with the light copper wire Ziegler had reported using. On the theory that, if he were to demonstrate the Ziegler Effect, it would be best to demonstrate a whole lot of it, Mr. Tedder contrived a battery of the new lithium reaction cells. The direct current from this powerful battery was transformed by an antique, but workable, automotive spark coil.

The bell rang as usual that morning, marking the beginning of the first class. Twenty pupils filed into the physics classroom and took their seats. Eighteen of them slumped down in an attitude which suggested that, although they were prepared to accept stoically the hour's ordeal, they weren't going to allow themselves to be taught anything. After all, Tech had lost last night's game to Walbash: what physical phenomenon could hope to shake off that grim memory? There was a shuffling of papers as the boys in the back seats pulled comic books from their notebooks. Guenther and Stetzel, sitting up front, pulled sheets of paper from notepads and headed them "The Ziegler Effect."

The classroom settled into an uneasy silence. Mr. Tedder waved an instructive hand toward the apparatus set up on the marble top of the demonstration bench. "As you can see, I have a set of three solenoids, or coils of insulated wire, connected to a source of alternating current. A sudden surge of this current through the outermost solenoid will give an iron-cerium alloy bar placed at the center of the apparatus an impetus toward horizontal motion." Stetzel and Guenther, who were conscientious, took rapid notes. The rest of the class was divided between those students who were surreptitiously catching up on the adventures of "The Rocket Patrol" and those who were quietly sinking into sleep.

Mr. Tedder continued. "The alloy bar's initial movement will be frustrated, as it were, by the action of a second solenoid placed within and at right angles to the first. A third coil, within and at right angles to each of the outer two, completes the process. The winding ratios of the three solenoids are 476:9:34." Stetzel and Guenther scribbled the numbers rapidly; Ned Norcross, in the back row, stirred in his sleep, and two members of the Class of '95 who shared a volume of the Rocket Patrol's exploits agreed to turn the page.

"What happens to the bar of iron-cerium at this point is a matter of conjecture. All observers are agreed only that it disappears. Perhaps it leaves the coils so rapidly that it neither injures the wires nor can it be seen. Perhaps the bar passes through a temporary fissure in the three-dimensional system we perceive, falling into some yet unconceivable other dimension. Doctor Ziegler, who first observed this effect, inclines to this latter belief." Mr. Tedder placed his fingers on the telegraph key he'd rigged up to close the circuit through his apparatus. "Watch closely," he cautioned, tapping down on the key.

On the twenty-third planet at a distant sun—a planet called by its inhabitants a name for which there are no equivalents in human phonetics—a Young Being in the early stages of prematurity tangled the minds of his elders with feelings of anguish. His teacher had disappeared!

Ned Norcross, who was taking Junior Physics II for the third time, had his mind on neither the Ziegler Effect nor the tragic results of last night's basketball game. He was slumped at his desk, dreamily rehearsing the topography of one Honey LaRue, a strip-teaser who nightly practiced her art at the Club Innuendo. Norcross pried himself up on one elbow to glance toward the clock above the demonstration bench, then slumped forward on his desk in a faint. Up on the marble top of the demonstration bench, pulling off a right silk glove in time to the lazy ripple of a snare drum, danced Honey LaRue.

Mr. Tedder yelped, and immediately regretted it. He'd had two beers three days before; could that bring on hallucination at this late date? But Honey had gone, taking the Ziegler coils with her. One terminal of the telegraph key was still connected to the plate on the spark coil, the other wire ended in a little knot of fused silver. No, this wasn't the effect that Doctor Ziegler had reported, not at all!

To cover his confusion, Mr. Tedder began to talk. "There, you've just seen the Ziegler Effect in action. Explain what you've just seen, and you'll be famous among men." Indeed, the iron-cerium alloy bar had disappeared; but so had 20,000 cm. of No. 40 silver wire, silk-insulated. But the boys—except, of course, Stetzel and Guenther—hadn't noticed. Mr. Tedder glanced over his shoulder to the clock, saw that it would be fifteen minutes before the class would end, and made a quick decision in the interest of his sanity. "Class dismissed!" he said.

There was a stupefied second while the news soaked into dormant nervous systems. Then the boys were shouting across the room, grabbing up books, and hurrying out into the hall to take noisy advantage of their moment of freedom. Stetzel and Guenther, as behooved the top pupils of the Class of '95, hurried up to Mr. Tedder to check their notes.

"The symbol for cerium is 'Ce,' isn't it?" Stetzel asked.

"Yes. But now . . ."

"How did you do that, Mr. Tedder?" Guenther interrupted.

"Do what?" Mr. Tedder glanced suspiciously at Guenther. Perhaps it hadn't been those two beers.

"You had a woman dancing, right up where those solenoids were," Guenther said.

"That's what I saw," Stetzel substantiated. "What a movie! She sure looked three-dimensional to me. Wow!"

"Yes," Mr. Tedder said, canceling his decision of a moment before to lay off beer. "That was just a little stunt I thought up to see how many of you were paying attention. New optical principle, you know. Now if you'll excuse me, I've got to get things ready for the next class. And wake up Norcross on your way out, will you?"

Stetzel jarred Norcross from unconsciousness and walked out into the hall, talking and gesturing significantly with Guenther. Norcross unfolded himself slowly, glanced with a furtive eye toward Mr. Tedder and the empty bench top, and walked rapidly out of the room, down the stairs, and into the school physician's office.

Alone, Mr. Tedder frowned at the bereft lithium battery and telegraph key. He had pressed the key, closing the circuit, and there'd been a spurt of flame. A strange girl had appeared, dancing on the marble top of the demonstration bench. He'd never seen the woman before—a tall blonde wearing very little.... What the devil! There she was again.

Mr. Coar, principal of Tech, walked toward the door to the physics classroom, rehearsing the speech he was going to deliver to Tedder. "Young man, Tech does not approve of the practice of letting students out into the halls before the end of the period. Their racket has shaken the walls of classrooms on three floors. What have you to say for yourself, Mr. Tedder?" Yes, that would do nicely. Mr. Coar opened the door.

Mr. Tedder was leaning against a front-row desk, nodding appreciatively as a sketchily clad young lady danced for him. "TEDDER!" the principal bellowed. "Stop that!"

Honey LaRue faded, and the space between telegraph key and lithium battery was empty again.

"Stop what?" Mr. Tedder inquired, wide-eyed with innocence.

"Stop letting your classes out early so that you can spend your time gloating over your... your..." Mr. Coar groped for a stinging adjective, drew a blank, and concluded weakly, "... your movies!"

"Did you see her, too?"

"I did, indeed. You came here highly recommended by Indiana University, Tedder; and, frankly, I didn't expect this sort of thing from you."

"Mr. Coar, I believe that I've stumbled across a novel physical phenomenon."

"Anatomy was being studied in 1600 A.D., young man," Mr. Coar observed, his voice dripping sarcasm, "and is scarcely any longer a 'novel physical phenomenon.'"

"Sit down, sir." Mr. Tedder offered the principal the top of a desk in the front row. "Now, what did you expect to see when you came in here?"

"The apparatus of a physics laboratory—all those gears and coils and tubes and... things," Mr. Coar vaguely enumerated. "Certainly not a..." The principal sat heavily on the desk top, bulge-eyed. On the marble top of the demonstration bench was a Goldbergesque network of machinery, a perfect reproduction of the principal's uncertain notions concerning scientific gadgetry.

"How the devil did you do that, Tedder?"

"People have been asking me all morning. I don't know. I don't think that I did do it."

"Has that girl..." Honey LaRue reappeared on the bench, and the air vibrated with the drums' seductive roll. "... been here before?"

"Yes, sir. Couple of boys in my class saw her, too."

"Where are they now?"

Mr. Tedder glanced up at the clock. "It's second period by now. Stetzel is in Latin III, I believe, and Guenther's in Microbiology II."

Mr. Coar went over to the loud-speaker in the corner of the room, pressed a button, and spoke to his secretary, up in the school office. "Ann, send me students Guenther and Stetzel. Rooms 103 and 309." He switched the blat-box off. He turned toward the empty demonstration bench, wrinkled his forehead in concentration, and looked up. A pot of geraniums was standing on the marble bench top.

"Whew! It knows what I'm thinking about!"

"Looks that way, doesn't it?"

"But nothing can do that. Not electricity, nor electronics, nor even cybernetics."

"Nothing that we know about could, sir. What would you suggest that I do with the screwy thing?"

Mr. Coar, caught off guard, made a suggestion that was more witty than helpful. The classroom door swung open, and Stetzel and Guenther hurried in together, vocally wondering at their release from schedule. "Good morning, Mr. Coar, Mr. Tedder. Did you want us?" Stetzel asked.

"Did you see a woman in here?" the principal demanded.

"Yes, sir," Guenther said. "The movie, you mean."

"So you saw her, too. That rules mass hypnosis out," Mr. Coar decided, illogically, glancing suspiciously toward the young physics instructor.

The classroom door swung open again, admitting two teachers. Mr. Percy N. Formeller, known to two generations of biology students as Old Preserved-In-Formaldehyde, was full of indignation at the preemption of Guenther from his microbiology class. Miss MacIntire, Latin I-V, followed, equally indignant over Stetzel's defection from Marcus Porcius Cato.

"Mr. Coar," Mr. Formeller demanded, "what is the meaning of this? Guenther left in the middle of a movie on *Trypanosoma gambiense*, disturbing my entire class. In Technicolor, too," the biology instructor finished, accusingly.

"And how about calling Stetzel out of my class during the Third Punic War!" Miss MacIntire said.

Mr. Coar defended himself. "We have something here which is unique, possibly of great value to science." Miss MacIntire sniffed. Science was something that students elected to take instead of Latin. "I'm happy that you two teachers came in. You may be able to help us throw some light on our problem. You took the precaution of placing your classes in the hands of responsible monitors, I hope?"

"Of course!" Miss MacIntire snapped.

"What is the nature of this 'unique something' that our Mr. Coar mentioned, Mr. Tedder?" Old Preserved-In-Formaldehyde spoke as one who seeks to calm troubled waters.

"I frankly believe it to be an unearthly life form," Mr. Tedder said. "Telepathic and hallucinative, by my guess, and definitely not from this earth."

Mr. Formeller, who kept his three-year subscription to *Improbable Stories* a closely guarded secret, glanced about him for the extraterrestrial life form. He shouted. There on the demonstration bench was a green-skinned monster, an eight-foot-tall caricature of a *Tyrannosaurus rex*, holding a nubile and light-clad young lady under its right foreleg. There was a "thump" beside the biology teacher as Miss MacIntire slumped to the floor. Stooping gallantly to pull his colleague back to her feet, Mr. Formeller stopped thinking of the telepathic, hallucinative, and green *Tyrannosaurus rex*, which, grinning, disappeared.

Mr. Coar stared toward the empty demonstration bench, wrinkled his forehead in concentration, and was again rewarded by the pot-of-geraniums-made-manifest. "See?" he asked rhetorically. "It becomes anything you want it to."

"Curious." Mr. Formeller glared toward the table. A small orange insect appeared. The biology teacher bent over it and counted the spots on the orange anterior wings. "Six spots. A real *bipunctata* of a common local variety, or I don't know my *Coleoptera*." An idea struck him, and he backed rapidly away from the bench. He turned to Mr. Tedder. "I wouldn't go too close to the thing, if I were you. It creates these things for a purpose. I believe that this hallucinative power, as you call it, is the logical development of protective coloration, mimicry, and similar devices used by earthly creatures to elude their enemies and to lure their prey."

"You mean, this beast on the table top mimics what we're thinking about in hopes of drawing us close enough to seize us and eat us?" asked Miss MacIntire.

"Roughly, yes," Mr. Formeller nodded. "We've no way of knowing the metabolic processes, the thought patterns, or even the true form of the creature. Its action in creating a pleasant picture may be as automatic as the *Starrkrampf reflex*, or playing 'possum, is to foxes and opossums and *Leptinotarsum decemlineatae*." Mr. Formeller paused, hoping that his erudition was showing.

Miss MacIntire, who had seated herself back at a third-row desk, remarked, "I'd wish that the beast were a rational creature."

There was a flurry in the air above the demonstration bench as a togaed Greek gentleman came into being. He raised a portentous index finger, exclaimed an involved Greek observation, and disappeared.

"It can talk!" Mr. Coar marveled.

"It said, 'You've got an eel by the tail,' " Miss MacIntire translated. "Greek."

"Like having a bull by the horns, or an armful of greased pig," Stetzel commented.

"If you'll excuse me," Guenther said, "it seems to me that the thing has some will of its own. For one thing, whatever form it takes, that form is not ambiguous or wavering, as an image in the mind's eye must be."

"What's more," Stetzel continued his friend's argument, "it can say things that are presumably not in the mind which called it into being. For example, using Greek to explain itself—I hope that I'm being clear—shows that the creature has imaginative power, as well as the ability to read our minds."

Percy N. Formeller hadn't been listening. Psychological investigations could wait until there was a good, solid foundation of physical fact on which to build. "I wonder if it's carnivorous?" he murmured.

Mr. Tedder nodded. He approved of Mr. Formeller's method. Strictly scientific. "I have some meat in my lunch," Mr. Tedder said. He walked carefully around the demonstration bench, staying a good five meters away from the potential carnivore. If the creature were a meat eater, Mr. Tedder had no desire to have its feeding habits demonstrated upon the person of a young physics instructor. Back in the stockroom, Mr. Tedder opened his brown paper lunch bag, unfolded the wax paper from the top sandwich, and shook out a slice of pimento loaf. He wished that he'd brought a less plebeian lunch. Pork chops, perhaps. Oh, well, Mr. Tedder walked out into the classroom holding the slice of meat by one catchup-moist corner.

Mr. Formeller impaled the slice of pimento loaf on a length of No. 8 galvanized wire the physics teacher provided. Like a keeper shoving a flank of horse meat into a cageful of lions, the biology teacher thrust the baited wire into the empty air above the demonstration bench.

The pimento-loaf slice disappeared.

"Carnivorous," Mr. Formeller noted with satisfaction.

"Do you suppose that the creature could get off the table and...walk around?" Miss MacIntire hoped that her maidenly caution wouldn't be thought an old-maid's foible.

"If it were readily mobile, it wouldn't have developed so complex a mechanism to lure its prey," Mr. Formeller said. "Its various... what's the classical word, Miss MacIntire?"

"Protean."

"Yes. Its protean manifestations are a clue to its habits. It is rooted to the spot, like a plant."

"Like Venus's-flytrap?" Guenther suggested.

"Yes," the biology teacher approved. *"Dionaea muscipula* is a cogent example of the sort of plant I'm talking about. By the way, don't you think we ought to name this thing? We've been calling it 'creature' and 'monster' and all sorts of things. Most unscientific.''

"We might call it *Rete proteanum*," Miss MacIntire suggested from her third-row seat. "A 'many-formed trap,' you know."

"No, we want a name which suggests its origin as well as its habits."

"It's not of this world nor of the known solar system," Mr. Tedder commented.

"That's it. It's an extrasolar—no, an extragalactic being-of-many-forms."

"*Polymorph metagalacticus*," Miss MacIntire said. "Not an inspired name, but it will do, it will suffice."

Mr. Coar stared at the empty space between the telegraph key and the bank of lithium reaction cells. His pot of geraniums appeared again, then the scarlet flowers wavered, faded, and became gold-and-purple pansies. "Polymorph it is," the principal said. His air was that of a bishop conferring imprimatur upon a lay brother's interpretation of a gospel passage.

The pot of pansies disappeared, giving way to Honey LaRue. The snare drums swished and chattered, and Honey, who'd rid herself of a good deal more than her gloves, winked knowingly at Miss MacIntire. Spotting Stetzel, Honey propelled her pelvis several centimeters in a horizontal direction, a movement known to the trade as the "bump." The Latin teacher uttered an unclassical yelp of outraged modesty and averted her head. Stetzel grew pink to his ear tips. This Extragalactic Polymorph had no tact at all! Honey disappeared with a regretful shrug, and the lascivious drum rolls ceased.

"This sort of thing could become dangerous," Mr. Tedder commented.

"What can we do with it?" Mr. Coar asked. "It wouldn't do to put a cage around it. It can't move any more than a . . . geranium plant can. And what will we feed it?"

"Pimento loaf," the physics instructor suggested.

"Think of the value this thing can have!" Stetzel enthused. "Psychiatrists can see the morbid mind-images of their disturbed patients, the paranoiacs and the like, and devise techniques of cure."

"By studying the metabolism of this polymorph, we can deduce the physical conditions of the world it came from," Mr. Formeller observed, a glint of the hunter instinct in his eyes.

"We might even ask it questions about the world it came from!" Guenther said. "Maybe it would show its real form to us, and talk or think to us. It's already shown a lot of initiative, you know."

Miss MacIntire, who'd recovered from the shock of Honey LaRue, spoke up. "We've got an eel by the tail, as it said. We can't handle it and we can't let it go. We'll have to call in experts in zoology and physics . . ." Mr. Formeller exchanged outraged glances with Mr.

Tedder,"... and have them study the polymorph with the best instruments available."

"All this is very well," Mr. Formeller said, "but what I'd like to know is how this polymorph got into your classroom, Tedder."

Mr. Tedder cautiously stepped up to the demonstration bench and took the knob of the telegraph key in his fingers. "This was the switch in a Ziegler's Effect apparatus I'd set up for demonstration. I just tapped it, like this..." Mr. Tedder slapped the key down.

There was a glare of sudden greenness, and the air popped like a broken vacuum tube as it rushed in to occupy space suddenly vacated.

The Extragalactic Polymorph was gone. Mr. Coar wrinkled his brow and thought furiously of geranium-plants-in-pots, to no avail. Miss MacIntire thought wistfully of the handsome Greek gentleman who'd addressed her with an obscure quotation. Mr. Tedder, Stetzel, and Guenther bent their combined brains to steady consideration of Miss Honey LaRue, and for a moment they thought they heard the lustful bellow of a supernal saxaphone. But Honey stayed away.

"If we'd only taken photographs!" Mr. Formeller wailed. "Maybe the things we saw, we saw only in our minds. The polymorph's real form would have registered on film."

"Maybe if Mr. Tedder would duplicate that apparatus of his and ..." Miss MacIntire paused uncertainly. The arcana of physics were as unknown to her as was the Greek ablative to Mr. Tedder. "Well, do the same thing that you did before. Maybe he'll come back."

"No." Mr. Tedder was glum. "It won't be back. When you think that all objects are constantly changing in space and time, you see how wonderful it is that anything ever gets anywhere. The Extragalactic Polymorph won't be back. Its appearance was an accident; a huge, incredible, once-in-all-history coincidence."

On the twenty-third planet of a sun of a galaxy that lay beyond the ken of even the two-hundred-inch mirror of Palomar and the giant refractors of Luna, a planet the name of which cannot be expressed in human phonetics, a Young Being in the early stages of prematurity chortled with its Id. Its teacher was back! Swiftly, the youngster threw aside the messy slice of pimento loaf that was draped across the silver cube and commanded, "Zzzrf me a Klompfr!" A Klompfr appeared, and the Young Being spilled its delight out into the minds of its elders.

This Star Shall Be Free

Murray Leinster

The urge was part of an Antarean experiment in artificial ecological imbalance, though of course the cave folk could not guess that. They were savages with no interest in science or, indeed, in anything much except filling their bellies and satisfying other primal urges. They inhabited a series of caves in a chalk formation above a river that ran through primordial England and France before it joined the Rhine and emptied into the sea.

They did not understand the urge at all—which was natural. It followed the disappearance of the ship from Antares by a full two hours, so they saw no connection between the two. Anyhow, it was just a vague, indefinite desire to move to the eastward—an impulse for which they had no explanation whatever.

Tork was spearing fish from a rock out in the river when the ship passed overhead. He was a young man, still gangling and awkward. He wasn't up to a fight with One-Ear yet, and had a bad time in consequence. One-Ear was the boss male of the cave-dwellers' colony in the cliff over the river. He wanted to chase Tork away or kill him, and Tork had to be on guard every second. But he felt safe out on his rock.

He had just speared a fine ganoid when he heard a howl of terror from the shore. He jerked his head around. He saw Bent-Leg, the other adult male, go hobbling in terror toward his own cave mouth, and he saw One-Ear knock two of his wives and three children off the ladder to his cave so he could get in first. The others shrieked and popped into whatever crevice was at hand, including the small opening in which Tork himself slept when he dared. Then there was stillness.

Tork stared blankly. He saw no cause for alarm ashore. He ran his eyes along the top of the cliff. He saw birch and beech and oak, growing above the chalk. His eyes swept the stream. There were old-men's stories of sea monsters coming all the way up from the deep bay (which would some day be the English Channel). But the surface of the river was undisturbed. He scanned the farther shore. There were still a few of the low-browed ogres from whom Tork's people had taken this land, but Tork knew that he could outrun or outswim them. And there were none of them in sight, either.

All was quiet. Tork grew curious and stood up on his rock. Then he saw the ship.

It was an ovoid of polished, silvery metal. It was huge, two hundred feet by three hundred, and it floated tranquilly a hundred yards above the treetops. It moved to the stream and then drifted smoothly in a new direction up the river. It was going to pass directly over Tork's head.

It was so strange as to be unthinkable, and therefore it smote Tork with a terror past expression. He froze into a paralytic stillness, staring up at it. It made no sound. It had no features. Its perfectly reflecting sides presented to Tork's dazed eyes a distorted oval reflection of the river and the stream banks and the cliffs and all the countryside for many miles around. He did not recognize the reflection. To him it seemed that the thing's hide was mottled and that the mottlings shifted in a horrifying fashion.

It floated on, unwavering, as if its mass were too great to be affected by the gentle wind. Tork stood frozen in the ultimate catalepsy of a man faced with terror neither to be fought nor fled from. He did not see the small, spidery frameworks built out from the shining hull. He did not see the tiny tubes moving this way and that, as if peering. He did not see several of the tubes converging upon him. He was numbed, dazed.

Nothing happened. The silver ovoid swam smoothly above the river. Presently the river curved, and the ship from Antares went on tranquilly above the land. A little later it rose to clear a range of low hills. Later still, it vanished behind them.

When he recovered, Tork swam ashore with his fish, shouting vain-gloriously that there was nothing to be afraid of. Heads popped timorously into view. Children appeared first, then grownups. One-Ear appeared last of all, with his red-rimmed eyes and whiskery truculence. There were babblings; then they died down. The cave folk could not talk about the thing. They had no words for it. There were no precedents, however farfetched, to compare it with. They babbled of their fright, but they could not talk about its cause.

In an hour, it appeared to have been forgotten. Tork cooked his fish. When his belly was quite full, a young girl named Berry stopped cautiously some yards away from him. She was at once shy and bold.

"You have much fish," she said, with a toss of her head.

"Too much," said Tork complacently. "I need a woman to help eat it."

He looked at her. She was probably One-Ear's daughter, but she was slim and curved and desirable where he was bloated and gross and bad-tempered. An interesting, speculative idea occurred to Tork. He grinned tentatively.

She said, "One-Ear smelled your fish. He sent me to get some. Shall I tell him he is a woman if he eats it?"

Her eyes were intent, not quite mocking. Tork scowled. To let her give such a message would be to challenge One-Ear to mortal combat, and One-Ear was twenty years older and sixty pounds heavier than Tork. He tossed the girl a fish, all cooked and greasy as it was.

"I give you the fish," said Tork grandly. "Eat it or give it to One-Ear. I don't care!"

She caught the fish expertly. Her eyes lingered on him as she turned away. She turned again to peer at him over her shoulder as she climbed the ladder to One-Ear's cave.

At just about that time the urge came to Tork. He suddenly wanted to travel eastward.

Travel, to the cave folk, was peril undiluted. They had clubs and fish spears which were simply sharpened sticks. They had nothing else. Wolves had not yet been taught to fear men. The giant hyena still prowled the wild. There were cave bears and innumerable beasts no man of Tork's people could hope to cope with save by climbing the nearest tree. To want to travel anywhere was folly. To travel eastward, where a sabertooth was rumored to den, was madness. Tork decided not to go.

But the urge remained exactly as strong as before. He summoned pictures of monstrous dangers. The urge did not deny them. It did not combat them. It simply ignored them. Tork wanted to travel to the east. He did not know why.

After half an hour, during which Tork struggled with himself, he saw the girl Berry come out of One-Ear's cave. She began to crack nuts for One-Ear's supper, using two stones. One-Ear's teeth were no longer sound enough to cope with nuts.

Tork looked at her. Presently an astounding idea came to him. He saw that the girl glanced furtively at him sometimes. He made a secret beckoning motion with his hand. After a moment, Berry got up and moved to throw a handful of nutshells into the stream. She stood idly watching them float away. She was only a few feet from Tork.

"I go to the east," said Tork in a low voice, "to look for a better cave than here."

Her eyes flicked sideways to him, but she gave no other sign. She did not move away, either. Tork elaborated: "A fine cave. A deep cave, where there is much game."

She glanced at him again out of the corners of her eyes. Tork's own eyes abruptly burned. He said, greatly daring, "Then I will come and take you to it!"

The girl tossed her head. Among the cave folk, property right to females—even one's own daughters—took precedence over all other forms of possession. Were One-Ear to hear of this invasion of his proprietary rights, there would be war to the death immediately. But the girl did not move away; she did not laugh. Tork felt vast pride and enormous ambition stir within him. After a long, breathless instant the girl turned away from the water and went back to the pounding of nuts for One-Ear. On the way her eyes flickered to Tork. She smiled a faint, almost frightened smile. That was all.

But it was enough to send Tork off within the next half hour with his club in his hand and high romantic dreamings in his heart—and a quite sincere conviction that he was moving eastward to find a cave in which to set up housekeeping.

Because of this, the journey became adventure. Once Tork was treed by a herd of small, piggish animals rather like the modern peccary. Once he fled to the river and dived in because of ominous rustlings which meant he was being stalked by something he didn't wait to identify. And when, near nightfall, he picked a tree to sleep in and started to climb it, he was halfway up to its lowest branch when he saw the ropelike doubling of the thickness of a slightly higher branch. He got down without rousing the great serpent and went shivering for three miles—eastward—before he chose another tree to sleep in. But before he went to sleep he arranged these incidents into quite heroic form, suitable to be recounted to Berry.

Tork went on at sunrise. He paused once to stuff himself with blackberries—and left that spot via nearby trees when something grunting and furry charged him. In midmorning he heard a faraway, earth-shaking sound that could come from nothing but sabertooth himself. Then he heard a curious popping noise that he had never heard before, and the snarl ceased abruptly. The hair fairly stood up on Tork's head. But now the urge to move eastward was very strong indeed. It seemed to grow stronger as he traveled. No other creatures seemed to feel it, however. Squirrels frisked in the trees. Once he saw a monstrous elk—the so-called Irish elk—whose antlers had a spread of yards. The monster looked at him with a stately air and did not flee. Tork was the one who gave ground, because the cave folk had no missile weapons save stones thrown by hand. He made a circuit around the great beast.

Then he abruptly ran into tumbled ground, where there were practically no trees but very many rocks. It would be a perfect place for lying in wait. Also, he saw the mouths of several very promising caves. If the urge had not become uncontrollably strong, he would have stopped to investigate them. But he went on. Once his sensitive nostrils smelled carrion, mingled with the musky animal odor of a great carnivore. Mentally he went into gibbering terror. In his mind he fled at top speed. But the urge was incredibly strong. He went on like someone possessed. He had freedom to dodge, to creep stealthily, to take every precaution for silence and to avoid the notice of the animals which had no need to fear one club-armed man. He could even run—provided he fled to eastward. It was no longer possible for him to turn back.

The urge continued to strengthen. After some miles he became an automaton—a blank-faced, gangling figure, sun-bronzed and partly clad in an untanned hide. He carried a club, and in his belt there was a sharpened stick which was his idea of a fish spear. He trudged onward, his eyes unseeing, automatically adjusting his steps to the ground, apathetically moving around great masses of stone in his way. He was, for a time, completely at the mercy of any carnivore that happened to see him.

He did not even falter when he saw the great, silvery ovoid which had passed over his head the day before. He marched toward it with glassy eyes and an expressionless face. Yet the ship was vastly more daunting on the ground than in the air. It was still absolutely mirror-like on its outer surface. It still seemed featureless, because the spidery mounts of its scanning tubes were tiny. But its monstrous size was more evident.

It rested on the ground on its larger, rounded end. Its smaller part pointed upward. It was three hundred feet high—three times the height of the tallest trees about it, some of which had been crushed by its weight as it descended. Their branches projected from beneath it. It was a gigantic silver egg, the height of a thirty-story building and a city block thick. It rested on squashed oak trees in completely enigmatic stillness, with no sign of life or motion anywhere about it.

Tork walked up to it stiffly, seeing nothing and hearing nothing. He moved into the very shadow of the thing. Then he stopped. The urge abruptly ceased.

Pure terror sent him into howling, headlong flight. And instantly the urge returned. Twenty yards from the outward-bulging silvery metal, he crashed to earth. Then he stood up and stiffly retraced his steps toward the ship. Again, compulsion left him and he wailed and fled—and within twenty yards he slowed to a walk, and turned, and came back in blind obedience.

Ten times in all he tried to flee, and each time returned to the shadow of the motionless, mirror-like ovoid. The tenth time he stood still, panting, his eyes wild. He saw his own reflection on the surface of the thing. He croaked at it, thinking that here was another captive. His image made faces at him, but no sound; he could not make it answer. In the end he turned his back upon it sullenly. He stood shivering violently, like any wild thing caught and made helpless.

Half an hour later he saw something moving across the ground toward the great silver egg. There was a faint, faint sound, and a gigantic curved section of the egg opened. Sloshing water poured out and made puddles. There was a smell as of the ocean. The approaching thing, a vehicle, floated nearer, six feet aboveground, with strange shapes upon it and a tawny-striped mass of fur which Tork knew could be nothing but sabertooth. Tork trembled in every limb, but he knew he could not flee.

Just before the vehicle floated into the opening made by the dropped curved plate, two of the shapes descended from it and approached Tork.

He shook like an aspen leaf. He half grasped his club and half raised it, but he was too much unnerved to attack.

The shapes regarded him interestedly. They wore suits of a rubbery fabric bulging as if from liquid within. There were helmets with transparent windows, from which eyes looked out. But the windows were filled with water.

The creatures from Antares halted some paces from Tork. One of them trained a small tube upon him, and immediately he seemed to hear voices.

"We called you here to be kind to you. We saw you yesterday, standing upon a rock."

Tork merely trembled. The second shape trained a tube upon him, and he heard another voice. There was no difference in the timbre, of course, because Tork's own brain was translating direct mental impressions into words; but he knew that the second figure spoke.

"It is an experiment, Man. We come from a far star, mapping out worlds our people may some day need. Yours is a good world, with much water. We do not care for the land. Therefore we do not mind being kind to you who live on the land. . . . You have fire."

Tork found his brain numbly agreeing. He thought of fire and cookery, and the two creatures seemed to find his thoughts interesting.

"You have intelligence," said the first creature brightly, "and it has occurred to us to make an experiment in ecology. How do you get food?"

Tork grasped only the final sentence. Again, he thought numbly. Gathering nuts. Picking berries. Spearing fish with a sharpened stick. Digging shellfish. Small animals such as rabbits and squirrels, knocked over by lucky stones. He thought also of One-Ear, who had been well fed enough yesterday merely to demand fish. On other occasions he had come bellowing, club in hand, and chased Tork away from the food he had gathered for himself.

"That is bad," said the voice in Tork's mind, but it seemed amused. "We shall show you ways to get much food. All the food you desire. We shall show you defenses against animals. It will be interesting to see what comes of an ecological imbalance so produced. You will wait here."

The two shapes moved away—they floated a little above the ground, Tork noted dazedly—and entered the ship. The curved plate closed behind them. There was a whistling of air somewhere. To men of later millennia, the sound might have suggested a water lock closing, being filled with water so that water-dwelling creatures could swim from it freely into the liquid-filled interior of the ship from Antares. To Tork, it suggested nothing.

Nothing happened for hours. Then, suddenly, Tork saw a great elk moving steadily and hypnotically toward the ship from Antares. It reached a spot less than fifty yards from the ship's side, and seemed suddenly to be released from compulsion. It turned and bounded away; then its flight slackened and stopped. It came back toward the ship. Fifty yards away, again it tried to escape, and again was recaptured.

Tork watched, wide-eyed.

Rabbits appeared, hopping toward the ship. They appeared by dozens and then by hundreds. The steady advance, converging from all directions, came to a halt in milling confusion at a fixed distance from the gigantic, glistening egg.

The curved plate opened again, and again there was a great sloshing of water and the smell of the sea. Four or five shapes emerged, floating above the ground. Even before he saw tubes trained upon him, Tork was aware of fragments of thought-conversation.

"I acknowledge that an experiment on land cannot possibly affect our later use of this planet." Another intonation, indignant: "But it is cruel! Give these creatures unlimited food and the means of defense, and you condemn their descendants to starvation!" Then other voices said disjointedly, "I insist that a new ecological balance of low birth rate will result—" "Land animals are of no concern to us—" "Stability of nature—" "Some new factor will nullify the experiment absolutely—"

Tork was a savage. He was of the cave folk, and he had never in his life come into contact with an abstraction. Because these were thoughts, he perceived them; he even understood them. But they had no reference to any of the other things in his mind or experience. So they lingered only like the fragments of a dream.

The creatures placed a sort of box before him. It seemed to Tork like a stone. There was a pattern of color leaning against it which after laborious study he discovered to be a reduced appearance of a human being. It was the first picture he had ever seen. Actually, it was a picture of him—the key pattern of the urge which had brought him, if the matter were fully understood. But he heeded the mental voices, referring to the box he thought a stone.

"This is a device which projects a desire. Since you are merely a man, we have stabilized the device so that it projects one desire only. That desire is of coming to the place from which the desire is projected. We drew you to this place by tuning the projection to you. It made you wish to come here."

Tork's brain assimilated the information after a fashion. Very patiently, the mental voices corrected his impressions. They went on:

"This device will now project only that desire, but we have left the tuning variable. Any human may change the tuning now. Stand close to the device and think of an animal, and the device will tune to animals of that sort and make them wish to come wherever the device may be."

Tork thought of sabertooth, and cringed. The mental voices were amused.

"Even that is arranged. Here is a picture of a man. Look at it and you will think only of a man, and the device will only call man to you. Here also is a picture of an elk. Place this by the device and look at it, and your thoughts of elk will tune the device, so elk will wish to come to you. Rabbits—"

Tork was frightened. It would be pleasant enough to be able to make squirrels or rabbits—he saw hundreds of rabbits now, out of the corner of his eye—come to be knocked on the head. But an elk? What could a man do with an elk? An elk could trample and toss—

"Naturally," said the voice in his mind, with some dryness, "we give you safety from animals also, if you change your habits to make use of our gifts. We have made spears with points of stone, which you can soon learn to duplicate. With the picture device you can draw animals to you, and with the spears you can kill them. Moreover—"

The voices in his mind went on and on. There were a bow and arrows. There were stone knives. For the purpose of the experiment, each instrument save the hypnotic device itself had been carefully designed to be understood by primitive minds.

"We of Antares seek new worlds for our race to inhabit. We have chosen your world for later use and shall remain upon it for perhaps a hundred of your years, to survey it. We shall be able to see the first results of what we do today. Then we shall go back to our own world, and when we return we will see the final result of our gifts to you. What happens on the land, of course, will not affect our use of the seas."

Another mental voice interrupted, protesting that the man was not given a fair chance to refuse the gifts. The instructor went on dryly, "Your species can now multiply without limit. We think that you will overrun all the land and destroy all other animals for food, and ultimately destroy yourselves. But we are not sure. We are curious to learn. You can refuse the gift if you choose."

Tork blinked. He understood—temporarily. But he was human and a savage. The prospect of unlimited food outweighed all other possible considerations. He was frightened, but he wanted all the food that could be had. Definitely.

Instructions continued. Presently Tork understood the spears, and was naïvely astonished. He understood the bows and arrows, and was amazed. He grew excited. He wanted to use the marvelous new things. He felt that the shapes were amused by him.

The land-suited figures floated back to the water lock of the ship. It closed. He was left alone. He fingered the weapons. Another great plate lowered. But this was not a lock; it was a window. A vast expanse of transparent stuff appeared. Behind it was water, and in the liquid the Antareans—no longer in their rubbery suits—swam within the great metal egg, watching.

Tork, newly instructed, examined the beautifully fashioned stone point of a spear and then lifted the spear as he had been told to do. He remembered sharp-pointed, sharp-edged stones he had seen. He remembered stones breaking when struck together. He knew he could make a point like this. But—

He was a savage. He went to that extraordinary circular confusion where rabbits hopped hypnotically toward the great silver egg and at a certain distance were released and turned to flee, and again became subject to the irresistible urge to approach it. Tork went out to them, his mouth slavering.

He made a monstrous slaughter before it palled on him. Then he saw the elk. Fifty yards from the ship it stopped, stared about it, and bounded away. It turned and came back toward the great ship until suddenly it stopped and stared. . . .

Tork killed it while it marched toward the ship in dazed obedience to the urge. Then he went crazy with triumph. He gorged himself upon the raw flesh and went back to the shadow of the ship—in his triumph he knew no more fear—and squatted down before the device he had been given. He thought of Berry. Inevitably, his thoughts went also to One-Ear and to the other members of the cave colony by the river. He wished each one of them to see his triumph and his greatness. With a reeking mass of raw meat beside him, he gloated over their admiration of him when they should come. . . .

They came. Berry remembered that Tork had gone to the east. She wished to follow him. One-Ear wished to go to the east.

Somehow, in his fumbling brain, the urge became associated with notions of vast quantities of food. The women wished to go east. Seeking unconsciously for a reason, they decided that their children would be safer there. So the colony of cave folk took up the march.

They did not all reach the giant egg. Bent-Leg succumbed to a giant hyena who tried to carry off one of his children. A woman died when she fell behind the others. The rest heard her shriek, but that was all. And there was one small boy missing when, moving like automatons, the rest of the cave people walked with blank faces and empty eyes to within yards of the grinning, triumphant Tork. Then they were released.

There were confusion and panic such as he had felt, until he seized them one by one and held them fast while he boasted and explained. Then they still cringed fearfully for a while—but there was food. One-Ear drooled when Tork thrust a haunch of elk meat upon him. He squatted down and wolfed it, tending to snarl and glare with his wicked, red-rimmed eyes if anyone drew near. But there was food for all. More, there were weapons. Tork shared them, expansively. Small boys killed rabbits. Women used the new stone knives and skinned them.

More humans came. They were not members of Tork's tribe, but fortunately Tork's people were so stuffed with food by the time the strangers came that they felt no inclination to rise and kill them. They howled with laughter at the strangers' release, instant panic and flight, and return and release and panic again. Presently, with vast amusement, they explained and offered food. The strangers stuffed themselves. Behind the great transparent window the Antareans swam and watched. The strangers were shown the new weapons. They wanted to try them. Tork languidly called more animals to be killed for demonstration—and food.

There was such festival and such feasting as had never before been known in the brief history of Man. By the end of the second day, no fewer than fifty humans either gobbled at more food than they had ever seen before in their lives, or else slept the noisy slumber of repletion, while the Antareans watched.

On the third morning, without any notice, the ship rose quietly from the ground and sped skyward. A thousand feet up, it slanted toward the west, toward the great ocean in which an exploring party from Antares would be most interested.

The humans' first reaction to the departure of the ship was panic. But Tork went to the box—the stone-that-calls-animals—and tried a new picture. He thought of graceful, timid deer. The device called a herd of the spotted creatures, and the cave folk killed them and were reassured.

The feasting might have gone on indefinitely, but that Tork was a savage and therefore like a child. He kept the neighborhood of

the camp so crowded with food animals that other creatures came
of their own accord to prey on them. When the brutish roaring of
the cave bear was heard, terror fell upon the people. They seized
the weapons and such food as they could carry, and they fled.
Mostly, they scattered.

But Tork's own tribe naturally stayed together. It fled back toward
its normal habitation, Tork carrying the stone-that-calls-animals.

Tork and Berry dissuaded the new members of the tribe from
looking covetously upon Berry. Berry, in fact, used a spear upon
an admirer who was pressing Tork too hard with a club. But
nevertheless, when Tork took possession of the one cave that had
been empty in the chalk cliff, Berry uttered a purely formal outburst
of shrieks as he dragged her inside to begin housekeeping.

Her father, One-Ear, did not go to her rescue. He was stuffed
to bursting with deer meat, and he merely cocked a tolerant, sleepy
eye when his daughter was thus kidnaped from his very presence.
In any case, he knew that she would have used a spear or knife
on him or anybody else who interfered, so he merely belched slightly
and settled back to slumber.

So Tork and Berry were married. But the end of the Antarean
experiment was not yet.

Those who had been called to the shadow of the silver ship and
there released spread through the land. Most of them had not joined
Tork's tribe. They had new, modern, priceless weapons. Non-
possessors of beautiful, up-to-date flint spears tried to do murder
for their possession. Their owners did a little murdering on their
own. Possessors of spears and arrows which would actually cut and
pierce were supermen. And in time it became apparent that a man
who practiced and gained skill with the even more scientific bow
and arrow was in a still better position to win wives and influence
the next generation. So every human who saw or heard of the new
weapons craved them passionately.

But, being humans and savages, they did not think of making
them for themselves. They tried to get them from Tork and his tribe.
At first they journeyed to the chalk-cliff village and asked for the
new weapons, naïvely. For a little while, Tork was flattered and
openhanded. Then he began to run short of worked flint. He grew
stingy; he gave no more away. Then envious men grew desperate.
They stole a spear here, an arrowhead there.... Tork had to establish
a flint curtain, permitting no visitors in his village. He was unques-
tioned chieftain now. One-Ear had become too fat either to hunt
or fight. And then furtive, burning-eyed sneak thieves hung about
the village. Some had traveled for weeks through dangers to make
the flesh crawl, merely in hope of a chance to steal a spear or flint
knife or arrowhead. They developed great adeptness at such sneak
thievery.

There came a day when Tork's own personal spear was stolen
from the mouth of his own cave. The thief was a youth of an
unknown tribe who seemed to appear from nowhere. He dashed
to the spear, seized it, and dived overboard with it. He swam underwater, rising only to gasp for breath, until so far offshore to be
out of range of thrown stones. Stone-tipped arrows were far too
precious to be fired into the river. He escaped.

Something had to be done. Tork needed that spear. Berry—being
now a wife of some months' standing—upbraided him shrilly for
his carelessness. Tork went gloomily into the deepest recesses of
his cave, to think. The stone-that-calls-animals was there. He
regarded it miserably. He thought of the creatures who had given
it to him. . . .

And Tork, the cave man, had the inspiration which, in the bumbling, unintentional manner in which men achieve their greatest
triumphs, actually determined the future of the human race.

There was a ship from Antares upon Earth. Its crew mapped the
Earth's oceans for later colonists. The Antarean civilization was
already a hundred thousand years old and very far advanced indeed.
Men had just been introduced to flint spears and knives and arrows
by the Antareans as an interesting experiment, to see what would
happen. But Tork had an inspiration. He thought about the
Antareans, while he squatted by the stone-that-calls-animals! It was
the greatest single inspiration that any man has ever known. But
for it, Earth would be an Antarean colony, and Man—Man would
be at best a tolerated animal on the continents the Antareans had
no use for.

Tork squatted by the Antarean device and remembered the
Antareans in their water-filled suits. Then he thought about them
as they had looked in the huge transparent window, paddling in
the monster aquarium which was their ship and looking out at the
cave folk. The effort made his head hurt.

Presently he called Berry to help him think.

Presently Berry grew impatient. She had housewifely tasks to perform. She told Tork that there should be a picture to look at; then
he could keep thinking of them without trouble.

It had long been a pastime of cave children to press one hand
against the cave wall and outline the outspread fingers with charcoal.
It produced a recognizable picture of a hand. Tork essayed to trace
his remembered image of what Antareans looked like, on the wall.
The result was extremely crude; but while he worked on it, it was
easy to keep thinking about Antareans.

Berry disapproved his drawing. She changed it, making it better.
Presently One-Ear, wheezing, came amiably into the cave of his
son-in-law and was informed of the enterprise. His sharp, red-
rimmed eyes perceived flaws even in Berry's artistry. He was the

first human art critic. Other members of the tribe appeared. Some criticized; others attempted drawings of their own. A continuous session of artistic effort began—with everybody thinking about Antareans all the time.

Of course, the Antareans felt the urge. Perhaps at the beginning it was very faint. But the cave-folk's memories of the Antareans grew sharper as they improved their drawings. The tuning of the device improved; and the impulse to move toward the calling device grew stronger. At best, it was nagging. In the end it grew unbearable.

So there came a day when the great silver ovoid appeared in the sky to westward. It came swiftly, undeviatingly, toward the cliff village. It landed on the solid ground above the caves. Instantly it had landed, it was within the space where the call did not operate, and its crew was freed of the urge. The ship took off again, instantly. But instantly it was back in the overwhelming grip of the device the Antareans themselves had made. It returned, took off and returned, and took off and returned. . . .

Presently it settled down solidly on the plateau above the river. Tork went, beaming, to meet the land-suited creatures who came out of the water lock. Two figures floated toward him, menacingly. Voices came in his brain, unreasonably irritated. One said severely, "Man, you should not use the calling device we gave you to call *us!*"

"We need more spears," said Tork, beaming, "and bows and arrows and knives. So we called you to ask you to give them to us."

Crackling, angry thought came into his mind. The Antareans raged. Tork could not understand it. He regarded them blankly. More Antareans came out. He caught comprehensible fragments of other thoughts.

"So long as they think about us, we are helpless to leave! We cannot go beyond the space of freedom. . . ." Another voice said furiously, "We cannot let mere animals call us! We must kill them!" Another voice said reasonably, "Better destroy the device. That will be enough. After all, the experiment—"

Then a dry voice asked, "Where is the device?"

The creatures fretted. Tork stood hopefully, waiting for them to give him spears and knives and arrowheads. He was aware of highly technical conversation. The Antareans located the device. It was deep in the sloping chalk cliff below the ship. But in order for an Antarean to get to it, he would first have to go away from it, to get down the cliff. And he could not go away from it!

A crackling mental voice suggested that they call the humans to them—away from the device. But the same objection applied. In order to approach a similar device inside the ship, the humans in the caves would have to go away from it, and they couldn't do that, either. It was a perfect stalemate. The Antareans were trapped.

They even considered blasting the cliff, to smash the instrument they had presented to Tork. But anything that would smash the device would blow up the ship. The hundred-thousand-year-old Antarean civilization was helpless against the naïve desires of cave men who simply wanted more pieces of worked flint.

"Man," snapped a voice in Tork's mind, "how did you creatures keep your thought steadily upon us so that we were called?"

"We made pictures of you," said Tork happily. "It was not easy to do, but we did it."

He beamed at them. There was pained silence. Then a mental voice said bitterly, "We will give you the spears and arrows, Man, if you will destroy every one of the pictures."

"We will do that," promised Tork brightly, "because now we can draw them again when we need you."

He seemed to hear groans inside his head. But the Antareans were civilized, after all. He seemed also to hear wry chucklings. And the dry voice said, inside his skull, "It is agreed. Go down and blot out the pictures of us. We will give you what you wish. Then we can go away.

"And—you will never be able to summon us again, Man! We had intended to stay on this earth for a hundred of your years, and if our experiment seemed too deadly to you, we would have stopped it. But now we will not take that risk. Your species is a land species, and we are of the sea, but we think it best that you disappear. We have given you the means to destroy yourselves. We will depart and let you do so. Now go and blot out the pictures."

Tork went happily down into his cave. He commanded the wiping out of the pictures of Antareans. Within an hour the ship was gone. And this time it rose straight into the sky, as if it weren't coming back.

At first Tork was made happy by a huge new store of worked flint; but within two months disaster fell. The pictures of animals —so needful when using the Antarean device—blew into a cooking fire and burned. Then there was deep mourning, and Tork and Berry and all the tribe tried earnestly to call back the ship to get a fresh supply.

But nothing happened.

This was catastrophe; they could no longer call animals to be killed. But then Berry suggested redrawing the burned pictures on the cave's walls, and again art was attempted, by men working from the motive which has produced most of the great art works of earth—to get something to eat.

The Antarean device worked just as well with pictures of the cave-folk's own drawing as with those the Antareans had provided. But of course the Antareans could not know about it, because they had left the planet altogether. . . .

Tork and Berry lived long lives and had many offspring, all of whom thrived mightily because of the Antarean experiment. Of course, the experiment was not ended. In time, the tribe in the chalk-cliff village had increased so much in numbers that there was lack of room for its members. Colonies were sent out from it, and they thrived, too. And every colony carried with it three distinct results of the Antarean experiment in ecological imbalance.

One was stone weapons, which in time they rather painfully learned to make for themselves. Another was the belief that it was a simple trick to call animals to be killed. The actual Antarean device—being tucked away in the back of Tork's cave—in time was covered over with rubbish and in two generations was forgotten. Since it needed no attention, it got none. In time, when its power grew weaker and its effect less, nobody even thought to uncover and tinker with it. And the third result of the Antarean contact with Tork's tribe was the practice of drawing and painting pictures of animals on cave walls. The art of those Cro-Magnon artists is still admired.

The experiment still went on. Men learned to make weapons. Presently they discovered metal. The spears and arrowheads became bronze, and then iron, and presently gunpowder replaced bowstrings to hurl metal missiles. Later still, there was the atom bomb. In the art line, there were Praxiteles and Rodin and Michelangelo and Picasso. . . . And the consequences of the experiment continued to develop. . . .

A good thirty thousand years after the time of Tork, the Antareans decided that they needed the oceans of Earth for the excess population of several already colonized planets. They prepared a colonizing fleet. The original survey was not complete, but it was good enough to justify a full-scale expedition for settlement.

More than two million Antareans swam in the vessels which launched themselves into space to occupy Earth. It was purely by accident that members of a society of learned Antareans, going over the original survey reports, came upon the record of the experiment. The learned society requested, without much hope, that an effort be made to trace the ancient meddling with the laws of nature and see if any results could be detected.

The Antarean fleet came out of overdrive beyond Jupiter and drove in toward Earth with placid confidence. There was blank amazement on board when small spacecraft hailed the newcomers with some belligerence. The Antareans were almost bewildered. There was no intelligent race here. . . . But they sent out a paralyzing beam to seize one ship and hold it for examination. Unfortunately, the beam was applied too abruptly and tore the Earthship to pieces.

So the many-times-removed great-great-grandchildren of Tork and Berry and the others of the cave-folk tribe—they blasted the Antarean fleet in seconds, and then very carefully examined the wreckage. They got an interstellar drive out of their examination, which well paid for the one lost Earthship. But the Antarean learned society never did learn the results of that experiment in ecological imbalance, started thirty thousand years before.

In fact, the results aren't all in yet.

A Pail of Air

Fritz Leiber

Pa had sent me out to get an extra pail of air. I'd just about scooped it full and most of the warmth had leaked from my fingers when I saw the thing.

You know, at first I thought it was a young lady. Yes, a beautiful young lady's face all glowing in the dark and looking at me from the fifth floor of the opposite apartment, which hereabouts is the floor just above the white blanket of frozen air. I'd never seen a live young lady before, except in the old magazines—Sis is just a kid an Ma is pretty sick and miserable—and it gave me such a start that I dropped the pail. Who wouldn't, knowing everyone on Earth was dead except Pa and Ma and Sis and you?

Even at that, I don't suppose I should have been surprised. We all see things now and then. Ma has some pretty bad ones, to judge from the way she bugs her eyes at nothing and just screams and screams and huddles back against the blankets hanging around the Nest. Pa says it is natural we should react like that sometimes.

When I'd recovered the pail and could look again at the opposite apartment, I got an idea of what Ma might be feeling at those times, for I saw it wasn't a young lady at all but simply a light—a tiny light that moved stealthily from window to window, just as if one of the cruel little stars had come down out of the airless sky to investigate why the Earth had gone away from the Sun, and maybe to hunt down something to torment or terrify, now that the Earth didn't have the Sun's protection.

I tell you, the thought of it gave me the creeps. I just stood there shaking, and almost froze my feet and did frost my helmet so solid on the inside that I couldn't have seen the light even if it had come out of one of the windows to get me. Then I had the wit to go back inside.

Pretty soon I was feeling my familiar way through the thirty or so blankets and rugs Pa has got hung around to slow down the escape of air from the Nest, and I wasn't quite so scared. I began to hear the tick-ticking of the clocks in the Nest and knew I was getting back into air, because there's no sound outside in the vacuum, of course. But my mind was still crawly and uneasy as I pushed through the last blankets—Pa's got them faced with aluminum foil to hold in the heat—and came into the Nest.

Let me tell you about the Nest. It's low and snug, just room for the four of us and our things. The floor is covered with thick woolly rugs. Three of the sides are blankets, and the blankets roofing it touch Pa's head. He tells me it's inside a much bigger room, but I've never seen the real walls or ceiling.

Against one of the blanket-walls is a big set of shelves, with tools and books and other stuff, and on top of it a whole row of clocks. Pa's very fussy about keeping them wound. He says we must never forget time, and without a sun or moon, that would be easy to do.

The fourth wall has blankets all over except around the fireplace, in which there is a fire that must never go out. It keeps us from freezing and does a lot more besides. One of us must always watch it. Some of the clocks are alarm and we can use them to remind us. In the early days there was only Ma to take turns with Pa—I think of that when she gets difficult—but now there's me to help, and Sis too.

It's Pa who is the chief guardian of the fire, though. I always think of him that way: a tall man sitting cross-legged, frowning anxiously at the fire, his lined face golden in its light, and every so often carefully placing on it a piece of coal from the big heap beside it. Pa tells me there used to be guardians of the fire sometimes in the very old days—vestal virgins, he calls them—although there was unfrozen air all around then and you didn't really need them.

He was sitting just that way now, though he got up quick to take the pail from me and bawl me out for loitering—he'd spotted my frozen helmet right off. That roused Ma and she joined in picking on me. She's always trying to get the load off her feelings, Pa explains. He shut her up pretty fast. Sis let off a couple of silly squeals too.

Pa handled the pail of air in a twist of cloth. Now that it was inside the Nest, you could really feel its coldness. It just seemed to suck the heat out of everything. Even the flames cringed away from it as Pa put it down close by the fire.

Yet it's that glimmery white stuff in the pail that keeps us alive. It slowly melts and vanishes and refreshes the Nest and feeds the fire. The blankets keep it from escaping too fast. Pa'd like to seal the whole place, but he can't—building's too earthquake-twisted, and besides he has to leave the chimney open for smoke.

Pa says air is tiny molecules that fly away like a flash if there isn't something to stop them. We have to watch sharp not to let the air run low. Pa always keeps a big reserve supply of it in buckets behind the first blankets, along with extra coal and cans of food and other things, such as pails of snow to melt for water. We have to go way down to the bottom floor for that stuff, which is a mean trip, and get it through a door to outside.

You see, when the Earth got cold, all the water in the air froze first and made a blanket ten feet thick or so everywhere, and then down on top of that dropped the crystals of frozen air, making another white blanket sixty or seventy feet thick maybe.

Of course, all the parts of the air didn't freeze and snow down at the same time.

First to drop out was the carbon dioxide—when you're shoveling for water, you have to make sure you don't go too high and get any of that stuff mixed in, for it would put you to sleep, maybe for good, and make the fire go out. Next there's the nitrogen, which doesn't count one way or the other, though it's the biggest part of the blanket. On top of that and easy to get at, which is lucky for us, there's the oxygen that keeps us alive. Pa says we live better than kings ever did, breathing pure oxygen, but we're used to it and don't notice. Finally, at the very top, there's a slick of liquid helium, which is funny stuff. All of these gases in neat separate layers. Like a pussy caffay, Pa laughingly says, whatever that is.

I was busting to tell them all about what I'd seen, and so as soon as I'd ducked out of my helmet and while I was still climbing out of my suit, I cut loose. Right away Ma got nervous and began making eyes at the entry-slit in the blankets and wringing her hands together—the hand where she'd lost three fingers from frostbite inside the good one, as usual. I could tell that Pa was annoyed at me scaring her and wanted to explain it all away quickly, yet could see I wasn't fooling.

"And you watched this light for some time, son?" he asked when I finished.

I hadn't said anything about first thinking it was a young lady's face. Somehow that part embarrassed me.

"Long enough for it to pass five windows and go to the next floor."

"And it didn't look like stray electricity or crawling liquid or starlight focussed by a growing crystal, or anything like that?"

He wasn't just making up those ideas. Odd things happen in a world that's about as cold as can be, and just when you think matter would be frozen dead, it takes on a strange new life. A slimy stuff comes crawling toward the Nest, just like an animal snuffing for heat—that's the liquid helium. And once, when I was little, a bolt of lightning—not even Pa could figure where it came from—hit the nearby steeple and crawled up and down it for weeks, until the glow finally died.

"Not like anything I ever saw," I told him.

He stood for a moment frowning. Then, "I'll go out with you, and you show it to me," he said.

Ma raised a howl at the idea of being left alone, and Sis joined in too, but Pa quieted them. We started climbing into our outside clothes—mine had been warming by the fire. Pa made them. They have plastic headpieces that were once big double-duty transparent food cans, but they keep heat and air in and can replace the air for a little while, long enough for our trips for water and coal and food and so on.

Ma started moaning again, "I've always known there was something outside there, waiting to get us. I've felt it for years—something that's part of the cold and hates all warmth and wants to destroy the Nest. It's been watching us all this time, and now it's coming after us. It'll get you and then come for me. Don't go, Harry!"

Pa had everything on but his helmet. He knelt by the fireplace and reached in and shook the long metal rod that goes up the chimney and knocks off the ice that keeps trying to clog it. Once a week he goes up on the roof to check if it's working all right. That's our worst trip and Pa won't let me make it alone.

"Sis," Pa said quietly, "come watch the fire. Keep an eye on the air, too. If it gets low or doesn't seem to be boiling fast enough, fetch another bucket from behind the blanket. But mind your hands. Use the cloth to pick up the bucket."

Sis quit helping Ma be frightened and came over and did as she was told. Ma quieted down pretty suddenly, though her eyes were still kind of wild as she watched Pa fix on his helmet tight and pick up a pail and the two of us go out.

Pa led the way and I took hold of his belt. It's a funny thing, I'm not afraid to go by myself, but when Pa's along I always want to hold on to him. Habit, I guess, and then there's no denying that this time I was a bit scared.

You see, it's this way. We know that everything is dead out there. Pa heard the last radio voices fade away years ago, and had seen some of the last folks die who weren't as lucky or well protected as us. So we knew that if there was something groping around out there, it couldn't be anything human or friendly.

Besides that, there's a feeling that comes with it always being night, *cold* night. Pa says there used to be some of that feeling even in the old days, but then every morning the Sun would come and chase it away. I have to take his word for that, not ever remembering the Sun as being anything more than a big star. You see, I hadn't been born when the dark star snatched us away from the Sun, and by now it's dragged us out beyond the orbit of the planet Pluto, Pa says, and taking us farther out all the time.

I found myself wondering whether there mightn't be something on the dark star that wanted us, and if that was why it had captured the Earth. Just then we came to the end of the corridor and I followed Pa out on the balcony.

I don't know what the city looked like in the old days, but now it's beautiful. The starlight lets you see it pretty well—there's quite a bit of light in those steady points speckling the blackness above. (Pa says the stars used to twinkle once, but that was because there was air.) We are on a hill and the shimmery plain drops away from us and then flattens out, cut up into neat squares by the troughs that used to be streets. I sometimes make my mashed potatoes look like it, before I pour on the gravy.

Some taller buildings push up out of the feathery plain, topped by rounded caps of air crystals, like the fur hood Ma wears, only whiter. On those buildings you can see the darker squares of windows, underlined by white dashes of air crystals. Some of them are on a slant, for many of the buildings are pretty badly twisted by the quakes and all the rest that happened when the dark star captured the Earth.

Here and there a few icicles hang, water icicles from the first days of the cold, other icicles of frozen air that melted on the roofs and dripped and froze again. Sometimes one of those icicles will catch the light of a star and send it to you so brightly you think the star has swooped into the city. That was one of the things Pa had been thinking of when I told him about the light, but I had thought of it myself first and known it wasn't so.

He touched his helmet to mine so we could talk easier and he asked me to point out the windows to him. But there wasn't any light moving around inside them now, or anywhere else. To my surprise, Pa didn't bawl me out and tell me I'd been seeing things. He looked all around quite a while after filling his pail, and just as we were going inside he whipped around without warning, as if to take some peeping thing off guard.

I could feel it too. The old peace was gone. There was something lurking out there, watching, waiting, getting ready.

Inside, he said to me, touching helmets, "If you see something like that again, son, don't tell the others. Your Ma's sort of nervous these days and we owe her all the feeling of safety we can give her. Once—it was when your sister was born—I was ready to give up and die, but your Mother kept me trying. Another time she kept the fire going a whole week all by herself when I was sick. Nursed me and took care of the two of you too.

"You know that game we sometimes play, sitting in a square in the Nest, tossing a ball around? Courage is like a ball, son. A person can hold it only so long, and then he's got to toss it to someone else. When it's tossed your way, you've got to catch it and hold it tight—and hope there'll be someone else to toss it to when you get tired of being brave."

His talking to me that way made me feel grown-up and good. But it didn't wipe away the thing outside from the back of my mind —or the fact that Pa took it seriously.

It's hard to hide your feelings about such a thing. When we got back in the Nest and took off our outside clothes, Pa laughed about it all and told them it was nothing and kidded me for having such an imagination, but his words fell flat. He didn't convince Ma and Sis any more than he did me. It looked for a minute like we were all fumbling the courage-ball. Something had to be done, and almost before I knew what I was going to say, I heard myself asking Pa to tell us about the old days, and how it all happened.

He sometimes doesn't mind telling that story, and Sis and I sure like to listen to it, and he got my idea. So we were all settled around the fire in a wink, and Ma pushed up some cans to thaw for supper, and Pa began. Before he did, though, I noticed him casually get a hammer from the shelf and lay it down beside him.

It was the same old story as always—I think I could recite the main thread of it in my sleep—though Pa always puts in a new detail or two and keeps improving it in spots.

He told us how the Earth had been swinging around the Sun ever so steady and warm, and the people on it fixing to make money and wars and have good time and get power and treat each other right or wrong, when without warning there comes charging out of space this dead star, this burned-out sun, and upsets everything.

You know, I find it hard to believe in the way those people felt, any more than I can believe in the swarming number of them. Imagine people getting ready for the horrible sort of war they were cooking up. Wanting it even, or at least wishing it were over so as to end their nervousness. As if all folks didn't have to hang together and pool every bit of warmth just to keep alive. And how can they have hoped to end danger, any more than we can hope to end the cold?

Sometimes I think Pa exaggerates and makes things out too black. He's cross with us once in a while and was probably cross with all those folks. Still, some of the things I read in the old magazines sound pretty wild. He may be right.

The dark star, as Pa went on telling it, rushed in pretty fast and there wasn't much time to get ready. At the beginning they tried to keep it a secret from most people, but then the truth came out, what with the earthquakes and floods—imagine, oceans of *unfrozen* water!—and people seeing stars blotted out by something on a clear night. First off they thought it would hit the Sun, and then they thought it would hit the Earth. There was even the start of a rush to get to a place called China, because people thought the star would hit on the other side. But then they found it wasn't going to hit either side, but was going to come very close to the Earth.

Most of the other planets were on the other side of the Sun and didn't get involved. The Sun and the newcomer fought over the Earth for a little while—pulling it this way and that, like two dogs growling over a bone, Pa described it this time—and then the newcomer won and carried us off. The Sun got a consolation prize, though. At the last minute it managed to hold on to the Moon.

That was the time of the monster earthquakes and floods, twenty times worse than anything before. It was also the time of the Big Jerk, as Pa calls it, when all Earth got yanked suddenly, just as Pa has done to me once or twice, grabbing me by the collar to do it, when I've been sitting too far from the fire.

You see, the dark star was going through space faster than the Sun, and in the opposite direction, and it had to wrench the world considerably in order to take it away.

The Big Jerk didn't last long. It was over as soon as the Earth was settled down in its new orbit around the dark star. But it was pretty terrible while it lasted. Pa says that all sorts of cliffs and buildings toppled, oceans slopped over, swamps and sandy deserts gave great sliding surges that buried nearby lands. Earth was almost jerked out of its atmosphere blanket and the air got so thin in spots that people keeled over and fainted—though of course, at the same time, they were getting knocked down by the Big Jerk and maybe their bones broke or skulls cracked.

We've often asked Pa how people acted during that time, whether they were scared or brave or crazy or stunned, or all four, but he's sort of leery of the subject, and he was again tonight. He says he was mostly too busy to notice.

You see, Pa and some scientist friends of his had figured out part of what was going to happen—they'd known we'd get captured and our air would freeze—and they'd been working like mad to fix up a place with airtight walls and doors, and insulation against the cold, and big supplies of food and fuel and water and bottled air. But the place got smashed in the last earthquakes and all Pa's friends were killed then and in the Big Jerk. So he had to start over and throw the Nest together quick without any advantages, just using any stuff he could lay his hands on.

I guess he's telling pretty much the truth when he says he didn't have any time to keep an eye on how other folks behaved, either then or in the Big Freeze that followed—followed very quick, you know, both because the dark star was pulling us away very fast and because Earth's rotation had been slowed in the tug-of-war, so that the nights were ten old nights long.

Still, I've got an idea of some of the things that happened from the frozen folk I've seen, a few of them in other rooms in our building, others clustered around the furnaces in the basements where we go for coal.

In one of the rooms, an old man sits stiff in a chair, with an arm and a leg in splints. In another, a man and woman are huddled together in a bed with heaps of covers over them. You can just see their heads peeking out, close together. And in another a beautiful young lady is sitting with a pile of wraps huddled around her, looking hopefully toward the door, as if waiting for someone who never came back with warmth and food. They're all still and stiff as statues, of course, but just like life.

Pa showed them to me once in quick winks of his flashlight, when he still had a fair supply of batteries and could afford to waste a little light. They scared me pretty bad and made my heart pound, especially the young lady.

Now, with Pa telling his story for the umpteenth time to take our minds off another scare, I got to thinking of the frozen folk again. All of a sudden I got an idea that scared me worse than anything yet. You see, I'd just remembered the face I'd thought I'd seen in the window. I'd forgotten about that on account of trying to hide it from the others.

What, I asked myself, if the frozen folk were coming to life? What if they were like the liquid helium that got a new lease on life and started crawling toward the heat just when you thought its molecules ought to freeze solid forever? Or like the electricity that moves endlessly when it's just about as cold as that? What if the ever-growing cold, with the temperature creeping down the last few degrees to the last zero, had mysteriously wakened the frozen folk to life—not warm-blooded life, but something icy and horrible?

That was a worse idea than the one about something coming down from the dark star to get us.

Or maybe, I thought, both ideas might be true. Something coming down from the dark star and making the frozen folk move, using them to do its work. That would fit with both things I'd seen—the beautiful young lady and the moving, star-like light.

The frozen folk with minds from the dark star behind their unwinking eyes, creeping, crawling, snuffing the way, following the heat to the Nest.

I tell you, that thought gave me a very bad turn and I wanted very badly to tell the others my fears, but I remembered what Pa had said and clenched my teeth and didn't speak.

We were all sitting very still. Even the fire was burning silently. There was just the sound of Pa's voice and the clocks.

And then, from beyond the blankets, I thought I heard a tiny noise. My skin tightened all over me.

Pa was telling about the early years in the Nest and had come to the place where he philosophizes.

"So I asked myself then," he said, "what's the use of going on? What's the use of dragging it out for a few years? Why prolong a doomed existence of hard work and cold and loneliness? The human race is done. The Earth is done. Why not give up? I asked myself—and all of a sudden I got the answer."

Again I heard the noise, louder this time, a kind of uncertain, shuffling tread, coming closer. I couldn't breathe.

"Life's always been a business of working hard and fighting the cold," Pa was saying. "The Earth's always been a lonely place, millions of miles from the next planet. And no matter how long the human race might have lived, the end would have come some night. Those things don't matter. What matters is that life is good. It has a lovely texture, like some rich cloth or fur, or the petals of flowers —you've seen pictures of those, but I can't describe how they feel—or the fire's glow. It makes everything else worth while. And that's as true for the last man as the first."

And still the steps kept shuffling closer. It seemed to me that the inmost blanket trembled and bulged a little. Just as if they were burned into my imagination, I kept seeing those peering, frozen eyes.

"So right then and there," Pa went on, and now I could tell that he heard the steps too, and was talking loud so we maybe wouldn't hear them, "right then and there I told myself that I was going on as if we had all eternity ahead of us. I'd have children and teach them all I could. I'd get them to read books. I'd plan for the future, try to enlarge and seal the Nest. I'd do what I could to keep everything beautiful and growing. I'd keep alive my feeling of wonder even at the cold and the dark and the distant stars."

But then the blanket actually did move and lift. And there was a bright light somewhere behind it. Pa's voice stopped and his eyes turned to the widening slit and his hand went out until it touched and gripped the handle of the hammer beside him.

In through the blanket stepped the beautiful young lady. She stood there looking at us the strangest way, and she carried something bright and unwinking in her hand. And two other faces peered over her shoulders—men's faces, white and staring.

Well, my heart couldn't have been stopped for more than four or five beats before I realized she was wearing a suit and helmet like Pa's homemade ones, only fancier, and that the men were too—and that the frozen folk certainly wouldn't be wearing those. Also, I noticed that the bright thing in her hand was just a kind of flashlight.

The silence kept on while I swallowed hard a couple of times, and after that there was all sorts of jabbering and commotion.

They were simply people, you see. We hadn't been the only ones to survive; we'd just thought so, for natural enough reasons. These three people had survived, and quite a few others with them. And when we found out *how* they'd survived, Pa let out the biggest whoop of joy.

They were from Los Alamos and they were getting their heat and power from atomic energy. Just using the uranium and plutonium intended for bombs, they had enough to go on for thousands of years. They had a regular little airtight city, with air locks and all. They even generated electric light and grew plants and animals by it. (At this Pa let out a second whoop, waking Ma from her faint.)

But if we were flabbergasted at them, they were double-flabbergasted at us.

One of the men kept saying, "But it's impossible, I tell you. You can't maintain an air supply without hermetic sealing. It's simply impossible."

That was after he had got his helmet off and was using our air. Meanwhile the young lady kept looking around at us as if we were saints, and telling us we'd done something amazing, and suddenly she broke down and cried.

They'd been scouting around for survivors, but they never expected to find any in a place like this. They had rocket ships at Los Alamos and plenty of chemical fuel. As for liquid oxygen, all you had to do was go out and shovel the air blanket at the top level. So after they'd got things going smoothly at Los Alamos, which had taken years, they'd decided to make some trips to likely places where there might be other survivors. No good trying long-distance radio signals, of course, since there was no atmosphere to carry them around the curve of the Earth.

Well, they'd found other colonies at Argonne and Brookhaven and way around the world at Harwell and Tanna Tuva. And now they'd been giving our city a look, not really expecting to find anything. But they had an instrument that noticed the faintest heat waves and it had told them there was something warm down here, so they'd landed to investigate. Of course we hadn't heard them land, since there was no air to carry the sound, and they'd had to investigate around quite a while before finding us. Their instruments had given them a wrong steer and they'd wasted some time in the building across the street.

By now, all five adults were talking like sixty. Pa was demonstrating to the men how he worked the fire and got rid of the ice in the chimney and all that. Ma had perked up wonderfully and was showing the young lady her cooking and sewing stuff, and even asking about how the women dressed at Los Alamos. The strangers marveled at everything and praised it to the skies. I could tell from the way they wrinkled their noses that they found the Nest a bit smelly, but they never mentioned that at all and just asked bushels of questions.

In fact, there was so much talking and excitement that Pa forgot about things, and it wasn't until they were all getting groggy that he looked and found the air had all boiled away in the pail. He got another bucket of air quick from behind the blankets. Of course that started them all laughing and jabbering again. The newcomers even got a little drunk. They weren't used to so much oxygen.

Funny thing, though—I didn't do much talking at all and Sis hung on to Ma all the time and hid her face when anybody looked at her. I felt pretty uncomfortable and disturbed myself, even about the young lady. Glimpsing her outside there, I'd had all sorts of mushy thoughts, but now I was just embarrassed and scared of her, even though she tried to be nice as anything to me.

I sort of wished they'd all quit crowding the Nest and let us be alone and get our feelings straightened out.

And when the newcomers began to talk about our all going to Los Alamos, as if that were taken for granted, I could see that something of the same feeling struck Pa and Ma too. Pa got very silent all of a sudden and Ma kept telling the young lady, "But I wouldn't know how to act there and I haven't any clothes."

The strangers were puzzled like anything at first, but then they got the idea. As Pa kept saying, "It just doesn't seem right to let this fire go out."

Well, the strangers are gone, but they're coming back. It hasn't been decided yet just what will happen. Maybe the Nest will be kept up as what one of the strangers called a "survival school." Or maybe we will join the pioneers who are going to try to establish a new colony at the uranium mines at Great Slave Lake or in the Congo.

Of course, now that the strangers are gone, I've been thinking a lot about Los Alamos and those other tremendous colonies. I have a hankering to see them for myself.

You ask me, Pa wants to see them too. He's been getting pretty thoughtful, watching Ma and Sis perk up.

"It's different, now that we know others are alive," he explains to me. "Your mother doesn't feel so hopeless any more. Neither do I, for that matter, not having to carry the whole responsibility for keeping the human race going, so to speak. It scares a person."

I looked around at the blanket walls and the fire and the pails of air boiling away and Ma and Sis sleeping in the warmth and the flickering light.

"It's not going to be easy to leave the Nest," I said, wanting to cry, kind of. "It's so small and there's just the four of us. I get scared at the idea of big places and a lot of strangers."

He nodded and put another piece of coal on the fire. Then he looked at the little pile and grinned suddenly and put a couple of handfuls on, just as if it was one of our birthdays or Christmas.

"You'll quickly get over that feeling, son," he said. "The trouble with the world was that it kept getting smaller and smaller, till it ended with just the Nest. Now it'll be good to have a real huge world again, the way it was in the beginning."

I guess he's right. You think the beautiful young lady will wait for me till I grow up? I'll be twenty in only ten years.

The Outsider

H. P. Lovecraft

Unhappy is he to whom the memories of childhood bring only fear and sadness. Wretched is he who looks back upon lone hours in vast and dismal chambers with brown hangings and maddening rows of antique books, or upon awed watches in twilight groves of grotesque, gigantic, and vine-encumbered trees that silently wave twisted branches far aloft. Such a lot the gods gave to me—to me, the dazed, the disappointed; the barren, the broken. And yet I am strangely content and cling desperately to those withered memories, when my mind momentarily threatens to reach beyond to *the other*.

I know not where I was born, save that the castle was infinitely old and infinitely horrible, full of dark passages and having high ceilings where the eye could find only cobwebs and shadows. The stones in the crumbling corridors seemed always hideously damp, and there was an accursed smell everywhere, as of the piled-up corpses of dead generations. It was never light, so that I used sometimes to light candles and gaze steadily at them for relief, nor was there any sun outdoors, since the terrible trees grew high above the topmost accessible tower. There was one black tower which reached above the trees into the unknown outer sky, but that was partly ruined and could not be ascended save by a well-nigh impossible climb up the sheer wall, stone by stone.

I must have lived years in this place, but I cannot measure the time. Beings must have cared for my needs, yet I cannot recall any person except myself, or anything alive but the noiseless rats and bats and spiders. I think that whoever nursed me must have been shockingly aged, since my first conception of a living person was that of something mockingly like myself, yet distorted, shrivelled, and decaying like the castle. To me there was nothing grotesque in the bones and skeletons that strewed some of the stone crypts deep down among the foundations. I fantastically associated these things with everyday events, and thought them more natural than the coloured pictures of living beings which I found in many of the mouldy books. From such books I learned all that I know. No teacher urged or guided me, and I do not recall hearing any human voice in all those years—not even my own; for although I had read of speech, I had never thought to try to speak aloud. My aspect was a matter equally unthought of, for there were no mirrors in the castle, and I merely regarded myself by instinct as akin to the youthful figures I saw drawn and painted in the books. I felt conscious of youth because I remembered so little.

Outside, across the putrid moat and under the dark mute trees, I would often lie and dream for hours about what I read in the books; and would longingly picture myself amidst gay crowds in the sunny world beyond the endless forests. Once I tried to escape from the forest, but as I went further from the castle the shade grew denser and the air more filled with brooding fear; so that I ran frantically back lest I lose my way in a labyrinth of nighted silence.

So through endless twilights I dreamed and waited, though I knew not what I waited for. Then in the shadowy solitude my longing for light grew so frantic that I could rest no more, and I lifted entreating hands to the single black ruined tower that reached above the forest into the unknown outer sky. And at last I resolved to scale that tower, fall though I might; since it were better to glimpse the sky and perish, than to live without ever beholding day.

In the dank twilight I climbed the worn and aged stone stairs till I reached the level where they ceased, and thereafter clung perilously to small footholds leading upwards. Ghastly and terrible was that dead, stairless cylinder of rock; black, ruined, and deserted, and sinister with startled bats whose wings made no noise. But more ghastly and terrible still was the slowness of my progress; for climb as I might, the darkness overhead grew no thinner, and a new chill as of haunted and venerable mould assailed me. I shivered as I wondered why I did not reach the light, and would have looked down had I dared. I fancied that night had come suddenly upon me, and vainly groped with one free hand for a window embrasure, that I might peer out and above, and try to judge the height I had attained.

All at once, after an infinity of awesome, sightless crawling up that concave and desperate precipice, I felt my head touch a solid thing, and I knew I must have gained the roof, or at least some kind of floor. In the darkness I raised my free hand and tested the barrier, finding it stone and immovable. Then came a deadly circuit of the tower, clinging to whatever holds the slimy wall could give; till finally my testing hand found the barrier yielding, and I turned upwards again, pushing the slab or door with my head as I used both hands in my fearful ascent. There was no light revealed above, and as my hands went higher I knew that my climb was for the nonce ended; since the slab was the trap-door of an aperture leading to a level stone surface of greater circumference than the lower tower, no doubt the floor of some lofty and capacious observation chamber. I crawled through carefully, and tried to prevent the heavy slab from falling back into place, but failed in the latter attempt. As I lay exhausted on the stone floor I heard the eerie echoes of its fall, but hoped when necessary to pry it up again.

Believing I was now at prodigious height, far above the accursed branches of the wood, I dragged myself up from the floor and fumbled about for windows, that I might look for the first time upon the sky, and the moon and stars of which I had read. But on every hand I was disappointed; since all that I found were vast shelves of marble, bearing odious oblong boxes of disturbing size. More and more I reflected, and wondered what hoary secrets might abide in this high apartment so many eons cut off from the castle below. Then unexpectedly my hands came upon a doorway, where hung a portal of stone, rough with strange chiselling. Trying it, I found it locked; but with a supreme burst of strength I overcame all obstacles and dragged it open inwards. As I did so there came to me the purest ecstasy I have ever known; for shining tranquilly through an ornate grating of iron, and down a short stone passageway of steps that ascended from the newly found doorway, was the radiant full moon, which I had never before seen save in dreams and in vague visions I dared not call memories.

Fancying now that I had attained the very pinnacle of the castle, I commenced to rush up the few steps beyond the door; but the sudden veiling of the moon by a cloud caused me to stumble, and I felt my way more slowly in the dark. It was still very dark when I reached the grating—which I tried carefully and found unlocked, but which I did not open for fear of falling from the amazing height to which I had climbed. Then the moon came out.

Most demoniacal of all shocks is that of the abysmally unexpected and grotesquely unbelievable. Nothing I had before undergone could compare in terror with what I now saw; with the bizarre marvels that sight implied. The sight itself was as simple as it was stupefying, for it was merely this: instead of a dizzying prospect of treetops seen from a lofty eminence, there stretched around me on the level through the grating nothing less than *the solid ground*, decked and diversified by marble slabs and columns, and overshadowed by an ancient stone church, whose ruined spire gleamed spectrally in the moonlight.

Half unconscious, I opened the grating and staggered out upon the white gravel path that stretched away in two directions. My mind, stunned and chaotic as it was, still held the frantic craving for light; and not even the fantastic wonder which had happened could stay my course. I neither knew nor cared whether my experience was insanity, dreaming, or magic; but was determined to gaze on brilliance and gaiety at any cost. I knew not who I was nor what I was, nor what my surroundings might be; though as I continued to stumble along I became conscious of a kind of fearsome latent memory that made my progress not wholly fortuitous. I passed under an arch out of that region of slabs and columns, and wandered through the open country; sometimes following the visible road, but sometimes leaving it curiously to tread across meadows where only occasional ruins bespoke the ancient presence of a forgotten road. Once I swam across a swift river where crumbling, mossy masonry told of a bridge long vanished.

Over two hours must have passed before I reached what seemed to be my goal, a venerable ivied castle in a thickly wooded park, maddeningly familiar, yet full of perplexing strangeness to me. I saw that the moat was filled in, and that some of the well-known towers were demolished; whilst new wings existed to confuse the beholder. But what I observed with chief interest and delight were the open windows—gorgeously ablaze with light and sending forth sound of the gayest revelry. Advancing to one of these I looked in and saw an oddly dressed company, indeed; making merry, and speaking brightly to one another. I had never, seemingly, heard human speech before and could guess only vaguely what was said. Some of the faces seemed to hold expressions that brought up incredibly remote recollections, others were utterly alien.

I now stepped through the low windows into the brilliantly lighted room, stepping as I did so from my single bright moment of hope to my blackest convulsion of despair and realisation. The nightmare was quick to come, for as I entered, there occurred immediately one of the most terrifying demonstrations I had ever conceived. Scarcely had I crossed the sill when there descended upon the whole company a sudden and unheralded fear of hideous intensity, distorting every face and evoking the most horrible screams from nearly every throat. Flight was universal, and in the clamour and panic several fell in a swoon and were dragged away by their madly fleeing companions. Many covered their eyes with their hands, and plunged blindly and awkwardly in their race to escape, overturning furniture and stumbling against the walls before they managed to reach one of the many doors.

The cries were shocking; and as I stood in the brilliant apartment alone and dazed, listening to their vanishing echoes, I trembled at the thought of what might be lurking near me unseen. At a casual inspection the room seemed deserted, but when I moved towards one of the alcoves I thought I detected a presence there—a hint of motion beyond the golden-arched doorway leading to another and somewhat similar room. As I approached the arch I began to perceive the presence more clearly; and then, with the first and last sound I ever uttered—a ghastly ululation that revolted me almost as poignantly as its noxious cause—I beheld in full, frightful vividness the inconceivable, indescribable, and unmentionable monstrosity which had by its simple appearance changed a merry company to a herd of delirious fugitives.

I cannot even hint what it was like, for it was a compound of all that is unclean, uncanny, unwelcome, abnormal, and detestable. It was the ghoulish shade of decay, antiquity, and desolation; the putrid, dripping eidolon of unwholesome revelation, the awful baring of that which the merciful earth should always hide. God knows it was not of this world—or no longer of this world—yet to my horror I saw in its eaten-away and bone-revealing outlines a leering, abhorrent travesty of the human shape; and in its mouldy, disintegrating apparel an unspeakable quality that chilled me even more.

I was almost paralysed, but not too much so to make a feeble effort towards flight; a backward stumble which failed to break the spell in which the nameless, voiceless monster held me. My eyes bewitched by the glassy orbs which stared loathsomely into them, refused to close; though they were mercifully blurred, and showed the terrible object but indistinctly after the first shock. I tried to raise my hand to shut out the sight, yet so stunned were my nerves that my arm could not fully obey my will. The attempt, however, was enough to disturb my balance; so that I had to stagger forward several steps to avoid falling. As I did so I became suddenly and agonisingly aware of the *nearness* of the carrion thing, whose hideous hollow breathing I half fancied I could hear. Nearly mad, I found myself yet able to throw out a hand to ward off the fetid apparition which pressed so close; when in one cataclysmic second of cosmic nightmarishness and hellish accident *my fingers touched the rotting outstretched paw of the monster beneath the golden arch.*

I did not shriek, but all the fiendish ghouls that ride the nightwind shrieked for me as in that same second there crashed down upon my mind a single and fleeting avalanche of soul-annihilating memory. I knew in that second all that had been; I remembered beyond the frightful castle and the trees, and recognised the altered edifice in which I now stood; I recognised, most terrible of all, the unholy abomination that stood leering before me as I withdrew my sullied fingers from its own.

But in the cosmos there is balm as well as bitterness, and that balm is nepenthe. In the supreme horror of that second I forgot what had horrified me, and the burst of black memory vanished in a chaos of echoing images. In a dream I fled from that haunted and accursed pile, and ran swiftly and silently in the moonlight. When I returned to the churchyard place of marble and went down the steps I found the stone trap-door immovable; but I was not sorry, for I had hated the antique castle and the trees. Now I ride with the mocking and friendly ghouls on the night wind, and play by day amongst the catacombs of Nephren-Ka in the sealed and unknown valley of Hadoth by the Nile. I know that light is not for me, save that of the moon over the rock tombs of Neb, nor any gaiety save the unnamed feasts of Nitokris beneath the Great Pyramid; yet in my new wildness and freedom I almost welcome the bitterness of alienage.

For although nepenthe has calmed me, I know always that I am an outsider; a stranger in this century and among those who are still men. This I have known ever since I stretched out my fingers to the abomination within that great gilded frame; stretched out my fingers and touched *a cold and unyielding surface of polished glass.*

Pictures Don't Lie

Katherine MacLean

The man from the *News* asked, "What do you think of the aliens, Mr. Nathen? Are they friendly? Do they look human?"

"Very human," said the thin young man.

Outside, rain sleeted across the big windows, blurring and dimming the view of the airfield where *they* would arrive. On the concrete runways, the puddles were pockmarked with rain, and the grass growing untouched between the runways of the unused airfield glistened wetly, bending before gusts of wind.

Back at a respectful distance from where the huge spaceship would land were the gray shapes of trucks, where TV camera crews huddled inside their mobile units, waiting. Farther back in the deserted sandy landscape, behind distant sandy hills, artillery was ranged in a great circle, and in the distance across the horizon, bombers stood ready at airfields, guarding the world against possible treachery from the first alien ship ever to land from space.

"Do you know anything about their home planet?" asked the man from the *Herald*.

The *Times* man stood with the others, listening absently; thinking of questions but reserving them. Joseph R. Nathen, the thin young man with the straight black hair and the tired lines on his face, was being treated with respect by his interviewers. He was obviously on edge, and they did not want to harry him with too many questions. They wanted to keep his good will. Tomorrow he would be one of the biggest celebrities ever to appear in headlines.

"No, nothing directly."

"Any ideas or deductions?" *Herald* persisted.

"Their world must be Earth-like to them," the weary-looking young man answered uncertainly. "The environment evolves the animal. But only in relative terms, of course." He looked at them with a quick glance and then looked away evasively, his lank black hair beginning to cling to his forehead with sweat. "That doesn't necessarily mean anything."

"Earth-like," muttered a reporter, writing it down as if he had noticed nothing more in the reply.

The *Times* man glanced at the *Herald*, wondering if he had noticed, and received a quick glance in exchange.

The *Herald* asked Nathen, "You think they are dangerous, then?"

It was the kind of question, assuming much, which usually broke reticence and brought forth quick facts —when it hit the mark. They all knew of the military precautions, although they were not supposed to know.

The question missed. Nathen glanced out the window vaguely. "No, I wouldn't say so."

"You think they are friendly, then?" said the *Herald*, equally positive on the opposite tack.

A fleeting smile touched Nathen's lips. "Those I know are."

There was no lead in this direction, and they had to get the basic facts of the story before the ship came. The *Times* asked, "What led up to your contacting them?"

Nathen answered, after a hesitation, "Static. Radio static. The Army told you my job, didn't they?"

The Army had told them nothing at all. The officer who had conducted them in for the interview stood glowering watchfully, as if he objected by instinct to telling the public anything.

Nathen glanced at him doubtfully. "My job is radio decoding for the Department of Military Intelligence. I use a directional pickup, tune in on foreign bands, record any scrambled or coded messages I hear, and build automatic decoders and descramblers for all the basic scramble patterns."

The officer cleared his throat but said nothing.

The reporters smiled, noting that down.

Security regulations had changed since arms inspection had been legalized by the U.S. Complete information being the only public security against secret rearmament, spying and prying had come to seem a public service. Its aura had changed. It was good public relations to admit to it.

Nathen continued, "I started directing the pickup at stars in my spare time. There's radio noise from stars, you know. Just stuff that sounds like spatter static, and an occasional squawk. People have been listening to it for a long time and researching, trying to work out why stellar radiation on those bands comes in such jagged bursts. It didn't seem natural."

He paused and smiled uncertainly, aware that the next thing he would say was the thing that would make him famous—an idea that had come to him while he listened—an idea as simple and as perfect as the one that came to Newton when he saw the apple fall.

"I decided it wasn't natural. I tried decoding it."

Hurriedly he tried to explain it away and make it seem obvious. "You see, there's an old intelligence trick: speeding up a message on a record until it sounds just like that, a short squawk of static, and then broadcasting it. Undergrounds use it. I'd heard that kind of screech before."

"You mean they broadcast at us in code?" asked the *News*.

"It's not exactly code. All you need to do is record it and slow it down. They're not broadcasting at us. If a star has planets, inhabited planets, and there is broadcasting between them, they would send it on a tight beam to save power." He looked for comprehension. "You know, like a spotlight. Theoretically, a tight beam can go on forever without losing power. But aiming would be difficult from planet to planet. You can't expect a beam to stay on target over such distances more than a few seconds at a time. So they'd naturally compress each message into a short half-second or one-second-long package and send it a few hundred times in one long blast to make sure it is picked up during the instant the beam swings across the target."

He was talking slowly and carefully, remembering that this explanation was for the newspapers. "When a stray beam swings through our section of space, there's a sharp peak in noise level from that direction. The beams are swinging to follow their own planets at home, and the distance between there and here exaggerates the speed of swing tremendously, so we wouldn't pick up more than a bip as it passes."

"How do you account for the number of squawks coming in?" the *Times* asked. "Do stellar systems rotate on the plane of the Galaxy?" It was a private question; he spoke impulsively from excitement.

The radio decoder grinned, the lines of strain vanishing from his face for a moment. "Maybe we're intercepting everybody's telephone calls, and the whole Galaxy is swarming with races that spend all day yakking at each other over the radio. Maybe the human type is a standard model."

"It would take something like that," the *Times* agreed. They smiled at each other.

The *News* asked, "How did you happen to pick up television instead of voices?"

"Not by accident," Nathen explained patiently. "I'd recognized a scanning pattern, and I wanted pictures. Pictures are understandable in any language."

Near the interviewers, a Senator paced back and forth, muttering his memorized speech of welcome and nervously glancing out the wide streaming windows into the gray sleeting rain.

Opposite the windows of the long room was a small raised platform flanked by the tall shapes of TV cameras and sound pickups on booms, and darkened floodlights, arranged and ready for the Senator to make his speech of welcome to the aliens and the world. A shabby radio sending set stood beside it without a case to conceal its parts, two cathode television tubes flickering nakedly on one side and the speaker humming on the other. A vertical panel of dials and knobs jutted up before them and a small hand-mike sat ready on the table before the panel. It was connected to a box-like, expensively cased piece of equipment with "Radio Lab, U. S. Property" stenciled on it.

"I recorded a couple of package screeches from Sagittarius and began working on them," Nathen added. "It took a couple of months to find the synchronizing signals and set the scanners close enough to the right time to even get a pattern. When I showed the pattern to the Department, they gave me full time to work on it, and an assistant to help. It took eight months to pick out the color bands, and assign them the right colors, to get anything intelligible on the screen."

The shabby-looking mess of exposed parts was the original receiver that they had labored over for ten months, adjusting and readjusting to reduce the maddening rippling plaids of unsynchronized color scanners to some kind of sane picture.

"Trial and error," said Nathen, "but it came out all right. The wide band-spread of the squawks had suggested color TV from the beginning."

He walked over and touched the set. The sPeaker bipped slightly and the gray screen flickered with a flash of color at the touch. The set was awake and sensitive, tuned to receive from the great interstellar spaceship which now circled the atmosphere.

"We wondered why there were so many bands, but when we got the set working and started recording and playing everything that came in, we found we'd tapped something like a lending-library line. It was all fiction, plays."

Between the pauses in Nathen's voice, the *Times* found himself unconsciously listening for the sound of roaring, swiftly approaching rocket jets.

The *Post* asked, "How did you contact the spaceship?"

"I scanned and recorded a film copy of *Rite of Spring*, the Disney-Stravinsky combination, and sent it back along the same line we were receiving from. Just testing. It wouldn't get there for a good number of years, if it got there at all, but I thought it would please the library to get a new record in.

"Two weeks later, when we caught and slowed a new batch of recordings, we found an answer. It was obviously meant for us. It was a flash of the Disney being played to a large audience, and then the audience sitting and waiting before a blank screen. The signal was very clear and loud. We'd intercepted a spaceship. They were asking for an encore, you see. They liked the film and wanted more...."

He smiled at them in sudden thought. "You can see them for yourself. It's all right down the hall where the linguists are working on the automatic translator."

The listening officer frowned and cleared his throat, and the thin young man turned to him quickly. "No security reason why they should not see the broadcasts, is there? Perhaps you should show them." He said to the reporters reassuringly, "It's right down the hall. You will be informed the moment the spaceship approaches."

The interview was very definitely over. The lank-haired, nervous young man turned away and seated himself at the radio set while the officer swallowed his objections and showed them dourly down the hall to a closed door.

They opened it and fumbled into a darkened room crowded with empty folding chairs and dominated by a glowing bright screen. The door closed behind them, bringing total darkness.

There was the sound of reporters fumbling their way into seats around him, but the *Times* man remained standing, aware of an enormous surprise, as if he had been asleep and wakened to find himself in the wrong country.

The bright colors of the double image seemed the only real thing in the darkened room. Even blurred as they were, he could see that the action was subtly different, the shapes subtly not right.

He was looking at aliens.

The impression was of two humans in disguise; humans moving oddly, half-dancing, half-crippled. Carefully, afraid the images would go away, he reached up to his breast pocket, took out his polarized glasses, rotated one lens at right angles to the other and put them on.

Immediately, the two beings came into sharp focus, real and solid, and the screen became a wide, illusively near window through which he watched them.

They were conversing with each other in a gray-walled room, discussing something with restrained excitement. The large man in the green tunic closed his purple eyes for an instant at something the other said and grimaced, making a motion with his fingers as if shoving something away from him.

Mellerdrammer.

The second, smaller, with yellowish-green eyes, stepped closer, talking more rapidly in a lower voice. The first stood very still, not trying to interrupt.

Obviously, the proposal was some advantageous treachery, and he wanted to be persuaded. The *Times* groped for a chair and sat down.

Perhaps gesture is universal: desire, a leaning forward; aversion, a leaning back; tension, relaxation. Perhaps these actors were masters. The scenes changed, a corridor, a parklike place in what he began to realize was a spaceship, a lecture room. There were others talking and working, speaking to the man in the green tunic, and never was it unclear what was happening or how they felt.

They talked a flowing language with many short vowels and shifts of pitch, and they gestured in the heat of talk, their hands moving with an odd lagging difference of motion, not slow but somehow drifting.

He ignored the language, but after a time the difference in motion began to arouse his interest. Something in the way they walked. . . .

With an effort he pulled his mind from the plot and forced his attention to the physical difference. Brown hair in short silky crew cuts, varied eye colors, the colors showing clearly because their irises were very large, their round eyes set very widely apart in tapering light brown faces. Their necks and shoulders were thick in a way that would indicate unusual strength for a human, but their wrists were narrow and their fingers long and thin and delicate.

There seemed to be more than the usual number of fingers.

Since he came in, a machine had been whirring and a voice muttering beside him. He called his attention from counting fingers and looked around. Beside him sat an alert-looking man wearing earphones, watching and listening with hawklike concentration. Beside him was a tall streamlined box. From the screen came the sound of the alien language. The man abruptly flipped a switch on the box, muttered a word into a small hand-microphone and flipped the switch back with nervous rapidity.

He reminded the *Times* man of the earphoned interpreters at the U.N. The machine was probably a vocal translator and the mutterer a linguist adding to its vocabulary. Near the screen were two other linguists taking notes.

The *Times* remembered the Senator pacing in the observatory room, rehearsing his speech of welcome. The speech would not be just an empty pompous gesture. It would be translated mechanically and understood by the aliens.

On the other side of the glowing window that was the stereo screen, the large protagonist in the green tunic was speaking to a pilot in a gray uniform. They stood in a brightly lit canary-yellow control room in a spaceship.

The *Times* tried to pick up the thread of the plot. Already he was interested in the fate of the hero, and liked him. That was the effect of good acting probably, for part of the art of acting is to win affection from the audience, and this actor might be the matinee idol of whole solar systems.

Controlled tension, betraying itself by a jerk of the hands, a too-quick answer to a question. The uniformed one, not suspicious, turned his back and busied himself at some task involving a map lit with glowing red points, his motions sharing the same fluid dragging grace of the others, as if they were underwater or on a slow-motion film. The other was watching a switch, a switch set into a panel, moving closer to it, talking casually—background music coming and rising in thin chords of tension.

There was a closeup of the alien's face watching the switch, and the *Times* noted that his ears were symmetrical half circles, almost perfect, with no earholes visible. The voice of the uniformed one answered, a brief word in a preoccupied deep voice. His back was still turned. The other glanced at the switch, moving closer to it, talking casually, the switch coming closer and closer stereoscopically. It was in reach, filling the screen. His hand came into view, darting out, closed over the switch—

There was a sharp clap of sound and his hand opened in a frozen shape of pain. Beyond him, as his gaze swung up, stood the figure of the uniformed officer, unmoving, a weapon rigid in his hand, in the startled position in which he had turned and fired, watching with widening eyes as the man in the green tunic swayed and fell.

The tableau held, the uniformed one drooping, looking down at his hand holding the weapon which had killed, and music began to build in from the background. Just for an instant, the room and the things within it flashed into one of those bewildering color changes which were the bane of color television, and switched to a color negative of itself, a green man standing in a violet control room, looking down at the body of a green man in a red tunic. It held for less than a second; then the color band alternator fell back into phase and the colors reversed to normal.

Another uniformed man came and took the weapon from the limp hand of the other, who began to explain dejectedly in a low voice while the music mounted and covered his words and the screen slowly went blank, like a window that slowly filmed over with gray fog.

The music faded.

In the dark, someone clapped appreciatively.

The earphoned man beside the *Times* shifted his earphones back from his ears and spoke briskly. "I can't get any more. Either of you want a replay?"

There was a short silence until the linguist nearest the set said, "I guess we've squeezed that one dry. Let's run the tape where Nathen and that ship's radio boy are diddling around CQing and tuning their beams. I have a hunch the boy is talking routine ham talk and giving the old radio count, one-two-three-testing. If he is, we have number words."

There was some fumbling in the semi-dark and then the screen came to life again.

It showed a flash of an audience sitting before a screen and gave a clipped chord of some familiar symphony. "Crazy about Stravinsky and Mozart," remarked the earphoned linguist to the *Times*, resettling his earphones. "Can't stand Gershwin. Can you beat that?" He turned his attention back to the screen as the right sequence came on.

The *Post*, who was sitting just in front of him, turned to the *Times* and said, "Funny how much they look like people." He was writing, making notes to telephone his report. "What color hair did that character have?"

"I didn't notice." He wondered if he should remind the reporter that Nathen had said he assigned the color bands on guess, choosing the colors that gave the most plausible images. The guests, when they arrived, could turn out to be bright green with blue hair. Only the gradations of color in the picture were sure, only the similarities and contrasts, the relationship of one color to another.

From the screen came the sound of the alien language again. This race averaged deeper voices than human. He liked deep voices. Could he write that?

No, there was something wrong with that, too. How had Nathen established the right sound-track pitch? Was it a matter of taking the modulation as it came in, or some sort of hetrodyning up and down by trial and error? Probably.

It might be safer to assume that Nathen had simply preferred deep voices.

As he sat there, doubting, an uneasiness he had seen in Nathen came back to memory. The tightness and uncertainty of Nathen's gestures. . . . He was afraid of something.

"What I still don't get, is why he went to all the trouble of building a special TV set to pick up their TV shows, instead of just talking to them on the radio," the *News* complained aloud. "They're good shows, but what's the point?"

Nobody bothered to answer. Pictures can be understood. Pictures need no translation. Pictures don't lie. Nathen's reasoning was obvious to the others.

On the screen now was the obviously unstaged and genuine scene of a young alien working over a bank of apparatus. He turned and waved, and opened his mouth in the comical O shape which the

Times was beginning to recognize as their equivalent of a grin, then went back to trying to explain something about the equipment, in elaborate awkward gestures and carefully mouthed words.

The *Times* got up quietly, went out into the bright, white stone corridor and walked back the way he had come, thoughtfully folding his stereo glasses and putting them away.

No one stopped him. Secrecy restrictions were ambiguous here. The reticence of the Army seemed a matter of habit, a reflex response of the Intelligence Department, in which all this had originated, rather than any reasoned policy of keeping the landing a secret.

The main room was more crowded than when he had left it. The TV camera and sound crew stood near their apparatus, the Senator had found a chair and was reading, and at the far end of the room eight men were grouped in a circle of chairs, arguing something with impassioned concentration. The *Times* recognized a few he knew personally, eminent names in science, workers in field theory.

A stray phrase reached him: "—reference to the universal constants as ratio—" It was probably a discussion of ways of converting formulas from one mathematics to another for a rapid exchange of information.

They had reason to be intent, aware of the flood of insights that novel viewpoints could bring if they could grasp them. He would have liked to go over and listen, but there was too little time left before the spaceship was due, and he had a question to ask.

The hand-rigged transceiver was still humming, tuned to the sending band of the circling ship, and the young man who had started it all was sitting on the edge of the TV platform with his chin resting in one hand. He did not look up as the *Times* approached, but it was the indifference of preoccupation, not discourtesy.

The *Times* sat down on the edge of the platform beside him and took out a pack of cigarettes, then remembered the coming TV broadcast and the ban on smoking. He put them away, thoughtfully watching the diminishing rain spray against the streaming windows.

"What's wrong?" he asked.

Nathen showed that he was aware and friendly by a slight motion of his head.

"*You* tell me."

"Hunch," said the *Times* man. "Sheer hunch. Everything sailing along too smoothly, everyone taking too much for granted."

Nathen relaxed slightly. "I'm still listening."

"Something about the way they move..."

Nathan shifted to glance at him.

"That's bothered me, too."

"Are you sure they're adjusted to the right speed?"

Nathen clenched his hands out in front of him and looked at them consideringly. "I don't know. When I turn the tape faster, they're all rushing, and you begin to wonder why their clothes don't stream behind them, why the doors close so quickly and yet you can't hear them slam, why things fall so fast. If I turn it slower, they all seem to be swimming." He gave the *Times* a considering sideways glance. "Didn't catch the name."

Country-bred guy, thought the *Times*. "Jacob Luke, *Times*," he said, extending his hand.

Nathen gave the hand a quick, hard grip, identifying the name. "Sunday Science Section editor. I read it. Surprised to meet you here."

"Likewise." The *Times* smiled. "Look, have you gone into this rationally, with formulas?" He found a pencil in his pocket. "Obviously, there's something wrong with our judgment of their weight-to speed-to momentum ratio. Maybe it's something simple like low gravity aboard ship, with magnetic shoes. Maybe they *are* floating slightly."

"Why worry?" Nathen cut in. "I don't see any reason to try to figure it out now." He laughed and shoved back his black hair nervously. "We'll see them in twenty minutes."

"Will we?" asked the *Times* slowly.

There was a silence while the Senator turned a page of his magazine with a slight crackling of paper, and the scientists argued at the other end of the room. Nathen pushed at his lank black hair again, as if it were trying to fall forward in front of his eyes and keep him from seeing.

"Sure." The young man laughed suddenly, talked rapidly. "Sure we'll see them. Why shouldn't we, with all the Government ready with welcome speeches, the whole Army turned out and hiding over the hill, reporters all around, newsreel cameras—everything set up to broadcast the landing to the world. The President himself shaking hands with me and waiting in Washington—"

He came to the truth without pausing for breath.

He said, "Hell, no, they won't get here. There's some mistake somewhere. Something's wrong. I should have told the brass hats yesterday when I started adding it up. Don't know why I didn't say anything. Scared, I guess. Too much top rank around here. Lost my nerve."

He clutched the *Times* man's sleeve. "Look. I don't know what—"

A green light flashed on the sending-receiving set. Nathan didn't look at it, but he stopped talking.

The loudspeaker on the set broke into a voice speaking in the alien's language. The Senator started and looked nervously at it, straightening his tie. The voice stopped.

Nathen turned and looked at the loudspeaker. His worry seemed to be gone.

"What is it?" the *Times* asked anxiously.

"He says they've slowed enough to enter the atmosphere now. They'll be here in five to ten minutes, I guess. That's Bud. He's all excited. He says holy smoke, what a murky-looking planet we live on." Nathen smiled. "Kidding."

The *Times* was puzzled. "What does he mean, murky? It can't be raining over much territory on Earth." Outside, the rain was slowing and bright blue patches of sky were shining through breaks in the cloud blanket, glittering blue light from the drops that ran down the windows. Murky? He tried to think of an explanation. "Maybe they're trying to land on Venus." The thought was ridiculous, he knew. The spaceship was following Nathen's sending beam. It couldn't miss Earth. "Bud" had to be kidding.

The green light on the set glowed again, and they stopped speaking, waiting for the message to be recorded, slowed, and replayed. The cathode screen came to life suddenly with a picture of the young man sitting at his sending-set, his back turned, watching a screen at one side which showed a glimpse of a huge dark plain approaching. As the ship plunged down toward it, the illusion of solidity melted into a boiling turbulence of black clouds. They expanded in an ink swirl, looked huge for an instant, and then blackness swallowed the screen. The young alien swung around to face the camera, speaking a few words as he moved, made the O of a smile again, then flipped the switch and the screen went gray.

Nathen's voice was suddenly toneless and strained. "He said something like break out the drinks, here they come."

"The atmosphere doesn't look like that," the *Times* said at random, knowing he was saying something too obvious even to think about. "Not Earth's atmosphere."

Some people drifted up. "What did they say?"

"Entering the atmosphere, ought to be landing in five or ten minutes," Nathen told them.

A ripple of heightened excitement ran through the room. Cameramen began adjusting the lens angles again, turning on mikes and checking them, turning on the floodlights. The scientists rose and stood near the window, still talking. The reporters trooped in from the hall and went to the windows to watch for the great event. The three linguists came in, trundling a large wheeled box that was the mechanical translator, supervising while it was hitched into the sound broadcasting system.

"Landing where?" the *Times* asked Nathen brutally. "Why don't you do something?"

"Tell me what to do and I'll do it," Nathen said quietly, not moving.

It was not sarcasm. Jacob Luke of the *Times* looked sidewise at the strained whiteness of his face, and moderated his tone. "Can't you contact them?"

"Not while they're landing."

"What now?" The *Times* took out a pack of cigarettes, remembered the rule against smoking, and put it back.

"We just wait." Nathen leaned his elbow on one knee and his chin in his hand.

They waited.

All the people in the room were waiting. There was no more conversation. A bald man of the scientist group was automatically buffing his fingernails over and over and inspecting them without seeing them, another absently polished his glasses, held them up to the light, put them on, and then a moment later took them off and began polishing again. The television crew concentrated on their jobs, moving quietly and efficiently, with perfectionist care, minutely arranging things which did not need to be arranged, checking things that had already been checked.

This was to be one of the great moments of human history, and they were all trying to forget that fact and remain impassive and wrapped up in the problems of their jobs as good specialists should.

After an interminable age the *Times* consulted his watch. Three minutes had passed. He tried holding his breath a moment, listening for a distant approaching thunder of jets. There was no sound.

The sun came out from behind the clouds and lit up the field like a great spotlight on an empty stage.

Abruptly the green light shone on the set again, indicating that a squawk message had been received. The recorder recorded it, slowed it, and fed it back to the speaker. The speaker clicked and the sound was very loud in the still, tense room.

The screen remained gray, but Bud's voice spoke a few words in the alien language. He stopped, the speaker clicked and the light went out. When it was plain that nothing more would occur and no announcement was to be made of what was said, the people in the room turned back to the windows. Talk picked up again.

Somebody told a joke and laughed alone.

One of the linguists remained turned toward the loudspeaker, then looked at the widening patches of blue sky showing out the window, his expression puzzled. He had understood.

"It's dark," the thin Intelligence Department decoder translated, low-voiced, to the man from the *Times*. "Your atmosphere is *thick*. That's precisely what Bud said."

Another three minutes. The *Times* caught himself about to light a cigarette and swore silently, blowing the match out and putting the cigarette back into its package. He listened for the sound of the rocket jets. It was time for the landing, yet he heard no blasts.

The green light came on in the transceiver.

Message in.

Instinctively he came to his feet. Nathen abruptly was standing beside him. Then the message came in the voice he was coming to think of as Bud. It spoke and paused. Suddenly the *Times* knew.

"We've landed." Nathen whispered the words.

The wind blew across the open spaces of white concrete and damp soil that was the empty airfield, swaying the wet, shiny grass. The people in the room looked out, listening for the roar of jets, looking for the silver bulk of a spaceship in the sky.

Nathen moved, seating himself at the transmitter, switching it on to warm up, checking and balancing dials. Jacob Luke of the *Times* moved softly to stand behind his right shoulder, hoping he could be useful. Nathan made a half motion of his head, as if to glance back at him, unhooked two of the earphone sets hanging on the side of the tall streamlined box that was the automatic translator, plugged them in and handed one back over his shoulder to the *Times* man.

The voice began to come from the speaker again.

Hastily, Jacob Luke fitted the earphones over his ears. He fancied he could hear Bud's voice tremble. For a moment it was just Bud's voice speaking the alien language, and then, very distant and clear in his earphones, he heard the recorded voice of the linguist say an English word, then a mechanical click and another clear word in the voice of one of the other translators, then another as the alien's voice flowed from the loudspeaker, the cool single words barely audible, overlapping and blending with it like translating thought, skipping unfamiliar words, yet quite astonishingly clear.

"Radar shows no buildings or civilization near. The atmosphere around us registers as thick as glue. Tremendous gas pressure, low gravity, no light at all. You didn't describe it like this. Where are you, Joe? This isn't some kind of trick, is it?" Bud hesitated, was prompted by a deeper official voice, and jerked out the words:

"If it is a trick, we are ready to repel attack."

The linguist stood listening. He whitened slowly and beckoned the other linguists over to him and whispered to them.

Joseph Nathen looked at them with unwarranted bitter hostility while he picked up the hand-mike, plugging it into the translator. "Joe calling," he said quietly into it in clear, slow English. "No trick. We don't know where you are. I am trying to get a direction fix from your signal. Describe your surroundings to us if at all possible."

Nearby, the floodlights blazed steadily on the television platform, ready for the official welcome of the aliens to Earth. The television channels of the world had been alerted to set aside their scheduled programs for an unscheduled great event. In the long room the people waited, listening for the swelling sound of rocket jets.

This time, after the light came on, there was a long delay. The speaker sputtered, and sputtered again, building to a steady scratching behind which they could barely sense a dim voice. It came through in a few tinny words and then wavered back to inaudibility. The machine translated in their earphones.

"Tried... seemed... repair..." Suddenly it came in clearly. "Can't tell if the auxiliary blew, too. Will try it. We might pick you up clearly on the next try. I have the volume down. Where is the landing port? Where are you?"

Nathen put down the hand-mike and carefully set a dial on the recording box, and flipped a switch, speaking over his shoulder. "This sets it to repeat what I said the last time. It keeps repeating." Then he sat with unnatural stillness, his head still half turned, as if he had suddenly caught a glimpse of answer and was trying to understand it.

The green warning light cut in, the recording clicked and the playback of Bud's face and voice appeared on the screen.

"We heard a few words, Joe, and then the receiver blew again. We're adjusting a viewing screen to pick up the long waves that go through the murk and convert them to visible light. We'll be able to see out soon. The engineer says that something is wrong with the stern jets, and the captain has had me broadcast a help call to our nearest space base." He made the mouth O of a grin. "The message won't reach it for some years. I trust you, Joe, but get us out of here, will you?—They're buzzing that the screen is finally ready. Hold everything."

The screen went gray, and the green light went off.

The *Times* considered the lag required for the help call, the speaking and recording of the message just received, the time needed to reconvert a viewing screen.

"They work fast." He shifted uneasily, and added at random, "Something wrong with the time factor. All wrong. They work *too* fast."

The green light came on again immediately. Nathen half turned to him, sliding his words hastily into the gap of time as the message was recorded and slowed. "They're close enough for our transmission power to blow their receiver."

If it was on Earth, why the darkness around the ship? "Maybe they see in the high ultra-violet—the atmosphere is opaque to that band," the *Times* suggested hastily as the speaker began to talk in the young extraterrestrial's voice.

That voice *was* really shaking now. "Stand by for the description." They tensed, waiting. The *Times* brought a map of the state before his mind's eye.

"A half circle of cliffs around the horizon. A wide, muddy lake, swarming with swimming things. Huge, strange white foliage all around the ship, and incredibly huge pulpy monsters attacking and eating each other on all sides. We almost landed in the lake, right on the soft edge. The mud can't hold the ship's weight, and we're sinking. The engineer says we might be able to blast free, but the tubes are mud-clogged and might blow up the ship.—When can you reach us?"

The description fitted nowhere on the map of the state. It fitted nowhere on a map of Earth.

Pulpy monsters... *Times* thought of the Carboniferous era. Dinosaurs? Cliffs... a muddy lake... monsters... Where?

"Right away," Nathen said. "We can reach them right away." Nathen obviously had seen something.

"Where are they?" the *Times* asked him quietly.

Nathen pointed to the antenna position indicators. The *Times* let his eyes follow the converging imaginary lines of focus out the window to the sunlit airfield, the empty airfield, the white drying concrete runways and green waving grass where the lines met.

Where the lines met. The spaceship was there!

The fear of something unknown gripped him suddenly.

The spaceship was broadcasting again. *"Where are you? Answer if possible! We are sinking! Where are you?"*

He saw that Nathen knew. "What is it?" the *Times* asked hoarsely. "How will we get them out of there? Are they in another dimension, or the past, or in another world or what?"

Nathen was smiling bitterly, and *Times* remembered that he had a good friend in the spaceship.

"My guess is that they evolved on a high-gravity planet with a thin atmosphere near a blue-white sun. Sure they see in the ultraviolet. Blue-white stars are normal. Our sun is small and dim and yellow, not normal. Our atmosphere is so thick, like under water...." He brought his gaze back to Jacob Luke of the *Times* without seeing him, seeing only some picture in his own mind. "We are giants, do you understand? Big, slow, stupid...."

"Where is the spaceship?"

"Slow...." Nathen laughed harshly. "A good joke on us, the weird place we live in, the thing it did to us."

The receiver squawked. The decoder machine caught the squawk, slowed it and replayed it immediately, spacing the tumbled frightened voice with cool English words.

"Where are you?" called the young voice from the alien spaceship. "Hurry, please, we're sinking."

The *Times* man took off the earphones and came to his feet. "We've got to hurry." He gripped Nathen's shoulder to get his attention. "Just tell me. Where are they?"

Nathen looked up into *Times'* face. "I want you to understand. We'll rescue them," he said quietly. "You were right about their way of moving, right about them moving at different speeds. This business I told you about them squawk-coding, speeding up their messages for better transmission. I was wrong."

"What do you mean?"

"They don't speed up their broadcasts."

"They don't—?"

Suddenly, in his mind's eye, the *Times* man began to see again the play he had just seen—but the actors were moving at blurring speed, the words jerking out in fluting, dizzying streams, thoughts and decisions passing with unnoticeable rapidity, rippling faces in a twisting blur of expressions, doors slamming wildly, shatteringly, as the actors leaped in and out of rooms.

No—faster, faster—he wasn't visualizing it as rapidly as it was, an hour of talk and action in one second of "squawk," a narrow peak of "noise" interfering with a single word in an Earth broadcast! Faster . . . faster. . . . It was impossible. Matter could not stand such stress—inertia—momentum—abrupt weight. . . .

It was insane. "Why?" he asked. "How?"

Nathen laughed again, harshly. "Get them out? There isn't a lake or a big river within a hundred miles of here! Where did you think they were?"

A shiver of unreality went down the *Times* man's spine. Automatically and inanely, he found himself delving in his pocket for a cigarette while he tried to understand what had happened. "Where are they, then? Why can't we see their spaceship?"

Nathen switched off the microphone in a gesture that showed the bitterness of his disappointment.

"We'll need a magnifying glass for that."

The Tartarus of Maids

Herman Melville

It lies not far from Woedolor Mountain in New England. Turning
to the east, right out from among bright farms and sunny meadows,
nodding in early June with odorous grasses, you enter ascendingly
among bleak hills. These gradually close in upon a dusky pass,
which, from the violent Gulf Stream of air unceasingly driving
between its cloven walls of haggard rock, as well as from the tradition
of a crazy spinster's hut having long ago stood somewhere hereabouts, is called the Mad Maid's Bellows-pipe.

Winding along at the bottom of the gorge is a dangerously narrow
wheel-road, occupying the bed of a former torrent. Following this
road to its highest point, you stand as within a Dantean gateway.
From the steepness of the walls here, their strangely ebon hue, and
the sudden contraction of the gorge, this particular point is called
the Black Notch. The ravine now expandingly descends into a great
purple, hopper-shaped hollow, far sunk among many Plutonian,
shaggy-wooded mountains. By the country people this hollow is
called the Devil's Dungeon. Sounds of torrents fall on all sides upon
the ear. These rapid waters unite at last in one turbid brick-colored
stream, boiling through a flume among enormous boulders. They
call this strange-colored torrent Blood River. Gaining a dark precipice
it wheels suddenly to the west, and makes one maniac spring of
sixty feet into the arms of a stunted wood of gray-haired pines,
between which it thence eddies on its further way down to the invisible low lands.

Conspicuously crowning a rocky bluff high to one side, at the
cataract's verge, is the ruin of an old saw-mill, built in those primitive times when vast pines and hemlocks superabounded
throughout the neighboring region. The black-mossed bulk of those
immense, rough-hewn, and spike-knotted logs, here and there tumbled all together, in long abandonment and decay, or left in solitary,

perilous projection over the cataract's gloomy brink, impart to this rude wooden ruin not only much of the aspect of one of rough-quarried stone, but also a sort of feudal Rhineland and Thurmberg look, derived from the pinnacled wildness of the neighboring scenery.

Not far from the bottom of the Dungeon stands a large white-washed building, relieved, like some great whited sepulchre, against the sullen background of mountain side firs, and other hardy evergreens, inaccessibly rising in grim terraces for some two thousand feet.

The building is a paper-mill.

Having embarked on a large scale in the seedsman's business (so extensively and broadcast, indeed, that at length my seeds were distributed through all the Eastern and Northern States, and even fell into the far soil of Missouri and the Carolinas), the demand for paper at my place became so great that the expenditure soon amounted to a most important item in the general account. It need hardly be hinted how paper comes into use with seedsmen, as envelopes. These are mostly made of yellowish paper, folded square; and when filled, are all but flat, and being stamped, and superscribed with the nature of the seeds contained, assume not a little the appearance of business-letters ready for the mail. Of these small envelopes I used an incredible quantity—several hundreds of thousands in a year. For a time I had purchased my paper from the wholesale dealers in a neighboring town. For economy's sake, and partly for the adventure of the trip, I now resolved to cross the mountains, some sixty miles, and order my future paper at the Devil's Dungeon paper-mill.

The sleighing being uncommonly fine toward the end of January, and promising to hold so for no small period, in spite of the bitter cold I started one gray Friday noon in my pung, well fitted with buffalo and wolf robes; and spending one night on the road, next noon came in sight of Woedolor Mountain.

The far summit fairly smoked with frost; white vapors curled up from its white-wooded top, as from a chimney. The intense congelation made the whole country look like one petrifaction. The steel shoes of my pung craunched and gritted over the vitreous, chippy snow, as if it had been broken glass. The forests here and there skirting the route, feeling the same all-stiffening influence, their inmost fibres penetrated with the cold, strangely groaned—not in the swaying branches merely, but likewise in the vertical trunk—as the fitful gusts remorselessly swept through them. Brittle with excessive frost, many colossal tough-grained maples, snapped in twain like pipestems, cumbered the unfeeling earth.

Flaked all over with frozen sweat, white as a milky ram, his nostrils at each breath sending forth two horn-shaped shoots of heated respiration, Black, my good horse, but six years old, started at a sudden turn, where, right across the track—not ten minutes fallen —an old distorted hemlock lay, darkly undulatory as an anaconda.

Gaining the Bellows-pipe, the violent blast, dead from behind, all but shoved my high-backed pung up-hill. The gust shrieked through the shivered pass, as if laden with lost spirits bound to the unhappy world. Ere gaining the summit, Black, my horse, as if exasperated by the cutting wind, slung out with his strong hind-legs, tore the light pung straight up-hill, and sweeping grazingly through the narrow notch, sped downward madly past the ruined saw-mill. Into the Devil's Dungeon horse and cataract rushed together.

With might and main, quitting my seat and robes, and standing backward, with one foot braced against the dashboard, I rasped and churned the bit, and stopped him just in time to avoid collision, at a turn, with the bleak nozzle of a rock, couchant like a lion in the way—a roadside rock.

At first I could not discover the paper-mill.

The whole hollow gleamed with the white, except, here and there, where a pinnacle of granite showed one windswept angle bare. The mountains stood pinned in shrouds—a pass of Alpine corpses. Where stands the mill? Suddenly a whirring, humming sound broke upon my ear. I looked, and there, like an arrested avalanche, lay the large whitewashed factory. It was subordinately surrounded by a cluster of other and smaller buildings, some of which, from their cheap, blank air, great length, gregarious windows, and comfortless expression, no doubt were boarding-houses of the operatives. A snow-white hamlet amidst the snows. Various rude, irregular squares and courts resulted from the somewhat picturesque cluster-ings of these buildings, owing to the broken, rocky nature of the ground, which forbade all method in their relative arrangement. Several narrow lanes and alleys, too, partly blocked with snow fallen from the roof, cut up the hamlet in all directions.

When, turning from the traveled highway, jingling with bells of numerous farmers—who, availing themselves of the fine sleighing, were dragging their wood to market—and frequently diversified with swift cutters dashing from inn to inn of the scattered vil-lages—when, I say, turning from that bustling main-road, I by degrees wound into the Mad Maid's Bellows-pipe, and saw the grim Black Notch beyond, then something latent, as well as something obvious in the time and scene, strangely brought back to my mind my first sight of dark and grimy Temple Bar. And when Black, my horse, went darting through the Notch, perilously grazing its rocky wall, I remembered being in a runaway London omnibus, which in much the same sort of style, though by no means at an equal rate, dashed through the ancient arch of Wren. Though the two objects did by no means completely correspond, yet this partial inadequacy but served to tinge the similitude not less with the vividness than the disorder of a dream. So that, when upon reining up at the protruding rock I at last caught sight of the quaint groupings of the factory-buildings and with the traveled highway and the Notch behind, found myself all alone, silently and privily stealing through deep-cloven passages into this sequestered spot, and saw the long, high-gabled main factory edifice, with a rude tower—for hoisting heavy boxes—at one end, standing among its crowded outbuildings and boarding-houses, as the Temple Church amidst the surrounding offices and dormitories, and when the marvelous retirement of this mysterious mountain nook fastened its whole spell upon me, then, what memory lacked, all tributary imagination furnished, and I said to myself, "This is the very counterpart of the Paradise of Bachelors, but snowed upon, and frost-painted to a sepulchre."

Dismounting and warily picking my way down the dangerous declivity—horse and man both sliding now and then upon the icy ledges—at length I drove, or the blast drove me, into the largest square, before one side of the main edifice. Piercingly and shrilly the shotted blast blew by the corner; and redly and demoniacally boiled Blood River at one side. A long wood-pile, of many scores of cords, all glittering in mail of crusted ice, stood crosswise in the square. A row of horse-posts, their north sides plastered with adhesive snow, flanked the factory wall. The bleak frost packed and paved the square as with some ringing metal.

The inverted similitude recurred—"The sweet, tranquil Temple garden, with the Thames bordering its green beds," strangely meditated I.

But where are the gay bachelors?

Then, as I and my horse stood shivering in the wind-spray, a girl ran from a neighboring dormitory door, and throwing her thin apron over her bare head, made for the opposite building.

"One moment, my girl; is there no shed hereabouts which I may drive into?"

Pausing, she turned upon me a face pale with work and blue with cold; an eye supernatural with unrelated misery.

"Nay," faltered I, "I mistook you. Go on; I want nothing."

Leading my horse close to the door from which she had come, I knocked. Another pale, blue girl appeared, shivering in the doorway as, to prevent the blast, she jealously held the door ajar.

"Nay, I mistake again. In God's name shut the door. But hold, is there no man about?"

That moment a dark-complexioned, well-wrapped personage passed, making for the factory door, and spying him coming, the girl rapidly closed the other one.

"Is there no horse-shed here, sir?"

"Yonder, the wood-shed," he replied, and disappeared inside the factory.

With much ado I managed to wedge in horse and pung between the scattered piles of wood all sawn and split. Then, blanketing my horse, and piling my buffalo on the blanket's top, and tucking in its edges well around the breast-band and breeching, so that the wind might not strip him bare, I tied him fast, and ran lamely for the factory door, stiff with frost, and cumbered with my driver's dreadnaught.

Immediately I found myself standing in a spacious place intolerably lighted by long rows of windows, focusing inward the snowy scene without.

At rows of blank-looking counters sat rows of blank-looking girls, with blank, white folders in their blank hands, all blankly folding blank paper.

In one corner stood some huge frame of ponderous iron, with a vertical thing like a piston periodically rising and falling upon a heavy wooden block. Before it—its tame minister—stood a tall girl, feeding the iron animal with half-quires of rose-hued notepaper which, at every downward dab of the piston-like machine, received in the corner the impress of a wreath of roses. I looked from the rosy paper to the pallid cheek, but said nothing.

Seated before a long apparatus, strung with long, slender strings like any harp, another girl was feeding it with foolscap sheets which, so soon as they curiously traveled from her on the cords, were withdrawn at the opposite end of the machine by a second girl. They came to the first girl blank; they went to the second girl ruled.

I looked upon the first girl's brow, and saw it was young and fair; I looked upon the second girl's brow, and saw it was ruled and wrinkled. Then, as I still looked, the two—for some small variety to the monotony—changed places; and where had stood the young, fair brow, now stood the ruled and wrinkled one.

Perched high upon a narrow platform, and still higher upon a high stool crowning it, sat another figure serving some other iron animal; while below the platform sat her mate in some sort of reciprocal attendance.

Not a syllable was breathed. Nothing was heard but the low, steady overruling hum of the iron animals. The human voice was banished from the spot. Machinery—that vaunted slave of humanity—here stood menially served by human beings, who served mutely and cringingly as the slave serves the Sultan. The girls did not so much seem accessory wheels to the general machinery as mere cogs to the wheels.

All this scene around me was instantaneously taken in at one sweeping glance—even before I had proceeded to unwind the heavy fur tippet from around my neck. But as soon as this fell from me, the dark-complexioned man, standing close by, raised a sudden cry, and seizing my arm, dragged me out into the open air, and without pausing for a word instantly caught up some congealed snow and began rubbing both my cheeks.

"Two white spots like the whites of your eyes," he said; "man, your cheeks are frozen."

"That may well be," muttered I; " 'tis some wonder the frost of the Devil's Dungeon strikes in no deeper. Rub away."

Soon a horrible, tearing pain caught at my reviving cheeks. Two gaunt blood-hounds, one on each side, seemed mumbling them. I seemed Actæon.

Presently, when all was over, I re-entered the factory, made known my business, concluded it satisfactorily, and then begged to be conducted throughout the place to view it.

"Cupid!" is the boy for that," said the dark-complexioned man. "Cupid!" and by this odd fancy-name calling a dimpled, red-cheeked, spirited-looking, forward little fellow who was rather impudently, I thought, gliding about among the passive-looking girls—like a gold-fish through hueless waves—yet doing nothing in particular that I could see, the man bade him lead the stranger through the edifice.

"Come first and see the water-wheel," said this lively lad, with the air of boyishly-brisk importance.

Quitting the folding-room, we crossed some damp, cold boards, and stood beneath a great wet shed, incessantly showering with foam, like the green barnacled bow of some East Indiaman in a gale. Round and round here went the enormous revolutions of the dark colossal water-wheel, grim with its one immutable purpose.

"This sets our whole machinery a-going, sir; in every part of all these buildings; where the girls work and all."

I looked, and saw that the turbid waters of Blood River had not changed their hue by coming under the use of man.

"You make only blank paper; no printing of any sort, I suppose? All blank paper, don't you?"

"Certainly; what else should a paper-factory make?"

The lad here looked at me as if suspicious of my common sense.

"Oh, to be sure!" said I, confused and stammering; "it only struck me as so strange that red waters should turn out pale chee—paper, I mean."

He took me up a wet and rickety stair to a great light room, furnished with no visible thing but rude, manger-like receptacles running all round its sides; and up to these mangers, like so many mares haltered to the rack, stood rows of girls. Before each was vertically thrust up a long, glittering scythe, immovably fixed at bottom to the manger-edge. The curve of the scythe, and its having no snath to it, made it look exactly like a sword. To and fro, across the sharp edge, the girls forever dragged long strips of rags, washed white, picked from baskets at one side; thus ripping asunder every seam, and converting the tatters almost into lint. The air swam with the fine, poisonous particles, which from all sides darted, subtilely, as motes in sunbeams, into the lungs.

"This is the rag-room," coughed the boy.

"You find it rather stifling here," coughed I in answer; "but the girls don't cough."

"Oh, they are used to it."

"Where do you get such hosts of rags?" picking up a handful from a basket.

"Some from the country round about; some from far over sea—Leghorn and London."

" 'Tis not unlikely, then," murmured I, "that among these heaps of rags there may be some old shirts, gathered from the dormitories of the Paradise of Bachelors. But the buttons are all dropped off. Pray, my lad, do you ever find any bachelor's buttons hereabouts?"

"None grow in this part of the country. The Devil's Dungeon is no place for flowers."

"Oh! you mean the *flowers* so called—the Bachelor's Buttons?"

"And was not that what you asked about? Or did you mean the gold bosom-buttons of our boss, Old Bach, as our whispering girls all call him?"

"The man, then, I saw below is a bachelor, is he?"

"Oh, yes, he's a Bach."

"The edges of those swords, they are turned outward from the girls, if I see right; but their rags and fingers fly so, I can not distinctly see."

"Turned outward."

Yes, murmured I to myself; I see it now; turned outward; and each erected sword is so borne, edge-outward, before each girl. If my reading fails me not, just so, of old, condemned state-prisoners went from the hall of judgment to their doom: an officer before, bearing a sword, its edge turned outward, in significance of their fatal sentence. So through consumptive pallors of this blank, raggy life, go these white girls to death.

"Those scythes look very sharp," again turning toward the boy.

"Yes; they have to keep them so. Look!"

That moment two of the girls, dropping their rags, plied each a whetstone up and down the swordblade. My unaccustomed blood curdled at the sharp shriek of the tormented steel.

Their own executioners; themselves whetting the very swords that slay them, meditated I.

"What makes those girls so sheet-white, my lad?"

"Why"—with a roguish twinkle, pure ignorant drollery, notknowing heartlessness—"I suppose the handling of such white bits of sheets all the time makes them so sheety."

"Let us leave the rag-room now, my lad."

More tragical and more inscrutably mysterious than any mystic sight, human or machine, throughout the factory, was the strange innocence of cruel-heartedness in this usage-hardened boy.

"And now," said he, cheerily, "I suppose you want to see our great machine, which cost us twelve thousand dollars only last autumn. That's the machine that makes the paper, too. This way, sir."

Following him, I crossed a large, bespattered place, with two great round vats in it, full of a white, wet, woolly-looking stuff, not unlike the albuminous part of an egg, soft-boiled.

"There," said Cupid, tapping the vats carelessly, "these are the first beginnings of the paper, this white pulp you see. Look how it swims bubbling round and round, moved by the paddle here. From hence it pours from both vats into that one common channel yonder, and so goes, mixed up and leisurely, to the great machine. And now for that."

He led me into a room, stifling with a strange, blood-like, abdominal heat, as if here, true enough, were being finally developed the germinous particles lately seen.

Before me, rolled out like some long Eastern manuscript, lay stretched one continuous length of iron framework—multitudinous and mystical, with all sorts of rollers, wheels, and cylinders, in slowly-measured and unceasing motion.

"Here first comes the pulp now," said Cupid, pointing to the highest end of the machine. "See; first it pours out and spreads itself upon this wide, sloping board; and then—look—slides, thin and quivering, beneath the first roller there. Follow on now, and see it as it slides from under that to the next cylinder. There; see how it has become just a very little less pulpy now. One step more, and it grows still more to some slight consistence. Still another cylinder, and it is so knitted—though as yet mere dragon-fly wing—that it forms an air-bridge here, like a suspended cobweb, between two more separated rollers; and flowing over the last one, and under again, and doubling about there out of sight for a minute among all those mixed cylinders you indistinctly see, it reappears here, looking now at last a little less like pulp and more like paper, but still quite delicate and defective yet awhile. But—a little further onward, sir, if you please—here now, at this further point, it puts on something of a real look, as if it might turn out to be something you might possibly handle in the end. But it's not yet done, sir. Good way to travel yet, and plenty more of cylinders must roll it."

"Bless my soul!" said I, amazed at the elongation, interminable convolutions, and deliberate slowness of the machine; "it must take a long time for the pulp to pass from end to end and come out paper."

"Oh! not so long," smiled the precocious lad, with a superior and patronizing air; "only nine minutes. But look; you may try it for yourself. Have you a bit of paper? Ah! here's a bit on the floor. Now mark that with any word you please, and let me dab it on here, and we'll see how long before it comes out at the other end."

"Well, let me see," said I, taking out my pencil; "come, I'll mark it with your name."

Bidding me take out my watch, Cupid adroitly dropped the inscribed slip on an exposed part of the incipient mass.

Instantly my eye marked the second-hand on my dial-plate.

Slowly I followed the slip, inch by inch; sometimes pausing for full half a minute as it disappeared beneath inscrutable groups of the lower cylinders, but only gradually to emerge again; and so, on, and on, and on—inch by inch; now in open sight, sliding along like a freckle on the quivering sheet; and then again wholly vanished; and so, on, and on, and on—inch by inch; all the time the main sheet growing more and more to final firmness—when, suddenly, I saw a sort of paper-fall, not wholly unlike a water-fall; a scissory sound smote my ear, as of some cord being snapped; and down dropped an unfolded sheet of perfect foolscap with my "Cupid" half faded out of it, and still moist and warm.

My travels were at an end, for here was the end of the machine.

"Well, how long was it?" said Cupid.

"Nine minutes to a second," replied I, watch in hand.

"I told you so."

For a moment a curious emotion filled me, not wholly unlike that which one might experience at the fulfillment of some mysterious prophecy. But how absurd, thought I again; the thing is a mere machine, the essence of which is unvarying punctuality and precision.

Previously absorbed by the wheels and cylinders, my attention was now directed to a sad-looking woman standing by.

"That is rather an elderly person so silently tending the machine-end here. She would not seem wholly used to it either."

"Oh," knowingly whispered Cupid, through the din, "she only came last week. She was a nurse formerly. But the business is poor in these parts, and she's left it. But look at the paper she is piling there."

"Aye, foolscap," handling the piles of moist, warm sheets, which continually were being delivered into the woman's waiting hands. "Don't you turn out anything but foolscap at this machine?"

"Oh, sometimes, but not often, we turn out finer work—cream-laid and royal sheets, we call them. But foolscap being in chief demand, we turn out foolscap most."

It was very curious. Looking at that blank paper continually dropping, dropping, dropping, my mind ran on in wonderings of those strange uses to which those thousand sheets eventually would be put. All sorts of writings would be writ on those now vacant things —sermons, lawyers' briefs, physicians' prescriptions, love-letters, marriage certificates, bills of divorce, registers of births, death-warrants, and so on, without end. Then, recurring back to them as they here lay all blank, I could not but bethink me of that celebrated comparison of John Locke, who, in demonstration of his theory that man had no innate ideas, compared the human mind at birth to a sheet of blank paper; something destined to be scribbled on, but what sort of characters no soul might tell.

Pacing slowly to and fro along the involved machine, still humming with its play, I was struck as well by the inevitability as the evolvement-power in all its motions.

"Does that thin cobweb there," said I, pointing to the sheet in its more imperfect stage, "does that never tear or break? It is marvelous fragile, and yet this machine it passes through is so mighty."

"It never is known to tear a hair's point."

"Does it never stop—get clogged?"

"No, It *must* go. The machinery makes it go just *so;* just that very way, and at that very pace you there plainly *see* it go. The pulp can't help going."

Something of awe now stole over me, as I gazed upon this inflexible iron animal. Always, more or less, machinery of this ponderous, elaborate sort strikes, in some moods, strange dread into the human heart, as some living, panting Behemoth might. But what made the thing I saw so specially terrible to me was the metallic necessity, the unbudging fatality which governed it. Though, here and there, I could not follow the thin, gauzy veil of pulp in the course of its more mysterious or entirely invisible advance, yet it was indubitable that, at those points where it eluded me, it still marched on in unvarying docility to the autocratic cunning of the machine. A fascination fastened on me. I stood spell-bound and wandering in my soul. Before my eyes—there, passing in slow procession along the wheeling cylinders, I seemed to see, glued to the pallid incipience of the pulp, the yet more pallid faces of all the pallid girls I had eyed that heavy day. Slowly, mournfully, beseechingly, yet unresistingly, they gleamed along, their agony dimly outlined on the imperfect paper, like the print of the tormented face on the handkerchief of Saint Veronica.

"Halloa! the heat of the room is too much for you," cried Cupid, staring at me.

"No—I am rather chill, if anything."

"Come out, sir—out—out," and, with the protecting air of a careful father, the precocious lad hurried me outside.

In a few moments, feeling revived a little, I went into the folding-room—the first room I had entered, and where the desk for transacting business stood, surrounded by the blank counters and blank girls engaged at them.

"Cupid here has led me a strange tour," said I to the dark-complexioned man before mentioned, whom I had ere this discovered not only to be an old bachelor, but also the principal proprietor. "Yours is a most wonderful factory. Your great machine is a miracle of inscrutable intricacy."

"Yes, all our visitors think it so. But we don't have many. We are in a very out-of-the-way corner here. Few inhabitants, too. Most of our girls come from far-off villages."

"The girls," echoed I, glancing round at their silent forms. "Why is it, sir, that in most factories, female operatives, of whatever age, are indiscriminately called girls, never women?"

"Oh! as to that—why, I suppose, the fact of their being generally unmarried—that's the reason, I should think. But it never struck me before. For our factory here, we will not have married women; they are apt to be off-and-on too much. We want none but steady workers: twelve hours to the day, day after day, through the three hundred and sixty-five days, excepting Sundays, Thanksgiving, and Fast-days. That's our rule. And so, having no married women, what females we have are rightly enough called girls."

"Then these are all maids," said I, while some pained homage to their pale virginity made me involuntarily bow.

"All maids."

Again the strange emotion filled me.

"Your cheeks look whitish yet, sir," said the man, gazing at me narrowly. "You must be careful going home. Do they pain you at all now? It's a bad sign, if they do."

"No doubt, sir," answered I, "when once I have got out of the Devil's Dungeon, I shall feel them mending."

"Ah, yes; the winter air in valleys, or gorges, or any sunken place, is far colder and more bitter than elsewhere. You would hardly believe it now, but it is colder here than at the top of Woedolor Mountain."

"I dare say it is, sir. But time presses me; I must depart."

With that, remuffling myself in dreadnaught and tippet, thrusting my hands into my huge seal-skin mittens, I sallied out into the nipping air, and found poor Black, my horse, all cringing and doubled up with the cold.

Soon, wrapped in furs and meditations, I ascended from the Devil's Dungeon.

At the Black Notch I paused, and once more bethought me of Temple Bar. Then, shooting through the pass, all alone with inscrutable nature, I exclaimed—Oh! Paradise of Bachelors! and oh! Tartarus of Maids!

That Only a Mother

Judith Merril

Margaret reached over to the other side of the bed where Hank should have been. Her hand patted the empty pillow, and then she came altogether awake, wondering that the old habit should remain after so many months. She tried to curl up, cat-style, to hoard her own warmth, found she couldn't do it any more, and climbed out of bed with a pleased awareness of her increasingly clumsy bulkiness.

Morning motions were automatic. On the way through the kitchenette, she pressed the button that would start breakfast cooking—the doctor had said to eat as much breakfast as she could—and tore the paper out of the facsimile machine. She folded the long sheet carefully to the "National News" section, and propped it on the bathroom shelf to scan while she brushed her teeth.

No accidents. No direct hits. At least none that had been officially released for publication. *Now, Maggie, don't get started on that. No accidents. No hits. Take the nice newspaper's word for it.*

The three clear chimes from the kitchen announced that breakfast was ready. She set a bright napkin and cheerful colored dishes on the table in a futile attempt to appeal to a faulty morning appetite. Then, when there was nothing more to prepare, she went for the mail, allowing herself the full pleasure of prolonged anticipation, because today there would *surely* be a letter.

There was. There were. Two bills and a worried note from her mother: "Darling, why didn't you write and tell me sooner? I'm thrilled, of course, but, well one hates to mention these things, but are you *certain* the doctor was right? Hank's been around all that uranium or thorium or whatever it is all these years, and I know you say he's a designer, not a technician, and he doesn't get near anything that might be dangerous, but you know he used to, back

381

at Oak Ridge. Don't you think... well, of course, I'm just being a foolish old woman, and I don't want you to get upset. You know much more about it than I do, and I'm sure your doctor was right. He *should* know..."

Margaret made a face over the excellent coffee, and caught herself refolding the paper to the medical news.

Stop it, Maggie, stop it! The radiologist said Hank's job couldn't have exposed him. And the bombed area we drove past... No, no. Stop it, now! Read the social notes or the recipes, Maggie girl.

A well-known geneticist, in the medical news, said that it was possible to tell with absolute certainty, at five months, whether the child would be normal, or at least whether the mutation was likely to produce anything freakish. The worst cases, at any rate, could be prevented. Minor mutations, of course, displacements in facial features, or changes in brain structure could not be detected. And there had been some cases recently, of normal embryos with atrophied limbs that did not develop beyond the seventh or eight month. But, the doctor concluded cheerfully, the *worst* cases could now be predicted and prevented.

"Predicted and prevented." We predicted it, didn't we? Hank and the others, they predicted it. But we didn't prevent it. We could have stopped it in '46 and '47. Now...

Margaret decided against the breakfast. Coffee had been enough for her in the morning for ten years; it would have to do for today. She buttoned herself into interminable folds of material that, the salesgirl had assured her, was the *only* comfortable thing to wear during the last few months. With a surge of pure pleasure, the letter and newspaper forgotten, she realized she was on the next to the last button. It wouldn't be long now.

The city in the early morning had always been a special kind of excitement for her. Last night it had rained, and the sidewalks were still damp-gray instead of dusty. The air smelled the fresher, to a city-bred woman, for the occasional pungency of acrid factory smoke. She walked the six blocks to work, watching the lights go out in the all-night hamburger joints, where the plate-glass walls were already catching the sun, and the lights go on in the dim interiors of cigar stores and dry-cleaning establishments.

The office was in a new Government building. In the rolovator, on the way up, she felt, as always, like a frankfurter roll in the ascending half of an old-style rotary toasting machine. She abandoned the air-foam cushioning gratefully at the fourteenth floor, and settled down behind her desk, at the rear of a long row of identical desks.

Each morning the pile of papers that greeted her was a little higher. These were, as everyone knew, the decisive months. The war might be won or lost on these calculations as well as any others. The man-power office had switched her here when her old expediter's job got to be too strenuous. The computer was easy to operate, and the work was absorbing, if not as exciting as the old job. But you didn't just stop working these days. Everyone who could do any-thing at all was needed.

And—she remembered the interview with the psychologist—*I'm probably the unstable type. Wonder what sort of neurosis I'd get sitting home reading that sensational paper*...

She plunged into the work without pursuing the thought.

February 18.

Hank darling,

Just a note—from the hospital, no less. I had a dizzy spell at work, and the doctor took it to heart. Blessed if I know what I'll do with myself lying in bed for weeks, just waiting—but Dr. Boyer seems to think it may not be so long.

There are too many newspapers around here. More infanticides all the time, and they can't seem to get a jury to convict any of them. It's the fathers who do it. Lucky thing you're not around, in case—

Oh, darling, that wasn't a very *funny* joke, was it? Write as often as you can, will you? I have too much time to think. But there really isn't anything wrong, and nothing to worry about.

Write often, and remember I love you.

Maggie.

SPECIAL SERVICE TELEGRAM

February 21, 1953
22:04 LK37G

From: Tech. Lieut. H. Marvell
X47—016 GCNY
To: Mrs. H. Marvell
Women's Hospital
New York City

HAD DOCTOR'S GRAM STOP WILL ARRIVE FOUR OH TEN STOP SHORT LEAVE STOP YOU DID IT MAGGIE STOP LOVE HANK

February 25.

Hank dear,

So you didn't see the baby either? You'd think a place this size would at least have visiplates on the incubators, so the fathers could get a look, even if the poor benighted mommas can't. They tell me I won't see her for another week, or maybe more—but of course, mother always warned me if I didn't slow my pace, I'd probably even have my babies too fast. Why must she *always* be right?

Did you meet that battle-ax of a nurse they put on here? I imagine they save her for people who've already had theirs, and don't let her get too near the prospectives—but a woman like that simply shouldn't be allowed in a maternity ward. She's obsessed with mutations, can't seem to talk about anything else. Oh, well, *ours* is all right, even if it was in an unholy hurry.

I'm tired. They warned me not to sit up so soon, but I *had* to write you. All my love, darling,

Maggie.

February 29.

Darling,

I finally got to see her! It's all true, what they say about new babies and the face that only a mother could love—but it's all there, darling, eyes, ears, and noses—no, only one—all in the right places. We're so *lucky*, Hank.

I'm afraid I've been a rambunctious patient. I kept telling that hatchet-faced female with the mutation mania that I wanted to *see* the baby. Finally the doctor came in to "explain" everything to me, and talked a lot of nonsense, most of which I'm sure no one could have understood, any more than I did. The only thing I got out of it was that she didn't Actually *have* to stay in the incubator; they just thought it was "wiser."

I think I got a little hysterical at that point. Guess I was more worried than I was willing to admit, but I threw a small fit about it. The whole business wound up with one of those hushed medical conferences outside the door, and finally the Woman in White said: "Well, we might as well. Maybe it'll work out better that way."

I'd heard about the way doctors and nurses in these places develop a God complex, and believe me it is as true figuratively as it is literally that a mother hasn't got a leg to stand on around here.

I *am* awfully weak, still. I'll write again soon. Love,

Maggie.

March 8.

Dearest Hank,

Well the nurse was wrong if she told you that. She's an idiot anyhow. It's a girl. It's easier to tell with babies than with cats, and I *know*. How about Henrietta?

I'm home again, and busier than a betatron. They got *everything* mixed up at the hospital, and I had to teach myself how to bathe her and do just about everything else. She's getting prettier, too. When can you get a leave, a *real* leave?

Love,
Maggie.

May 26.

Hank dear,

You should see her now—and you shall. I'm sending along a reel of color movie. My mother sent her those nighties with drawstrings all over. I put one on, and right now she looks like a snow-white potato sack with that beautiful, beautiful flower-face blooming on top. Is that *me* talking? Am I a doting mother? But wait till you *see* her!

July 10.

...Believe it or not, as you like, but your daughter can talk, and I don't mean baby talk. Alice discovered it—she's a dental assistant in the WACs, you know—and when she heard the baby giving out what I thought was a string of gibberish, she said the kid knew words and sentences, but couldn't say them clearly because she has no teeth yet. I'm taking her to a speech specialist.

September 13.

...We have a prodigy for real! Now that all her front teeth are in, her speech is perfectly clear and—a new talent now—she can sing! I mean really carry a tune! At seven months! Darling my world would be perfect if you could only get home.

November 19.

...at last. The little goon was so busy being clever, it took her all this time to learn to crawl. The doctor says development in these cases is always erratic...

SPECIAL SERVICE TELEGRAM

December 1, 1953
08:47 LK59F

From: Tech. Lieut. H. Marvell
      X47—016 GCNY
        To: Mrs. H. Marvell
          Apt. K-17
          504 E. 19 St.
          N.Y. N.Y.

WEEK'S LEAVE STARTS TOMORROW STOP WILL ARRIVE AIRPORT TEN OH FIVE STOP DON'T MEET ME STOP LOVE LOVE LOVE HANK

Margaret let the water run out of the bathinette until only a few inches were left, and then loosed her hold on the wriggling baby.

"I think it was better when you were retarded, young woman," she informed her daughter happily. "You *can't* crawl in a bathinette, you know."

"Then why can't I go in the bathtub?" Margaret was used to her child's volubility by now, but every now and then it caught her unawares. She swooped the resistant mass of pink flesh into a towel, and began to rub.

"Because you're too little, and your head is very soft, and bathtubs are very hard."

"Oh. Then when can I go in the bathtub?"

"When the outside of your head is as hard as the inside, brainchild." She reached toward a pile of fresh clothing. "I cannot understand," she added, pinning a square of cloth through the nightgown, "why a child of your intelligence can't learn to keep a diaper on the way other babies do. They've been used for centuries, you know, with perfectly satisfactory results."

The child disdained to reply; she had heard it too often. She waited patiently until she had been tucked, clean and sweet-smelling, into a white-painted crib. Then she favored her mother with a smile that inevitably made Margaret think of the first golden edge of the sun bursting into a rosy pre-dawn. She remembered Hank's reaction to the color pictures of his beautiful daughter, and with the thought, realized how late it was.

"Go to sleep, puss. When you wake up, you know, your *Daddy* will be here."

"Why?" asked the four-year-old mind, waging a losing battle to keep the ten-month-old body awake.

Margaret went into the kitchenette and set the timer for the roast. She examined the table, and got her clothes from the closet, new dress, new shoes, new slip, new everything, bought weeks before and saved for the day Hank's telegram came. She stopped to pull a paper from the facsimile, and, with clothes and news, went into the bathroom, and lowered herself gingerly into the steaming luxury of a scented tub.

She glanced through the paper with indifferent interest. Today at least there was no need to read the national news. There was an article by a geneticist. The same geneticist. Mutations, he said, were increasing disproportionately. It was too soon for recessives; even the first mutants, born near Hiroshima and Nagasaki in 1946 and 1947 were not old enough yet to breed. *But my baby's all right.* Apparently, there was some degree of free radiation from atomic explosions causing the trouble. *My baby's fine. Precocious, but normal.* If more attention had been paid to the first Japanese mutations, he said . . .

There was that little notice in the paper in the spring of '47. That was when Hank quit at Oak Ridge. "Only two or three per cent of those guilty of infanticide are being caught and punished in Japan today..." *But* MY BABY'S *all right.*

She was dressed, combed, and ready to the last light brush-on of lip paste, when the door chime sounded. She dashed for the door, and heard, for the first time in eighteen months the almost-forgotten sound of a key turning in the lock before the chime had quite died away.

"Hank!"

"Maggie!"

And then there was nothing to say. So many days, so many months, of small news piling up, so many things to tell him, and now she just stood there, staring at a khaki uniform and a stranger's pale face. She traced the features with the finger of memory. The same high-bridged nose, wide-set eyes, fine feathery brows; the same long jaw, the hair a little farther back now on the high forehead, the same tilted curve to his mouth. Pale... Of course, he'd been underground all this time. And strange, stranger because of lost familiarity than any newcomer's face could be.

She had time to think all that before his hand reached out to touch her, and spanned the gap of eighteen months. Now, again, there was nothing to say, because there was no need. They were together, and for the moment that was enough.

"Where's the baby?"

"Sleeping. She'll be up any minute."

No urgency. Their voices were as casual as though it were a daily exchange, as though war and separation did not exist. Margaret picked up the coat he'd thrown on the chair near the door, and hung it carefully in the hall closet. She went to check the roast, leaving him to wander through the rooms by himself, remembering and coming back. She found him, finally, standing over the baby's crib.

She couldn't see his face, but she had no need to.

"I think we can wake her just this once." Margaret pulled the covers down, and lifted the white bundle from the bed. Sleepy lids pulled back heavily from smoky brown eyes.

"Hello." Hank's voice was tentative.

"Hello." The baby's assurance was more pronounced.

He had heard about it, of course, but that wasn't the same as hearing it. He turned eagerly to Margaret. "She really can—?"

"Of course she can, darling. But what's more important, she can even do nice normal things like other babies do, even stupid ones. Watch her crawl!" Margaret set the baby on the big bed.

For a moment young Henrietta lay and eyed her parents dubiously.

"Crawl?" she asked.

"That's the idea. Your Daddy is new around here, you know. He wants to see you show off."

"Then put me on my tummy."

"Oh, of course." Margaret obligingly rolled the baby over.

"What's the matter?" Hank's voice was still casual, but an undercurrent in it began to charge the air of the room. "I thought they turned over first."

"This baby," Margaret would not notice the tension, *"This* baby does things when she wants to."

This baby's father watched with softening eyes while the head advanced and the body hunched up propelling itself across the bed.

"Why the little rascal," he burst into relieved laghter. "She looks like one of those potato-sack racers they used to have on picnics. Got her arms pulled out of the sleeves already." He reached over and grabbed the knot at the bottom of the long nightie.

"I'll do it, darling." Margaret tried to get there first.

"Don't be silly, Maggie. This may be *your* first baby, but *I* had five kid brothers." He laughed her away, and reached with his other hand for the string that closed one sleeve. He opened the sleeve bow, and groped for an arm.

"The way you wriggle," he addressed his child sternly, as his hand touched a moving knob of flesh at the shoulder, "anyone might think you are a worm, using your tummy to crawl on, instead of your hands and feet."

Margaret stood and watched, smiling. "Wait till you hear her sing, darling—"

His right hand traveled down from the shoulder to where he thought an arm would be, traveled down, and straight down, over firm small muscles that writhed in an attempt to move against the pressure of his hand. He let his fingers drift up again to the shoulder. With infinite care, he opened the knot at the bottom of the nightgown. His wife was standing by the bed, saying: "She can do 'Jingle Bells,' and—"

His left hand felt along the soft knitted fabric of the gown, up towards the diaper that folded, flat and smooth, across the bottom end of his child. No wrinkles. No kicking. *No . . .*

"Maggie." He tried to pull his hands from the neat fold in the diaper, from the wriggling body. "Maggie." His throat was dry; words came hard, low and grating. He spoke very slowly, thinking the sound of each word to make himself say it. His head was spinning, but he had to *know* before he let it go. "Maggie, why . . . didn't you . . . tell me?"

"Tell you what, darling?" Margaret's poise was the immemorial patience of woman confronted with man's childish impetuosity. Her sudden laugh sounded fantastically easy and natural in that room; it was all clear to her now. "Is she wet? I didn't know."

She didn't know. His hands, beyond control, ran up and down the soft-skinned baby body, the sinuous, limbless body. *Oh God, dear God*—his head shook and his muscles contracted, in a bitter spasm of hysteria. His fingers tightened on his child—*Oh God, she didn't know ...*

Neutron Star

Larry Niven

I

The Skydiver dropped out of hyperspace an even million miles above the neutron star. I needed a minute to place myself against the stellar background and another to find the distortion Sonya Laskin had mentioned before she died. It was to my left, an area the apparent size of the Earth's moon. I swung the ship around to face it.

Curdled stars, muddled stars, stars that had been stirred with a spoon.

The neutron star was in the center, of course, though I couldn't see it and hadn't expected to. It was only eleven miles across, and cool. A billion years had passed since BVS-1 burned by fusion fire. Millions of years, at least, since the cataclysmic two weeks during which BVS-1 was an X-ray star, burning at a temperature of five billion degrees Kelvin. Now it showed only by its mass.

The ship began to turn by itself. I felt the pressure of the fusion drive. Without help from me, my faithful metal watchdog was putting me in hyperbolic orbit that would take me within one mile of the neutron star's surface. Twenty-four hours to fall, twenty-four hours to rise... and during that time, something would try to kill me. As something had killed the Laskins.

The same type of autopilot, with the same program, had chosen the Laskins' orbit. It had not caused their ship to collide with the star. I could trust the autopilot. I could even change its program.

I really ought to.

How did I get myself into this hole?

The drive went off after ten minutes of maneuvering. My orbit was established, in more ways than one. I knew what would happen if I tried to back out now.

All I'd done was walk into a drugstore to get a new battery for my lighter!

Right in the middle of the store, surrounded by three floors of sales counters, was the new 2603 Sinclair intrasystem yacht. I'd come for a battery, but I stayed to admire. It was a beautiful job, small and sleek and streamlined and blatantly different from anything that's ever been built. I wouldn't have flown it for anything, but I had to admit it was pretty. I ducked my head through the door to look at the control panel. You never saw so many dials. When I pulled my head out, all the customers were looking in the same direction. The place had gone startlingly quiet.

I can't blame them for staring. A number of aliens were in the store, mainly shopping for souvenirs, but they were staring too. A puppeteer is unique. Imagine a headless, three-legged centaur wearing two Cecil the Seasick Sea Serpent puppets on his arms, and you'll have something like the right picture. But the arms are weaving necks, and the puppets are real heads, flat and brainless, with wide flexible lips. The brain is under a bony hump set between the bases of the necks. This puppeteer wore only its own coat of brown hair, with a mane that extended all the way up its spine to form a thick mat over the brain. I'm told that the way they wear the mane indicates their status in society, but to me it could have been anything from a dock worker to a jeweler to the president of General Products.

I watched with the rest as it came across the floor, not because I'd never seen a puppeteer, but because there is something beautiful about the dainty way they move on those slender legs and tiny hooves. I watched it come straight toward me, closer and closer. It stopped a foot away, looked me over and said, "You are Beowulf Shaeffer, former chief pilot for Nakamura Lines."

Its voice was a beautiful contralto with not a trace of accent. A puppeteer's mouths are not only the most flexible speech organs around, but also the most sensitive hands. The tongues are forked and pointed, the wide, thick lips have little fingerlike knobs along the rims. Imagine a watchmaker with a sense of taste in his fingertips...

I cleared my throat. "That's right."

It considered me from two directions. "You would be interested in a high-paying job?"

"I'd be fascinated in a high-paying job."

"I am our equivalent of the regional president of General Products. Please come with me, and we will discuss this elsewhere."

I followed it into a displacement booth. Eyes followed me all the way. It was embarrassing, being accosted in a public drugstore by a two-headed monster. Maybe the puppeteer knew it. Maybe it was testing me to see how badly I needed money.

My need was great. Eight months had passed since Nakamura Lines folded. For some time before that, I had been living very high on the hog, knowing that my back pay would cover my debts. I never saw that back pay. It was quite a crash, Nakamura Lines. Respectable middle-aged businessmen took to leaving their hotel windows without their lift belts. Me, I kept spending. If I'd started living frugally, my creditors would have done some checking...and I'd have ended in debtor's prison.

The puppeteer dialed thirteen fast digits with its tongue. A moment later we were elsewhere. Air puffed out when I opened the booth door, and I swallowed to pop my ears.

"We are on the roof of the General Products building." The rich contralto voice thrilled along my nerves, and I had to remind myself that it was an alien speaking, not a lovely woman. "You must examine this spacecraft while we discuss your assignment."

I stepped outside a little cautiously, but it wasn't the windy season. The roof was at ground level. That's the way we build on We Made It. Maybe it has something to do with the fifteen-hundred-mile-an-hour winds we get in summer and winter, when the planet's axis of rotation runs through its primary, Procyon. The winds are our planet's only tourist attraction, and it would be a shame to slow them down by planting skyscrapers in their path. The bare, square concrete roof was surrounded by endless square miles of desert, not like the deserts of other inhabited worlds, but an utterly lifeless expanse of fine sand just crying to be planted with ornamental cactus. We've tried that. The wind blows the plants away.

The ship lay on the sand beyond the roof. It was a #2 General Products hull: a cylinder three hundred feet long and twenty feet through, pointed at both ends and with a slight wasp-waist constriction near the tail. For some reason it was lying on its side, with the landing shocks still folded in at the tail.

Ever notice how all ships have begun to look the same? A good ninety-five percent of today's spacecrafts are built around one of the four General Products hulls. It's easier and safer to build that way, but somehow all ships end as they began: mass-produced look-alikes.

The hulls are delivered fully transparent, and you use paint where you feel like it. Most of this particular hull had been left transparent. Only the nose had been painted, around the life-system. There was no major reaction drive. A series of retractable attitude jets had been mounted in the sides, and the hull was pierced with smaller holes, square and round—for observational instruments. I could see them gleaming through the hull.

The puppeteer was moving toward the nose, but something made me turn toward the stern for a closer look at the landing shocks.

They were bent. Behind the curved, transparent hull panels, some tremendous pressure had forced the metal to flow like warm wax, back and into the pointed stern.

"What did this?" I asked.

"We do not know. We wish strenuously to find out."

"What do you mean?"

"Have you heard of the neutron star BVS-1?"

I had to think a moment. "First neutron star ever found, and so far the only. Someone located it two years ago by stellar displacement."

"BVS-1 was found by the Institute of Knowledge on Jinx. We learned through a go-between that the Institute wished to explore the star. They needed a ship to do it. They had not yet sufficient money. We offered to supply them with a ship's hull, with the usual guarantees, if they would turn over to us all data they acquired through using our ship."

"Sounds fair enough." I didn't ask why they hadn't done their own exploring. Like most sentient vegetarians, puppeteers find discretion to be the *only* part of valor.

"Two humans named Peter Laskin and Sonya Laskin wished to use the ship. They intended to come within one mile of the surface in a hyperbolic orbit. At some point during their trip, an unknown force apparently reached through the hull to do this to the landing shocks. The unknown force also seems to have killed the pilots."

"But that's impossible. Isn't it?"

"You see the point. Come with me." The puppeteer trotted toward the bow.

I saw the point, all right. Nothing, but nothing can get through a General Products hull. No kind of electromagnetic energy except visible light. No kind of matter, from the smallest subatomic particle to the fastest meteor. That's what the company's advertisements claim, and the guarantee backs them up. I've never doubted it, and I've never heard of a General Products hull being damaged by a weapon or by anything else.

On the other hand, a General Products hull is as ugly as it is functional. The puppeteer-owned company could be badly hurt if it got around that something *could* get through a company hull. But I didn't see where I came in.

We rode an escalladder into the nose.

The lifesystem was in two compartments. Here the Laskins had used heat-reflective paint. In the conical control cabin the hull had been divided into windows. The relaxation room behind it was a windowless reflective silver. From the back wall of the relaxation room an access tube ran aft, opening on various instruments and the hyperdrive motors.

There were two acceleration couches in the control cabin. Both had been torn loose from their mountings and wadded into the nose like so much tissue paper, crushing the instrument panel. The backs of the crumpled couches were splashed with rust brown. Flecks of the same color were all over everything, the walls, the windows, the viewscreens. It was as if something had hit the couches from behind: something like a dozen paint-filled toy balloons, striking with tremendous force.

"That's blood," I said.

"That is correct. Human circulatory fluid."

II

Twenty-four hours to fall.

I spent most of the first twelve hours in the relaxation room, trying to read. Nothing significant was happening, except that a few times I saw the phenomenon Sonya Laskin had mentioned in her last report. When a star went directly behind the invisible BVS-1, a halo formed. BVS-1 was heavy enough to bend light around it, displacing most stars to the sides; but when a star went directly behind the neutron star, its light was displaced to all sides at once. Result: a tiny circle which flashed once and was gone almost before the eye could catch it.

I'd known next to nothing about neutron stars the day the puppeteer picked me up. Now I was an expert. But I still had no idea what was waiting for me when I got down there.

All the matter you're ever likely to meet will be normal matter, composed of a nucleus of protons and neutrons surrounded by electrons in quantum energy states. In the heart of any star there is a second kind of matter: for there, the tremendous pressure is enough to smash the electron shells. The result is degenerate matter: nuclei forced together by pressure and gravity, but held apart by the mutual repulsion of the more or less continuous electron 'gas' around them. The right circumstances may create a third type of matter.

Given: a burnt-out white dwarf with a mass greater than 1.44 times the mass of the Sun—Chandrasekhar's Limit, named for an Indian-American astronomer of the nineteen hundreds. In such a mass the electron pressure alone would not be able to hold the electrons back from the nuclei. Electrons would be forced against protons—to make neutrons. In one blazing explosion most of the star would change from a compressed mass of degenerate matter to a closely packed lump of neutrons: neutronium, theoretically the densest matter possible in this universe. Most of the remaining normal and degenerate matter would be blown away by the liberated heat.

For two weeks the star would give off X-rays, as its core temperature dropped from five billion degrees Kelvin to five hundred million. After that it would be a light-emitting body perhaps ten to twelve miles across: the next best thing to invisible. It was not strange that BVS-1 was the first neutron star ever found.

Neither is it strange that the Institute of Knowledge on Jinx would have spent a good deal of time and trouble looking. Until BVS-1 was found, neutronium and neutron stars were only theories. The examination of an actual neutron star could be of tremendous importance. Neutron stars could give us the key to true gravity control.

Mass of BVS-1: 1.3 times the mass of Sol, approximately.

Diameter of BVS-1 (estimated): eleven miles of neutronium, covered by half a mile of degenerate matter, covered by maybe twelve feet of ordinary matter.

Escape velocity: 130,000 mps, approximately.

Nothing else was known of the tiny black star until the Laskins went in to look. Now the Institute knew one thing more. The star's spin.

"A mass that large can distort space by its rotation," said the puppeteer. "The Institute ship's projected hyperbola was twisted across itself in such a way that we can deduce the star's period of rotation to be two minutes, twenty-seven seconds."

The bar was somewhere in the General Products building. I don't know just where, and with the transfer booths it doesn't matter. I kept staring at the puppeteer bartender. Naturally only a puppeteer would be served by a puppeteer bartender, since any biped would resent knowing that somebody made his drink with his mouth. I had already decided to get dinner somewhere else.

"I see your problem," I said. "Your sales will suffer if it gets out that something can reach through one of your hulls and smash a crew to bloody smears. But where do I fit in?"

"We wish to repeat the experiment of Sonya Laskin and Peter Laskin. We must find—"

"With me?"

"Yes. We must find out what it is that our hulls cannot stop. Naturally you may—"

"But I won't."

"We are prepared to offer one million stars."

I was tempted, but only for a moment. "Forget it."

"Naturally you will be allowed to build your own ship, starting with a #2 General Products hull."

"Thanks, but I'd like to go on living."

"You would dislike being confined. I find that We Made It has reestablished the debtor's prison. If General Products made public your accounts..."

"Now, *just* a—"

"You owe money in the close order of five hundred thousand stars. We will pay your creditors before you leave. If you return—" I had to admire the creature's honesty in not saying *when*—"we will pay you the remainder. You may be asked to speak to news commentators concerning the voyage, in which case there will be more stars."

"You say I can build my own ship?"

"Naturally. This is not a voyage of exploration. We want you to return safely."

"It's a deal," I said.

After all, the puppeteer had tried to blackmail me. What happened next would be its own fault.

They built my ship in two weeks flat. They started with a #2 General Products hull, just like the one around the Institute of Knowledge ship, and the lifesystem was practically a duplicate of the Laskins', but there the resemblance ended. There were no instruments to observe neutron stars. Instead, there was a fusion motor big enough for a Jinx warliner. In my ship, which I now called Skydiver, the drive would produce thirty gees at the safety limit. There was a laser cannon big enough to punch a hole through We Made It's moon. The puppeteer wanted me to feel safe, and now I did, for I could fight and I could run. Especially I could run.

I heard the Laskins' last broadcast through half a dozen times. Their unnamed ship had dropped out of hyperspace a million miles above BVS-1. Gravity warp would have prevented their getting closer in hyperspace. While her husband was crawling through the access tube for an instrument check, Sonya Laskin had called the Institute of Knowledge. " . . . we can't see it yet, not with the naked eye. But we can see where it is. Every time some star or other goes behind it, there's a little ring of light. Just a minute. Peter's ready to use the telescope . . ."

Then the star's mass had cut the hyperspacial link. It was expected, and nobody had worried—then. Later, the same effect must have stopped them from escaping whatever attacked them, into hyperspace.

When would-be rescuers found the ship, only the radar and the cameras were still running. They didn't tell us much. There had been no camera in the cabin. But the forward camera gave us, for one instant, a speed-blurred view of the neutron star. It was a featureless disc the orange color of perfect barbecue coals, if you know someone who can afford to burn wood. This object had been a neutron star a long time.

"There'll be no need to paint the ship," I told the president.

"You should not make such a trip with the walls transparent. You would go insane."

"I'm no flatlander. The mind-wrenching sight of naked space fills me with mild, but waning interest. I want to know nothing's sneaking up behind me."

The day before I left, I sat alone in the General Products bar letting the puppeteer bartender make me drinks with his mouth. He did it well. Puppeteers were scattered around the bar in twos and threes, with a couple of men for variety; but the drinking hour had not yet arrived. The place felt empty.

I was pleased with myself. My debts were all paid, not that that would matter where I was going. I would leave with not a mini-credit to my name; with nothing but the ship . . .

All told, I was well out of a sticky situation. I hoped I'd like being a rich exile.

I jumped when the newcomer sat down across from me. He was a foreigner, a middle-aged man wearing an expensive night-black business suit and a snow-white asymmetric beard. I let my face freeze and started to get up.

"Sit down, Mr. Shaeffer."

"Why?"

He told me by showing me a blue disc. An Earth-government ident. I looked it over to show I was alert, not because I'd know an ersatz from the real thing.

"My name is Sigmund Ausfaller," said the government man. "I wish to say a few words concerning your assignment on behalf of General Products."

I nodded, not saying anything.

"A record of your verbal contract was sent to us as a matter of course. I noticed some peculiar things about it. Mr. Shaeffer, will you really take such a risk for only five hundred thousand stars?"

"I'm getting twice that."

"But you only keep half of it. The rest goes to pay debts. Then there are taxes. But never mind. What occurred to me was that a spaceship is a spaceship, and yours is very well armed and has powerful legs. An admirable fighting ship, if you were moved to sell it."

"But it isn't mine."

"There are those who would not ask. On Canyon, for example, or the Isolationist party of Wonderland."

I said nothing.

"Or, you might be planning a career of piracy. A risky business, piracy, and I don't take the notion seriously."

I hadn't even thought about piracy. But I'd have to give up on Wonderland . . .

"What I would like to say is this, Mr. Shaeffer. A single entrepreneur, if he were sufficiently dishonest, could do terrible damage to the reputation of all human beings everywhere. Most species find it necessary to police the ethics of their own members, and we are no exception. It occurred to me that you might not take your ship to the neutron star at all; that you would take it elsewhere and sell it. The puppeteers do not make invulnerable war vessels. They are pacifists. Your Skydiver is unique.

"Hence I have asked General Products to allow me to install a remote control bomb in the Skydiver. Since it is inside the hull, the hull cannot protect you. I had it installed this afternoon.

"Now, notice! If you have not reported within a week I will set off the bomb. There are several worlds within a week's hyperspace flight of here, but all recognize the dominion of Earth. If you flee, you must leave your ship within a week, so I hardly think you will land on a nonhabitable world. Clear?"

"Clear."

"If I am wrong, you may take a lie-detector test and prove it. Then you may punch me in the nose, and I will apologize handsomely."

I shook my head. He stood up, bowed and left me sitting there cold sober.

Four films had been taken from the Laskins' cameras. In the time left to me, I ran through them several times, without seeing anything out of the way. If the ship had run through a gas cloud, the impact could have killed the Laskins. At perihelion they were moving at better than half the speed of light. But there would have been friction, and I saw no sign of heating in the films. If something alive had attacked them, the beast was invisible to radar and to an enormous range of light frequencies. If the attitude jets had fired accidentally—I was clutching at straws—the light showed on none of the films.

There would be savage magnetic forces near BVS-1, but that couldn't have done any damage. No such force could penetrate a General Products hull. Neither could heat, except in special bands of radiated light, bands visible to at least one of the puppeteers' alien customers. I hold adverse opinions on the General Products hull, but they all concern the dull anonymity of the design. Or maybe I resent the fact that General Products holds a near-monopoly on spacecraft hulls and isn't owned by human beings. But if I'd had to trust my life to, say, the Sinclair yacht I'd seen in the drugstore, I'd have chosen jail.

Jail was one of my three choices. But I'd be there for life. Ausfaller would see to that.

Or I could run for it in the Skydiver. But no world within reach would have me, that is. Of course, if I could find an undiscovered Earthlike world within a week of We Made It...

Fat chance. I preferred BVS-1 to that any day.

III

I thought that flashing circle of light was getting bigger, but it flashed so seldom I couldn't be sure. BVS-1 wouldn't show even in my telescope. I gave that up and settled for just waiting.

Waiting, I remembered a long-ago summer I spent on Jinx. There were days when, unable to go outside because a dearth of clouds had spread the land with raw blue-white sunlight, we amused ourselves by filling party balloons with tap water and dropping them on the sidewalk from three stories up. They made lovely splash patterns—which dried out too fast. So we put a little ink in each balloon before filling it. Then the patterns stayed.

Sonya Laskin had been in her chair when the chairs collapsed. Blood samples showed that it was Peter, who had struck them from behind, like a water balloon dropped from a great height.

What could get through a General Products hull?

Ten hours to fall.

I unfastened the safety net and went for an inspection tour. The access tunnel was three feet wide, just right to push through in free fall. Below me was the length of the fusion tube; to the left, the laser cannon; to the right, a set of curved side tubes leading to inspection points for the gyros, the batteries and generator, the air plant, the hyperspace shunt motors. All was in order—except me. I was clumsy. My jumps were always too short or too long. There was no room to turn at the stern end, so I had to back fifty feet to a side tube.

Six hours to go, and still I couldn't find the neutron star. Probably I would see it only for an instant, passing at better than half the speed of light. Already my speed must be enormous.

Were the stars turning blue?

Two hours to go, I was sure they were turning blue. Was my speed that high? Then the stars behind should be red. Machinery blocked the view behind me, so I used the gyros. The ship turned with peculiar sluggishness. And the stars behind were blue, not red. All around me were blue-white stars.

Imagine light falling into a savagely steep gravitational well. It won't accelerate. Light can't move faster than light. But it can gain in energy, in frequency. The light was falling on me, harder and harder as I dropped.

I told the dictaphone about it. That dictaphone was probably the best protected item on the ship. I had already decided to earn my money by using it, just as if I expected to collect. Privately I wondered just how intense the light would get.

Skydiver had drifted back to vertical, with its axis through the neutron star, but now it faced outward. I'd thought I had the ship stopped horizontally. More clumsiness. I used the gyros. Again the ship moved mushily, until it was halfway through the swing. Then it seemed to fall automatically into place. It was as if the Skydiver preferred to have its axis through the neutron star.

I didn't like that in the least.

I tried the maneuver again, and again the Skydiver fought back. But this time there was something else. Something was pulling at me.

So I unfastened my safety net and fell headfirst into the nose.

The pull was light, about a tenth of a gee. It felt more like sinking through honey than falling. I climbed back into my chair, tied myself in with the net, now hanging face down, turned on the dictaphone. I told my story in such nitpicking detail that my hypothetical listeners could not but doubt my hypothetical sanity. "I think this is what happened to the Laskins," I finished. "If the pull increases, I'll call back."

Think? I never doubted it. This strange, gentle pull was inexplicable. Something inexplicable had killed Peter and Sonya Laskin. Q.E.D.

Around the point where the neutron star must be, the stars were like smeared dots of oilpaint, smeared radially. They glared with an angry, painful light. I hung face down in the net and tried to think.

It was an hour before I was sure. The pull was increasing. And I still had an hour to fall.

Something was pulling on me, but not on the ship.

No, that was nonsense. What could reach out to me through a General Products hull? It must be the other way around. Something was pushing on the ship, pushing it off course.

If it got worse I could use the drive to compensate. Meanwhile, the ship was being pushed *away* from BVS-1, which was fine by me.

But if I was wrong, if the ship were not somehow being pushed away from BVS-1, the rocket motor would send the Skydiver crashing into eleven miles of neutronium.

And why wasn't the rocket already firing? If the ship was being pushed off course, the autopilot should be fighting back. The accelerometer was in good order. It had looked fine when I made my inspection tour down the access tube.

Could something be pushing on the ship *and* on the accelerometer, but not on me?

It came down to the same impossibility. Something that could reach through a General Products hull.

To hell with theory, said I to myself, said I. I'm getting out of here. To the dictaphone I said, "The pull has increased dangerously. I'm going to try to alter my orbit."

Of course, once I turned the ship outward and used the rocket, I'd be adding my own acceleration to the X force. It would be a strain, but I could stand it for a while. If I came within a mile of BVS-1, I'd end like Sonya Laskin.

She must have waited face down in a net like mine, waited without a drive unit, waited while the pressure rose and the net cut into her flesh, waited until the net snapped and dropped her into the nose, to lie crushed and broken until the X force tore the very chairs loose and dropped them on her.

I hit the gyros.

The gyros weren't strong enough to turn me. I tried it three times. Each time the ship rotated about fifty degrees and hung there, motionless, while the whine of the gyros went up and up. Released, the ship immediately swung back to position. I was nose down to the neutron star, and I was going to stay that way.

Half an hour to fall, and the X force was over a gee. My sinuses were in agony. My eyes were ripe and ready to fall out. I don't know if I could have stood a cigarette, but I didn't get the chance. My pack of Fortunados had fallen out of my pocket, when I dropped into the nose. There it was, four feet beyond my fingers, proof that the X force acted on other objects besides me. Fascinating.

I couldn't take any more. If it dropped me shrieking into the neutron star, I had to use the drive. And I did. I ran the thrust up until I was approximately in free fall. The blood which had pooled in my extremities went back where it belonged. The gee dial registered one point two gee. I cursed it for a lying robot.

The soft-pack was bobbing around in the nose, and it occurred to me that a little extra nudge on the throttle would bring it to me. I tried it. The pack drifted toward me, and I reached, and like a sentient thing it speeded up to avoid my clutching hand. I snatched at it again as it went past my ear, but again it was moving too fast. That pack was going at a hell of a clip, considering that here I was, practically in free fall. It dropped through the door to the relaxation room, still picking up speed, blurred and vanished as it entered the access tube. Seconds later I heard a solid Thump.

But that was *crazy*. Already the X force was pulling blood into my face. I pulled my lighter out, held it at arm's length and let go. It fell gently into the nose. But the pack of Fortunados had hit like I'd dropped it from a *building*.

Well.

I nudged the throttle again. The mutter of fusing hydrogen reminded me that if I tried to keep this up all the way, I might well put the General Products hull to its toughest test yet: smashing it into a neutron star at half lightspeed. I could see it now: a transparent hull containing only a few cubic inches of dwarf star matter wedged into the tip of the nose.

At one point four gee, according to that lying gee dial, the lighter came loose and drifted toward me. I let it go. It was clearly falling when it reached the doorway. I pulled the throttle back. The loss of power jerked me violently forward, but I kept my face turned. The lighter slowed and hesitated at the entrance to the access tube. Decided to go through. I cocked my ears for the sound, then jumped as the whole ship rang like a gong.

And the accelerometer was right at the ship's center of mass. Otherwise the ship's mass would have thrown the needle off. The puppeteers were fiends for ten-decimal-point accuracy.

I favored the dictaphone with a few fast comments, then got to work reprogramming the autopilot. Luckily what I wanted was simple. The X force was but an X force to me, but now I knew how it behaved. I might actually live through this.

The stars were fiercely blue, warped to streaked lines near that special point. I thought I could see it now, very small and dim and red; but it might have been imagination. In twenty minutes, I'd be rounding the neutron star. The drive grumbled behind me. In effective free fall, I unfastened the safety net and pushed myself out of the chair.

A gentle push aft—and ghostly hands grasped my legs. Ten pounds of weight hung by my fingers from the back of the chair. The pressure should drop fast. I'd programmed the autopilot to reduce the thrust from two gees to zero during the next two minutes. All I had to do was be at the center of mass, in the access tube, when the thrust went to zero.

Something gripped the ship through a General Products hull. A psychokinetic life form stranded on a sun twelve miles in diameter? But how could anything alive stand such gravity?

Something might be stranded in orbit. There is life in space: outsiders and sailseeds and maybe others we haven't found yet. For all I knew or cared, BVS-1 itself might be alive. It didn't matter. I knew what the X force was trying to do. It was trying to pull the ship apart.

There was no pull on my fingers. I pushed aft and landed on the back wall, on bent legs. I knelt over the door, looking aft/down. When free fall came, I pulled myself through and was in the relaxation room looking down/forward into the nose.

Gravity was changing faster than I liked. The X force was growing as zero hour approached, while the compensating rocket thrust dropped. The X force tended to pull the ship apart; it was two gee forward at the nose, two gee backward at the tail and diminished to zero at the center of mass. Or so I hoped. The pack and lighter had behaved as if the force pulling them had increased for every inch they moved sternward.

The dictaphone was fifty feet below, utterly unreachable. If I had anything more to say to General Products, I'd have to say it in person. Maybe I'd get the chance. Because I knew what force was trying to tear the ship apart.

It was the tide.

The motor was off, and I was at the ship's midpoint. My spread-eagled position was getting uncomfortable. It was four minutes to perihelion.

Something creaked in the cabin below me. I couldn't see what it was, but I could clearly see a red point glaring among blue radial lines, like a lantern at the bottom of a well. To the sides, between the fusion tube and the tanks and other equipment, the blue stars glared at me with a light that was almost violet. I was afraid to look too long. I actually thought they might blind me.

There must have been hundreds of gravities in the cabin. I could even feel the pressure change. The air was thin at this height, one hundred and fifty feet above the control room.

And now, almost suddenly, the red dot was more than a dot. My time was up. A red disc leapt up at me; the ship swung around me; and I gasped and shut my eyes tight. Giants' hands gripped my arms and legs and head, gently but with great firmness, and tried to pull me in two. In that moment it came to me that Peter Laskin had died like this. He'd made the same guesses I had, and he'd tried to hide in the access tube. But he'd slipped. As I was slipping . . .

When I got my eyes open the red dot was shrinking into nothing.

IV

The puppeteer president insisted I be put in a hospital for observation. I didn't fight the idea. My face and hands were flaming red, with blisters rising, and I ached like I'd been beaten. Rest and tender loving care, that's what I wanted.

I was floating between a pair of sleeping plates, hideously uncomfortable, when the nurse came to announce a visitor. I knew who it was from her peculiar expression.

"What can get through a General Products hull?" I asked it.

"I hoped you would tell me." The president rested on its single back leg, holding a stick that gave off green, incense-smelling smoke.

"And so I will. Gravity."

"Do not play with me, Beowulf Shaeffer. This matter is vital."

"I'm not playing. Does your world have a moon?"

"That information is classified." The puppeteers are cowards. Nobody knows where they come from, and nobody is likely to find out.

"Do you know what happens when a moon gets too close to its primary?"

"It falls apart."

"Why?"

"I do not know."

"Tides."

"What is a tide?"

Oho, said I to myself, said I. "I'm going to try to tell you. The Earth's moon is almost two thousand miles in diameter and does not rotate with respect to Earth. I want you to pick two rocks on the Moon, one at the point nearest the Earth, one at the point furthest away."

"Very well."

"Now, isn't it obvious that if those rocks were left to themselves they'd fall away from each other? They're in two different orbits, mind you, concentric orbits, one almost two thousand miles outside the other. Yet those rocks are forced to move at the same orbital speed."

"The one outside is moving faster."

"Good point. So there *is* a force trying to pull the Moon apart. Gravity holds it together. Bring the Moon close enough to Earth, and those two rocks would simply float away."

"I see. Then this *tide* tried to pull your ship apart. It was powerful enough in the lifesystem of the Institute ship to pull the acceleration chairs out of their mounts."

"And to crush a human being. Picture it. The ship's nose was just seven miles from the center of BVS-1. The tail was three hundred feet further out. Left to themselves they'd have gone in completely different orbits. My head and feet tried to do the same thing, when I got close enough."

"I see. Are you moulting?"

"What?"

"I noticed you are losing your outer integument in spots."

"Oh, *that*. I got a bad sunburn from exposure to starlight."

Two heads stared at each other for an eyeblink. A shrug? The puppeteer said, "We have deposited the remainder of your pay with the Bank of We Made It. One Sigmund Ausfaller, human, has frozen the account until your taxes are computed."

"Figures."

"If you will talk to reporters now, explaining what happened to the Institute ship, we will pay you ten thousand stars. We will pay cash so that you may use it immediately. It is urgent. There have been rumors."

"Bring 'em in." As an afterthought I added, "I can also tell them that your world is moonless. That should be good for a footnote somewhere."

"I do not understand." But two long necks had drawn back, and the puppeteer was watching me like a pair of pythons.

"You'd know what a tide was if you had a moon. You couldn't avoid it."

"Would you be interested in . . ."

" . . . a million stars? I'd be fascinated. I'll even sign a contract if it includes what we're hiding. How do *you* like being black-mailed?"

Mellonta Tauta

Edgar Allan Poe

To the Editor of the Lady's Book:

*I have the honor of sending you, for your magazine, an article which
I hope you will be able to comprehend rather more distinctly than I
do myself. It is a translation, by my friend Martin Van Buren Mavis
(sometimes called the "Poughkeepsie Seer,") of an odd-looking MS. which
I found, about a year ago, tightly corked up in a jug floating in the
Mare Tenebrarum—a sea well described by the Nubian geographer, but
seldom visited, now-a-days, except by the transcendentalists and divers
for crotchets.*

> *Very Truly,*
> EDGAR A. POE

On Board Balloon "Skylark"

April 1, 2848

Now, my dear friend—now, for your sins, you are to suffer the
infliction of a long gossiping letter. I tell you distinctly that I am
going to punish you for all your impertinences by being as tedious,
as discursive, as incoherent, and as unsatisfactory as possible.
Besides, here I am, cooped in a dirty balloon, with some one or
two hundred of the *canaille,* all bound on a *pleasure* excursion, (what
a funny idea some people have of pleasure!) and I have no prospect
of touching *terra firma* for a month at least. Nobody to talk to.
Nothing to do. When one has nothing to do, then is the time to
correspond with one's friends. You perceive, then, why it is that
I write you this letter—it is on account of my *ennui* and your sins.

Get ready your spectacles and make up your mind to be annoyed.
I mean to write at you every day during this odious voyage.

Heigho! when will any *Invention* visit the human pericranium?
Are we forever to be doomed to the thousand inconveniences of
the balloon? Will *nobody* contrive a more expeditious mode of prog-

ress? This jog-trot movement, to my thinking, is little less than positive torture. Upon my word we have not made more than a hundred miles the hour since leaving home! The very birds beat us—at least some of them. I assure you that I do not exaggerate at all. Our motion, no doubt, seems slower than it actually is—this on account of our having no objects about us by which to estimate our velocity, and on account of our going *with* the wind. To be sure, whenever we meet a balloon we have a chance of perceiving our rate, and then, I admit, things do not appear so very bad. Accustomed as I am to this mode of traveling, I cannot get over a kind of giddiness whenever a balloon passes us in a current directly overhead. It always seems to me like an immense bird of prey about to pounce upon us and carry us off in its claws. One went over us this morning about sunrise, and so nearly overhead that its drag rope actually brushed the net-work suspending our car, and caused us very serious apprehension. Our captain said that if the material of the bag had been the trumpery varnished "silk" of five hundred or a thousand years ago, we should inevitably have been damaged. This silk, as he explained it to me, was a fabric composed of the entrails of a species of earth-worm. The worm was carefully fed on mulberries—a kind of fruit resembling a water-melon—and, when sufficiently fat, was crushed in a mill. The paste thus arising was called *papyrus* in its primary state, and went through a variety of processes until it finally became "silk." Singular to relate, it was once much admired as an article of *female dress!* Balloons were also very generally constructed from it. A better kind of material, it appears, was subsequently found in the down surrounding the seed-vessels of a plant vulgarly called *euphorbium*, and at that time botanically termed milkweed. This latter kind of silk was designated as silk-buckingham, on account of its superior durability, and was usually prepared for use by being varnished with a solution of gum caoutchouc—a substance which in some respects must have resembled the *gutta percha* now in common use. This caoutchouc was occasionally called India rubber or rubber of whist, and was no doubt one of the numerous *fungi*. Never tell me again that I am not at heart an antiquarian.

Talking of drag-ropes our own, it seems, has this moment knocked a man overboard from one of the small magnetic propellers that swarm in ocean below us—a boat of about six thousand tons, and, from all accounts, shamefully crowded. These diminutive barques should be prohibited from carrying more than a definite number of passengers. The man, of course, was not permitted to get on board again, and was soon out of sight, he and his life-preserver. I rejoice, my dear friend, that we live in an age so enlightened that no such thing as an individual is supposed to exist. It is the mass for which the true Humanity cares. By the by, talking of Humanity, do you know that our immortal Wiggins is not so original in his views of the Social Condition and so forth, as his contemporaries are inclined to suppose? Pundit assures me that the same ideas were put, nearly in the same way, about a thousand years ago, by an Irish philosopher called Furrier, on account of his keeping a retail shop for cat-peltries and other furs. Pundit *knows*, you know; there can be no mistake about it. How very wonderfully do we see verified, every day, the profound observation of the Hindoo Aries Tottle (as quoted by Pundit)—"Thus must we say that, not once or twice, or a few times, but with almost infinite repetitions, the same opinions come round in a circle among men."

April 2.—Spoke to-day the magnetic cutter in charge of the middle section of floating telegraph wires. I learn that when this species of telegraph was first put into operation by Horse, it was considered quite impossible to convey the wires over sea; but now we are at a loss to comprehend where the difficulty lay! So wags the world. *Tempora mutantur*—excuse me for quoting the Etruscan. What *would* we do without the Atalantic telegraph? (Pundit says Atlantic was the ancient adjective.) We lay to a few minutes to ask the cutter some questions, and learned, among other glorious news, that civil war is raging in Africa, while the plague is doing its good work beautifully both in Yurope and Ayesher. Is it not truly remarked that, before the magnificent light shed upon philosophy by Humanity, the world was accustomed to regard War and Pestilence as calamities? Do you know that prayers were actually offered up in the ancient temples to the end that these *evils*(!) might not be visited upon mankind? Is it not really difficult to comprehend upon what principle of interest our forefathers acted? Were they so blind as not to perceive that the destruction of a myriad of individuals is only so much positive advantage to the mass!

April 3.—It is really a very fine amusement to ascend the rope-ladder leading to the summit of the balloon-bag and thence survey the surrounding world. From the car below, you know, the prospect is not so comprehensive—you can see little vertically. But seated here (where I write this) in the luxuriously-cushioned open piazza of the summit, one can see everything that is going on in all directions. Just now, there is quite a crowd of balloons in sight, and they present a very animated appearance, while the air is resonant with the hum of so many millions of human voices. I have heard it asserted that when Yellow or (as Pundit *will* have it) Violet, who is supposed to have been the first aeronaut, maintained the practicability of traversing the atmosphere in all directions, by merely ascending or descending until a favorable current was attained, he was scarcely hearkened to at all by his contemporaries, who looked upon him as merely an ingenious sort of madman, because the philosophers (?) of the day declared the thing impossible. Really now it does seem to me *quite* unaccountable how anything so obviously feasible could have escaped the sagacity of the ancient *savans.* But in all ages the great obstacles to advancement in Art have been opposed by the so-called men of science. To be sure, *our* men of science are not quite so bigoted as those of old:—oh, I have something *so* queer to tell you on this topic. Do you know that it is not more than a thousand years ago since the metaphysicians consented to relieve the people of the singular fancy that there existed but *two possible roads for the attainment of Truth!* Believe it if you can! It appears that long, long ago, in the night of Time, there lived a Turkish philosopher (or Hindoo possibly) called Aries Tottle. This person introduced, or at all events propagated what was termed the deductive or *à priori* mode of investigation. He started with what he maintained to be *axioms* or "self-evident truths," and thence proceeded "logically" to results. His greatest disciples were one Neuclid and one Cant. Well, Aries Tottle flourished supreme until the advent of one Hog, surnamed the "Ettrick Shepherd," who preached an entirely different system, which he called the *à posteriori* or inductive. His plan referred altogether to Sensation. He proceeded by observing, analyzing and classifying facts—*instantiae naturae,* as they were affectedly called—into general laws. Aries Tottle's mode, in a word, was based on *noumena;* Hog's on *phenomena.* Well, so great was the admiration excited by this latter system that, at its first introduction, Aries Tottle fell into disrepute; but finally he recovered ground, and was permitted to divide the realm of Truth with his more modern rival. The *savans* now maintained that the Aristotelian and *Baconian* roads were the sole possible avenues to knowledge. "Baconian," you must know, was an adjective invented as equivalent to Hog-ian and more euphonious and dignified.

Now, my dear friend, I do assure you, most positively, that I represent this matter fairly, on the soundest authority; and you can easily understand how a notion so absurd on its very face must have operated to retard the progress of all true knowledge—which makes its advances almost invariably by intuitive bounds. The ancient idea confined investigation to *crawling;* and for hundreds of years so great was the infatuation about Hog especially, that a virtual end was put to all thinking properly so called. No man dared utter a truth to which he felt himself indebted to his *Soul* alone. It mattered not whether the truth was even *demonstrably* a truth, for the bullet-headed *savans* of the time regarded only *the road* by which he had attained it. They would not even *look* at the end. "Let us see the means," they cried, "the means!" If, upon investigation of the means, it was found to come neither under the category of Aries (that is to say Ram) nor under the category Hog, why then the savans went no farther, but pronounced the "theorist" a fool, and would have nothing to do with him or his truth.

Now, it cannot be maintained, even, that by the crawling system the greatest amount of truth would be attained in any long series of ages, for the repression of *imagination* was an evil not to be compensated for by any superior *certainty* in the ancient modes of investigation. The error of these Jurmains, these Vrinch, these Inglitch and these Amriccans (the latter, by the way, were our own immediate progenitors) was an error quite analogous with that of the wiseacre who fancies that he must necessarily see an object the better the more closely he holds it to his eyes. These people blinded themselves by details. When they proceeded Hoggishly, their "facts" were by no means always facts—a matter of little consequence had it not been for assuming that they *were* facts and must be facts because they appeared to be such. When they proceeded on the path of the Ram, their course was scarcely as straight as a ram's horn, for they *never had* an axiom which was an axiom at all. They must have been very blind not to see this, even in their own day; for even in their own day many of the long "established" axioms had been rejected. For example—"*Ex nihilo nihil fit*"; "a body cannot act where it is not"; "there cannot exist antipodes"; "darkness cannot come out of light"—all these, and a dozen other similar propositions, formerly admitted without hesitation as axioms, were, even at the period of which I speak, seen to be untenable. How absurd in these people, then, to persist in putting faith in "axioms" as immutable bases of Truth! But even out of the mouths of their soundest reasoners it is easy to demonstrate the futility, the impalpability of their axioms in general. Who *was* the soundest of their logicians? Let me see! I will go and ask Pundit and be back in a minute.... Ah, here we have it! Here is a book written nearly a thousand years ago and lately translated from the Inglitch—which, by the way, appears to have been the rudiments of the Amriccans. Pundit says it is decidedly the cleverest ancient work on its topic, Logic. The author (who was much thought of in his day) was one Miller, or Mill; and we find it recorded of him, as a point of some importance, that he had a millhorse called Bentham. But let us glance at the treatise!

Ah!—"Ability or inability to conceive," says Mr. Mill, very properly, "is in no case to be received as a criterion of axiomatic truth." What *modern* in his senses would ever think of disputing this truism? The only wonder with us must be, how it happened that Mr. Mill conceived it necessary even to hint at any thing so obvious. So far good—but let us turn over another page. What have we here?—"Contradictories cannot both be true—that is, cannot co-exist in nature." Here Mr. Mill means, for example, that a tree must be either a tree or not a tree—that it cannot be at the same time a tree and not a tree. Very well; but I ask him *why*. His reply is this—and never pretends to be any thing else than this—"Because it is impossible to conceive that contradictories can both be true." But this is no answer at all, by his own showing; for has he not just admitted as a truism that "ability or inability to conceive is *in no case* to be received as a criterion of axiomatic truth."

Now I do not complain of these ancients so much because their logic is, by their own showing, utterly baseless, worthless and fantastic altogether, as because of their pompous and imbecile proscription of all *other* roads of truth, of all *other* means for its attainment than the two preposterous paths—the one of creeping and the one of crawling—to which they have dared to confine the Soul that loves nothing so well as to *soar*.

By the by, my dear friend, do you not think it would have puzzled these ancient dogmaticians to have determined by *which* of their two roads it was that the most important and most sublime of *all* their truths was, in effect, attained? I mean the truth of Gravitation. Newton owed it to Kepler. Kepler admitted that his three laws were *guessed at*—these three laws of all laws which led the great Inglitch mathematician to his principle, the basis of all physical principle—to go behind which we must enter the Kingdom of Metaphysics. Kepler guessed—that is to say, *imagined*. He was essentially a "theorist" —that word now of so much sanctity, formerly an epithet of contempt. Would it not have puzzled these old moles, too, to have explained by which of the two "roads" a cryptographist unriddles a cryptograph of more than usual secrecy, or by which of the two roads Champollion directed mankind to those enduring and almost innumerable truths which resulted from his deciphering the Hieroglyphics?

One word more on this topic and I will be done boring you. Is it not *passing* strange that, with their eternal prating about *roads* to Truth, these bigoted people missed what we now so clearly perceive to be the great highway—that of Consistency? Does it not seem singular how they should have failed to deduce from the works of God the vital fact that a perfect consistency *must be* in absolute truth! How plain has been our progress since the late announcement of this proposition! Investigation has been taken out of the hands of the ground-moles and given, as a task, to the true and only true thinkers, the men of ardent imagination. These latter *theorize*. Can you not fancy the shout of scorn with which my words would be received by our progenitors were it possible for them to be now looking over my shoulder? These men, I say, *theorize*; and their theories are simply corrected, reduced, systematized—cleared, little by little, of their dross of inconsistency—until, finally, a perfect consistency stands apparent which even the most stolid admit, because it *is* a consistency, to be an absolute and an unquestionable *truth*.

April 4.—The new gas is doing wonders, in conjunction with the new improvement in gutta percha. How very safe, commodious,

Fiction

manageable, and in every respect convenient are our modern balloons! Here is an immense one approaching us at the rate of at
least a hundred and fifty miles an hour. It seems to be crowded
with people—perhaps there are three or four hundred passengers—and yet it soars to an elevation of nearly a mile, looking
down upon poor us with sovereign contempt. Still a hundred or
even two hundred miles an hour is slow traveling, after all. *Do* you
remember our flight on the railroad across the Kanadaw continent?
—fully three hundred miles the hour—*that* was traveling. Nothing
to be seen, though—nothing to be done but flirt, feast and dance
in the magnificent saloons. Do you remember what an odd sensation
was experienced when, by chance, we caught a glimpse of external
objects while the cars were in full flight? Everything seemed
unique—in one mass. For my part, I cannot say but that I preferred
the traveling by the slow train of a hundred miles the hour. Here
we were permitted to have glass windows—even to have them
open—and something like a distinct view of the country was
attainable. . . . Pundit says that *the route* for the great Kanadaw railroad must have been in some measure marked out about nine
hundred years ago! In fact, he goes so far as to assert that actual
traces of a road are still discernible—traces referable to a period quite
as remote as that mentioned. The track, it appears, was *double* only;
ours you know, has twelve paths; and three or four new ones are in
preparation. The ancient rails were very slight, and placed so close
together as to be, according to modern notions, quite frivolous, if
not dangerous in the extreme. The present width of track—fifty
feet—is considered, indeed, scarcely secure enough. For my part,
I make no doubt that a track of some sort *must* have existed in very
remote times, as Pundit asserts; for nothing can be clearer, to my
mind, than that, at some period—not less than seven centuries ago,
certainly—the Northern and Southern Kanadaw continents were
united; the Kanawdians, then, would have been driven, by necessity,
to a great railroad across the continent.

April 5.—I am almost devoured by *ennui.* Pundit is the only conver-
sible person on board; and he, poor soul! can speak of nothing but
antiquities. He has been occupied all the day in the attempt to convince me that the ancient Amriccans *governed themselves!*—did ever
anybody hear of such an absurdity?—that they existed in a sort of
every-man-for-himself confederacy, after the fashion of the "prairie
dogs" that we read of in fable. He says that they started with the
queerest idea conceivable, viz: that all men are born free and
equal—this in the very teeth of the laws of *gradation* so visibly
impressed upon all things both in the moral and physical universe.
Every man "voted," as they called it—that is to say, meddled with
public affairs—until, at length, it was discovered that what is
everybody's business is nobody's and that the "Republic" (so the

absurd thing was called) was without a government at all. It is related, however, that the first circumstance which disturbed, very particularly, the self-complacency of the philosophers who constructed this "Republic," was the startling discovery that universal suffrage gave opportunity for fraudulent schemes, by means of which any desired number of votes might at any time be polled, without the possibility of prevention or even detection, by any party which should be merely villainous enough not to be ashamed of the fraud. A little reflection upon this discovery sufficed to render evident the consequences, which were that rascality *must* predominate—in a word, that a republican government *could* never be anything but a rascally one. While the philosophers, however, were busied in blushing at their stupidity in not having foreseen these inevitable evils, and intent upon the invention of new theories, the matter was put to an abrupt issue by a fellow of the name of *Mob*, who took everything into his own hands and set up a despotism, in comparison with which those of the fabulous Zeros and Hellofagabaluses were respectable and delectable. This Mob (a foreigner, by the by) is said to have been the most odious of all men that ever encumbered the earth. He was a giant in stature—insolent, rapacious, filthy; had the gall of a bullock with the heart of an hyena and the brains of a peacock. He died, at length, by dint of his own energies, which exhausted him. Nevertheless, he had his uses, as everything has, however vile, and taught mankind a lesson which to this day it is in no danger of forgetting—never to run directly contrary to the natural analogies. As for Republicanism, no analogy could be found for it upon the face of the earth—unless we except the case of the "prairie dogs," an exception which seems to demonstrate, if anything, that democracy is a very admirable form of government—for dogs.

April 6.—Last night had a fine view of Alpha Lyrae, whose disk, through our captain's spy-glass, subtends an angle of half a degree, looking very much as our sun does to the naked eye on a misty day. Alpha Lyrae, although so *very* much larger than our sun, by the by, resembles him closely as regards its spots, its atmosphere, and in many other particulars. It is only within the last century, Pundit tells me, that the binary relation existing between these two orbs began even to be suspected. The evident motion of our system in the heavens was (strange to say!) referred to an orbit about a prodigious star in the centre of the galaxy. About this star, or at all events about a centre of gravity common to all the globes of the Milky Way and supposed to be near Alcyone in the Pleiades, every one of these globes was declared to be revolving, our own performing the circuit in a period of 117,000,000 of years! *We,* with our present lights, our vast telescopic improvements and so forth, of course find it difficult to comprehend *the ground* of an idea such as this. Its first propagator was one Mudler. He was led, we must presume, to this wild hypothesis by mere analogy in the first instance; but, this being the case, he should have at least adhered to analogy in its development. A great central orb *was*, in fact, suggested; so far Mudler was consistent. This central orb, however, dynamically, should have been greater than all its surrounding orbs taken together. The question might then have been asked—"Why do we not see it?"—*we*, especially, who occupy the mid region of the cluster—the very locality *near* which, at least, must be situated this inconceivable central sun. The astronomer, perhaps, at this point, took refuge in the suggestion of non-luminosity; and here analogy was suddenly let fall. But even admitting the central orb non-luminous, how did he manage to explain its failure to be rendered visible by the incalculable host of glorious suns glaring in all directions about it? No doubt what he finally maintained was merely a centre of gravity common to all the revolving orbs—but here again analogy must have been let fall. Our system revolves, it is true, about a common centre of gravity, but it does this in connection with and in consequence of a material sun whose mass more than counterbalances the rest of the system. The mathematical circle is a curve composed of an infinity of straight lines; but this idea of the circle—this idea of it which, in regard to all earthly geometry, we consider as merely the mathematical, in contradistinction from the practical, idea—is, in sober fact, the *practical* conception which alone we have any right to entertain in respect to those Titanic circles with which we have to deal, at least in fancy, when we suppose our system, with its fellows, revolving about a point in the centre of the galaxy. Let the most vigorous of human imaginations but attempt to take a single step towards the comprehension of a circuit so unutterable! It would scarcely be paradoxical to say that a flash of lightning itself, traveling *forever* upon the circumference of this inconceivable circle, would still *forever* be traveling in a straight line. That the path of our sun along such a circumference —that the direction of our system in such an orbit—would, to any human perception, deviate in the slightest degree from a straight line even in a million of years, is a proposition not to be entertained; and yet these ancient astronomers were absolutely cajoled, it appears, into believing that a decisive curvature had become apparent during the brief period of their astronomical history—during the mere point—during the utter nothingness of two or three thousand years! How incomprehensible, that considerations such as this did not at once indicate to them the true state of affairs—that of the binary revolution of our sun and Alpha Lyrae around a common centre of gravity!

April 7.—Continued last night our astronomical amusements. Had a fine view of the five Nepturian asteroids, and watched with much interest the putting up of a huge impost on a couple of lintels in the new temple at Daphnis in the moon. It was amusing to think that creatures so diminutive as the lunarians, and bearing so little resemblance to humanity, yet evinced a mechanical ingenuity so much superior to our own. One finds it difficult, too, to conceive the vast masses which these handle so easily, to be as light as our reason tells us they actually are.

April 8.—Eureka! Pundit is in his glory. A balloon from Kanadaw spoke us to-day and threw on board several late papers: they contain some exceedingly curious information relative to Kanawdian or rather to Amriccan antiquities. You know, I presume, that laborers have for some months been employed in preparing the ground for a new fountain at Paradise, the emperor's principal pleasure garden. Paradise, it appears, has been, *literally* speaking, an island time out of mind—that is to say, its northern boundary was always (as far back as any records extend) a rivulet, or rather a very narrow arm of the sea. This arm was gradually widened until it attained its present breadth—a mile. The whole length of the island is nine miles; the breadth varies materially. The entire area (so Pundit says) was, about eight hundred years ago, densely packed with houses, some of them twenty stories high; land (for some most unaccountable reason) being considered as specially precious just in this vicinity. The disastrous earthquake, however, of the year 2050, so totally uprooted and overwhelmed the town (for it was almost too large to be called a village) that the most indefatigable of our antiquarians have never yet been able to obtain from the site any sufficient data (in the shape of coins, medals or inscriptions) wherewith to build up even the ghost of a theory concerning the manners, customs, &c. &c., of the aboriginal inhabitants. Nearly all that we have hitherto known of them is, that they were a portion of the Knicker-bocker tribe of savages infesting the continent at its first discovery by Recorder Riker, a knight of the Golden Fleece. They were by no means uncivilized, however, but cultivated various arts and even sciences after a fashion of their own. It is related of them that they were acute in many respects, but were oddly afflicted with a monomania for building what, in the ancient Amriccan, was denominated "churches"—a kind of pagoda instituted for the wor-ship of two idols that went by the names of Wealth and Fashion. In the end, it is said, the island became, nine-tenths of it, church. The women, too, it appears were oddly deformed by a natural pro-tuberance of the region just below the small of the back—although, most unaccountably, this deformity was looked upon altogether in the light of a beauty. One or two pictures of these singular women have, in fact, been miraculously preserved. They look very odd, *very*—like something between a turkey-cock and a dromedary.

Well, these few details are nearly all that have descended to us respecting the ancient Knickerbockers. It seems, however, that while digging in the centre of the emperor's garden (which, you know,

covers the whole island), some of the workmen unearthed a cubical
and evidently chiseled block of granite, weighing several hundred
pounds. It was in good preservation, having received, apparently,
little injury from the convulsion which entombed it. On one of its
surfaces was a marble slab with (only think of it!) *an inscription—a
legible inscription.* Pundit is in ecstasies. Upon detaching the slab,
a cavity appeared, containing a leaden box filled with various coins,
a long scroll of names, several documents which appear to resemble
newspapers, with other matters of intense interest to the antiquarian! There can be no doubt that all these are genuine Amriccan relics
belonging to the tribe called Knickerbocker. The papers thrown on
board our balloon are filled with fac-similes of the coins, MSS.,
typography, &c. &c. I copy for your amusement the Knickerbocker
inscription on the marble slab:—

THIS CORNER STONE OF A MONUMENT TO THE
MEMORY OF
GEORGE WASHINGTON,
WAS LAID WITH APPROPRIATE CEREMONIES ON THE
19TH DAY OF OCTOBER, 1847,
THE ANNIVERSARY OF THE SURRENDER OF
LORD CORNWALLIS
TO GENERAL WASHINGTON AT YORKTOWN,
A.D. 1781,
UNDER THE AUSPICES OF THE
WASHINGTON MONUMENT ASSOCIATION OF THE
CITY OF NEW YORK.

This, as I give it, is a verbatim translation done by Pundit himself,
so there *can* be no mistake about it. From the few words thus preserved, we glean several important items of knowledge, not the least
interesting of which is the fact that a thousand years ago *actual*
monuments had fallen into disuse—as was all very proper—the
people contenting themselves, as we do now, with a mere indication
of the design to erect a monument at some future time; a cornerstone
being cautiously laid by itself "solitary and alone" (excuse me for
quoting the great Amriccan poet Benton!) as a guarantee of the mag-
nanimous *intention*. We ascertain, too, very distinctly, from this
admirable inscription, the how, as well as the where and the what,
of the great surrender in question. As to the *where*, it was Yorktown
(wherever that was), and as to the *what*, it was General Cornwallis
(no doubt some wealthy dealer in corn). *He* was surrendered. The
inscription commemorates the surrender of—what?—why, "of Lord
Cornwallis." The only question is what could the savages wish him
surrendered for. But when we remember that these savages were
undoubtedly cannibals, we are led to the conclusion that they

intended him for sausage. As to the *how* of the surrender, no language can be more explicit. Lord Cornwallis was surrendered (for sausage) "under the auspices of the Washington Monument Association"—no doubt a charitable institution for the depositing of corner-stones.—But Heaven bless me! what is the matter? Ah! I see—the balloon has collapsed, and we shall have a tumble into the sea, I have, therefore, only time enough to add that, from a hasty inspection of fac-similes of newspapers, &c., I find that *the* great men in those days among the Amriccans were one John, a smith, and one Zacchary, a tailor.

Good bye, until I see you again. Whether you ever get this letter or not is a point of little importance, as I write altogether for my own amusement. I shall cork the MS. up in a bottle however, and throw it into the sea.

Yours everlastingly,
PUNDITA

What to Do
until the Analyst Comes

Frederik Pohl

I just sent my secretary out for a container of coffee and she brought me back a lemon Coke.

I can't really blame her. Who in all the world do I have to blame, except myself? Hazel was a good secretary to me for fifteen years, fine at typing, terrific at brushing off people I didn't want to see, and the queen of them all at pumping office gossip out of the ladies' lounge. She's a little fuzzy-brained most of the time now, sure. But after all!

I can say this for myself, I didn't exactly know what I was getting into. No doubt you remember the—Well, let me start that sentence over again, because naturally there is a certain doubt. Perhaps, let's say, *perhaps* you remember the two doctors and their headline report about cigarettes and lung cancer. It hit us pretty hard at VandenBlumer & Silk, because we've been eating off the Mason-Dixon Tobacco account for twenty years. Just figure what our fifteen per cent amounted to on better than ten million dollars net billing a year, and you'll see that for yourself. What happened first was all to the good, because naturally the first thing that the client did was scream and reach for his checkbook and pour another couple million dollars into special promotions to counteract the bad press, but that couldn't last. And we knew it. VB. & S. is noted in the trade as an advertising agency that takes the long view; we saw at once that if the client was in danger, no temporary spurt of advertising was going to pull him out of it, and it was time for us to climb up on top of the old mountain and take a good look at the countryside ahead.

The Chief called a special Plans meeting that morning and laid it on the line for us. "There goes the old fire bell, boys," he said, "and it's up to us to put the fire out. I'm listening, so start talking."

Baggott cleared his throat and said glumly, "It may only be the paper, Chief. Maybe if they make them without paper...." He's

418

the a.e. for Mason-Dixon, so you couldn't really blame him for taking the client's view.

The Chief twinkled: "If they make them without paper they aren't cigarettes any more, are they? Let's not wander off into side issues, boys. I'm still listening."

None of us wanted to wander off into side issues, so we all looked patronizingly at Baggott for a minute. Finally, Ellen Silk held up her hand. "I don't want you to think," she said, "that just because Daddy left me a little stock I'm going to push my way into things, Mr. VandenBlumer, but—well, did you have in mind finding some, uh, angle to play on that would take the public's mind off the report?"

You have to admire the Chief. "Is that your recommendation, my dear?" he inquired fondly, bouncing the ball right back to her.

She said weakly, "*I* don't know. I'm confused."

"Naturally, my dear," he beamed. "So are we all. Let's see if Charley here can straighten us out a little. Eh, Charley?"

He was looking at me. I said at once, "I'm glad you asked me for an opinion, Chief. I've been doing a little thinking, and here's what I've come up with." I ticked off the points on my fingers. "One, tobacco makes you cough. Two, liquor gives you a hangover. Three, reefers and the other stuff—well, let's just say they're against the law." I slapped the three fingers against the palm of my other hand. "So what's left for us, Chief? That's my question. Can we come up with something new, something different, something that, one, is not injurious to the health, two, does not give you a hangover, three, is not habit-forming and therefore against the law?"

Mr. VandenBlumer said approvingly, "That's good thinking, Charley. When you hear that fire bell, you really jump, boy."

Baggott's hand was up. He said, "Let me get this straight, Chief. Is it Charley's idea that we recommend to Mason-Dixon that they go out of the tobacco business and start making something else?"

The old man looked at him blandly for a moment. "Why should it be Mason-Dixon?" he asked softly, and left it at that while we all thought of the very good reasons why it *shouldn't* be Mason-Dixon. After all, loyalty to a client is one thing, but you've got an obligation to your own people too.

The old man let it sink in, then he turned back to me. "Well, Charley?" he asked. "We've heard you pinpoint what we need. Got any specific suggestions?"

They were all looking at me to see if I had anything concrete to offer.

Unfortunately, I had.

I just asked Hazel to get me the folder on Leslie Clary Cloud, and she came in with a copy of my memo putting him on the payroll two years back. "That's all there was in the file," she said dreamily, her jaw muscles moving rhythmically. There wasn't any use arguing with her, so I handed her the container of lemon Coke and told her to ditch it and bring me back some *coffee*, C-O-F-F-E-E, coffee. I tried going through the files myself when she was gone, but *that* was a waste of time.

So I'll have to tell you about Leslie Clary Cloud from memory. He came into the office without an appointment and why Hazel ever let him in to see me I'll never know. But she did. He told me right away, "I've been fired, Mr. McGory. Canned. After eleven years with the Wyoming Bureau of Standards as a senior chemist."

"That's too bad, Dr. Cloud," I said, shuffling the papers on my desk. "I'm afraid, though, that our organization doesn't—"

"No, no," he said hastily, " I don't know anything about advertising. Organic chemistry's my field. I have a, well, a suggestion for a process that might interest you. You have the Mason-Dixon Tobacco account, don't you? Well, in my work for my doctorate I—" He drifted off into a fog of long-chain molecules and short-chain molecules and pentose sugars and common garden herbs. It took me a little while, but I listened patiently and I began to see what he was driving at. There was, he was saying, a substance in a common plant which, by cauliflamming the whingdrop and ditricolating the residual glom, or words something like that, you could convert into another substance which appeared to have many features in common with what is sometimes called hop, snow or joy-dust. In other words, dope.

I stared at him aghast. "Dr. Cloud," I demanded, "do you know what you're suggesting? If we added this stuff to our client's cigarettes we'd be flagrantly violating the law. That's the most unheard-of thing I ever heard of! Besides, we've already looked into this matter, and the cost estimates are—"

"No, no!" he said again. "You don't understand, Mr. McGory. This isn't any of the drugs currently available, it's something new and different."

"Different?"

"Non-habit-forming, for instance."

"Non-habit-forming?"

"Totally. Chemically it is entirely unrelated to any narcotic in the pharmacopeia. Legally—well, I'm no lawyer, but I swear, Mr. McGory, this isn't covered by any regulation. No reason it should be. It doesn't hurt the user, it doesn't form a habit, it's cheap to manufacture, it—"

"Hold it," I said, getting to my feet. "Don't go away—I want to catch the boss before he goes to lunch."

So I caught the boss, and he twinkled thoughtfully at me. No, he didn't want me to discuss it with Mason-Dixon just yet, and yes, it did seem to have some possibilities, and certainly, put this man on the payroll and see if he turns up with something.

So we did; and he did.

Auditing raised the roof when the vouchers began to come through, but I bucked them up to the Chief and he calmed them down. It took a lot of money, though, and it took nearly six months. But then Leslie Clary Cloud called up one morning and said, "Come on down, Mr. McGory. We're in."

The place we'd fixed up for him was on the lower East Side and it reeked of rotten vegetables. I made a mental note to double-check all our added-chlorophyll copy and climbed up the two flights of stairs to Cloud's private room. He was sitting at a lab bench, beaming at a row of test tubes in front of him.

"This is it?" I asked, gleaming at the test tubes.

"This is it." He smiled dreamily at me and yawned. "Excuse me," he blinked amiably. "I've been sampling the little old product."

I looked him over very carefully. He had been sampling something or other, that was clear enough. But no whisky breath; no dilated pupils; no shakes; no nothing. He was relaxed and cheerful, and that was all you could say.

"Try a little old bit," he invited, gesturing at the test tubes.

Well, there are times when you have to pay your dues in the club. VB. & S. had been mighty good to me, and if I had to swallow something unfamiliar to justify the confidence the Chief had in me, why I just had to go ahead and do it. Still, I hesitated for a moment.

"Aw," said Leslie Clary Cloud, "don't be scared. Look, I just had a shot but I'll take another one." He fumbled one of the test tubes out of the rack and, humming to himself, slopped a little of the colorless stuff into a beaker of some other colorless stuff—water, I suppose. He drank it down and smacked his lips. "Tastes awful," he observed cheerfully, "but we'll fix that. Whee!"

I looked him over again, and he looked back at me, giggling. "Too strong," he said happily. "Got it too strong. We'll fix that too." He rattled beakers and test tubes aimlessly while I took a deep breath and nerved myself up to it.

"All right," I said, and took the fresh beaker out of his hand. I swallowed it down almost in one gulp. It tasted terrible, just as he said, tasted like the lower floors had smelled, but that was all I noticed right away. Nothing happened for a moment except that Cloud looked at me thoughtfully and frowned.

"Say," he said, "I guess I should have diluted that."

I guess he should have. *Wham.*

But a couple of hours later I was all right again.

Cloud was plenty apologetic. "Still," he said consolingly, standing over me as I lay on the lab bench, "it proves one thing. You had a dose about the equivalent of ten thousand normal shots, and you have to admit it hasn't hurt you."

"I do?" I asked, and looked at the doctor. He swung his stethoscope by the earpieces and shrugged.

Nothing organically wrong with you, Mr. McGory—not that I can find, anyway. Euphoria, yes. Temporarily high pulse, yes. Delirium there for a little while, yes—though it was pretty mild. But I don't think you even have a headache now."

"I don't," I admitted. I swung my feet down and sat up, apprehensively. But no hammers started in my head. I had to confess it: I felt wonderful.

Well, between us we tinkered it into what Cloud decided would be a "normal" dosage—just enough to make you feel good—and he saturated some sort of powder and rolled it into pellets and clamped then in a press and came out with what looked as much like aspirins as anything else. "They'd probably work that way too," he said. "A psychogenic headache would melt away in five minutes with one of those."

"We'll bear that in mind," I said.

What with one thing and another, I couldn't get to the old man that day before he left, and the next day was the weekend and you *don't* disturb the Chief's weekends, and it was Monday evening before I could get him alone for long enough to give him the whole pitch. He was delighted.

"Dear, dear," he twinkled. "So much out of so little. Why, they hardly look like anything at all."

"Try one, Chief," I suggested.

"Perhaps I will. You checked the legal angle?"

"On the quiet. It's absolutely clean."

He nodded and poked at the little pills with his finger. I scratched the back of my neck, trying to be politely inconspicuous, but the Chief doesn't miss much. He looked at me inquiringly.

"Hives," I explained, embarrassed. "I, uh, got an overdose the first time, like I said. I don't know much about these things, but what they told me at the clinic was I set up an allergy."

"Allergy?" Mr. VandenBlumer looked at me thoughtfully. "We don't want to spread allergies with this stuff, do we?"

"Oh, no danger of that, Chief. It's Cloud's fault, in a way; he handed me an undiluted dose of the stuff, and I drank it down. The clinic was very positive about that: Even twenty or thirty times the normal dose won't do you any harm."

"Um." He rolled one of the pills in his finger and thumb and sniffed it thoughtfully. "How long are you going to have your hives?"

"They'll go away. I just have to keep away from the stuff. I wouldn't have them now, but—well, I liked it so much I tried another shot yesterday." I coughed, and added, "It works out pretty well, though. You see the advantages, of course, Chief. I have to give it up, and I can swear that there's no craving, no shakes, no kick-off symptoms, no nothing. I, well, I wish I could enjoy it like anyone else, sure. But I'm here to testify that Cloud told the simple truth: It isn't habit-forming."

"Um," he said again; and that was the end of the discussion.

Oh, the Chief is a cagey man. He gave me my orders: Keep my mouth shut about it. I have an idea that he was waiting to see what happened to my hives, and whether any craving would develop, and what the test series on animals and Cloud's Bowery-derelict volunteers would show. But even more, I think he was waiting until the time was exactly, climactically right.

Like at the Plans meeting, the day after the doctors' report and the panic at Mason-Dixon.

And that's how Cheery-Gum was born.

Hazel just came in with the cardboard container from the drug store, and I could tell by looking at it—no steam coming out from under the lid, beads of moisture clinging to the sides—that it wasn't the coffee I ordered. "Hey!" I yelled after her as she was dreamily waltzing through the door. "Come back here!"

"Sure 'nough, Massa," she said cheerfully, and two-stepped back, "S'matter?"

I took a grip on my temper. "Open that up," I ordered. "Take a look at what's in it."

She smiled at me and popped the lid off the container. Half the contents spilled across my desk. "Oh, dear," said Hazel, "excuse me while I get a cloth."

"Never mind the cloth," I said, mopping at the mess with my handkerchief. "What's in there?"

She gazed wonderingly into the container for a moment; then she said, "Oh, *honestly*, boss! I see what you mean. These idiots in the drug store, they're gummed up higher than a kite, morning, noon and night. I always say, if you can't handle it, you shouldn't touch it during working hours. I'm sorry about this, boss. No lemon! How can they call it a lemon Coke when they forget the—

"Hazel," I said, "what I wanted was coffee. Coffee."

She looked at me. "You mean *I* got it wrong? Oh, I'm sorry, Mr. McGory. I'll go right down and get it now." She smiled repentantly and hummed her way toward the door. With her hand on the knob, she stopped and turned to look at me. "All the same, boss," she said, "that's a funny combination. Coffee *and* Coke. But I'll see what I can do."

And she was gone, to bring me heaven knows what incredible concoction. But what are you going to do?

No, that's no answer. I know it's what *you* would do. But it makes me break out in hives.

The first week we were delighted, the second week we were triumphant, the third week we were millionaires.

The sixth week I skulked along the sidewalks all the way across town and down, to see Leslie Clary Cloud. Even so I almost got it when a truckdriver dreamily piled into the glass front of a saloon a yard or two behind me.

When I saw Cloud sitting at his workbench, feet propped up, hands clasped behind his head, eyes half-closed, I could almost have kissed him. For his jaws were not moving. Alone in New York, except for me, he wasn't chewing Cheery-Gum.

"Thank heaven!" I said sincerely.

He blinked and smiled at me. "Mr. McGory," he said in a pleasant drawl. "Nice of you."

His manner disturbed me, and I looked more closely. "You're not—you're not gummed up, are you?"

He said gently, "Do I looked gummed up? I never chew the stuff."

"Good!" I unfolded the newspaper I had carried all the way from Madison Avenue and showed him the inside pages—the ones that were not a mere smear of ink. "See here, Cloud. Planes crashing into Radio City. Buses driving off the George Washington Bridge. Ships going aground at the Battery. We did it, Cloud, you and I!"

"Oh, I wouldn't get upset about it, old man," he said comfortably. "All local, isn't it?"

"Isn't that bad enough? And it isn't local—it can't be. It's just that there isn't any communication outside the city any more—outside of any city, I guess. The shipments of Cheery-Gum, that's all that ever gets delivered anywhere. Because that's all anybody cares about any more, and we did it, you and I!"

He said sympathetically, "That's too bad, McGory."

"Curse you!" I shrieked at him. "You said it wasn't a drug! You said it wasn't habit-forming! You said—"

"Now, now," he said with gentle firmness. "Why not chew a stick yourself?"

"Because I can't! It gives me hives!"

"Oh, that's right." He looked self-reproachful. "Well," he said dreamily at last, "I guess that's about the size of it, McGory." He was staring at the ceiling again.

"What is?"

"What is what?"

"What's about the—Oh, the devil with it. Cloud, you got us into this, you have to get us out of it. There must be some way of curing this habit."

"But there isn't any habit to cure, McGory," he pointed out.

"But there is!"

"Tem-per," he said waggishly, and took a corked test tube out of his workbench. He drank it down, every drop, and tossed the tube in a wastebasket. "You see?" he demanded severely. "*I* don't chew Cheery-Gum."

So I appealed to a Higher Authority.

In the eighteenth century I would have gone to the Church, in the nineteenth, to the State. I went to an office fronting on Central Park where the name on the bronze plaque was *Theodor Yust, Analyst*.

It wasn't easy. I almost walked out on him when I saw that his jaws were chewing as rhythmically as his secretary's. But Cloud's concoction is not, as he kept saying, a drug, and though it makes you relax and makes you happy and, if you take enough of it, makes you drunk, it doesn't make you unfit to talk to. So I took a grip on my temper, the only bad temper left, and told him what I wanted.

He laughed at me—in the friendliest way. "Put a stop to Cheery-Gum? Mr. McGory!"

"But the plane crashes—"

"No more suicides, Mr. McGory!"

"The train wrecks—"

"Not a murder or a mugging in the whole city in a month."

I said hopelessly, "But it's *wrong!*"

"Ah," he said in the tone of a discoverer, "now we come down to it. Why is it wrong, Mr. McGory?"

That was the second time I almost walked out. But I said, "Let's get one thing straight: I don't want you digging into my problems. That's not why I'm here. Cheery-Gum *is* wrong, and I am *not* biased against it. You can take a detached view of collisions and sudden death if you want to, but what about slow death? All over the city, all over the country, people are lousing up their jobs. Nobody cares. Nobody does anything but go through the motions. They're happy. What happens when they get hungry because the farmers are feeling too good to put in their crops?"

He sighed patiently. He took the wad of gum out of his mouth, rolled it neatly into a Kleenex and dropped it in the wastebasket. He took a fresh stick out of a drawer and unwrapped it, but stopped when he saw me looking at him. He chuckled. "Rather I didn't," Mr. McGory? Well, why not oblige you? It's not habit-forming, after all." He dropped the gum back into the drawer and said: "Answering your questions, they won't starve. The farmers are farming, the workers are working, the policemen are policing, and I'm analyzing. And you're worrying. Why? Work's getting done."

"But my secretary—"

"Forget about your secretary, Mr. McGory. Sure, she's a little fuzzy-brained, a little absent-minded. Who isn't? But she comes to work, because why shouldn't she?"

"Sure she does, but—"

"But she's happy. Let her be happy, Mr. McGory!"

I looked scandalized at him. "You, a doctor! How can you say that? Suppose *you* were fuzzy-brained and so on when a patient desperately needed—"

He stopped me. "In the past three weeks," he said gently, "you're the first to come in that door."

I changed tack: "All right, you're an analyst. What about a G.P. or a surgeon?"

He shrugged. "Perhaps," he conceded, "perhaps in one case out of a thousand—somebody hurt in an accident, say—he'd get to the hospital too late, or the surgeon would make some little mistake. Perhaps. Not even one in a thousand—one in a million, maybe. But Cheery-Gum isn't a drug. A quarter-grain of sodium amytol, and your surgeon's as good as new." Absent-mindedly he reached into the drawer for the stick of gum.

"And you say," I said accusingly, "that it's not habit-forming!"

He stopped with his hand halfway to his mouth. "Well," he said wryly, "it *is* a habit. Don't confuse semantics, Mr. McGory. It is not a narcotic addiction. If my supply were cut off this minute, I would feel bad—as bad as if I couldn't play bridge any more for some reason, and no worse." He put the stick of gum away again and rummaged through the bottom drawers of his desk until he found a dusty pack of cigarettes. "Used to smoke three packs a day," he wheezed, choking on the first drag.

He wiped his streaming eyes. "You know, Mr. McGory," he said sharply, "you're a bit of a prig. You don't want people to be happy."

"I—"

He stopped me before I could work up a full explosion. "Wait! Don't think that you're the only person who thinks about what's good for the world. When I first heard of Cheery-Gum, I worried." He stubbed the cigarette out distastefully, still talking. "Euphoria is well and good, I said, but what about emergencies? And I looked around, and there weren't any. Things were getting done, maybe slowly and erratically, but they were getting done. And then I said, on a high moral plane, that's well and good, but what about the ultimate destiny of man? Should the world be populated by cheerful near-morons? And that worried me, until I began looking at my patients." He smiled reflectively. "I had 'em all, Mr. McGory. You name it, I had it coming in to see me twice a week. The worst wrecks of psyches you ever heard of, twisted and warped and destroying themselves; and they stopped. They stopped eating themselves up with worry and fear and tension, and then they weren't my patients any more. And what's more, they weren't morons. Give them a stimulus, they respond. Interest them, they react. I played bridge the other night with a woman who was catatonic last month; we had to put the first stick of gum in her mouth. She beat the hell out of me, Mr. McGory. I had a mathematician coming here who—well, never mind. It was bad. He's happy as a clam, and the last time I saw him he had finished a paper he began ten years ago, and couldn't touch. Stimulate them—they respond. When things are dull—Cheery-Gum. What could be better?"

I looked at him dully, and said, "So you can't help me."

"I didn't say that. Do you want me to help you?"

"Certainly!"

"Then answer my question: Why don't you chew a stick yourself?"

"Because I can't!" It all tumbed out, the Plans meeting and Leslie Clary Cloud and the beaker that hadn't been diluted and the hives. "A terrific allergy," I emphasized. "Even antihistamines don't help. They said at the clinic that the antibodies formed after a massive initial—"

He said comfortably, "Soma over psyche, eh? Well, what would you expect? But believe me, Mr. McGory, allergies are psychogenic. Now, if you'll just—"

Well, if you can't lick 'em, join 'em, that's what the old man used to say.

But I can't join them. Theodore Yust offered me an invitation, but I guess I was pretty rude to him. And when, at last, I went back, ready to crawl and apologize, there was a scrawled piece of cardboard over the bronze nameplate; it said: *Gone fishing.*

I tried to lay it on the line with the Chief. I opened the door of the Plans room, and there he was with Baggott and Wayber, from Mason-Dixon. They were sitting there whittling out model ships, and so intent on what they were doing that they hardly noticed me. After a while the Chief said idly, "Bankrupt yet?" And moments passed, and Wayber finally replied, in an absent-minded tone:

"Guess so. Have to file some papers or something." And they went on with their whittling.

So I spoke sharply to them, and the minute they looked up and saw me, it was like the Rockettes: the hands into the pockets, the paper being unwrapped, the gum into the mouth. And naturally I couldn't make any sense with them after that. So what are you going to do?

No! I can't!

Hazel hardly comes in to see me any more, even. I bawled her out for it—what would happen, I demanded, if I suddenly had to answer a letter. But she only smiled dreamily at me. "There hasn't been a letter in a month," she pointed out amiably. "Don't worry, though. If anything comes up, I'll be with you in a flash. This stuff isn't a habit with me, I can stop it any time, you just say the word and ol' Hazel'll be there. . . ."

And she's right because, when you get right down to it, there's the trouble. It isn't a habit.

So how can you break it?

You can stop Cheery-Gum any time. You can stop it this second, or five minutes from now, or tomorrow.

So why worry about it?

It's completely voluntary, entirely under your control; it won't hurt you, it won't make you sick.

I wish Theodor Yust would come back. Or maybe I'll just cut my throat.

Sredni Vashtar

Saki

Conradin was ten years old, and the doctor had pronounced his professional opinion that the boy would not live another five years. The doctor was silky and effete, and counted for little, but his opinion was endorsed by Mrs. De Ropp, who counted for nearly everything. Mrs. De Ropp was Conradin's cousin and guardian, and in his eyes she represented those three-fifths of the world that are necessary and disagreeable and real; the other two-fifths, in perpetual antagonism to the foregoing, were summed up in himself and his imagination. One of these days Conradin supposed he would succumb to the mastering pressure of wearisome necessary things—such as illnesses and coddling restrictions and drawnout dullness. Without his imagination, which was rampant under the spur of loneliness, he would have succumbed long ago.

Mrs. De Ropp would never, in her honestest moments, have confessed to herself that she disliked Conradin, though she might have been dimly aware that thwarting him "for his good" was a duty which she did not find particularly irksome. Conradin hated her with a desperate sincerity which he was perfectly able to mask. Such few pleasures as he could contrive for himself gained an added relish from the likelihood that they would be displeasing to his guardian, and from the realm of his imagination she was locked out—an unclean thing, which should find no entrance.

In the dull, cheerless garden, overlooked by so many windows that were ready to open with a message not to do this or that, or a reminder that medicines were due, he found little attraction. The few fruit-trees that it contained were set jealously apart from his plucking, as though they were rare specimens of their kind blooming in an arid waste; it would probably have been difficult to find a market-gardener who would have offered ten shillings for their entire yearly produce. In a forgotten corner, however, almost hidden behind a dismal shrubbery, was a disused tool-shed of respectable proportions, and within its walls Conradin found a haven, something that took on the varying aspects of a playroom and a cathedral. He had peopled it with a legion of familiar phantoms, evoked partly from fragments of history and partly from his own brain, but it also boasted two inmates of flesh and blood. In one corner lived a ragged-plumaged Houdan hen, on which the boy lavished an affection that had scarcely another outlet. Further back in the gloom stood a large hutch, divided into two compartments, one of which was fronted with close iron bars. This was the abode of a large polecat-ferret, which a friendly butcher-boy had once smuggled, cage and all, into its present quarters, in exchange for a long-secret hoard of small silver. Conradin was dreadfully afraid of the lithe, sharp-fanged beast, but it was his most treasured possession. Its very presence in the tool-shed was a secret and fearful joy, to be kept scrupulously from the knowledge of the Woman, as he privately dubbed his cousin. And one day, out of Heaven knows what material, he spun the beast a wonderful name, and from that moment it grew into a god and a religion. The Woman indulged in religion once a week at a church near by, and took Conradin with her, but to him the church service was an alien rite in the House of Rimmon. Every Thursday, in the dim and musty silence of the tool-shed, he worshiped with mystic and elaborate ceremonial before the wooden hutch where dwelt Sredni Vashtar, the great ferret. Red flowers in their season and scarlet berries in the winter-time were offered at his shrine, for he was a god who laid some special stress on the fierce impatient side of things, as opposed to the Woman's religion, which, as far as Conradin could observe, went to great lengths in the contrary direction. And on great festivals powdered nutmeg was strewn in front of his hutch, an important feature of the offering being that the nutmeg had to be stolen. These festivals were of irregular occurrence, and were chiefly appointed to celebrate some passing event. On one occasion, when Mrs. De Ropp suffered from acute toothache for three days, Conradin kept up the festival during the entire three days, and almost succeeded in persuading himself that Sredni Vashtar was personally responsible for the toothache. If the malady had lasted another day the supply of nutmeg would have given out.

The Houdan hen was never drawn into the cult of Sredni Vashtar. Conradin had long ago settled that she was an Anabaptist. He did not pretend to have the remotest knowledge as to what an Anabaptist was, but he privately hoped that it was dashing and not very respectable. Mrs. De Ropp was the ground plan on which he based and detested all respectability.

After a while Conradin's absorption in the tool-shed began to attract the notice of his guardian. "It is not good for him to be pottering down there in all weathers," she promptly decided, and at breakfast one morning she announced that the Houdan hen had been sold and taken away overnight. With her shortsighted eyes she peered at Conradin, waiting for an outbreak of rage and sorrow, which she was ready to rebuke with a flow of excellent precepts and reasoning. But Conradin said nothing: there was nothing to be said. Something perhaps in his white set face gave her a momentary qualm, for at tea that afternoon there was toast on the table, a delicacy which she usually banned on the ground that it was bad for him; also because the making of it "gave trouble," a deadly offense in the middle-class feminine eye.

"I thought you liked toast," she exclaimed, with an injured air, observing that he did not touch it.

"Sometimes," said Conradin.

In the shed that evening there was an innovation in the worship of the hutch-god. Conradin had been wont to chant his praises, tonight he asked a boon.

"Do one thing for me, Sredni Vashtar."

The thing was not specified. As Sredni Vashtar was a god he must be supposed to know. And choking back a sob as he looked at that other empty corner, Conradin went back to the world he so hated.

And every night, in the welcome darkness of his bedroom, and every evening in the dusk of the tool-shed, Conradin's bitter litany went up: "Do one thing for me, Sredni Vashtar."

Mrs. De Ropp noticed that the visits to the shed did not cease, and one day she made a further journey of inspection.

"What are you keeping in that locked hutch?" she asked. "I believe it's guinea-pigs. I'll have them all cleared away."

Conradin shut his lips tight, but the Woman ransacked his bedroom till she found the carefully hidden key, and forthwith marched down to the shed to complete her discovery. It was a cold afternoon, and Conradin had been bidden to keep to the house. From the furthest window of the dining-room the door of the shed could just be seen beyond the corner of the shrubbery, and there Conradin stationed himself. He saw the Woman enter, and then he imagined her opening the door of the sacred hutch and peering down with her shortsighted eyes into the thick straw bed where his god lay hidden. Perhaps she would prod at the straw in her clumsy impatience. And Conradin fervently breathed his prayer for the last time. But he knew as he prayed that he did not believe. He knew that the Woman would come out presently with that pursed smile he loathed so well on her face, and that in an hour or two the gardener would carry away his wonderful god, a god no longer, but a simple brown ferret in a hutch. And he knew that the Woman would triumph always as she triumphed now, and that he would grow ever more sickly under her pestering and domineering and superior wisdom, till one day nothing would matter much more with him, and the doctor would be proved right. And in the sting and misery of his defeat, he began to chant loudly and defiantly the hymn of his threatened idol:

> Sredni Vashtar went forth,
> His thoughts were red thoughts and his teeth were white.
> His enemies called for peace, but he brought them death.
> Sredni Vashtar the Beautiful.

And then of a sudden he stopped his chanting and drew closer to the window-pane. The door of the shed still stood ajar as it had been left, and the minutes were slipping by. They were long minutes, but they slipped by nevertheless. He watched the starlings running and flying in little parties across the lawn; he counted them over and over again, with one eye always on that swinging door. A sour-faced maid came in to lay the table for tea, and still Conradin stood and waited and watched. Hope had crept by inches into his heart, and now a look of triumph began to blaze in his eyes that had only known the wistful patience of defeat. Under his breath, with a furtive exultation, he began once again the paean of victory and devastation. And presently his eyes were rewarded: out through that doorway came a long, low, yellow-and-brown beast, with eyes the garden, drank for a moment, then crossed a little plank bridge of jaws and throat. Conradin dropped on his knees. The great polecat-ferret made its way down to a small brook at the foot of the garden, drank for a moment, then crossed a little plank bridge and was lost to sight in the bushes. Such was the passing of Sredni Vashtar.

"Tea is ready," said the sour-faced maid; "where is the mistress?"
"She went down to the shed some time ago," said Conradin.

And while the maid went to summon her mistress to tea, Conradin fished a toasting-fork out of the sideboard drawer and proceeded to toast himself a piece of bread. And during the toasting of it and the buttering of it with much butter and the slow enjoyment of eating it, Conradin listened to the noises and silences which fell in quick spasms beyond the dining-room door. The loud foolish screaming of the maid, the answering chorus of wondering ejaculations from the kitchen region, the scuttering footsteps and hurried embassies for outside help, and then, after a lull, the scared sobbings and the shuffling tread of those who bore a heavy burden into the house.

"Whoever will break it to the poor child? I couldn't for the life of me!" exclaimed a shrill voice. And while they debated the matter among themselves, Conradin made himself another piece of toast.

Street of Dreams,
Feet of Clay

Robert Sheckley

I

Carmody had never really planned to leave New York. Why he did so is inexplicable. A born urbanite, he had grown accustomed to the minor inconveniences of metropolitan life. His snug apartment on the 290th floor of Levitfrack Towers on West Ninety-ninth Street was nicely equipped in the current "Spaceship" motif. The windows were double-sealed in tinted lifetime plexiglas, and the air ducts worked through a blind baffle filtration system which sealed automatically when the Combined Atmosphere Pollution Index reached 999.8 on the Con Ed scale. True, his oxygen-nitrogen air recirculation system was old, but it was reliable. His water purification cells were obsolete and ineffective; but then, nobody drank water anyhow.

Noise was a continual annoyance, unstoppable and inescapable. But Carmody knew that there was no cure for this, since the ancient art of soundproofing had been lost. It was urban man's lot to listen, a captive audience, to the arguments, music and watery gurglings of his adjacent neighbors. Even this torture could be alleviated, however, by producing similar sounds of one's own.

Going to work each day entailed certain dangers; but these were more apparent than real. Disadvantaged snipers continued to make their ineffectual protests from rooftops and occasionally succeeded in potting an unwary out-of-towner. But as a rule, their aim was abominable. Additionally, the general acceptance of lightweight personal armor had taken away most of their sting, and the sternly administered state law forbidding the personal possession of surplus cannon had rendered them ineffectual.

Thus, no single factor can be adduced for Carmody's sudden decision to leave what was generally considered the world's most exciting megapolitan agglomeration. Blame it on a vagrant impulse, a pastoral fantasy, or on sheer perversity. The simple, irreducible fact is, one day Carmody opened his copy of the *Daily Times-News* and saw an advertisement for a model city in New Jersey.

"Come live in Bellwether, the city that cares," the advertisement proclaimed. There followed a list of utopian claims which need not be reproduced here.

"Huh," said Carmody, and read on.

Bellwether was within easy commuting distance. One simply drove through the Ulysses S. Grant Tunnel at 43rd Street, took the Hoboken Shunt Subroad to the Palisades Interstate Crossover, followed that for 3.2 miles on the Blue-Charlie Sorter Loop that led onto U.S. 5 (The Hague Memorial Tollway), proceeded along that a distance of 6.1 miles to the Garden State Supplementary Access Service Road (Provisional), upon which one tended west to Exit 1731A, which was King's Highbridge Gate Road, and then continued along that for a distance of 1.6 miles. And there you were.

"By jingo," said Carmody, "I'll do it."

And he did.

II

King's Highbridge Gate Road ended on a neatly trimmed plain. Carmody got out of his car and looked around. Half a mile ahead of him he saw a small city. A single modest signpost identified it as Bellwether.

This city was not constructed in the traditional manner of American cities, with outliers of gas stations, tentacles of hot-dog stands, fringes of motels and a protective carapace of junkyards; but rather, as some Italian hill towns are fashioned, it rose abruptly, without physical preamble, the main body of the town presenting itself at once and without amelioration.

Carmody found this appealing. He advanced into the city itself.

Bellwether had a warm and open look. Its streets were laid out generously, and there was a frankness about the wide bay windows of its store-fronts. As he penetrated deeper, Carmody found other delights. Just within the city he entered a piazza, like a Roman piazza, only smaller; and in the center of the piazza there was a fountain, and standing in the fountain was a marble representation of a boy with a dolphin, and from the dolphin's mouth a stream of clear water issued.

"I do hope you like it," a voice said from behind Carmody's left shoulder.

"It's nice," Carmody said.

"I constructed it and put it there myself," the voice told him. "It seemed to me that a fountain, despite the antiquity of its concept, is esthetically functional. And this piazza, with its benches and shady chestnut trees, is copied from a Bolognese model. Again, I did not inhibit myself with the fear of seeming old-fashioned. The true artist uses what is necessary, be it a thousand years old or one second new."

"I applaud your sentiment," Carmody said. "Permit me to introduce myself. I am Edward Carmody." He turned, smiling.

But there was no one behind his left shoulder, or behind his right shoulder, either. There was no one in the piazza, nobody at all in sight.

"Forgive me," the voice said. "I didn't mean to startle you. I thought you knew."

"Knew what?" Carmody asked.

"Knew about me."

"Well, I don't," Carmody said. "Who are you and where are you speaking from?"

"I am the voice of the city," the voice said. "Or to put it another way, I am the city itself, Bellwether, the actual and veritable city, speaking to you."

"Is that a fact?" Carmody said sardonically. "Yes," he answered himself, "I suppose it is a fact. So all right, you're a city. Big deal!"

He turned away from the fountain and strolled across the piazza like a man who conversed with cities every day of his life, and who was slightly bored with the whole thing. He walked down various streets and up certain avenues. He glanced into store windows and noted houses. He paused in front of statuary, but only briefly.

"Well?" the city of Bellwether asked after a while.

"Well what?" Carmody answered at once.

"What do you think of me?"

"You're okay," Carmody said.

"Only okay? Is that all?"

"Look," Carmody said, "a city is a city. When you've seen one, you've pretty much seen them all."

"That's untrue!" the city said, with some show of pique. "I am distinctly different from other cities. I am unique."

"Are you indeed?" Carmody said scornfully. "To me you look like a conglomeration of badly assembled parts. You've got an Italian piazza, a couple of Greek-type buildings, a row of Tudor houses, an old-style New York tenement, a California hot-dog stand shaped like a tugboat and God knows what else. What's so unique about that?"

"The combination of those forms into a meaningful entity is unique," the city said. "These older forms are not anachronisms, you understand. They are representative styles of living, and as such are appropriate in a well wrought machine for living. Would you care for some coffee and perhaps a sandwich or some fresh fruit?"

"Coffee sounds good," Carmody said. He allowed Bellwether to guide him around the corner to an open-air cafe. The cafe was called *O You Kid* and was a replica of a Gay Nineties saloon, right down to the Tiffany lamps and the cutglass chandelier and the player piano. Like everything else that Carmody had seen in the city, it was spotlessly clean, but without people.

"Nice atmosphere, don't you think?" Bellwether asked.

"Campy," Carmody pronounced. "Okay if you like that sort of thing."

A foaming mug of cappucino was lowered to his table on a stainless steel tray. Carmody sipped.

"Good?" Bellwether asked.

"Yes, very good."

"I rather pride myself on my coffee," the city said quietly. "And on my cooking. Wouldn't you care for a little something? An omelette, perhaps, or a souffle?"

"Nothing," Carmody said firmly. He leaned back in his chair and said, "So you're a model city, huh?"

"Yes, that is what I have the honor to be," Bellwether said. "I am the most recent of all model cities; and, I believe, the most satisfactory. I was conceived by a joint study group from Yale and the University of Chicago, who were working on a Rockefeller fellowship. Most of my practical details were devised by M.I.T., although some special sections of me came from Princeton and from the RAND Corporation. My actual construction was a General Electric project, and the money was procured by grants from the Ford and Carnegie Foundations, as well as several other institutions I am not at liberty to mention."

"Interesting sort of history," Carmody said, with hateful nonchalance. "That's a Gothic cathedral across the street, isn't it?"

"Modified Romanesque," the city said. "Also interdenominational and open to all faiths, with a designed seating capacity for three hundred people."

"That doesn't seem like many for a building of that size."

"It's not, of course. Designedly. My idea was to combine awesomeness with coziness."

"Where are the inhabitants of this town, by the way?" Carmody asked.

"They have left," Bellwether said mournfully. "They have all departed."

"Why?"

The city was silent for a while, then said, "There was a breakdown in city-community relations. A misunderstanding, really. Or perhaps I should say, an unfortunate series of misunderstandings. I suspect that rabble-rousers played their part."

"But what *happened*, precisely?"

"I don't know," the city said. "I really don't know. One day they simply all left. Just like that! But I'm sure they'll be back."

"I wonder," Carmody said.

"I am convinced of it," the city said. "But putting that aside: why don't *you* stay here, Mr. Carmody?"

"I haven't really had time to consider it," Carmody said.

"How could you help but like it?" Bellwether said. "Just think —you would have the most modern up-to-date city in the world at your beck and call."

"That does sound interesting," Carmody said.

"So give it a try, how could it hurt you?" the city asked.

"All right, I think I will," Carmody said.

He was intrigued by the city of Bellwether. But he was also apprehensive. He wished he knew exactly why the city's previous occupants had left.

At Bellwether's insistence, Carmody slept that night in the sumptuous bridal suite of the King George V Hotel. Bellwether served him breakfast on the terrace and played a brisk Hayden quartet while Carmody ate. The morning air was delicious. If Bellwether hadn't told him, Carmody would never have guessed it was reconstituted.

When he was finished, Carmody leaned back and enjoyed the view of Bellwether's western quarter—a pleasing jumble of Chinese pagodas, Venetian footbridges, Japanese canals, a green Burmese hill, a Corinthian temple, a California parking lot, a Norman tower and much else besides.

"You have a splendid view," he told the city.

"I'm so glad you appreciate it," Bellwether replied. "The problem of style was argued from the day of my inception. One group held for consistency: a harmonious group of shapes blending into a harmonious whole. But quite a few model cities are like that. They are uniformly dull, artificial entities created by one man or one committee, unlike real cities."

"You're sort of artificial yourself, aren't you?" Carmody asked.

"Of course! But I do not pretend to be anything else. I am not a fake 'city of the future' or a mock-Florentine bastard. I am a true agglutinated congeries. I am supposed to be interesting and stimulating in addition to being functional and practical."

"Bellwether, you look okay to me," Carmody said, in a sudden rush of expansiveness. "Do all model cities talk like you?"

"Certainly not. Most cities up to now, model or otherwise, never said a word. But their inhabitants didn't like that. It made the city seem too huge, too masterful, too soulless, too impersonal. That is why I was created with a voice and an artificial consciousness to guide it."

"I see," Carmody said.

"The point is, my artificial consciousness personalizes me, which is very important in an age of depersonalization. It enables me to be truly responsive. It permits me to be creative in meeting the demands of my occupants. We can reason with each other, my people and I. By carrying on a continual and meaningful dialogue, we can help each other to establish a dynamic, flexible and truly viable urban environment. We can modify each other without any significant loss of individuality."

"It sounds fine," Carmody said. "Except, of course, that you don't have anyone here to carry on a dialogue with."

"That is the only flaw in the scheme," the city admitted. "But for the present, I have you."

"Yes, you have me," Carmody said, and wondered why the words rang unpleasantly on his ear.

"And, naturally, you have me," the city said. "It is a reciprocal relationship, which is the only kind worth having. But now, my dear Carmody, suppose I show you around myself. Then we can get you settled in and regularized."

"Get me what?"

"I didn't mean that the way it sounded," the city said. "It simply is an unfortunate scientific expression. But you understand, I'm sure, that a reciprocal relationship necessitates obligations on the part of both involved parties. It couldn't very well be otherwise, could it?"

"Not unless it was a *laissez-faire* relationship."

"We're trying to get away from all that," Bellwether said. "*Laissez-faire* becomes a doctrine of the emotions, you know, and leads non-stop to *anomie*. If you will just come this way...."

III

Carmody went where he was asked and beheld the excellencies of Bellwether. He toured the power plant, the water filtration center, the industrial park and the light industries section. He saw the children's park and the Odd Fellow's Hall. He walked through a museum and an art gallery, a concert hall and a theater, a bowling alley, a billiards parlor, a Go-Kart track and a movie theater. He became tired and wanted to stop. But the city wanted to show itself off, and Carmody had to look at the five-story American Express building, the Portuguese synagogue, the statue of Buckminster Fuller, the Greyhound Bus Station and several other attractions.

At last it was over. Carmody concluded that beauty was in the eye of the beholder, except for a small part of it that was in the beholder's feet.

"A little lunch now?" the city asked.

"Fine," Carmody said.

He was guided to the fashionable Rochambeau Cafe, where he began with *potage au petit pois* and ended with *petits fours*.

"What about a nice Brie to finish off?" the city asked.

"No, thanks," Carmody said. "I'm full. Too full, as a matter of fact."

"But cheese isn't filling. A bit of first-rate Camembert?"

"I couldn't possibly."

"Perhaps a few assorted fruits. *Very* refreshing to the palate."

"It's not my palate that needs refreshing," Carmody said.

"At least an apple, a pear and a couple of grapes?"

"Thanks, no."

"A couple of cherries?"

"No, no, no!"

"A meal isn't complete without a little fruit," the city said.

"My meal is," Carmody said.

"There are important vitamins only found in fresh fruit."

"I'll just have to struggle along without them."

"Perhaps half an orange, which I will peel for you? Citrus fruits have no bulk at all."

"I couldn't possibly."

"Not even one quarter of an orange? If I take out all the pits?"

"Most decidedly not."

"It would make me feel better," the city said. "I have a completion compulsion, you know, and no meal is complete without a piece of fruit."

"No! No! No!"

"All right, don't get so excited," the city said. "If you don't like the sort of food I serve, that's up to you."

"But I do like it!"

"Then if you like it so much, why won't you eat some fruit?"

"Enough," Carmody said. "Give me a couple of grapes."

"I wouldn't want to force anything on you."

"You're not forcing. Give me, please."

"You're quite sure?"

"Gimme!" Carmody shouted.

"So take," the city said and produced a magnificent bunch of muscatel grapes. Carmody ate them all. They were very good.

"Excuse me," the city said. "What are you doing?" Carmody sat upright and opened his eyes. "I was taking a little nap," he said. "Is there anything wrong with that?"

"What should be wrong with a perfectly natural thing like that?" the city said.

"Thank you," Carmody said, and closed his eyes again.

"But why nap in a chair?" the city asked.

"Because I'm *in* a chair, and I'm already half asleep."

"You'll get a crick in your back," the city warned him.

"Don't care," Carmody mumbled, his eyes still closed.

"Why not take a proper nap? Over here, on the couch?"

"I'm already napping comfortably right here."

"You're not really comfortable," the city pointed out. "The human anatomy is not constructed for sleeping sitting up."

"At the moment, mine is," Carmody said.

"It's not. Why not try the couch?"

"The chair is fine."

"But the couch is finer. Just try it, please, Carmody. Carmody?"

"Eh? What's that?" Carmody said, waking up.

"The couch. I really think you should rest on the couch."

"All right!" Carmody said, struggling to his feet. "Where is this couch?"

He was guided out of the restaurant, down the street, around the corner, and into a building marked *The Snoozerie*. There were a dozen couches. Carmody went to the nearest.

"Not that one," the city said. "It's got a bad spring."

"It doesn't matter," Carmody said. "I'll sleep around it."

"That will result in a cramped posture."

"Christ!" Carmody said, getting to his feet. "Which couch would you recommend?"

"This one right back here," the city said. "It's a king-size, the best in the place. The yield-point of the mattress has been scientifically determined. The pillows—"

"Right, fine, good," Carmody said, lying down on the indicated couch.

"Shall I play you some soothing music?"

"Don't bother."

"Just as you wish. I'll put out the lights, then."

"Fine."

"Would you like a blanket? I control the temperature here, of course, but sleepers often get a subjective impression of chilliness."

"It doesn't matter! Leave me alone!"

"All right!" the city said. "I'm not doing this for myself, you know. Personally, I never sleep."

"Okay, sorry," Carmody said.

"That's perfectly all right."

There was a long silence. Then Carmody sat up.

"What's the matter?" the city asked.

"Now I can't sleep," Carmody said.

"Try closing your eyes and consciously relaxing every muscle in your body, starting with the big toe and working upward to—"

"I can't sleep!" Carmody shouted.

"Maybe you weren't very sleepy to begin with," the city suggested. "'But at least you could close your eyes and try to get a little rest. Won't you do that for me?"

"No!" Carmody said. "I'm not sleepy and I don't need a rest."

"Stubborn!" the city said. "Do what you like. I've tried my best."

"Yeah!" Carmody said, getting to his feet and walking out of the Snoozerie.

IV

Carmody stood on a little curved bridge and looked over a blue lagoon.

"This is a copy of the Rialto bridge in Venice," the city said. "Scaled down, of course."

"I know," Carmody said. "I read the sign."

"It's rather enchanting, isn't it?"

"Sure, it's fine," Carmody said, lighting a cigarette.

"You're doing a lot of smoking," the city pointed out.

"I know. I feel like smoking."

"As your medical advisor, I must point out that the link between smoking and lung cancer is conclusive."

"I know."

"If you switched to a pipe your chances would be improved."

"I don't like pipes."

"What about a cigar, then?"

"I don't like cigars." He lit another cigarette.

"That's your third cigarette in five minutes," the city said.

"Goddamn it, I'll smoke as much and as often as I please!" Carmody shouted.

"Well, of course you will!" the city said. "I was merely trying to advise you for your own good. Would you want me to simply stand by and not say a word while you destroyed yourself?"

"Yes," Carmody said.

"I can't believe that you mean that. There is an ethical imperative involved here. Man can act against his best interests; but a machine is not allowed that degree of perversity."

"Get off my back," Carmody said sullenly. "Quit pushing me around."

"Pushing you around? My dear Carmody, have I coerced you in any way? Have I done any more than advise you?"

"Maybe not. But you talk too much."

"Perhaps I don't talk enough," the city said. "To judge from the response I get."

"You talk too much," Carmody repeated and lit a cigarette.

"That is your fourth cigarette in five minutes."

Carmody opened his mouth to bellow an insult. Then he changed his mind and walked away.

"What's this?" Carmody asked.

"It's a candy machine," the city told him.

"It doesn't look like one."

"Still, it is one. This design is a modification of a design by Saarionmen for a silo. I have miniaturized it, of course, and—"

"It still doesn't look like a candy machine. How do you work it?"

"It's very simple. Push the red button. Now wait. Press down one of those levers on Row A; now press the green button. There!"

A Baby Ruth bar slid into Carmody's hand.

"Huh," Carmody said. He stripped off the paper and bit into the bar. "Is this a real Baby Ruth bar or a copy of one?" he asked.

"It's a real one. I had to subcontract the candy concession because of the pressure of work."

"Huh," Carmody said, letting the candy wrapper slip from his fingers.

"That," the city said, "is an example of the kind of thoughtlessness I always encounter."

"It's just a piece of paper," Carmody said, turning and looking at the candy wrapper lying on the spotless street.

"Of course it's just a piece of paper," the city said. "But multiply it by a hundred thousand inhabitants and what do you have?"

"A hundred thousand Baby Ruth wrappers," Carmody answered at once.

"I don't consider that funny," the city said. "You wouldn't want to *live* in the midst of all that paper, I can assure you. You'd be the first to complain if this street were strewn with garbage. But do you do your share? Do you even clean up after yourself? Of course not! You leave it to me, even though I have to run all of the other functions of the city, night and day, without even Sundays off."

Carmody bent down to pick up the candy wrapper. But just before his fingers could close on it, a pincer arm shot out of the nearest sewer, snatched the paper away and vanished from sight.

"It's all right," the city said. "I'm used to cleaning up after people. I do it all the time."

"Yuh," said Carmody.

"Nor do I expect any gratitude."

"I'm grateful, I'm grateful!" Carmody said.

"No, you're not," Bellwether said.

"So okay, maybe I'm not. What do you want me to say?"

"I don't want you to say anything," the city said. "Let's us consider the incident closed."

"Had enough?" the city said, after dinner.

"Plenty," Carmody said.

"You didn't eat much."

"I ate all I wanted. It was very good."

"If it was so good, why didn't you eat more?"

"Because I couldn't hold any more."

"If you hadn't spoiled your appetite with that candy bar..."

"Goddamn it, the candy bar didn't spoil my appetite! I just—"

"You're lighting a cigarette," the city said.

"Yeah," Carmody said.

"Couldn't you wait a little longer?"

"Now look," Carmody said. "Just what in hell do you—"

"But we have something more important to talk about," the city said quickly. "Have you thought about what you're going to do for a living?"

"I haven't really had much time to think about it."

"Well, I have been thinking about it. It would be nice if you became a doctor."

"Me? I'd have to take special college courses, then get into medical school, and so forth."

"I can arrange all that," the city said.

"Not interested."

"Well. . . . What about law?"

"Never."

"Engineering is an excellent line."

"Not for me."

"What about accounting?"

"Not on your life."

"What do you want to be?"

"A jet pilot," Carmody said impulsively.

"Oh, come now!"

"I'm quite serious."

"I don't even have an air field here."

"Then I'll pilot somewhere else."

"You're only saying that to spite me!"

"Not at all," Carmody said. "I want to be a pilot, I really do. I've *always* wanted to be a pilot! Honest I have!"

There was a long silence. Then the city said, "The choice is entirely up to you." This was said in a voice like death.

"Where are you going now?"

"Out for a walk," Carmody said.

"At nine-thirty in the evening?"

"Sure. Why not?"

"I thought you were tired."

"That was quite some time ago."

"I see. And I also thought that you could sit here and we could have a nice chat."

"How about if we talk after I get back?" Carmody asked.

"No, it doesn't matter," the city said.

"The walk doesn't matter," Carmody said, sitting down. "Come on, we'll talk."

"I no longer care to talk," the city said. "Please go for your walk."

V

"Well, good night," Carmody said.

"I beg your pardon?"

"I said, 'good night.' "

"You're going to sleep?"

"Sure. It's late, I'm tired."

"You're going to sleep now?"

"Well, why not?"

"No reason at all," the city said, "except that you have forgotten to wash."

"Oh.... I guess I did forget. I'll wash in the morning."

"How long is it since you've had a bath?"

"Too long. I'll take one in the morning."

"Wouldn't you feel better if you took one right now?"

"No."

"Even if I drew the bath for you?"

"No! Goddamn it, no! I'm going to sleep!"

"Do exactly as you please," the city said. "Don't wash, don't study, don't eat a balanced diet. But also, don't blame me."

"Blame you? For what?"

"For anything," the city said.

"Yes. But what did you have in mind, specifically?"

"It isn't important."

"Then why did you bring it up in the first place?"

"I was only thinking of you," the city said.

"I realize that."

"You must know that it can't benefit *me* if you wash or not."

"I'm aware of that."

"When one cares," the city went on, "when one feels one's responsibilities, it is not nice to hear oneself sworn at."

"I didn't swear at you."

"Not this time. But earlier today you did."

"Well.... I was nervous."

"That's because of the smoking."

"Don't start that again!"

"I won't," the city said. "Smoke like a furnace. What does it matter to me?"

"Damned right," Carmody said, lighting a cigarette.

"But my failure," the city said.

"No, no," Carmody said. "Don't say it, please don't!"

"Forget I said it," the city said.

"All right."

"Sometimes I get overzealous."

"Sure."

"And it's especially difficult because I'm right. I am right, you know."

"I know," Carmody said. "You're right, you're right, you're always right. Right right right right right—"

"Don't overexcite yourself betime," the city said. "Would you care for a glass of milk?"

"No."

"You're sure?"

Carmody put his hands over his eyes. He felt very strange. He also felt extremely guilty, fragile, dirty, unhealthy and sloppy. He felt generally and irrevocably bad, and it would always be this way unless he changed, adjusted, adapted. . . .

But instead of attempting anything of the sort he rose to his feet, squared his shoulders, and marched away past the Roman piazza and the Venetian bridge.

"Where are you going?" the city asked. "What's the matter?"

Silent, tight-lipped, Carmody continued past the children's park and the American Express building.

"What did I do wrong?" the city cried. "What, just tell me what?"

Carmody made no reply but strode past the Rochambeau Cafe and the Portuguese synagogue, coming at last to the pleasant green plain that surrounded Bellwether.

"Ingrate!" the city screamed after him. "You're just like all the others. All of you humans are disagreeable animals, and you're never really satisfied with anything."

Carmody got into his car and started the engine.

"But of course," the city said, in a more thoughtful voice, "you're never really *dissatisfied* with anything either. The moral, I suppose, is that a city must learn patience."

Carmody turned the car onto King's Highbridge Gate Road and started east, toward New York.

"Have a nice trip!" Bellwether called after him. "Don't worry about me, I'll be waiting up for you."

Carmody stepped down hard on the accelerator. He really wished he hadn't heard that last remark.

The Last Man
Mary Wollstonecraft Shelley

Abridged from the first edition published in three volumes by Henry Colburn, New Burlington Street, London, 1826.

I lived far from the busy haunts of men, and the rumour of wars or political changes came worn to a mere sound, to our mountain abodes. England had been the scene of momentous struggles, during my early boyhood. In the year 2073, the last of its kings, the ancient friend of my father, had abdicated in compliance with the gentle force of the remonstrances of his subjects, and a republic was instituted. Large estates were secured to the dethroned monarch and his family; he received the title of Earl of Windsor, and Windsor Castle, an ancient royalty, with its wide demesnes were a part of his allotted wealth. He died soon after, leaving two children, a son and a daughter.

The ex-queen, a princess of the house of Austria, had long impelled her husband to withstand the necessity of the times. When she became a widow, she turned all her thoughts to educating her son Adrian, second Earl of Windsor, so as to accomplish her ambitious ends; and with his mother's milk he imbibed, and was intended to grow up in the steady purpose of re-acquiring his lost crown. Adrian was now fifteen years of age. He was addicted to study, and imbued beyond his years with learning and talent: report said that he had already begun to thwart his mother's views, and to entertain republican principles.

At this period the name and exploits of one of my countrymen filled the world with admiration. Relations of what he had done, conjectures concerning his future actions, were the never-failing topics of the hour. I was not angry on my own account, but I felt as if the praises which this idol received were leaves torn from laurels destined for Adrian. But I must enter into some account of this darling of fame—this favourite of the wonder-loving world.

Lord Raymond was the sole remnant of a noble but impoverished family. From early youth he had considered his pedigree with complacency, and bitterly lamented his want of wealth. His first wish was aggrandisement; and the means that led towards this end were secondary considerations. Haughty, yet trembling to every demonstration of respect; ambitious, but too proud to shew his ambition; willing to achieve honour, yet a votary of pleasure,—he entered upon life. He was met on the threshold by some insult, real or imaginary; some repulse, where he least expected it; some disappointment, hard for his pride to bear. He writhed beneath an injury he was unable to revenge; and he quitted England with a vow not to return, till the good time should arrive, when she might feel the power of him she now despised.

He became an adventurer in the Greek wars. His reckless courage and comprehensive genius brought him into notice. He became the darling hero of this rising people. His foreign birth, and he refused to throw off his allegiance to his native country, alone prevented him from filling the first offices in the state. But, though others might rank higher in title and ceremony, Lord Raymond held a station above and beyond all this. He led the Greek armies to victory; their triumphs were all his own. When he appeared, whole towns poured forth their population to meet him; new songs were adapted to their national airs, whose themes were his glory, valour, and munificence.

A truce was concluded between the Greeks and Turks.

Lord Raymond returned from Greece. No two persons could be more opposite than Adrian and he. With all the incongruities of his character, Raymond was emphatically a man of the world. His passions were violent; as these often obtained the mastery over him, he could not always square his conduct to the obvious line of self-interest, but self-gratification at least was the paramount object with him. He looked on the structure of society as but a part of the machinery which supported the web on which his life was traced. The earth was spread out as an highway for him; the heavens built up as a canopy for him.

Adrian felt that he made a part of a great whole. He owned affinity not only with mankind, but all nature was akin to him; the mountains and sky were his friends; the winds of heaven and the offspring of earth his playmates; while he the focus only of this mighty mirror, felt his life mingle with the universe of existence. His soul was sympathy, and dedicated to the worship of beauty and excellence. Adrian and Raymond now came into contact, and a spirit of aversion rose between them. Adrian despised the narrow views of the politician, and Raymond held in supreme contempt the benevolent visions of the philanthropist.

Everything in the English constitution had been regulated for the better preservation of peace. To our extreme surprise, when it was moved that we should resolve ourselves into a committee for the election of the Lord Protector, the chairman declared Lord Raymond duly chosen.

The selected passion of the soul of Raymond was ambition. Readiness of talent, a capacity of entering into, and leading the dispositions of men; earnest desire of distinction were the awakeners and nurses of his ambition. But other ingredients mingled with these, and prevented him from becoming the calculating, determined character, which alone forms a successful hero. He was obstinate, but not firm; benevolent in his first movements; harsh and reckless when provoked. Above all, he was remorseless and unyielding in the pursuit of any object of desire, however lawless.

[Later] said Raymond, "This is only part of a system:—a scheme of tyranny to which I will never submit. Because I am Protector of England, am I to be the only slave in its empire?" and he took the star, insignia of office, from his breast, and threw it on the table. "I renounce my office. I abdicate my power—assume it who will! Adrian, I am about to return to Greece, to become again a soldier, perhaps a conquerer. Will you accompany me?

"I will," replied Adrian.

After the lapse of more than a year, Adrian returned from Greece.

When our exiles had first arrived, a truce was in existence between the Turks and Greeks; a truce that was as sleep to the mortal frame, signal of renewed activity on waking. With the numerous soldiers of Asia, with all of warlike stores, ships, and military engines, that wealth and power could command, the Turks at once resolved to crush an enemy, which creeping on by degrees, had from their stronghold in the Morea, acquired Thrace and Macedonia, and had led their armies even to the gates of Constantinople, while their extensive commercial relations gave every European nation an interest in their success.

Each vessel brought exhilarating tidings from Greece. The presence of a friend in its armies and councils made us enter into the details with enthusiasm; and a short letter now and then from Raymond told us how he was engrossed by the interests of his adopted country. The Greeks were strongly attached to their commercial pursuits, and would have been satisfied with their present acquisitions, had not the Turks roused them by invasion. The patriots were victorious; a spirit of conquest was instilled; and already they looked on Constantinople as their own. Raymond rose perpetually in their estimation; but one man held a superior command to him in their armies. He was conspicuous for his conduct and choice of position in a battle fought in the plains of Thrace, on the banks of the Hebrus, which was to decide the fate of Islam. The Mahometans were defeated, and driven entirely from the country west of this river. The battle was sanguinary, the loss of the Turks apparently irreparable; the Greeks, in losing one man, forgot the nameless crowd strewed upon the bloody field, and they ceased to value themselves on a victory, which cost them—Raymond.

The Athenians had expected their hero to return in triumph; the women had taught their children to lisp his name joined to thanksgiving; his manly beauty, his courage, his devotion to their cause, made him appear in their eyes almost as one of the ancient deities of the soil descended from their native Olympus to defend them. When they spoke of his probable death and certain captivity, tears streamed from their eyes; even as the women of Syria sorrowed for Adonis, did the wives and mothers of Greece lament our English Raymond—Athens was a city of mourning.

I joined Raymond and his staff, now on their way to the Golden City.

I rode one morning with Raymond to the lofty mound, not far from the Top Kapou, (Cannon-gate), on which Mahmoud planted his standard, and first saw the city. Still the same lofty domes and minarets towered above the verdurous walls, where Constantine had died, and the Turk had entered the city. The plain around was interspersed with cemeteries, Turk, Greek, and Armenian, with their growth of cypress trees; and other woods of more cheerful aspect, diversified the scene. Among them the Greek army was encamped, and their squadrons moved to and fro—now in regular march, now in swift career.

Raymond's eyes were fixed on the city. "I have counted the hours of her life," said he; "one month, and she falls. Remain with me till then; wait till you see the cross on St. Sophia; and then return to your peaceful glades."

The empire of the Mahometans in Europe was at its close. The Greek fleet blockading every port of Stamboul, prevented the arrival of succour from Asia; all egress on the side towards land had become impracticable, except to such desperate sallies, as reduced the numbers of the enemy without making any impression on our lines. The garrison was now so much diminished, that it was evident that the city could easily have been carried by storm; but both humanity and policy dictated a slower mode of proceeding. We could hardly doubt that, if pursued to the utmost, its palaces, its temples and store of wealth would be destroyed in the fury of contending triumph and defeat.

Suddenly the system of warfare was changed. We experienced no more assaults; and by night and day we continued our labours unimpeded. Stranger still, when the troops advanced near the city, the walls were vacant, and no cannon was pointed against the intruders. . . . Scouts returned, reporting only the continued silence and desolation of the city, he commanded the army to be drawn out before the gates. No one appeared on the walls; the very portals, though locked and barred, seemed unguarded; above, the many domes and glittering crescents pierced heaven; while the old walls, survivors of ages, with ivy-crowned tower and weed-tangled buttress, stood as rocks in an uninhabited waste. From within the city neither shout nor cry, nor aught except the casual howling of a dog, broke the noon-day stillness. Even our soldiers were awed to silence; the music paused; the clang of arms was hushed.

The men disdainfully repelled the idea of having deserted the defence of their city; and one, the youngest among them, in answer to the taunt of a sailor, exclaimed, "Take it, Christian dogs! take the palaces, the gardens, the mosques, the abode of our fathers—take plague with them; pestilence is the enemy we fly; if she be your friend, hug her to your bosoms. The curse of Allah is on Stamboul, share ye her fate."

An universal shudder and fearful whispering passed through the lines; not a soldier moved. "Cowards!" exclaimed their general, exasperated, "give me an hatchet! I alone will enter! I will plant your standard; and when you see it wave from yon highest minaret, you may gain courage, and rally round it!"

One of the officers now came forward: "General," he said, "we neither fear the courage, nor arms, the open attack, nor secret ambush of the Moslems. We are ready to expose our breasts, exposed ten thousand times before, to the balls and scymetars of the infidels, and to fall gloriously for Greece. But we will not die in heaps, like dogs poisoned in summer-time, by the pestilential air of that city—we dare not go against the plague!"

A multitude of men are feeble and inert, without a voice, a leader; give them that, and they regain the strength belonging to their numbers. Shouts from a thousand voices now rent the air—the cry of applause became universal. Raymond saw the danger; he was willing to save his troops from the crime of disobedience; for he knew, that contention once begun between the commander and his army, each act and word added to the weakness of the former, and bestowed power on the latter. He gave orders for the retreat to be sounded, and the regiments repaired in good order to the camp.

We were soon joined by Raymond. He looked gloomy and perturbed. "The prayer of my youth was to be one among those who render the pages of earth's history splendid; who exalt the race of man, and make this little globe a dwelling of the mighty. Alas, for Raymond! the prayer of his youth is wasted—the hopes of his manhood are null!

"From my dungeon in yonder city I cried, soon I will be thy lord! When Evadne pronounced my death, I thought that the title of Victor of Constantinople would be written on my tomb, and I subdued all mortal fear. I stand before its vanquished walls, and dare not call myself a conqueror. So shall it not be! Did not Alexander leap from the walls of the city of the Oxydracæ, to shew his coward troops the way to victory, encountering alone the swords of its defenders? Even so will I brave the plague—and though no man follow, I will plant the Grecian standard on the height of St. Sophia."

Reason came unavailing to such high-wrought feelings. In vain I shewed him, that when winter came, the cold would dissipate the pestilential air, and restore courage to the Greeks. "Talk not of other season than this!" he cried. "I have lived my last winter, and the date of this year, 2092, will be carved upon my tomb. Already do I see," he continued, looking up mournfully, "the bourne and precipitate edge of my existence, over which I plunge into the gloomy mystery of the life to come.

I then came to a resolution of pursuing our journey to England overland. My own heart was racked by regrets and remorse. The apprehension, that Raymond had departed for ever, that his name, blended eternally with the past, must be erased from every anticipation of the future, had come slowly upon me. I had always admired his talents; his noble aspirations; his grand conceptions of the glory and majesty of his ambition: his utter want of mean passions; his fortitude and daring.

A heavy rain made this mode of travelling now incommodious; so we embarked in a steam-packet; and after a short passage landed at Portsmouth.

A strange story was rife here. A few days before, a tempest-struck vessel had appeared off the town: the hull was parched-looking and cracked, the sails rent, and bent in a careless, unseamanlike manner, the shrouds tangled and broken. She drifted towards the harbour, and was stranded on the sands at the entrance. In the morning the custom-house officers, together with a crowd of idlers, visited her. One only of the crew appeared to have arrived with her. He had got to shore, and had walked a few paces towards the town, and then, vanquished by malady and approaching death, had fallen on the inhospitable beach. He was found stiff, his hands clenched, and pressed against his breast. His skin, nearly black, his matted hair and bristly beard, were signs of a long protracted misery. It was whispered that he had died of the plague. No one ventured on board the vessel, and strange sights were averred to be seen at night, walking the deck, and hanging on the masts and shrouds. She soon went to pieces; I was shewn where she had been, and saw her disjoined timbers tossed on the waves. The body of the man who had landed, had been buried deep in the sands; and none could tell more, than that the vessel was American built, and that several months before the *Fortunatus* had sailed from Philadelphia, of which no tidings were afterwards received.

The plague at Athens had been preceded and caused by the contagion from the east; and the scene of havoc and death continued to be acted there, on a scale of fearful magnitude. A hope that the visitation of the present year would prove the last, kept up the spirits of the merchants connected with these countries; but the inhabitants were driven to despair, or to a resignation which, arising from fanaticism, assumed the same dark hue. America had also received the taint; and, were it yellow fever or plague, the epidemic was gifted with a virulence before unfelt. The devastation was not confined to the towns, but spread throughout the country; the hunter died in the woods, the peasant in the corn-fields, and the fisher on his native waters.

A strange story was brought to us from the East, to which little credit would have been given, had not the fact been attested by a multitude of witnesses, in various parts of the world. On the twenty-first of June, it was said that an hour before noon, a black sun arose: an orb, the size of that luminary, but dark, defined, whose beams were shadows, ascended from the west; in about an hour it had reached the meridian, and eclipsed the bright parent of day. Night fell upon every country, night, sudden, rayless, entire. The stars came out, shedding their ineffectual glimmerings on the light-widowed earth. But soon the dim orb passed from over the sun, and lingered down the eastern heaven. As it descended, its dusky rays crossed the brilliant ones of the sun, and deadened or distorted them. The shadows of things assumed strange and ghastly shapes. The wild animals in the woods took fright at the unknown shapes figured on the ground. They fled they knew not whither; and the citizens were filled with greater dread, at the convulsion which "shook lions into civil streets;"—birds, strong-winged eagles, suddenly blinded, fell in the market-places, while owls and bats shewed themselves welcoming the early night. Gradually the object of fear sank beneath the horizon, and to the last shot up shadowy beams into the otherwise radiant air. Such was the tale sent us from Asia, from the eastern extremity of Europe, and from Africa as far west as the Golden Coast.

Whether this story were true or not, the effects were certain. Through Asia, from the banks of the Nile to the shores of the Caspian, from the Hellespont even to the sea of Omar, a sudden panic was driven. The men filled the mosques; the women, veiled, hastened to the tombs, and carried offerings to the dead, thus to preserve the living. The plague was forgotten, in this new fear which the black sun had spread; and, though the dead multiplied, and the streets of Ispahan, of Pekin, and of Delhi were strewed with pestilence-struck corpses, men passed on, gazing on the ominous sky, regardless of the death beneath their feet. The christians sought their churches,—christian maidens, even at the feast of roses, clad in white, with shining veils, sought, in long procession, the places consecrated to their religion, filling the air with their hymns; while, ever and anon, from the lips of some poor mourner in the crowd, a voice of wailing burst, and the rest looked up, fancying they could discern the sweeping wings of angels, who passed over the earth, lamenting the disasters about to fall on man.

In the sunny clime of Persia, in the crowded cities of China, amidst the aromatic groves of Cashmere, and along the southern shores of the Mediterranean, such scenes had place. Even in Greece the tale of the sun of darkness encreased the fears and despair of the dying multitude. We, in our cloudy isle, were far removed from danger, and the only circumstance that brought these disasters at all home to us, was the daily arrival of vessels from the east, crowded with emigrants, mostly English; for the Moslems, though the fear of death was spread keenly among them, still clung together; that, if they were to die (and if they were, death would as readily meet them on the homeless sea, or in far England, as in Persia),—if they were to die, their bones might rest in earth made sacred by the relics of true believers. Mecca had never before been so crowded with pilgrims; yet the Arabs neglected to pillage the caravans, but, humble and weaponless, they joined the procession, praying Mahomet to avert plague from their tents and deserts.

What are we, the inhabitants of this globe, least among the many that people infinite space? Our minds embrace infinity; the visible mechanism of our being is subject to merest accident. Day by day we are forced to believe this. He whom a scratch has disorganized, he who disappears from apparent life under the influence of the hostile agency at work around us, had the same powers as I—I also am subject to the same laws. In the face of all this we call ourselves lords of the creation, wielders of the elements, masters of life and death, and we allege in excuse of this arrogance, that though the individual is destroyed, man continues for ever.

Thus, losing our identity, that of which we are chiefly conscious, we glory in the continuity of our species, and learn to regard death without terror. But when any whole nation becomes the victim of the destructive powers of exterior agents, then indeed man shrinks into insignificance, he feels his tenure of life insecure, his inheritance on earth cut off.

Thus we began to feel, with regard to many-visaged death let loose on the chosen districts of our fair habitation, and above all, with regard to the plague. We feared the coming summer. Nations, bordering on the already infected countries, began to enter upon serious plans for the better keeping out of the enemy. We, a commercial people, were obliged to bring such schemes under consideration; and the question of contagion became a matter of earnest disquisition.

That the plague was not what is commonly called contagious, like the scarlet fever, or extinct small-pox, was proved. It was called an epidemic. But the grand question was still unsettled of how this epidemic was generated and increased. If infection depended upon the air, the air was subject to infection. As for instance, a typhus fever has been brought by ships to one sea-port town; yet the very people who brought it there, were incapable of communicating it in a town more fortunately situated. But how are we to judge of airs, and pronounce—in such a city plague will die unproductive; in such another, nature has provided for it a plentiful harvest? In the same way, individuals may escape ninety-nine times, and receive the death-blow at the hundredth; because bodies are sometimes in a state to reject the infection of malady, and at others, thirsty to imbibe it. These reflections made our legislators pause, before they could decide on the laws to be put in force. The evil was so wide-spreading, so violent and immedicable, that no care, no prevention could be judged superfluous, which even added a chance to our escape.

These were questions of prudence; there was no immediate necessity for an earnest caution. England was still secure. France, Germany, Italy and Spain, were interposed, walls yet without a breach, between us and the plague. Our vessels truly were the sport of winds and waves, even as Gulliver was the toy of the Brobdignagians; but we on our stable abode could not be hurt in life or limb by these eruptions of nature. We could not fear—we did not. Yet a feeling of awe, a breathless sentiment of wonder, a painful sense of the degradation of humanity, was introduced into every heart. Nature, our mother, and our friend, had turned on us a brow of menace. She showed us plainly, that, though she permitted us to assign her laws and subdue her apparent powers, yet, if she put forth but a finger, we must quake. She could take our glove, fringed with mountains, girded by the atmosphere, containing the condition of our being, and all that man's mind could invent or his force achieve; she could take the ball in her hand, and cast it into space, where life would be drunk up, and man and all his efforts for ever annihilated.

These speculations were rife among us; yet not the less we proceeded in our daily occupations, and our plans, whose accomplishment demanded the lapse of many years. No voice was heard telling us to hold! When foreign distresses came to be felt by us through the channels of commerce, we set ourselves to apply remedies. Subscriptions were made for the emigrants, and merchants bankrupt by the failure of trade. The English spirit awoke to its full activity, and, as it had ever done, set itself to resist the evil, and to stand in the breach which diseased nature had suffered chaos and death to make in the bounds and banks which had hitherto kept them out.

At the commencement of summer, we began to feel, that the mischief which had taken place in distant countries was greater than we had at first suspected. Quito was destroyed by an earthquake. Mexico laid waste by the united effects of storm, pestilence and famine. Crowds of emigrants inundated the west of Europe; and our island had become the refuge of thousands. In the mean time Ryland had been chosen Protector. He had sought this office with eagerness, under the idea of turning his whole forces to the suppression of the privileged orders of our community. His measures were thwarted, and his schemes interrupted by this new state of things. Many of the foreigners were utterly destitute; and their increasing numbers at length forbade a recourse to the usual modes of relief. Trade was stopped by the failure of the interchange of cargoes usual between us, and America, India, Egypt and Greece. A sudden break was made in the routine of our lives. In vain our Protector and his partizans sought to conceal this truth; in vain, day after day, he appointed a period for the discussion of the new laws concerning hereditary rank and privilege; in vain he endeavoured to represent the evil as partial and temporary. These disasters came home to so many bosoms, and, through the various channels of commerce, were carried so entirely into every class and division of the community, that of necessity they became the first question in the state, the chief subjects to which we must turn our attention.

Can it be true, each asked the other with wonder and dismay, that whole countries are laid waste, whole nations annihilated, by these disorders in nature? The vast cities of America, the fertile plains of Hindostan, the crowded abodes of the Chinese, are menaced with utter ruin. Where late the busy multitudes assembled for pleasure or profit, now only the sound of wailing and misery is heard. The air is empoisoned, and each human being inhales death, even while in youth and health, their hopes are in the flower. We called to mind the plague of 1348, when it was calculated that a third of mankind had been destroyed. As yet western Europe was uninfected; would it always be so?

Half England was desolate, when October came, and the equinoctial winds swept over the earth, chilling the ardours of the unhealthy season. The summer, which was uncommonly hot, had been protracted into the beginning of this month, when on the eighteenth a sudden change was brought about from summer temperature to winter frost. Pestilence then made a pause in her death-dealing career. Gasping, not daring to name our hopes, yet full even to the brim with intense expectation, we stood as a shipwrecked sailor stands on a barren rock islanded by the ocean, watching a distant vessel, fancying that now it nears, and then again that it is bearing from sight. This promise of a renewed lease of life turned rugged natures to melting tenderness, and by contrast filled the soft with harsh and unnatural sentiments. When it seemed destined that all were to die, we were reckless of the how and when—now that the virulence of the disease was mitigated, and it appeared willing to spare some, each was eager to be among the elect, and clung to life with dastard tenacity. Instances of desertion became more frequent; and even murders, which made the hearer sick with horror, where the fear of contagion had armed those nearest in blood against each other. But these smaller and separate tragedies were about to yield to a mightier interest—and, while we were promised calm from infectious influences, a tempest arose wilder than the winds, a tempest bred by the passions of man, nourished by his most violent impulses, unexampled and dire.

A number of people from North America, the relics of that populous continent, had set sail for the east with mad desire of change, leaving their native plains for lands not less afflicted than their own. Several hundreds landed in Ireland, about the first of November, and took possession of such vacant habitations as they could find; seizing upon the superabundant food, and the stray cattle. As they exhausted the produce of one spot, they went on to another. At length they began to interfere with the inhabitants, and strong in their concentrated numbers, ejected the natives from their dwellings, and robbed them of their winter store. A few events of this kind roused the fiery nature of the Irish; and they attacked the invaders. Some were destroyed; the major part escaped by quick and well ordered movements; and danger made them careful. Their numbers ably arranged; the very deaths among them concealed; moving on in good order, and apparently given up to enjoyment, they excited the envy of the Irish. The Americans permitted a few to join their band, and presently the recruits outnumbered the strangers—nor did they join with them, nor imitate the admirable order which, preserved by the Trans-Atlantic chiefs, rendered them at once secure and formidable. The Irish followed their tack in disorganized multitudes; each day increasing; each day becoming more lawless. The Americans were eager to escape from the spirit they had roused, and, reaching the eastern shores of the island, embarked for England. Their incursion would hardly have been felt had they come alone; but the Irish, collected in unnatural numbers, began to feel the inroads of famine, and they followed in the wake of Americans for England also. The crossing of the sea could not arrest their progress. The harbours of the desolate sea-ports of the west of Ireland were filled with vessels of all sizes, from the man of war to the small fishers' boat, which lay sailorless, and rotting on the lazy deep. The emigrants embarked by hundreds, and unfurling their sails with rude hands, made strange havoc of buoy and cordage. Those who modestly betook themselves to the smaller craft, for the most part

achieved their watery journey in safety. Some, in the true spirit
of reckless enterprise, went on board a ship of an hundred and
twenty guns; the vast hull drifted with the tide out of the bay, and
after many hours its crew of landsmen contrived to spread a great
part of her enormous canvass—the wind took it, and while a
thousand mistakes of the helmsman made her present her head now
to one point, and now to another, the vast fields of canvass that
formed her sails flapped with a sound like that of a huge cataract;
or such as a sea-like forest may give forth when buffeted by an
equinoctial north-wind. The portholes were open, and with every
sea, which as she lurched, washed her decks, they received whole
tons of water. The difficulties were increased by a fresh breeze which
began to blow, whistling among the shrowds, dashing the sails this
way and that, and rending them with horrid split, and such whir
as may have visited the dreams of Milton, when he imagined the
winnowing of the arch-fiend's van-like wings, which increased the
uproar of wild chaos. These sounds were mingled with the roaring
of the sea, the splash of the chafed billows round the vessel's sides,
and the gurgling up of the water in the hold. The crew, many of
whom had never seen the sea before, felt indeed as if heaven and
earth came ruining together, as the vessel dipped her bows in the
waves, or rose high upon them. Their yells were drowned in the
clamour of elements, and the thunder rivings of their unwieldy
habitation—they discovered at last that the water gained on them,
and they betook themselves to their pumps; they might as well have
laboured to empty the ocean by bucketfuls. As the sun went down,
the gale increased; the ship seemed to feel her danger, she was now
completely water-logged, and presented other indications of settling
before she went down. The bay was crowded with vessels, whose
crews, for the most part, were observing the uncouth sportings of
this huge unwieldy machine—they saw her gradually sink; the
waters now rising above her lower decks—they could hardly wink
before she had utterly disappeared, nor could the place where the
sea had closed over her be at all discerned. Some few of her crew
were saved, but the greater part clinging to her cordage and masts
went down with her, to rise only when death loosened their hold.

This event caused many of those who were about to sail, to put
foot again on firm land, ready to encounter any evil rather than
to rush into the yawning jaws of the pitiless ocean. But these were
few, in comparison to the numbers who actually crossed. Many went
up as high as Belfast to ensure a shorter passage, and then journeying
south through Scotland, they were joined by the poorer natives of
that country, and all poured with one consent into England.

Such incursions struck the English with affright, in all those towns
where there was still sufficient population to feel the change. There
was room enough indeed in our hapless country for twice the

number of invaders; but their lawless spirit instigated them to violence; they took a delight in thrusting the possessors from their
houses; in seizing on some mansion of luxury, where the noble
dwellers secluded themselves in fear of the plague; in forcing these
of either sex to become their servants and purveyors; till, the ruin
complete in one place, they removed their locust visitation to
another. When unopposed they spread their ravages wide; in cases
of danger they clustered, and by dint of numbers overthrew their
weak and despairing foes. They came from the east and north, and
directed their course without apparent motive, but unanimously
towards our unhappy metropolis.

Communication had been to a great degree cut off through the
paralyzing effects of pestilence, so that the van of our invaders had
proceeded as far as Manchester and Derby, before we received notice
of their arrival. They swept the country like a conquering army,
burning—laying waste—murdering. The lower and vagabond English joined with them. Some few of the Lords Lieutenant who
remained, endeavoured to collect the militia—but the ranks were
vacant, panic seized on all, and the opposition that was made only
served to increase the audacity and cruelty of the enemy. They talked
of taking London, conquering England—calling to mind the long
detail of injuries which had for many years been forgotten. Such
vaunts displayed their weakness, rather than their strength—yet still
they might do extreme mischief, which, ending in their destruction,
would render them at last objects of compassion and remorse.

We were now taught how, in the beginning of the world, mankind
clothed their enemies in impossible attributes—and how details proceeding from mouth to mouth, might, like Virgil's ever-growing
Rumour, reach the heavens with her brow, and clasp Hesperus and
Lucifer with her outstretched hands. Gorgon and Centaur, dragon
and iron-hoofed lion, vast sea-monster and gigantic hydra, were
but types of the strange and appalling accounts brought to London
concerning our invaders. Their landing was long unknown, but having now advanced within an hundred miles of London, the country
people flying before them arrived in successive troops, each exaggerating the numbers, fury, and cruelty of the assailants. Tumult
filled the before quiet streets—women and children deserted their
homes, escaping they knew not whither—fathers, husbands, and
sons, stood trembling, not for themselves, but for their loved and
defenceless relations. As the country people poured into London,
the citizens fled southwards—they climbed the higher edifices of
the town, fancying that they could discern the smoke and flames
the enemy spread around them. As Windsor lay, to a great degree,
in the line of march from the west, I removed my family to London,
assigning the Tower for their sojourn, and joining Adrian, acted
as his Lieutenant in the coming struggle.

We employed only two days in our preparations, and made good use of them. Artillery and arms were collected; the remnants of such regiments, as could be brought through many losses into any show of muster, were put under arms, with that appearance of military discipline which might encourage our own party, and seem most formidable to the disorganized multitude of our enemies. Even music was not wanting: banners floated in the air, and the shrill fife and loud trumpet breathed forth sounds of encouragement and victory. A practised ear might trace an undue faltering in the step of the soldiers; but this was not occasioned so much by fear of the adversary, as by disease, by sorrow, and by fatal prognostications, which often weighed most potently on the brave, and quelled the manly heart to abject subjection.

Adrian led the troops. He was full of care. It was small relief to him that our discipline should gain us success in such a conflict; while plague still hovered to equalize the conqueror and the conquered, it was not victory that he desired, but bloodless peace. As we advanced, we were met by bands of peasantry, whose almost naked condition, whose despair and horror, told at once the fierce nature of the coming enemy. The senseless spirit of conquest and thirst of spoil blinded them, while with insane fury they deluged the country in ruin. The sight of the military restored hope to those who fled, and revenge took place of fear. They inspired the soldiers with the same sentiment. Languor was changed to ardour, the slow step converted to a speedy pace, while the hollow murmur of the multitude, inspired by one feeling, and that deadly, filled the air, drowning the clang of arms and sound of music. Adrian perceived the change, and feared that it would be difficult to prevent them from wreaking their utmost fury on the Irish. He rode through the lines, charging the officers to restrain the troops, exhorting the soldiers, restoring order, and quieting in some degree the violent agitation that swelled every bosom.

We first came upon a few stragglers of the Irish at St. Albans. They retreated, and joining others of their companions, still fell back, till they reached the main body. Tidings of an armed and regular opposition recalled them to a sort of order. They made Buckingham their head-quarters, and scouts were sent out to ascertain our situation. We remained for the night at Luton. In the morning a simultaneous movement caused us each to advance. It was early dawn, and the air, impregnated with freshest odour, seemed in idle mockery to play with our banners, and bore onwards towards the enemy the music of the bands, the neighings of the horses, and regular step of the infantry. The first sound of martial instruments that came upon our undisciplined foe, inspired surprise, not unmingled with dread. It spoke of other days, of days of concord and order; it was associated with times when plague was not, and man lived beyond the shadow of imminent fate. The pause was momentary. Soon we heard their disorderly clamour, the barbarian shouts, the untimed step of thousands coming on in disarray. Their troops now came pouring on us from the open country or narrow lanes; a large extent of unenclosed fields lay between us; we advanced to the middle of this, and then made a halt: being somewhat on superior ground, we could discern the space they covered. When their leaders perceived us drawn out in opposition, they also gave the word to halt, and endeavoured to form their men into some imitation of military discipline. The first ranks had muskets; some were mounted, but their arms were such as they had seized during their advance, their horses those they had taken from the peasantry; there was no uniformity, and little obedience, but their shouts and wild gestures showed the untamed spirit that inspired them. Our soldiers received the word, and advanced to quickest time, but in perfect order: their uniform dresses, the gleam of their polished arms, their silence, and looks of sullen hate, were more appalling than the savage clamour of our innumerous foe. Thus coming nearer and nearer each other, the howls and shouts of the Irish increased; the English proceeded in obedience to their officers, until they came near enough to distinguish the faces of their enemies; the sight inspired them with fury: with one cry, that rent heaven and was re-echoed by the furthest lines, they rushed on; they disdained the use of the bullet, but with fixed bayonet dashed among the opposing foe, while the ranks opening at intervals, the matchmen lighted the cannon, whose deafening roar and blinding smoke filled up the horror of the scene.

I was beside Adrian; a moment before he had again given the word to halt, and had remained a few yards distant from us in deep meditation: he was forming swiftly his plan of action, to prevent the effusion of blood; the noise of cannon, the sudden rush of the troops, and yell of the foe, startled him: with flashing eyes he exclaimed, "Not one of these must perish!" and plunging the rowels into his horse's sides, he dashed between the conflicting bands. We, his staff, followed him to surround and protect him; obeying his signal, however, we fell back somewhat. The soldiery perceiving him, paused in their onset; he did not swerve from the bullets that passed near him, but rode immediately between the opposing lines. Silence succeeded to clamour; about fifty men lay on the ground dying or dead. Adrian raised his sword in act to speak: "By whose command," he cried, addressing his own troops, "do you advance? Who ordered your attack? Fall back; these misguided men shall not be slaughtered, while I am your general. Sheath your weapons; these are your brothers, commit not fratricide; soon the plague will not leave one for you to glut your revenge upon: will you be more pitiless than pestilence? As you honour me—as you worship God, in whose image those also are created—as your children and friends are dear to you,—shed not a drop of precious human blood."

He spoke with outstretched hand and winning voice, and then turning to our invaders, with a severe brow, he commanded them to lay down their arms: "Do you think," he said, "that because we are wasted by plague, you can overcome us; the plague is also among you, and when ye are vanquished by famine and disease, the ghosts of those you have murdered will arise to bid you not hope in death. Lay down your arms, barbarous and cruel men—men whose hands are stained with the blood of the innocent, whose souls are weighed down by the orphan's cry! We shall conquer, for the right is on our side; already your cheeks are pale—the weapons fall from your nerveless grasp. Lay down your arms, fellow men! brethren! Pardon, succour, and brotherly love await your repentance. You are dear to us, because you wear the frail shape of humanity; each one among you will find a friend and host among these forces. Shall man be the enemy of man, while plague, the foe to all, even now is above us, triumphing in our butchery, more cruel than her own?"

Each army paused. On our side the soldiers grasped their arms firmly, and looked with stern glances on the foe. These had not thrown down their weapons, more from fear than the spirit of contest; they looked at each other, each wishing to follow some example given him,—but they had no leader. Adrian threw himself from his horse, and approaching one of those just slain: "He was a man," he cried, "and he is dead. O quickly bind up the wounds of the fallen—let not one die; let not one more soul escape through your merciless gashes, to relate before the throne of God the tale of fratricide; bind up their wounds—restore them to their friends. Cast away the hearts of tigers that burn in your breasts; throw down those tools of cruelty and hate; in this pause of exterminating destiny, let each man be brother, guardian, and stay to the other. Away with those blood-stained arms, and hasten some of you to bind up these wounds."

As he spoke, he knelt on the ground, and raised in his arms a man from whose side the warm tide of life gushed—the poor wretch gasped—so still had either host become, that his moans were distinctly heard, and every heart, late fiercely bent on universal massacre, now beat anxiously in hope and fear for the fate of this one man. Adrian tore off his military scarf and bound it round the sufferer—it was too late—the man heaved a deep sigh, his head fell back, his limbs lost their sustaining power.—"He is dead!" said Adrian, as the corpse fell from his arms on the ground, and he bowed his head in sorrow and awe. The fate of the world seemed bound up in the death of this single man. On either side the bands threw down their arms, even the veterans wept, and our party held out

their hands to their foes, while a gush of love and deepest amity
filled every heart. The two forces mingling, unarmed and hand in
hand, talking only how each might assist the other, the adversaries
conjoined; each repenting, the one side their former cruelties, the
other their late violence, they obeyed the orders of the General to
proceed towards London.

Hear you not the rushing sound of the coming tempest? Do you
not behold the clouds open, and destruction lurid and dire pour
down on the blasted earth? See you not the thunderbolt fall, and
are deafened by the shout of heaven that follows its descent? Feel
you not the earth quake and open with agonizing groans, while
the air is pregnant with shrieks and wailings,—all announcing the
last days of man?

No! none of these things accompanied our fall! The balmy air
of spring, breathed from nature's ambrosial home, invested the
lovely earth, which wakened as a young mother about to lead forth
in pride her beauteous offspring to meet their sire who had been
long absent.

Plague is the companion of spring, of sunshine, and plenty. We
no longer struggle with her. We have forgotten what we did when
she was not.

At first the increase of sickness in spring brought increase of toil
to such of us, who, as yet spared to life, bestowed our time and
thoughts on our fellow creatures. We nerved ourselves to the task:
"in the midst of despair we performed the tasks of hope." We went
out with the resolution of disputing with our foe. We aided the
sick, and comforted the sorrowing; turning from the multitudinous
dead to the rare survivors, with an energy of desire that bore the
resemblance of power, we bade them—live. Plague sat paramount
the while, and laughed us to scorn.

In the autumn of this year 2096, the spirit of emigration crept
in among the few survivors, who, congregating from various parts
of England, met in London. This spirit existed as a breath, a wish,
a far off thought, until communicated to Adrian, who imbibed it
with ardour, and instantly engaged himself in plans for its execution.
The fear of immediate death vanished with the heats of September.
Another winter was before us, and w might elect our mode of passing it to the best advantage. Perhaps in rational philosophy none
could be better chosen than this scheme of migration, which would
draw us from the immediate scene of our woe, and, leading us
through pleasant and picturesque countries, amuse for a time our
despair. The idea once broached, all were impatient to put it in
execution.

We were still at Windsor; our renewed hopes medicined the
anguish we had suffered from the late tragedies. The death of many
of our inmates had weaned us from the fond idea, that Windsor

Castle was a spot sacred from the plague; but our lease of life was renewed for some months, and even Idris lifted her head, as a lily after a storm, when a last sunbeam tinges its silver cup. Just at this time Adrian came down to us; his eager looks shewed us that he was full of some scheme. He hastened to take me aside, and disclosed to me with rapidity his plan of emigration from England.

To leave England for ever! to turn from its polluted fields and groves, and, placing the sea between us, to quit it, as a sailor quits the rock on which he has been wrecked, when the saving ship rides by. Such was his plan.

To leave the country of our fathers, made holy by their graves!—We could not feel even as a voluntary exile of old, who might for pleasure or convenience forsake his native soil; though thousands of miles might divide him, England was still a part of him, as he of her. He heard of the passing events of the day; he knew that, if he returned, and resumed his place in society, the entrance was still open, and it required but the will, to surround himself at once with the associations and habits of boyhood. Not so with us, the remnant. We left none to represent us, none to repeople the desert land, and the name of England died, when we left her,

> In vagabond pursuit of dreadful safety.

Yet let us go! England is in her shroud,—we may not enchain ourselves to a corpse. Let us go—the world is our country now, and we will choose for our residence its most fertile spot. Shall we, in these desert halls, under this wintry sky, sit with closed eyes and folded hands, expecting death? Let us rather go out to meet it gallantly:—or perhaps—for all this pendulous orb, this fair gem in the sky's diadem, is not surely plague-striken—perhaps, in some secluded nook, amidst eternal spring, and waving trees, and purling streams, we may find Life. The world is vast, and England, though her many fields and wide spread woods seem interminable, is but a small part of her. At the close of a day's march over high mountains and through snowy vallies, we may come upon health, and committing our loved ones to its charge, replant the uprooted tree of humanity, and send to late posterity the tale of the ante-pestilential race, the heroes and sages of the lost state of things.

On the twentieth of November, Adrian and I rode for the last time through the streets of London. They were grass-grown and desert. The open doors of the empty mansions creaked upon their hinges; rank herbage, and deforming dirt, had swiftly accumulated on the steps of the houses; the voiceless steeples of the churches pierced the smokeless air; the churches were open, but no prayer was offered at the altars; mildew and damp had already defaced their ornaments; birds, and tame animals, now homeless, had built nests, and made their lairs in consecrated spots. We passed St. Paul's. London, which had extended so far in suburbs in all direction, had been somewhat deserted in the midst, and much of what had in former days obscured this vast building was removed. Its ponderous mass, blackened stone, and high dome, made it look, not like a temple, but a tomb. Methought above the portico was engraved the *Hic jacet* of England. We passed on eastwards, engaged in such solemn talk as the times inspired. No human step was heard, nor human form discerned. Troops of dogs, deserted of their masters, passed us; and now and then a horse, unbridled and unsaddled, trotted towards us, and tried to attract the attention of those which we rode, as if to allure them to seek like liberty. An unwieldy ox, who had fed in an abandoned granary, suddenly lowed, and shewed his shapeless form in a narrow door-way; every thing was desert; but nothing was in ruin. And this medley of undamaged buildings, and luxurious accommodation, in trim and fresh youth, was contrasted with the lonely silence of the unpeopled streets.

When we arrived at Dover, after a fatiguing day's journey, we all required rest and sleep; but the scene acting around us soon drove away such ideas. We were drawn, along with the greater part of our companions, to the edge of the cliff, there to listen and make a thousand conjectures. A fog narrowed our horizon to about a quarter of a mile, and the misty veil, cold and dense, enveloped sky and sea in equal obscurity. What added to our inquietude was the circumstance that two-thirds of our original number were now waiting for us in Paris, and clinging, as we now did most painfully, to any addition to our melancholy remnant, this division, with the tameless impassable ocean between, struck us with affright. At length, after loitering for several hours on the cliff, we retired to Dover Castle, whose roof sheltered all who breathed the English air, and sought the sleep necessary to restore strength and courage to our worn frames and languid spirits.

Our journey was impeded by a thousand obstacles. As our horses grew tired, we had to seek for others; and hours were wasted, while we exhausted our artifices to allure some of these enfranchised slaves of man to resume the yoke; or as we went from stable to stable through the towns, hoping to find some who had not forgotten the shelter of their native stalls. Our ill success in procuring them, obliged us continually to leave some one of our companions behind; and on the first of February, Adrian and I entered Paris, wholly unaccompanied. The serene morning had dawned when we arrived at Saint Denis, and the sun was high, when the clamour of voices, and the clash, as we feared, of weapons, guided us to where our countrymen had assembled on the Place Vendome. We passed a knot of Frenchmen, who were talking earnestly of the madness of the insular invaders, and then coming by a sudden turn upon the Place, we saw the sun glitter on drawn swords and fixed bayonets, while yells and clamours rent the air. It was a scene of unaccustomed confusion in these days of depopulation. Roused by fancied wrongs, and insulting scoffs, the opposite parties had rushed to attack each other; while the elect, drawn up apart, seemed to wait an opportunity to fall with better advantage on their foes, when they should have mutually weakened each other. A merciful power interposed, and no blood was shed; for, while the insane mob were in the very act of attack, the females, wives, mothers and daughters, rushed between; they seized the bridles; they embraced the knees of the horsemen, and hung on the necks, or enweaponed arms of their enraged relatives; the shrill female scream was mingled with the manly shout, and formed the wild clamour that welcomed us on our arrival.

The last events that marked our progress through France were so full of strange horror and gloomy misery, that I dare not pause too long in the narration. If I were to dissect each incident, every small fragment of a second would contain an harrowing tale, whose minutest word would curdle the blood in thy young veins. It is right that I should erect for thy instruction this monument of the foregone race; but not that I should drag thee through the wards of an hospital, nor the secret chambers of the charnel-house. This tale, therefore, shall be rapidly unfolded. Images of destruction, pictures of despair, the procession of the last triumph of death, shall be drawn before thee, swift as the rack driven by the north wind along the blotted splendour of the sky.

Weed-grown fields, desolate towns, the wild approach of riderless horses had now become habitual to my eyes; nay, sights far worse, of the unburied dead, and human forms which were strewed on the road side, and on the steps of once frequented habitations, where,

> Through the flesh that wastes away
> Beneath the parching sun, the whitening bones
> Start forth, and moulder in the sable dust.

Sights like these had become—ah, woe the while! so familiar, that we had ceased to shudder, or spur our stung horses to sudden speed, as we passed them. France in its best days, at least that part of France through which we travelled, had been a cultivated desert, and the absence of enclosures, of cottages, and even of peasantry, was saddening to a traveller from sunny Italy, or busy England.

Thus we continued travelling during the hottest season; and it was not till the first of August, that we, the emigrants,—reader, there were just eighty of us in number,—entered the gates of Dijon.

We had expected this moment with eagerness, for now we had accomplished the worst part of our drear journey, and Switzerland was near at hand. Yet how could we congratulate ourselves on any event thus imperfectly fulfilled? Were these miserable beings, who, worn and wretched, passed in sorrowful procession, the sole remnants of the race of man, which, like a flood, had once spread over and possessed the whole earth? It had come down clear and unimpeded from its primal mountain source in Ararat, and grew from a puny streamlet to a vast perennial river, generation after generation flowing on ceaselessly. The same, but diversified, it grew, and swept onwards towards the absorbing ocean, whose dim shores we now reached. It had been the mere plaything of nature, when first it crept out of uncreative void into light; but thought brought forth power and knowledge; and, clad with these, the race of man assumed dignity and authority. It was then no longer the mere gardener of earth, or the shepherd of her flocks; "it carried with it an imposing and majestic aspect; it had a pedigree and illustrious ancestors; it had its gallery of portraits, its monumental inscriptions, its records and titles."*

This was all over, now that the ocean of death had sucked in the slackening tide, and its source was dried up. We first had bidden adieu to the state of things which having existed many thousand years, seemed eternal; such a state of government, obedience, traffic, and domestic intercourse, as had moulded our hearts and capacities, as far back as memory could reach. Then to patriotic zeal, to the arts, to reputation, to enduring fame, to the name of country, we had bidden farewell. We saw depart all hope of retrieving our ancient state—all expectation, except the feeble one of saving our individual lives from the wreck of the past. To preserve these we had quitted England—England, no more; for without her children, what name could that barren island claim? With tenacious grasp we clung to such rule and order as could best save us; trusting that, if a little colony could be preserved, that would suffice at some remoter period to restore the lost community of mankind.

But the game is up! We must all die; nor leave survivor nor heir to the wide inheritance of earth. We must all die! The species of man must perish; his frame of exquisite workmanship; the wondrous mechanism of his senses; the noble proportion of his godlike limbs; his mind, the throned king of these; must perish. Will the earth still keep her place among the planets; will she still journey with unmarked regularity round the sun; will the seasons change, the trees adorn themselves with leaves, and flowers shed their fragrance, in solitude? Will the mountains remain unmoved, and streams still keep a downward course towards the vast abyss; will

*Burke's *Reflections on the French Revolution.*

the tides rise and fall, and the winds fan universal nature; will beasts pasture, birds fly, and fishes swim, when man, the lord, possessor, perceiver, and recorder of all these things, has passed away, as though he had never been? O, what mockery is this! Surely death is not death, and humanity is not extinct; but merely passed into other shapes, unsubjected to our perceptions. Death is a vast portal, an high road to life: let us hasten to pass; let us exist no more in this living death, but die that we may live!

We had now reached Switzerland, so long the final mark and aim of our exertions. We had looked, I know not wherefore, with hope and pleasing expectation on her congregation of hills and snowy crags, and opened our bosoms with renewed spirits to the icy Biz, which even at Midsummer used to come from the northern glacier laden with cold. Yet how could we nourish expectation of relief? Like our native England, and the vast extent of fertile France, this mountain-embowered land was desolate of its inhabitants. Nor bleak mountain-top, nor snow-nourished rivulet; not the ice-laden Biz, nor thunder, the tamer of contagion, had preserved them—why therefore should we claim exemption?

Who was there indeed to save? What troop had we brought fit to stand at bay, and combat with the conqueror? We were a failing remnant, tamed to mere submission to the coming blow. A train half dead, through fear of death—a hopeless, unresisting, almost reckless crew, which, in the tossed bark of life, had given up all pilotage, and resigned themselves to the destructive force of ungoverned winds. So on the fifteenth of August we departed on our pilgrimage towards Rome.

I sat at the prow, watching our course; when suddenly I heard the waters break with redoubled fury. We were certainly near the shore—at the same time I cried, "About there!" and a broad lightning filling the concave, shewed us for one moment the level beach a-head, disclosing even the sands, and stunted, ooze-sprinkled beds of reeds, that grew at high water mark.

For a moment the gale paused, and ocean sank to a comparative silence—it was a breathless interval; the wind which, as a practised leaper, had gathered itself up before it sprung, now with terrific roar rushed over the sea, and the waves struck our stern. Adrian exclaimed that the rudder was gone.

We were without a rudder—we rushed prow foremost into the vast billows piled up a-head—they broke over and filled the tiny skiff; one scream I heard—one cry that we were gone, I uttered; I found myself in the waters; darkness was around. When the light of the tempest flashed, I saw the keel of our upset boat close to me—I clung to this, grasping it with clenched hand and nails, while I endeavoured during each flash to discover any appearance of my companions. I thought I saw Adrian at no great distance from me,

clinging to an oar; I sprung from my hold, and with energy beyond
my human strength, I dashed aside the waters as I strove to lay
hold of him. As that hope failed, instinctive love of life animated
me.

The shelving shore suddenly presented a footing for me. I rose,
and was again thrown down by the breakers—a point of rock to
which I was enabled to cling, gave me a moment's respite; and then,
taking advantage of the ebbing of the waves, I ran forwards—gained
the dry sands, and fell senseless on the oozy reeds that sprinkled
them.

The day passed; each moment contained eternity; although when
hour after hour had gone by, I wondered at the quick flight of time.
Yet even now I had not drunk the bitter potion to the dregs; I was
not yet persuaded of my loss; I did not yet feel in every pulsation,
in every nerve, in every thought, that I remained alone of my
race,—that I was the LAST MAN.

Now—soft awhile—have I arrived so near the end? Yes! it is all
over now—a step or two over those new made graves, and the wearisome way is done. Can I accomplish my task? Can I streak my paper
with words capacious of the grand conclusion? Arise, black
Melancholy! quit thy Cimmerian solitude! Bring with thee murky
fogs from hell, which may drink up the day; bring blight and pes-
tiferous exhalations, which, entering the hollow caverns and breathing places of earth, may fill her stony veins with corruption, so
that not only herbage may no longer flourish, the trees may rot,
and rivers run with gall—but the everlasting mountains be decom-
posed, and the mighty deep putrify, and the genial atmosphere
which clips the globe, lose all powers of generation and sustenance.
Do this, sad visaged power, while I write, while eyes read these
pages.

And who will read them? Beware, tender offspring of the reborn
world—beware, fair being, with human heart, yet untamed by care,
and human brow, yet unploughed by time—beware, lest the cheerful
current of thy blood be checked, thy golden locks turn grey, thy
sweet dimpling smiles be changed to fixed, harsh wrinkles! Let not
day look on these lines, lest garish day waste, turn pale, and die.
Seek a cypress grove, whose moaning boughs will be harmony befitting; seek some cave, deep embowered in earth's dark entrails,
where no light will penetrate, save that which struggles, red and
flickering, through a single fissure, staining thy page with grimmest
livery of death.

I found the granaries of Rome well stored with grain, and particularly with Indian corn; this product requiring less art in its preparation for food, I selected as my principal support. I now found
the hardships and lawlessness of my youth turn to account. A man
cannot throw off the habits of sixteen years. Since that age, it is

true, I had lived luxuriously, or at least surrounded by all the conveniences civilization afforded. But before that time, I had been "as uncouth a savage, as the wolf-bred founder of old Rome"—and now, in Rome itself, robber and shepherd propensities, similar to those of its founder, were of advantage to its sole inhabitant. I spent the morning riding and shooting in the Campagna—I passed long hours in the various galleries—I gazed at each statue, and lost myself in a reverie before many a fair Madonna or beauteous nymph. I haunted the Vatican, and stood surrounded by marble forms of divine beauty. Each stone deity was possessed by sacred gladness, and the eternal früition of love. They looked on me with unsympathizing complacency, and often in wild accents I reproached them for their supreme indifference—for they were human shapes, the human form divine was manifest in each fairest limb and lineament. The perfect moulding brought with it the idea of colour and motion; often, half in bitter mockery, half in self-delusion, I clasped their icy proportions, and, coming between Cupid and his Psyche's lips, pressed the unconceiving marble.

I endeavoured to read. I visited the libraries of Rome. I selected a volume, and choosing some sequestered, shady nook, on the banks of the Tiber, or opposite the fair temple in the Borghese Gardens, or under the old pyramid of Cestius, I endeavoured to conceal me from myself, and immerse myself in the subject traced on the pages before me. As if in the same soil you plant nightshade and a myrtle tree, they will each appropriate the mould, moisture, and air administered, for the fostering their several properties—so did my grief find sustenance, and power of existence, and growth, in what else had been divine manna, to feed radiant meditation. Ah! while I streak this paper with the tale of what my so named occupations were—while I shape the skeleton of my days—my hand trembles—my heart pants, and my brain refuses to lend expression, or phrase, or idea, by which to image forth the veil of unutterable woe that clothed these bare realities. Oh, worn and beating heart, may I dissect thy fibres, and tell how in each unmitigable misery, sadness, dire, repinings, and despair, existed? May I record my many ravings—the wild curses I hurled at torturing nature—and how I have passed days shut out from light and food—from all except the burning hell alive in my own bosom?

I was presented, meantime, with one other occupation, the one best fitted to discipline my melancholy thoughts, which strayed backwards, over many a ruin, and through many a flowery glade, even to the mountain recess, from which in early youth I had first emerged.

During one of my rambles through the habitations of Rome, I found writing materials on a table in an author's study. Parts of a manuscript lay scattered about. It contained a learned disquisition on the Italian language; one page an unfinished dedication to posterity, for whose profit the writer had sifted and selected the niceties of this harmonious language—to whose everlasting benefit he bequeathed his labours.

I also will write a book, I cried—for whom to read?—to whom dedicated? And then with silly flourish (what so capricious and childish as despair?) I wrote,

DEDICATION
TO THE ILLUSTRIOUS DEAD.
SHADOWS, ARISE, AND READ YOUR FALL!
BEHOLD THE HISTORY OF THE
LAST MAN.

Yet, will not this world be repeopled, and the children of a saved pair of lovers, in some to me unknown and unattainable seclusion, wandering to these prodigious relics of the ante-pestilential race, seek to learn how beings so wondrous in their achievements, with imagination infinite, and powers godlike, had departed from their home to an unknown country?

I will write and leave in this most ancient city, this "world's sole monument," a record of these things. I will leave a monument of the existence of Verney, the Last Man. At first I thought only to speak of plague, of death, and last, of desertion; but I lingered fondly on my early years, and recorded with sacred zeal the virtues of my companions. They have been with me during the fulfilment of my task. I have brought it to an end—I lift my eyes from my paper—again they are lost to me. Again I feel that I am alone.

A year has passed since I have been thus occupied. The seasons have made their wonted round, and decked this eternal city in a changeful robe of surpassing beauty. A year has passed; and I no longer *guess* at my state or my prospects—loneliness is my familiar, sorrow my inseparable companion. I have endeavoured to brave the storm—I have endeavoured to school myself to fortitude—I have sought to imbue myself with the lessons of wisdom. It will not do. My hair has become nearly grey—my voice, unused now to utter sound, comes strangely on my ears. My person, with its human powers and features, seem to me a monstrous excrescence of nature. How express in human language a woe human being until this hour never knew! How give intelligible expression to a pang none but I could ever understand!—No one has entered Rome. None will ever come. I smile bitterly at the delusion I have so long nourished, and still more, when I reflect that I have exchanged it for another as delusive, as false, but to which I now cling with the same fond trust.

Winter has come again; and the gardens of Rome have lost their leaves—the sharp air comes over the Campagna, and has driven its brute inhabitants to take up their abode in the many dwellings of the deserted city—frost has suspended the gushing fountains —and Trevi has stilled her eternal music. I had made a rough calculation, aided by the stars, by which I endeavoured to ascertain the first day of the new year. In the old out-worn age, the Sovereign Pontiff was used to go in solemn pomp, and mark the renewal of the year by driving a nail in the gate of the temple of Janus. On that day I ascended St. Peter's, and carved on its topmost stone the æra 2100, last year of the world!

My only companion was a dog, a shaggy fellow, half water and half shepherd's dog, whom I found tending sheep in the Campagna. His master was dead, but nevertheless he continued fulfilling his duties in expectation of his return. If a sheep strayed from the rest, he forced it to return to the flock, and sedulously kept off every intruder. Riding in the Campagna I had come upon his sheep-walk, and for some time observed his repetition of lessons learned from man, now useless, though unforgotten. His delight was excessive when he saw me. He sprung up to my knees; he capered round and round, wagging his tail, with the short, quick bark of pleasure: he left his fold to follow me, and from that day has never neglected to watch by and attend on me, shewing boisterous gratitude whenever I caressed or talked to him. His pattering steps and mine alone were heard, when we entered the magnificent extent of nave and aisle of St. Peter's. We ascended the myriad steps together, when on the summit I achieved my design, and in rough figures noted the date of the last year. I then turned to gaze on the country, and to take leave of Rome. I had long determined to quit it, and I now formed the plan I would adopt for my future career, after I had left this magnificent abode.

A solitary being is by instinct a wanderer, and that I would become. A hope of amelioration always attends on change of place, which would even lighten the burthen of my life. I had been a fool to remain in Rome all this time: Rome noted for Mal'aria, the famous caterer for death. But it was still possible, that, could I visit the whole extent of earth, I should find in some part of the wide extent a survivor. Methought the sea-side was the most probable retreat to be chosen by such a one. If left alone in an inland district, still they could not continue in the spot where their last hopes had been extinguished; they would journey on, like me, in search of a partner for their solitude, till the watery barrier stopped their further progress.

To that water—cause of my woes, perhaps now to be their cure, I would betake myself. Farewell, Italy!—farewell, thou ornament of the world, matchless Rome, the retreat of the solitary one during long months!—to civilized life—to the settled home and succession of monotonous days, farewell! Peril will now be mine; and I hail her as a friend—death will perpetually cross my path, and I will meet him as a benefactor; hardship, inclement weather, and dangerous tempests will be my sworn mates. Ye spirits of storm, receive me! ye powers of destruction, open wide your arms, and clasp me for ever! if a kinder power have not decreed another end, so that after long endurance I may reap my reward, and again feel my heart beat near the heart of another like to me.

Tiber, the road which is spread by nature's own hand, threading her continent, was at my feet, and many a boat was tethered to the banks. I would with a few books, provisions, and my dog, embark in one of these and float down the current of the stream into the sea; and then, keeping near land, I would coast the beauteous shores and sunny promontories of the blue Mediterranean, pass Naples, along Calabria, and would dare the twin perils of Scylla and Charybdis; then, with fearless aim (for what had I to lose?), skim ocean's surface towards Malta and the further Cyclades. I would avoid Constantinople, the sight of whose well-known towers and inlets belonged to another state of existence from my present one; I would coast Asia Minor, and Syria, and, passing the seven-mouthed Nile, steer northward again, till losing sight of forgotten Carthage and deserted Lybia, I should reach the pillars of Hercules. And then—no matter where—the oozy caves, and soundless depths of ocean may be my dwelling, before I accomplish this long-drawn voyage, or the arrow of disease find my heart as I float singly on the weltering Mediterranean; or, in some place I touch at, I may find what I seek—a companion; or if this may not be—to endless time, decrepid and grey headed—youth already in the grave with those I love—the lone wanderer will still unfurl his sail, and clasp the tiller—and, still obeying the breezes of heaven, for ever round another and another promontory, anchoring in another and another bay, still ploughing seedless ocean, leaving behind the verdant land of native Europe, adown the tawny shore of Africa, having weathered the fierce seas of the Cape, I may moor my worn skiff in a creek, shaded by spicy groves of the odorous islands of the far Indian ocean.

These are wild dreams. Yet since, now a week ago, they came on me, as I stood on the height of St. Peter's, they have ruled my imagination. I have chosen my boat, and laid in my scant stores. I have selected a few books; the principal are Homer and Shakespeare—But the libraries of the world are thrown open to me—and in any port I can renew my stock. I form no expectation of alteration for the better; but the monotonous present is intolerable to me. Neither hope nor joy are my pilots—restless despair and fierce desire of change lead me on. I long to grapple with danger, to be excited by fear, to have some task, however slight or voluntary, for each day's fulfilment. I shall witness all the variety of appearance, that the elements can assume—I shall read fair augury in the rainbow—menace in the cloud—some lesson or record dear to my heart in everything. Thus around the shores of deserted earth, while the sun is high, and the moon waxes or wanes, angels, the spirits of the dead, and the ever-open eye of the Supreme, will behold the tiny bark, freighted with Verney—the LAST MAN.

Black Is Beautiful

Robert Silverberg

my nose is flat my lips are thick my hair is frizzy my skin is black
is beautiful
is black is beautiful

I am James Shabazz age seventeen born august 13 1983 I am black
I am afro I am beautiful this machine writes my words as I speak
them and the machine is black
is beautiful

Elijah Muhammad's *The Supreme Wisdom* says:

*Separation of the so-called Negroes from their slave masters' children
is a MUST. It is the only SOLUTION to our problem. It was the only
solution, according to the Bible, for Israel and the Egyptians, and it will
prove to be the only solution for America and her slaves, whom she
mockingly calls her citizens, without granting her citizenship. We must
keep this in our minds at all times that we are actually being mocked.*

Catlike, moving as a black panther would, James Shabazz stalked
through the city. It was late summer, and the pumps were working
hard, sucking the hot air out from under the Manhattan domes and
squirting it into the suburbs. There had been a lot of grinding about
that lately. Whitey out there complained that all that hot air was
wilting his lawns and making his own pumps work too hard. Screw
Whitey, thought James Shabazz pleasantly. Let his lawns wilt. Let
him complain. Let him get black in the face with complaining. Do
the mother some good.

Silently, pantherlike, down Fifth Avenue to Fifty-third, across to
Park, down Park to Forty-eighth. Just looking around. A big boy,
sweat-shiny, black but not black enough to suit him. He wore a
gaudy five-colored dashiki, beads from Mali, flowing white belled
trousers, a neat goatee, a golden earring. In his left rear pocket:
a beat-up copy of the new novel about Malcolm. In his right rear
pocket: a cute little sonic blade.

Saturday afternoon and the air was quiet. None of the hopterbuses coming through the domes and dumping Whitey onto the rooftops. They stayed home today, the commuters, the palefaces. Saturday and Sunday, the city was black. Likewise all the other days of the week after 4 P.M. Run, Whitey, run! See Whitey run! Why does Whitey run? Because he don't belong here no more.

Sorry teach. I shouldn't talk like that no more, huh?

James Shabazz smiled. The identity card in his pocket called him James Lincoln, but when he walked alone through the city he spurned that name. The slave master name. His parents stuck with it, proud of it, telling him that no black should reject a name like Lincoln. The dumb geeps! What did they think, that great-great-grandpappy was owned by Honest Abe? Lincoln was a tag some belching hillbilly stuck on the family a hundred fifty years ago. If anyone asks me today, I'm James Shabazz. Black. Proud of it.

Black faces mirrored him on every street. Toward him came ten diplomats in tribal robes, not Afros but Africans, a bunch of Yorubas, Ibos, Baules, Mandingos, Ashantis, Senufos, Bakongos, Balubas, who knew what, the real thing, anyway, black as night, so black they looked purple. No slave master blood in them! James Shabazz smiled, nodded. Good afternoon, brothers. Nice day! They took no notice of him, but swept right on, their conversation unbroken. They were not speaking Swahili, which he would have recognized, but some other foreign language, maybe French. He wasn't sure. He scowled after them. Who they think they are, walking around a black man's city, upnosing people like that?

He studied his reflection for a while in the burnished window of a jewelry shop. Ground floor, Martin Luther King Building. Eighty stories of polished black marble. Black. Black man's money built that tower! Black man's sweat!

Overhead came the buzz of a hopter after all. No commuters today, so they had to be tourists. James Shabazz stared up at the beetle of a hopter crossing the dull translucent background of the distant dome. It landed on the penthouse hopter stage of the King Building. He crossed the street and tried to see the palefaces stepping out, but the angle was too steep. Even so, he bowed ceremoniously. Welcome, massa! Welcome to the black man's metropolis! Soul food for lunch? Real hot jazz on 125th? Dancing jigaboo girls stripping at the Apollo? Sightseeing tour of Bedford-Stuyvesant and Harlem?

Can't tell where Bedford-Stuyvesant ends and Harlem begins, can you? But you'll come looking anyway.

Like to cut your guts up, you honkie mothers.

Martin Luther King said in Montgomery, Alabama, instructing the bus desegregators:

If cursed, do not curse back. If pushed, do not push back. If struck,
do not strike back, but evidence love and goodwill at all times.

He sat down for a while in Lumumba Park, back of the Forty-second Street Library, to watch the girls go by. The new summer styles were something pretty special: Congo Revival, plenty of beads and metal coils, but not much clothing except a sprayon sarong around the middle. There was a lot of grumbling by the old people. But how could you tell a handsome Afro girl that she shouldn't show her beautiful black breasts in public? Did they cover the boobies in the Motherland? Not until the missionaries came. Christ can't stand a pair of bares. The white girls cover up because they don't got much up there. Or maybe to keep from getting sunburned.

He admired the parade of proud jiggling black globes. The girls smiled to themselves as they cut through the park. They all wore their hair puffed out tribal style, and some of them even with little bone doodads thrust through it. There was no reason to be afraid of looking too primitive anymore. James Shabazz winked, and some of them winked back. A few of the girls kept eyes fixed rigidly ahead; plainly it was an ordeal for them to strip down this way. Most of them enjoyed it as much as the men did. The park was full of men enjoying the show. James Shabazz wished they'd bring those honkie tourists here. He'd love a chance to operate on a few of them.

Gradually he became aware of a huge, fleshy, exceedingly black man with grizzled white hair, sitting across the way pretending to be reading his paper, but really stealing peeks at the cuties going by. James Shabazz recognized him: Powell 43X Nissim, Coordinating Chairman of the Afro-Muslim Popular Democratic Party of Greater New York. He was one of the biggest men in the city, politically—maybe even more important than Mayor Abdulrahman himself. He was also a good friend of the father of James Shabazz, who handled some of Powell 43X's legal work. Four or five times a year he came around to discuss some delicate point, and stayed far into the night, drinking pot after pot of black coffee and telling jokes in an uproarious bellow. Most of his jokes were anti-black; he could tell them like any Kluxer. James Shabazz looked on him as coarse, vulgar, seamy, out of date, an old-line pol. But yet you had to respect a man with that much power.

Powell 43X Nissim peered over the top of his *Amsterdam News*, saw him, let out a whoop, and yelled, "Hey, Jimmy Lincoln! What you doin' here?"

James Shabazz stood up and walked stiffly over. "Getting me some fresh air, sir."

"Been working at the library, huh? Studying hard? Gonna be the first nigger president, maybe?"

"No, sir. Just walkin' around on a Saturday."

"Ought to be in the library," Powell 43X said. "Read. Learn. That's how we got where we are. You think we took over this city because we a bunch of dumb niggers?" He let out a colossal laugh. "We *smart*, man!"

James Shabazz wanted to say, "We took over the city because Whitey ran out. He dumped it on us, is all. Didn't take no brains, just staying power."

Instead he said, "I got a little time to take it easy yet, sir. I don't go to college for another year."

"Columbia, huh?"

"You bet. Class of '05, that's me."

"You gonna fool with football when you get to college?"

"Thought I would."

"You listen to me," said Powell 43X. "Football's okay for high school. You get yourself into politics instead up there. Debating team. Malcolm X Society. Afro League. Smart boy like you, you got a career in government ahead of you if you play it right." He jerked his head to one side and indicated a girl striding by. "You get to be somebody, maybe you'll have a few of those to play with." He laughed. The girl was almost six feet tall, majestic, deep black, with great heavy swinging breasts and magnificent buttocks switching saucily from side to side beneath her sprayon wrap. Conscious that all eyes were on her, she crossed the park on the diagonal, heading for the Sixth Avenue side. Suddenly three whites appeared at the park entrance: weekend visitors, edgy, conspicuous. As the black girl went past them, one turned, gaping, his eyes following the trajectory of her outthrust nipples. He was a wiry redhead, maybe twenty years old, in town for a good time in boogieville, and you could see the hunger popping out all over him.

"Honkie mother," James Shabazz muttered. "Could use a blade you know where."

Powell 43X clucked his tongue. "Easy, there. Let him look! What it hurt you if he thinks she's worth lookin' at?"

"Don't belong here. No right to look. Why can't they stay where they belong?"

"Jimmy—"

"Honkies right in Times Square! Don't they know this here's our city?"

Marcus Garvey said:

The Negro needs a Nation and a country of his own, where he can best show evidence of his own ability in the art of human progress. Scattered as an unmixed and unrecognized part of alien nations and civilizations is but to demonstrate his imbecility, and point him out as an unworthy derelict, fit neither for the society of Greek, Jew, or Gentile.

While he talked with Powell 43X, James Shabazz kept one eye
on the honkie from the suburbs. The redhead and his two pals cut
out in the direction of Forty-first Street. James Shabazz excused himself finally and drifted away, toward that side of the park. Old wind-
bag, he thought. Nothing but a Tom underneath. Tolerance for the
honkies! When did they tolerate *us*?

Easy, easy, like a panther. Walk slow and quiet.

Follow the stinking mother. Show him how it really is.

Malcolm X said:

*Always bear in mind that our being in the Western hemisphere differs
from anyone else, because everyone else came here voluntarily. Everyone
that you see in this part of the world got on a boat and came here voluntarily; whether they were immigrants or what have you, they came here
voluntarily. So they don't have any real squawk, because they got what
they were looking for. But you and I can squawk because we didn't
come here voluntarily. We didn't ask to be brought here. We were brought
here forcibly, against our will, and in chains. And at no time since we
have been here, have they even acted like they wanted us here. At no
time. At no time have they ever tried to pretend that we were brought
here to be citizens. Why, they don't even* pretend. *So why should we
pretend?*

The cities had been theirs for fifteen or twenty years. It had been
a peaceful enough conquest. Each year there were fewer whites and
more blacks, and the whites kept moving out, and the blacks kept
getting born, and one day Harlem was as far south as Seventy-second
Street, and Bedford-Stuyvesant had slopped over into Flatbush and
Park Slope, and there was a black mayor and a black city council,
and that was it. In New York the tipping point had come about
1986. There was a special problem there, because of the Puerto
Ricans, who thought of themselves as a separate community; but
they were outnumbered, and most of them finally decided it was
cooler to have a city of their own. They took Yonkers, the way the
Mexicans took San Diego. What it shuffled down to, in the end,
was a city about eighty-five percent black and ten percent Puerto,
with some isolated pockets of whites who stuck around out of stubbornness or old age or masochism or feelings of togetherness with
their black brothers. Outside the city were the black suburbs, like
Mount Vernon and Newark and New Rochelle, and beyond them,
fifty, eighty, a hundred miles out, were the towns of the whites.
It was apartheid in reverse.

The honkie commuters still came into the city, those who had
to, quick-in quick-out, do your work and scram. There weren't many
of them, really, a hundred thousand a day or so. The white ad
agencies were gone north. The white magazines had relocated

editorial staffs in the green suburbs. The white book publishers had followed the financial people out. Those who came in were corporate executives, presiding over all-black staffs; trophy whites, kept around by liberal-minded blacks for decoration; government employees, trapped by desegregation edicts; and odds and ends of other sorts, all out of place, all scared.

It was a black man's city. It was pretty much the same all across the country. Adjustments had been made.

Stokely Carmichael said:

We are oppressed as a group because we are black, not because we are lazy, not because we're apathetic, not because we're stupid, not because we smell, not because we eat watermelon and have good rhythm. We are oppressed because we are black, and in order to get out of that oppression, one must feel the group power that one has. . . . If there's going to be any integration it's going to be a two-way thing. If you believe in integration, you can come live in Watts. You can send your children to the ghetto schools. Let's talk about that. If you believe in integration, then we're going to start adopting us some white people to live in our neighborhood. . . .

We are not gonna wait for white people to sanction black power. We're tired of waiting.

South of Forty-second Street things were pretty quiet on a Saturday, or any other time. Big tracts of the city were still empty. Some of the office buildings had been converted into apartment houses to catch the overflow, but a lot of them were still awaiting development. It took time for a black community to generate enough capital to run a big city, and though it was happening fast, it wasn't happening fast enough to make use of all the facilities the whites had abandoned. James Shabazz walked silently through silence, keeping his eyes on the three white boys who strolled, seemingly aimlessly, a block ahead of him.

He couldn't dig why more tourists didn't get cut up. Hardly any of them did, except those who got drunk and pawed some chick. The ones who minded their own business were left alone, because the top men had passed the word that the sightseers were okay, that they injected cash into the city and shouldn't be molested. It amazed James Shabazz that everybody listened. Up at the Audubon, somebody would get up and read from Stokely or Malcolm or one of the other black martyrs, and call for a holy war on Whitey, really socking it to 'em. Civil rights! Equality! Black power! Retribution for four hundred years of slavery! Break down the ghetto walls! Keep the faith, baby! Tell it how it is! All about the exploitation of the black man, the exclusion of the Afros from the lily-white suburbs, the concentration of economic power in Whitey's hands. And the audience would shout amen and stomp its feet and sing hymns, but nobody would ever do anything. *Nobody would ever do anything.* He couldn't understand that. Were they satisfied to live in a city with an invisible wall around it? Did they really think they had it so good? They talked about owning New York, and maybe they did, but didn't they know that it was all a fraud, that Whitey had given them the damn city just so they'd stay out of *his* backyard?

Someday we gonna run things. Not the Powell 43X cats and the other Toms, but *us.* And we gonna keep the city, but we gonna take what's outside, too.

And none of this crap about honkie mothers coming in to look our women over.

James Shabazz noted with satisfaction that the three white boys were splitting up. Two of them were going into Penn Station to grab the tube home, looked like. The third was the redhead, and he was standing by himself on Seventh Avenue, looking up at Uhuru Stadium, which he probably called Madison Square Garden. Good boy. Dumb enough to leave yourself alone. Now I gonna teach you a thing or two.

He moved forward quickly.

Robert F. Williams said:
When an oppressed people show a willingness to defend themselves, the enemy, who is a moral weakling and coward, is more willing to grant concessions and work for a respectable compromise.

He walked up smiling and said, "Hi, man. I'm Jimmy Lincoln."
Whitey looked perplexed. "Hi, man."
"You lookin' for some fun, I bet."
"Just came in to see the city a little."
"To find some fun. Lots of great chicks around here." Jimmy Lincoln winked broadly. "You can't kid me none. I go for 'em too. Where you from, Red?"
"Nyack."
"That's upstate somewhere, huh?"
"Not so far. Just over the bridge. Rockland County."
"Yeah. Nice up there, I bet. I never seen it."
"Not so different from down here. Buildings are smaller, that's all. Just as crowded."
"I bet they got a different looking skin in Nyack," said Jimmy Lincoln. He laughed. "I bet I right, huh?"
The red-haired boy laughed too. "Well, I guess you are."
"Come on with me. I find you some fun. You and me. What's your name?"
"Tom."

"Tom. That's a good one. Lookee, Tom, I know a place, lots of girls, something to drink, a pill to pop, real soul music, yeah? Eh, man? Couple blocks from here. You came here to see the city, let me show it to you. Right?"

"Well—" uneasily.

"Don't be so uptight, man. You don't trust your black brother? Look, we got no feud with you. All that stuff's ancient history! You got to realize this is the year 2000, we all free men, we got what we after. Nobody gonna hurt you." Jimmy Lincoln moved closer and winked confidentially. "Lemme tell you something, too. That red hair of yours, the girls gonna orbit over that! They don't see that kind hair every day. Them freckles. Them blue eyes. Man, blue eyes, it turn them on! You in for the time of your life!"

Tom from Nyack grinned. He pointed toward Penn Station. "I came in with two pals. They went home, the geeps! Tomorrow they're going to feel awful dopey about that."

"You know they will," said Jimmy Lincoln.

They walked west, across Eighth Avenue, across Ninth, into the redevelopment area where the old warehouses had been ripped down. Signs sprouting from the acreage of rubble proclaimed that the Afro-American Cultural Center would shortly rise here. Just now the area looked bombed out. Tom from Nyack frowned as if he failed to see where a swinging nightclub was likely to be located in this district. Jimmy Lincoln led him up to Thirty-fifth Street and around the hollow shell of a not quite demolished building.

"Almost there?" Tom asked.

"We here right now, man."

"Where?"

"Up against that wall, that's where," said James Shabazz. The sonic blade glided into his hand. He studded it and it began to whir menacingly. In a quiet voice he said, "Honkie, I saw you look at a black girl a little while ago like you might just be thinking about what's between her legs. You shouldn't think thoughts like that about black girls. You got an itch, man, you scratch it on your own kind. I think I'm gonna fix you so you don't itch no more."

Minister James 3X said:

First, there is fear—first and foremost there is inborn fear, and hatred for the black man. There is a feeling on the part of the white man of inferiority. He thinks within himself that the black man is the best man.

The white man is justified in feeling that way because he has discovered that he is weaker than the black man. His mental power is less than that of the black man—he has only six ounces of brain and the Original Man has seven-and-a-half ounces. . . . The white man's physical power is one-third less than that of the black man.

He had never talked this long with a honkie before. You didn't
see all that many of them about, when you spent your time in high
school. But now he stared into those frightened blue eyes and
watched the blood drain from the scruffy white skin and he felt
power welling up inside himself. He was Chaka Zulu and Malcolm
and Stokely and Nkrumah and Nat Turner and Lumumba all rolled
into one. He, James Shabazz, was going to lead the new black revolution, and he was going to begin by sacrificing this cowering honkie.
Through his mind rolled the magnificent phrases of his prophets.
He heard them talking, yes, Adam and Ras Tafari and Floyd, heard
them singing down the ages out of Africa, kings in chains, martyrs,
the great ones, he heard Elijah Muhammad and Muhammad Ali,
Marcus Garvey, Sojourner Truth, du Bois, Henry Garnet, Rap Brown,
rattling the chains, shouting for freedom, and all of them telling
him, go on, man, how long you want to be a nigger anyhow? Go
on! You think you got it so good? You gonna go to college, get
a job, live in a house, eat steak and potatoes, and that's enough,
eh, nigger, even if you can't set foot in Nyack, Peekskill, Wantaugh,
Suffern, Morristown? Be happy with what you got, darkie! You got
more than we ever did, so why bitch about things? You got a city!
You got power! You got freedom! It don't matter that they call you
an ape. Don't matter that they don't let you near their daughters.
Don't matter that you never seen Nyack. Be grateful for what you
got, man, is that the idea?

He heard their cosmic laughter, the thunder of their derision.

And he moved toward Tom the honkie and said, "Here's where
the revolution gets started again. Trash like you fooling with our
women, you gonna get a blade in the balls. You go home to Nyack
and give 'em that message, man."

Tom said lamely, "Look out behind you!"

James Shabazz laughed and began to thrust the blade home, but
the anesthetic dart caught him in the middle of the back and his
muscles surrendered, and the blade fell, and he turned as he folded
up and saw the black policeman with the dart gun in his black fist,
and he realized that he had known all along that this was how it
would turn out, and he couldn't say he really cared.

Robert Moses of SNCC was questioned in May 1962 on the voter
registration drive in Mississippi:

Q. Mr. Moses, did you know a Herbert Lee?

A. Yes, he was a Negro farmer who lived near Liberty.

*Q. Would you tell the Committee what Mr. Lee was doing and what
happened?*

*A. He was killed on September 25th. That morning I was in McComb.
The Negro doctor came by the voter registration office to tell us he had*

just taken a bullet out of a Negro's head. We went over to see who it was because I thought it was somebody in the voting program, and were able to identify the man as Mr. Herbert Lee, who had attended our classes and driven us around the voting area, visiting other farmers.

Powell 43X Nissim said heavily, folding his hands across his paunch, "I got you off because you're your daddy's son. But you try a fool thing like that again, I gon' let them put you away."

James Shabazz said nothing.

"What you think you was doing, anyway, Jimmy? You know we watch all the tourists. We can't afford to let them get cut up. There was tracers on that kid all the time."

"I didn't know."

"You sit there mad as hell, thinking I should have let you cut him. You know who you really would have cut? Jimmy Lincoln, that's who. We still got jails. Black judges know the law too. You get ruined for life, a thing like that. And what for?"

"To show the honkie a thing or two."

"Jimmy, Jimmy, Jimmy! What's to show? We got the whole city!"

"Why can't we live outside?"

"Because we don't *want* to. Those of us who can afford it, even, we stay here. They got laws against discrimination in this country. We stay here because we like it with our own kind. Even the black millionaires, and don't think there ain't plenty of 'em. We got a dozen men, they could *buy* Nyack. They stay."

"And why do you stay?"

"I'm in politics," said Powell 43X. "You know what a power base means? I got to stay where my people are. I don't care about living with the whites."

"You talk like you aren't even sore about it," James Shabazz said. "Don't you hate Whitey?"

"No. I don't hate no one."

"We all hate Whitey!"

"Only you hate Whitey," said Powell 43X. "And that's because you don't know nothin' yet. The time of hating's over, Jimmy. We got to be practical. You know, we got ourselves a good deal now, and we ain't gon' get more by burning nobody. Well, maybe the Stock Exchange moved to Connecticut, and a lot of banks and stuff like that, but *we run the city*. Black men. Black men hold the mortgages. We got a black upper crust here now. Fancy shops for black folk, fancy restaurants, black banks, gorgeous mosques. Nobody oppressing us now. When a mortgage gets foreclosed these days, it's a *black* man doin' the foreclosin'. Black men ownin' the sweatshops. Ownin' the hockshops. Good and bad, we got the city,

Jimmy. And maybe this is the way it's meant to be: us in the cities, them outside."

"You talk like a Tom!"

"And you talk like a fool." Powell 43X chuckled. "Jimmy, wake up! We all Toms today. We don't do revolutions now."

"I go to the Audubon," James Shabazz said. "I listen to them speak. They talk revolution there. They don't sound like no Toms to me!"

"It's all politics, son. Talk big, yell for equality. It don't make sense to let a good revolution die. They do it for show. A man don't get anywhere politickin' in black New York by sayin' that everything's one hundred percent all right in the world. And you took all that noise seriously? You didn't know that they just shoutin' because it's part of the routine? You went out to spear you a honkie? I figured you for smarter than that. Look, you all mixed up, boy. A smart man, black or white, he don't mess up a good deal for himself, even if he sometimes say he *want* to change everything all around. You full of hate, full of dreams. When you grow up, you'll understand. Our problem, it's not how to get out into the suburbs, it's how to keep Whitey from wanting to come back and live in here! We got to keep what we got. We got it pretty good. Who oppressing you, Jimmy? You a slave? Wake up! And now you understand the system a little better, clear your rear end outa my office. I got to phone up the mayor and have a little talk."

Jimmy Lincoln stumbled out, stunned, shaken. His eyes felt hot and his tongue was dry. The system? The *system?* How cynical could you get? The whole revolution phony? All done for show?

No. No. No. No.

He wanted to smash down the King Building with his fists. He wanted to see buildings ablaze, as in the old days when the black man was still fighting for what ought to be his.

I don't believe it, he thought. Not any of it. I'm not gonna stop fighting for my rights. I'm gonna live to see us overcome. I won't sell out like the others. Not me!

And then he thought maybe he was being a little dumb. Maybe Powell 43X was right: there wasn't anything left worth fighting for, and only a dopey kid would take the slogans at face value. He tried to brush that thought out of his head. If Powell 43X was right, everything he had read was a lot of crap. Stokely. Malcolm. All the great martyrs. Just so much ancient history?

He stepped out into the summer haze. Overhead, a hopterbus was heading for the suburbs. He shook his fist at it; and instantly he felt foolish for the gesture, and wondered why he felt foolish. And knew. And beneath his rebellious fury, began to suspect that one day he'd give in to the system too. But not yet. Not yet!

time to do my homework now

machine, spell everything right today's essay is on black power as a revolutionary force I am James Lincoln, Class 804, Frederick Douglass High School put that heading on the page yeah

the concept of black power as a revolutionary force first was heard during the time of oppression forty years ago, when

crap on that, machine we better hold it until I know what I going to say

I am James Shabazz age seventeen born august 13 1983 I am black I am afro I am beautiful

black is beautiful

let's start over, machine

let's make an outline first

black power its origin its development the martyrdoms and lynchings the first black mayors the black congressmen and senators the black cities and then talk about black power as a continuing thing, the never-ending revolution no matter what pols like 43X say, never give in never settle for what they give you never sell out

that's it, machine

black power

black

black is beautiful

Sundance

Robert Silverberg

Today you liquidated about 50,000 Eaters in Sector A, and now you are spending an uneasy night. You and Herndon flew east at dawn, with the green-gold sunrise at your backs, and sprayed the neural pellets over a thousand hectares along the Forked River. You flew on into the prairie beyond the river, where the Eaters have already been wiped out, and had lunch sprawled on that thick, soft carpet of grass where the first settlement is expected to rise. Herndon picked some juiceflowers, and you enjoyed half an hour of mild hallucinations. Then, as you headed toward the copter to begin an afternoon of further pellet spraying, he said suddenly, "Tom, how would you feel about this if it turned out that the Eaters weren't just animal pests? That they were *people*, say, with a language and rites and a history and all?"

You thought of how it had been for your own people.

"They aren't," you said.

"Suppose they were. Suppose the Eaters—"

"They aren't. Drop it."

Herndon has this streak of cruelty in him that leads him to ask such questions. He goes for the vulnerabilities; it amuses him. All night now his casual remark has echoed in your mind. Suppose the Eaters ... Suppose the Eaters ... Suppose ... Suppose ...

You sleep for a while, and dream, and in your dreams you swim through rivers of blood.

Foolishness. A feverish fantasy. You know how important it is to exterminate the Eaters fast, before the settlers get here. They're just animals, and not even harmless animals at that; ecology-wreckers is what they are, devourers of oxygen-liberating plants, and they have to go. A few have been saved for zoological study. The rest must be destroyed. Ritual extirpation of undesirable beings, the old, old story. But let's not complicate our job with moral qualms, you tell yourself. Let's not dream of rivers of blood.

486

The Eaters don't even *have* blood, none that could flow in rivers, anyway. What they have is, well, a kind of lymph that permeates every tissue and transmits nourishment along the interfaces. Waste products go out the same way, osmotically. In terms of process, it's structurally analogous to your own kind of circulatory system, except there's no network of blood vessels hooked to a master pump. The life-stuff just oozes through their bodies, as though they were amoebas or sponges or some other low-phylum form. Yet they're definitely high-phylum in nervous system, digestive setup, limb-and-organ template, etc. Odd, you think. The thing about aliens is that they're alien, you tell yourself, not for the first time.

The beauty of their biology for you and your companions is that it lets you exterminate them so neatly.

You fly over the grazing grounds and drop the neural pellets. The Eaters find and ingest them. Within an hour the poison has reached all sectors of the body. Life ceases; a rapid breakdown of cellular matter follows, the Eater literally falling apart molecule by molecule the instant that nutrition is cut off; the lymph-like stuff works like acid; a universal lysis occurs; flesh and even the bones, which are cartilaginous, dissolve. In two hours, a puddle on the ground. In four, nothing at all left. Considering how many millions of Eaters you've scheduled for extermination here, it's sweet of the bodies to be self-disposing. Otherwise what a charnel house this world would become!

Suppose the Eaters . . .

Damn Herndon. You almost feel like getting a memory-editing in the morning. Scrape his stupid speculations out of your head. If you dared. If you dared.

In the morning he does not dare. Memory-editing frightens him; he will try to shake free of his new-found guilt without it. The Eaters, he explains to himself, are mindless herbivores, the unfortunate victims of human expansionism, but not really deserving of passionate defense. Their extermination is not tragic; it's just too bad. If Earthmen are to have this world, the Eaters must relinquish it. There's a difference, he tells himself, between the elimination of the Plains Indians from the American prairie in the nineteenth century and the destruction of the bison on that same prairie. One feels a little wistful about the slaughter of the thundering herds; one regrets the butchering of millions of the noble brown woolly beasts, yes. But one feels outrage, not mere wistful regret, at what was done to the Sioux. There's a difference. Reserve your passions for the proper cause.

He walks from his bubble at the edge of the camp toward the center of things. The flagstone path is moist and glistening. The morning fog has not yet lifted, and every tree is bowed, the long, notched leaves heavy with droplets of water. He pauses, crouching, to observe a spider-analog spinning its asymmetrical web. As he watches, a small amphibian, delicately shaded turquoise, glides as inconspicuously as possible over the mossy ground. Not inconspicuously enough; he gently lifts the little creature and puts it on the back of his hand. The gills flutter in anguish, and the amphibian's sides quiver. Slowly, cunningly, its color changes until it matches the coppery tone of the hand. The camouflage is excellent. He lowers his hand and the amphibian scurries into a puddle. He walks on.

He is forty years old, shorter than most of the other members of the expedition, with wide shoulders, a heavy chest, dark glossy hair, a blunt, spreading nose. He is a biologist. This is his third career, for he has failed as an anthropologist and as a developer of real estate. His name is Tom Two Ribbons. He has been married twice but has had no children. His great-grandfather died of alcoholism; his grandfather was addicted to hallucinogens; his father had compulsively visited cheap memory-editing parlors. Tom Two Ribbons is conscious that he is failing a family tradition, but he has not yet found his own mode of self-destruction.

In the main building he discovers Herndon, Julia, Ellen, Schwartz, Chang, Michaelson, and Nichols. They are eating breakfast; the others are already at work. Ellen rises and comes to him and kisses him. Her short soft yellow hair tickles his cheeks. "I love you," she whispers. She has spent the night in Michaelson's bubble. "I love you," he tells her, and draws a quick vertical line of affection between her small pale breasts. He winks at Michaelson, who nods, touches the tops of two fingers to his lips, and blows them a kiss. We are all good friends here, Tom Two Ribbons thinks.

"Who drops pellets today?" he asks.

"Mike and Chang," says Julia. "Sector C."

Schwartz says, "Eleven more days and we ought to have the whole peninsula clear. Then we can move inland."

"If our pellet supply holds up," Chang points out.

Herndon says, "Did you sleep well, Tom?"

"No," says Tom. He sits down and taps out his breakfast requisition. In the west, the fog is beginning to burn off the mountains. Something throbs in the back of his neck. He has been on this world nine weeks now, and in that time it has undergone its only change of season, shading from dry weather to foggy. The mists will remain for many months. Before the plains parch again, the Eaters will be gone and the settlers will begin to arrive. His food slides down the chute and he seizes it. Ellen sits beside him. She is a little more than half his age; this is her first voyage; she is their keeper of records, but she is also skilled at editing. "You look troubled," Ellen tells him. "Can I help you?"

"No. Thank you."

"I hate it when you get gloomy."

"It's a racial trait," says Tom Two Ribbons.

"I doubt that very much."

"The truth is that maybe my personality reconstruct is wearing thin. The trauma level was so close to the surface. I'm just a walking veneer, you know."

Ellen laughs prettily. She wears only a sprayon halfwrap. Her skin looks damp; she and Michaelson have had a swim at dawn. Tom Two Ribbons is thinking of asking her to marry him, when this job is over. He has not been married since the collapse of the real estate business. The therapist suggested divorce as part of the reconstruct. He sometimes wonders where Terry has gone and whom she lives with now. Ellen says, "You seem pretty stable to me, Tom."

"Thank you," he says. She is young. She does not know.

"If its just a passing gloom I can edit it out in one quick snip."

"Thank you," he says. "No."

"I forgot. You don't like editing."

"My father—"

"Yes?"

"In fifty years he pared himself down to a thread," Tom Two Ribbons says. "He had his ancestors edited away, his whole heritage, his religion, his wife, his sons, finally his name. Then he sat and smiled all day. Thank you, no editing."

"Where are you working today?" Ellen asks.

"In the compound, running tests."

"Want company? I'm off all morning."

"Thank you, no," he says, too quickly. She looks hurt. He tries to remedy his unintended cruelty by touching her arm lightly and saying, "Maybe this afternoon, all right? I need to commune a while. Yes?"

"Yes," she says, and smiles, and shapes a kiss with her lips.

After breakfast he goes to the compound. It covers a thousand hectares east of the base; they have bordered it with neural-field projectors at intervals of eighty meters, and this is a sufficient fence to keep the captive population of two hundred Eaters from straying. When all the others have been exterminated, this study group will remain. At the southwest corner of the compound stands a lab bubble from which the experiments are run: metabolic, psychological, physiological, ecological. A stream crosses the compound diagonally. There is a low ridge of grassy hills at its eastern edge. Five distinct copses of tightly clustered knifeblade trees are separated by patches of dense savanna. Sheltered beneath the grass are the oxygen-plants, almost completely hidden except for the photosynthetic spikes that jut to heights of three or four meters at regular intervals, and for the lemon-colored respiratory bodies, chest high, that make the grassland sweet and dizzying with exhaled gases. Through the fields move the Eaters in a straggling herd, nibbling delicately at the respiratory bodies.

Tom Two Ribbons spies the herd beside the stream and goes toward it. He stumbles over an oxygen-plant hidden in the grass but deftly recovers his balance and, seizing the puckered orifice of the respiratory body, inhales deeply. His despair lifts. He approaches the Eaters. They are spherical, bulky, slow-moving creatures, covered by masses of coarse orange fur. Saucer-like eyes protrude above narrow rubbery lips. Their legs are thin and scaly, like a chicken's, and their arms are short and held close to their bodies. They regard him with bland lack of curiosity. "Good morning, brothers!" is the way he greets them this time, and he wonders why.

I noticed something strange today. Perhaps I simply sniffed too much oxygen in the fields; maybe I was succumbing to a suggestion Herndon planted; or possibly it's the family masochism cropping out. But while I was observing the Eaters in the compound, it seemed to me, for the first time, that they were behaving intelligently, that they were functioning in a ritualized way.

I followed them around for three hours. During that time they uncovered half a dozen outcroppings of oxygen-plants. In each case they went through a stylized pattern of action before starting to munch. They:

Formed a straggly circle around the plants.

Looked toward the sun.

Looked toward their neighbors on left and right around the circle.

Made fuzzy neighing sounds *only* after having done the foregoing.

Looked toward the sun again.

Moved in and ate.

If this wasn't a prayer of thanksgiving, a saying of grace, then what was it? And if they're advanced enough spiritually to say grace, are we not therefore committing genocide here? Do chimpanzees say grace? Christ, we wouldn't even wipe out chimps the way we're cleaning out the Eaters! Of course, chimps don't interfere with human crops, and some kind of coexistence would be possible, whereas Eaters and human agriculturalists simply can't function on the same planet. Nevertheless, there's a moral issue here. The liquidation effort is predicated on the assumption that the intelligence level of the Eaters is about on a par with that of oysters, or, at best, sheep. Our consciences stay clear because our poison is quick and painless and because the Eaters thoughtfully dissolve upon dying, sparing us the mess of incinerating millions of corpses. But if they pray—

I won't say anything to the others just yet. I want more evidence, hard, objective. Films, tapes, record cubes. Then we'll see. What if I can show that we're exterminating intelligent beings? My family knows a little about genocide, after all, having been on the receiving end just a few centuries back. I doubt that I could halt what's going on here. But at the very least I could withdraw from the operation. Head back to Earth and stir up public outcries.

I hope I'm imagining this.

I'm not imagining a thing. They gather in circles; they look to the sun; they neigh and pray. They're only balls of jelly on chicken-legs, but they give thanks for their food. Those big round eyes now seem to stare accusingly at me. Our tame herd here knows what's going on: that we have descended from the stars to eradicate their kind, and that they alone will be spared. They have no way of fighting back or even of communicating their displeasure, but they *know*. And hate us. Jesus, we have killed two million of them since we got here, and in a metaphorical way I'm stained with blood, and what will I do, what can I do?

I must move very carefully, or I'll end up drugged and edited.

I can't let myself seem like a crank, a quack, an agitator. I can't stand up and *denounce!* I have to find allies. Herndon, first. He surely is on to the truth; he's the one who nudged *me* to it, that day we dropped pellets. And I thought he was merely being vicious in his usual way!

I'll talk to him tonight.

He says, "I've been thinking about that suggestion you made. About the Eaters. Perhaps we haven't made sufficiently close psychological studies. I mean, if they really *are* intelligent—"

Herndon blinks. He is a tall man with glossy dark hair, a heavy beard, sharp cheekbones. "Who says they are, Tom?"

"You did. On the far side of the Forked River, you said—"

"It was just a speculative hypothesis. To make conversation."

"No, I think it was more than that. You really believed it."

Herndon looks troubled. "Tom, I don't know what you're trying to start, but don't start it. If I for a moment believed we were killing intelligent creatures, I'd run for an editor so fast I'd start an implosion wave."

"Why did you ask me that thing, then?" Tom Two Ribbons says.

"Idle chatter."

"Amusing yourself by kindling guilts in somebody else? You're a bastard, Herndon. I mean it."

"Well, look, Tom, if I had any idea that you'd get so worked up about a hypothetical suggestion—" Herndon shakes his head. "The Eaters aren't intelligent beings. Obviously. Otherwise we wouldn't be under orders to liquidate them."

"Obviously," says Tom Two Ribbons.

Ellen said, "No, I don't know what Tom's up to. But I'm pretty sure he needs a rest. It's only a year and a half since his personality reconstruct, and he had a pretty bad breakdown back then."

Michaelson consulted a chart. "He's refused three times in a row to make his pellet-dropping run. Claiming he can't take time away from his research. Hell, we can fill in for him, but it's the idea that he's ducking chores that bothers me."

"What kind of research is he doing?" Nichols wanted to know.

"Not biological," said Julia. "He's with the Eaters in the compound all the time, but I don't see him making any tests on them. He just watches them."

"And talks to them," Chang observed.

"And talks, yes," Julia said.

"About what?" Nichols asked.

"Who knows?"

Everyone looked at Ellen. "You're closest to him," Michaelson said. "Can't you bring him out of it?"

"I've got to know what he's in, first," Ellen said. "He isn't saying a thing."

You know that you must be very careful, for they outnumber you, and their concern for your mental welfare can be deadly. Already they realize you are disturbed, and Ellen has begun to probe for the source of the disturbance. Last night you lay in her arms and she questioned you, obliquely, skillfully, and you knew what she is trying to find out. When the moons appeared she suggested that you and she stroll in the compound, among the sleeping Eaters. You declined, but she sees that you have become involved with the creatures.

You have done probing of your own—subtly, you hope. And you are aware that you can do nothing to save the Eaters. An irrevocable commitment has been made. It is 1876 all over again; these are the bison, these are the Sioux, and they must be destroyed, for the railroad is on its way. If you speak out here, your friends will calm you and pacify you and edit you, for they do not see what you see. If you return to Earth to agitate, you will be mocked and recommended for another reconstruct. You can do nothing. You can do nothing.

You cannot save, but perhaps you can record.

Go out into the prairie. Live with the Eaters; make yourself their friend; learn their ways. Set it down, a full account of their culture, so that at least that much will not be lost. You know the techniques of field anthropology. As was done for your people in the old days, do now for the Eaters.

He finds Michaelson. "Can you spare me for a few weeks?" he asks.

"Spare you, Tom? What do you mean?"

"I've got some field studies to do. I'd like to leave the base and work with Eaters in the wild."

"What's wrong with the ones in the compound?"

"It's the last chance with wild ones, Mike. I've got to go."

"Alone, or with Ellen?"

"Alone."

Michaelson nods slowly. "All right, Tom. Whatever you want. Go. I won't hold you here."

I dance in the prairie under the green-gold sun. About me the Eaters gather. I am stripped; sweat makes my skin glisten; my heart pounds. I talk to them with my feet, and they understand.

They understand.

They have a language of soft sounds. They have a god. They know love and awe and rapture. They have rites. They have names. They have a history. Of all this I am convinced.

I dance on thick grass.

How can I reach them? With my feet, with my hands, with my grunts, with my sweat. They gather by the hundreds, by the thousands, and I dance. I must not stop. They cluster about me and make their sounds. I am a conduit for strange forces. My great-grandfather should see me now! Sitting on his porch in Wyoming, the firewater in his hand, his brain rotting—see me now, old one! See the dance of Tom Two Ribbons! I talk to these strange ones with my feet under a sun that is the wrong color. I dance. I dance.

"Listen to me," I say. "I am your friend, I alone, the only one you can trust. Trust me, talk to me, teach me. Let me preserve your ways, for soon the destruction will come."

I dance, and the sun climbs, and the Eaters murmur.

There is the chief, I dance toward him, back, toward, I bow, I point to the sun, I imagine the being that lives in that ball of flame, I imitate the sounds of these people, I kneel, I rise, I dance. Tom Two Ribbons dances for you.

I summon skills my ancestors forgot. I feel the power flowing in me. As they danced in the days of the bison, I dance now, beyond the Forked River.

I dance, and now the Eaters dance too. Slowly, uncertainly, they move toward me, they shift their weight, lift leg and leg, sway about. "Yes, like that!" I cry. "Dance!"

We dance together as the sun reaches noon height.

Now their eyes are no longer accusing. I see warmth and kinship. I am their brother, their redskinned tribesman, he who dances with them. No longer do they seem clumsy to me. There is a strange ponderous grace in their movements. They dance. They dance. They caper about me. Closer, closer, closer!

We move in holy frenzy.

They sing, now, a blurred hymn of joy. They throw forth their arms, unclench their little claws. In unison they shift weight, left foot forward, right, left, right. Dance, brothers, dance, dance, dance! They press against me. Their flesh quivers; their smell is a sweet one. They gently thrust me across the field, to a part of the meadow where the grass is deep and untrampled. Still dancing, we seek for the oxygen-plants, and find clumps of them beneath the grass, and they make their prayer and seize them with their awkward arms, separating the respiratory bodies from the photosynthetic spikes. The plants, in anguish, release floods of oxygen. My mind reels. I laugh and sing. The Eaters are nibbling the lemon-colored perforated globes, nibbling the stalks as well. They thrust their plants at me. It is a religious ceremony, I see. Take from us, eat with us, join with us, this is the body, this is the blood, take, eat, join. I bend forward and put a lemon-colored globe to my lips. I do not bite; I nibble, as they do, my teeth slicing away the skin of the globe. Juice spurts into my mouth, while oxygen drenches my nostrils. The Eaters sing hosannas. I should be in full paint for this, paint of my forefathers, feathers too, meeting their religion in the regalia of what should have been mine. Take, eat, join. The juice of the oxygen-plant flows in my veins. I embrace my brothers. I sing, and as my voice leaves my lips it becomes an arch that glistens like new steel, and I pitch my song lower, and the arch turns to tarnished silver. The Eaters crowd close. The scent of their bodies is fiery red to me. Their soft cries are puffs of steam. The sun is very warm; its rays are tiny jagged pings of puckered sound, close to the top of my range of hearing, plink! plink! plink! The thick grass hums to me, deep and rich, and the wind hurls points of flame along the prairie. I devour another oxygen-plant, and then a third. My brothers laugh and shout. They tell me of their gods, the god of warmth, the god of food, the god of pleasure, the god of death, the god of holiness, the god of wrongness, and the others. They recite for me the names of their kings, and I hear their voices as splashes of green mold on the clean sheet of the sky. They instruct me in their holy rites. I must remember this, I tell myself, for when it is gone it will never come again. I continue to dance. They continue to dance. The color of the hills becomes rough and coarse, like abrasive gas. Take, eat, join. Dance. They are so gentle!

I hear the drone of the copter, suddenly.

It hovers far overhead. I am unable to see who flies in it. "No," I scream. "Not here! Not these people! Listen to me! This is Tom Two Ribbons! Can't you hear me? I'm doing a field study here! You have no right—!"

My voice makes spirals of blue moss edged with red sparks. They drift upward and are scattered by the breeze.

I yell, I shout, I bellow. I dance and shake my fists. From the wings of the copter the jointed arms of the pellet-distributors unfold. The gleaming spigots extend and whirl. The neural pellets rain down into the meadow, each tracing a blazing track that lingers in the sky. The sound of the copter becomes a furry carpet stretching to the horizon, and my shrill voice is lost in it.

The Eaters drift away from me, seeking the pellets, scratching at the roots of the grass to find them. Still dancing, I leap into their midst, striking the pellets from their hands, hurling them into the stream, crushing them to powder. The Eaters growl black needles at me. They turn away and search for more pellets. The copter turns and flies off, leaving a trail of dense oily sound. My brothers are gobbling the pellets eagerly.

There is no way to prevent it.

Joy consumes them and they topple and lie still. Occasionally a limb twitches; then even this stops. They begin to dissolve. Thousands of them melt on the prairie, sinking into shapelessness, losing their spherical forms, flattening, ebbing into the ground. The bonds of the molecules will no longer hold. It is the twilight of protoplasm. They perish. They vanish. For hours I walk the prairie. Now I inhale oxygen; now I eat a lemon-colored globe. Sunset begins with the ringing of leaden chimes. Black clouds make brazen trumpet calls in the east and the deepening wind is a swirl of coaly bristles. Silence comes. Night falls. I dance. I am alone.

The copter comes again, and they find you, and you do not resist as they gather you in. You are beyond bitterness. Quietly you explain what you have done and what you have learned, and why it is wrong to exterminate these people. You describe the plant you have eaten and the way it affects your senses, and as you talk of the blessed synesthesia, the texture of the wind and the sound of the clouds and the timbre of the sunlight, they nod and smile and tell you not to worry, that everything will be all right soon, and they touch something cold to your forearm, so cold that it is a whir and a buzz and the deintoxicant sinks into your vein and soon the ecstasy drains away, leaving only the exhaustion and the grief.

He says, "We never learn a thing, do we? We export all our horrors to the stars. Wipe out the Armenians, wipe out the Jews, wipe out the Tasmanians, wipe out the Indians, wipe out everyone who's in the way, and then come out here and do the same damned murderous thing. You weren't with me out there. You didn't dance with them. You didn't see what a rich, complex culture the Eaters have. Let me tell you about their tribal structure. It's dense: seven levels of matrimonial relationships, to begin with, and an exogamy factor that requires—"

Softly Ellen says, "Tom, darling, nobody's going to harm the Eaters."

"And the religion," he goes on. "Nine gods, each one an aspect of *the* god. Holiness and wrongness both worshiped. They have hymns, prayers, a theology. And we, the emissaries of the god of wrongness—"

"We're not exterminating them," Michaelson says. "Won't you understand that, Tom? This is all a fantasy of yours. You've been under the influence of drugs, but now we're clearing you out. You'll be clean in a little while. You'll have perspective again."

"A fantasy?" he says bitterly. "A drug dream? I stood out in the prairie and saw you drop pellets. And I watched them die and melt away. I didn't dream that."

"How can we convince you?" Chang asks earnestly. "What will make you believe? Shall we fly over the Eater country with you and show you how many millions there are?"

"But how many millions have been destroyed?" he demands.

They insist that he is wrong. Ellen tells him again that no one has ever desired to harm the Eaters. "This is a scientific expedition, Tom. We're here to *study* them. It's a violation of all we stand for to injure intelligent lifeforms."

"You admit that they're intelligent?"

"Of course. That's never been in doubt."

"Then why drop the pellets?" he asks. "Why slaughter them?"

"None of that has happened, Tom," Ellen says. She takes his hand between her cool palms. "Believe us. Believe us."

He says bitterly, "If you want me to believe you, why don't you do the job properly? Get out the editing machine and go to work on me. You can't simply *talk* me into rejecting the evidence of my own eyes."

"You were under drugs all the time," Michaelson says.

"I've never taken drugs! Except for what I ate in the meadow, when I danced—and that came after I had watched the massacre going on for weeks and weeks. Are you saying that it's a retroactive delusion?"

"No, Tom," Schwartz says. "You've had this delusion all along. It's part of your therapy, your reconstruct. You came here programmed with it."

"Impossible," he says.

Ellen kisses his fevered forehead. "It was done to reconcile you to mankind, you see. You had this terrible resentment of the displacement of your people in the nineteenth century. You were unable to forgive the industrial society for scattering the Sioux, and you were terribly full of hate. Your therapist thought that if you could be made to participate in an imaginary modern extermination, if you could come to see it as a necessary operation, you'd be purged of your resentment and able to take your place in society as—"

He thrusts her away. "Don't talk idiocy! If you knew the first thing about reconstruct therapy, you'd realize that no reputable therapist could be so shallow. There are no one-to-one correlations in reconstructs. No, don't touch me. Keep away. Keep away."

He will not let them persuade him that this is merely a drug-born dream. It is no fantasy, he tells himself, and it is no therapy. He rises. He goes out. They do not follow him. He takes a copter and seeks his brothers.

Again I dance. The sun is much hotter today. The Eaters are more numerous. Today I wear paint, today I wear feathers. My body shines with my sweat. They dance with me, and they have a frenzy in them that I have never seen before. We pound the trampled meadow with our feet. We clutch for the sun with our hands. We sing, we shout, we cry. We will dance until we fall.

This is no fantasy. These people are real, and they are intelligent, and they are doomed. This I know.

We dance. Despite the doom, we dance.

My great-grandfather comes and dances with us. He too is real. His nose is like a hawk's, not blunt like mine, and he wears the big headdress, and his muscles are like cords under his brown skin. He sings, he shouts, he cries.

Others of my family join us.

We eat the oxygen-plants together. We embrace the Eaters. We know, all of us, what it is to be hunted.

The clouds make music and the wind takes on texture and the sun's warmth has color.

We dance, We dance. Our limbs know no weariness.

The sun grows and fills the whole sky, and I see no Eaters now, only my own people, my father's fathers across the centuries, thousands of gleaming skins, thousands of hawk's noses, and we eat the plants, and we find sharp sticks and thrust them into our flesh, and the sweet blood flows and dries in the blaze of the sun, and we dance, and we dance, and some of us fall from weariness, and we dance, and the prairie is a sea of bobbing headdresses, an ocean of feathers, and we dance, and my heart makes thunder, and my knees become water, and the sun's fire engulfs me, and I dance, and I fall, and I dance, and I fall, and I fall, and I fall.

Again they find you and bring you back. They give you the cool snout on your arm to take the oxygen-plant drug from your veins, and then they give you something else so you will rest. You rest and you are very calm. Ellen kisses you and you stroke her soft skin, and then the others come in and they talk to you, saying soothing things, but you do not listen, for you are searching for realities. It is not an easy search. It is like falling through many trapdoors, looking for the one room whose floor is not hinged. Everything that has happened on this planet is your therapy, you tell yourself, designed to reconcile an embittered aborigine to the white man's conquest; nothing is really being exterminated here. You reject that and fall through and realize that this must be the therapy of your friends; they carry the weight of accumulated centuries of guilts and have come here to shed that load, and you are here to ease them of their burden, to draw their sins into yourself and give them forgiveness. Again you fall through, and see that the Eaters are mere animals who threaten the ecology and must be removed; the culture you imagined for them is your hallucination, kindled out of old churnings. You try to withdraw your objections to this necessary extermination, but you fall through again and discover that there is no extermination except in your mind, which is troubled and disordered by your obsession with the crime against your ancestors, and you sit up, for you wish to apologize to these friends of yours, these innocent scientists whom you have called murderers. And you fall through.

Slow Sculpture

Theodore Sturgeon

I

He didn't know who he was when she met him—well, not many
people did. He was in the high orchard doing something under
a pear tree. The land smelled of late summer and wind—bronze,
it smelled bronze.

He looked up at a compact girl in her mid-twenties, at a fearless
face and eyes the same color as her hair, which was extraordinary
because her hair was red-gold. She looked down at a leather-skinned
man in his forties, at a gold-leaf electroscope in his hand, and felt
she was an intruder.

She said, "Oh—" in what was apparently the right way.

Because he nodded once and said, "Hold this—" and there could
then be no thought of intrusion.

She knelt down beside him and took the instrument, holding
it exactly where he positioned her hand. He moved away a little
and struck a tuning fork against his kneecap.

"What's it doing?"

He had a good voice, the kind of voice strangers notice and listen
to.

She looked at the delicate leaves of gold in the glass shield of
the electroscope.

"They're moving apart."

He struck the tuning fork again and the leaves pressed away from
one another.

"Much?"

"About forty-five degrees when you hit the fork."

"Good—that's about the most we'll get." From a pocket of his
bush jacket he drew a sack of chalk dust and dropped a small handful
on the ground. "I'll move now. You stay right there and tell me
how much the leaves separate."

499

He traveled around the pear tree in a zigzag course, striking his tuning fork while she called out numbers—ten degrees, thirty, five, twenty, nothing. Whenever the gold foil pressed apart to maximum—forty degrees or more—he dropped more chalk. When he was finished the tree was surrounded by a rough oval of white dots. He took out a notebook and diagramed them and the tree, put away the book and took the electroscope out of her hands.

"Were you looking for something?" he asked her.

"No," she said. "Yes."

He could smile. Though it did not last long she found the expression surprising in a face like his.

"That's not what is called, in a court of law, a responsive answer."

She glanced across the hillside, metallic in that late light. There wasn't much on it—rocks, weeds the summer was done with, a tree or so, the orchard. Anyone present had come a long way to get here.

"It wasn't a simple question," she said, tried to smile and burst into tears.

She was sorry and said so.

"Why?" he asked.

This was the first time she was to experience this ask-the-next-question thing of his. It was unsettling. It always would be—never less, sometimes a great deal more.

"Well—one doesn't have emotional explosions in public."

"You do. I don't know this 'one' you're talking about."

"I—guess I don't either, now that you mention it."

"Tell the truth then. No sense in going around and around about it: *He'll think that I . . .* and the like. I'll think what I think, whatever you say. Or—go down the mountain and just don't say any more." She did not turn to go, so he added: "Try the truth, then. If it's important, it's simple. And if it's simple it's easy to say."

"I'm going to die!" she cried.

"So am I."

"I have a lump in my breast."

"Come up to the house and I'll fix it."

Without another word he turned away and started through the orchard. Startled half out of her wits, indignant and full of insane hope, experiencing, even, a quick curl of astonished laughter, she stood for a moment watching him go and then found herself (at what point did I decide?) running after him.

She caught up with him on the uphill margin of the orchard.

"Are you a doctor?"

He appeared not to notice that she had waited, had run.

"No," he said and, walking on, appeared not to see her stand again pulling at her lower lip, then run again to catch up.

"I must be out of my mind," she said, joining him on a garden path.

She said it to herself. He must have known because he did not answer. The garden was alive with defiant chrysanthemums and a pond in which she saw the flicker of a pair of redcap imperials —silver, not gold fish—the largest she had ever seen. Then—the house.

First it was part of the garden with its colonnaded terrace—and then, with its rock walls (too massive to be called fieldstone) part of the mountain. It was on and in the hillside. Its roofs paralleled the skylines, front and sides, and part of it was backed against an outjutting cliff face. The door, beamed and studded and featuring two archers' slits, was opened for them (but there was no one there) and when it closed it was silent, a far more solid exclusion of things outside than any click or clang of latch or bolt.

She stood with her back against it watching him cross what seemed to be the central well of the house, or at least this part of it. It was a kind of small court in the center of which was an atrium, glazed on all of its five sides and open to the sky at the top. In it was a tree, a cypress or juniper, gnarled and twisted and with the turnedback, paralleled, sculptured appearance of what the Japanese call bonsai.

"Aren't you coming?" he called, holding open a door behind the atrium.

"Bonsai just aren't fifteen feet tall," she said.

"This one is."

She walked past it slowly, looking.

"How long have you had it?"

His tone of voice said he was immensely pleased. It is a clumsiness to ask the owner of a bonsai how old it is—you are then demanding to know if it is his work or if he has acquired and continued the concept of another; you are tempting him to claim for his own the concept and the meticulous labor of someone else and it becomes rude to tell a man he is being tested. Hence, *How long have you had it?* is polite, forbearing, profoundly courteous.

He answered, "Half my life."

She looked at the tree. Trees can be found, sometimes, not quite discarded, not quite forgotten, potted in rusty gallon cans in not quite successful nurseries, unsold because they are shaped oddly or have dead branches here and there, or because they have grown too slowly in whole or part. These are the ones which develop interesting trunks and a resistance to misfortune that makes them flourish if given the least excuse for living. This one was far older than half this man's life, or all of it. Looking at it, she was terrified by the unbidden thought that a fire, a family of squirrels, some subterra-

nean worm or termite could end this beauty—something working
outside any concept of rightness or justice or—of respect.

She looked at the tree. She looked at the man.

"Coming?"

"Yes," she said and went with him into his laboratory. "Sit down
over there and relax," he told her. "This might take a little while."

"Over there" was a big leather chair by the bookcase. The books
were right across the spectrum—reference works in medicine and
engineering, nuclear physics, chemistry, biology, psychiatry. Also
tennis, gymnastics, chess, the oriental war game Go, and golf. And
then drama, the techniques of fiction, *Modern English Usage, The
American Language* and supplement, Wood's and Walker's *Rhyming
Dictionaries* and an array of other dictionaries and encyclopedias.
A whole long shelf of biographies.

"You have quite a library."

He answered her rather shortly—clearly he did not want to talk
just now, for he was very busy.

He said only, "Yes I have—perhaps you'll see it some
time"—which left her to pick away at his words to find out what
on earth he meant by them.

He could only have meant, she decided, that the books beside
her chair were what he kept handy for his work—that his real library
was elsewhere. She looked at him with a certain awe.

And she watched him. She liked the way he moved—swiftly, decisively. Clearly he knew what he was doing. He used some equipment that she recognized—a glass still, titration equipment, a cen-
trifuge. There were two refrigerators, one of which was not a
refrigerator at all, for she could see the large indicator on the door.
It stood at 70°F. It came to her that a modern refrigerator is perfectly
adaptable to the demand for controlled environment, even a warm
one.

But all that—and the equipment she did not recognize—was only
furniture. It was the man who was worth watching, the man who
kept her occupied so that not once in all the long time she sat there
was she tempted toward the bookshelves.

At last he finished a long sequence at the bench, threw some
switches, picked up a tall stool and came over to her. He perched
on the stool, hung his heels on the cross-spoke and lay a pair of
long brown hands over his knees.

"Scared."

He made it a statement.

"I suppose I am."

"You don't have to stay."

"Considering the alternative"—she began bravely but the
courage-sound somehow oozed out. "It can't matter much."

"Very sound," he said almost cheerfully. "I remember when I
was a kid there was a fire scare in the apartment house where we

lived. It was a wild scramble to get out and my ten-year-old brother found himself outside in the street with an alarm clock in his hand. It was an old one and it didn't work—but of all the things in the place he might have snatched up at a time like that, it turned out to be the clock. He's never been able to figure out why."

"Have you?"

"Not why he picked that particular thing—no. But I think I know why he did something obviously irrational. You see, panic is a very special state. Like fear and flight, or fury and attack, it's a pretty primitive reaction to extreme danger. It's one of the expressions of the will to survive. What makes it so special is that it's irrational. Now, why would the abandonment of reason be a survival mechanism?"

She thought about this seriously. There was that about this man which made serious thought imperative.

"I can't imagine," she said finally. "Unless it's because, in some situations, reason just doesn't work."

"You can imagine," he said, again radiating that huge approval, making her glow. "And you just did. If you are in danger and you try reason and reason doesn't work—you abandon it. You can't say it's unintelligent to abandon what doesn't work, right? So then you are in panic. You start to perform random acts. Most of them—far and away most—will be useless. Some might even be dangerous. But that doesn't matter—you're in danger already. Where the survival factor comes in is that way down deep you know that one chance in a million is better than no chance at all. So—here you sit—you're scared and you could run. Something says you should run but you won't."

She nodded.

He went on: "You found a lump. You went to a doctor and he made some tests and gave you the bad news. Maybe you went to another doctor and he confirmed it. You then did some research and found out what was to happen next—the exploratory, the radical, the questionable recovery, the whole long agonizing procedure of being what they call a terminal case. You then flipped out. Did some things you hope I won't ask you about. Took a trip somewhere, anywhere, wound up in my orchard for no reason." He spread the good hands and let them go back to their kind of sleep. "Panic. The reason for little boys in their pajamas standing at midnight with a broken alarm clock in their arms—and for the existence of quacks." Something chimed over on the bench and he gave her a quick smile and went back to work, saying over his shoulder, "I'm not a quack, by the way. To qualify as a quack you have to claim to be a doctor. I don't."

She watched him switch off, switch on, stir, measure and calculate. A little orchestra of equipment chorused and soloed around him as he conducted, whirring, hissing, clicking, flickering. She wanted to laugh, to cry and to scream. She did not one of these things for fear of not stopping, ever.

When he came over again, the conflict was not raging within her but was exerting steady and opposed tensions. The result was a terrible stasis and all she could do when she saw the instrument in his hand was to widen her eyes. She quite forgot to breathe.

"Yes, it's a needle," he said, his tone almost bantering. "A long shiny sharp needle. Don't tell me you are one of those needle-shy people." He flipped the long power cord that trailed from the black housing around the hypodermic to get some slack, straddled the stool. "Want something to steady your nerves?"

She was afraid to speak. The membrane containing her sane self was very thin, stretched very tight.

He said, "I'd rather you didn't, because this pharmaceutical stew is complex enough as it is. But if you need it—"

She managed to shake her head a little and again felt the wave of approval from him. There were a thousand questions she wanted to ask—had meant to ask—needed to ask. What was in the needle? How many treatments must she have? What would they be like? How long must she stay and where? And most of all—oh, could she live, could she live?

II

He seemed concerned with the answer to only one of these.

"It's mostly built around an isotope of potassium. If I told you all I know about it and how I came on it in the first place it would take—well, more time than we've got. But here's the general idea. Theoretically, every atom is electrically balanced—never mind ordinary exceptions. Likewise all electrical charges in the molecule are supposed to be balanced—so much plus, so much minus, total zero. I happened on the fact that the balance of charges in a wild cell is not zero—not quite. It's as if there were a submicroscopic thunderstorm going on at the molecular level, with little lightning bolts flashing back and forth and changing the signs. Interfering with communications—static—and that," he said, gesturing with the shielded hypo in his hand, "is what this is all about. When something interferes with communications—especially the RNA mechanism that says, *Read this blueprint, build accordingly and stop when it's done* —when that message gets garbled lopsided things get built. Off balance things. Things that do almost what they should, do it almost right—they're wild cells and the messages they pass on are even worse.

"Okay. Whether these thunderstorms are caused by viruses or chemicals or radiation or physical trauma or even anxiety—and don't think anxiety can't do it—is secondary. The important thing is to fix it so the thunderstorm can't happen. If you can do that the cells have plenty of ability all by themselves to repair and replace what's gone wrong. And biological systems aren't like ping-pong balls with static charges waiting for the charge to leak away or to discharge into a grounded wire. They have a kind of resilience—I call it forgiveness—that enables them to take on a little more charge, or a little less, and do all right. Well, then—say a certain clump of cells is wild and say it carries an aggregate of a hundred units extra on the positive side. Cells immediately around it are affected—but not the next layer or the next.

"If they could be opened to the extra charge—if they could help to drain it off—they would, well, *cure* the wild cells of the surplus. You see what I mean? And they would be able to handle that little overage themselves or pass it on to other cells and still others who could deal with it. In other words if I can flood your body with a medium that can drain off and distribute a concentration of this unbalanced charge, the ordinary bodily processes will be free to move in and clear up the wild-cell damage. And that's what I have here."

He held the shielded needle between his knees and from a side pocket of his lab coat he took a plastic box, opened it and drew out an alcohol swab. Still cheerfully talking, he took her terror-numbed arm and scrubbed at the inside of her elbow.

"I am not for one second implying that nuclear charges in the atom are the same thing as static electricity. They're in a different league altogether. But the analogy holds. I could use another analogy. I could liken the charge in the wild cells to accumulations of fat. And this gunk of mine to a detergent that would break it up and spread it so far it couldn't be detected anymore. But I'm led to the static analogy by an odd side effect—organisms injected with this stuff do build up one hell of a static charge. It's a byproduct and, for reasons I can only theorize about at the moment, it seems to be keyed to the audio spectrum. Tuning forks and the like. That's what I was playing with when I met you. That tree is drenched with this stuff. It used to have a whorl of wild-cell growth. It hasn't anymore."

He gave her the quick, surprising smile and let it flicker away as he held the needle point upward and squirted it. With his other hand wrapped around her left bicep he squeezed gently and firmly. The needle was lowered and placed and slid into the big vein so deftly that she gasped—not because it hurt but because it did not. Attentively he watched the bit of glass barrel protruding from the black housing as he withdrew the plunger a fraction and saw the puff of red into the colorless fluid inside.

Then he bore steadily on the plunger again.

"Please don't move. I'm sorry, this will take a little time. I have to get quite a lot of this into you. Which is fine, you know," he said, resuming the tone of his previous remarks about audio spectra, "because side effect or no, it's consistent. Healthy bio systems develop a strong electrostatic field, unhealthy ones a weak one or none at all. With an instrument as primitive and simple as that little electroscope you can tell if any part of the organism has a community of wild cells and if so, where it is and how big and how wild." Deftly he shifted his grip on the encased hypodermic without moving the point or varying the plunger pressure. It was beginning to be uncomfortable—an ache turning into a bruise. "And if you're wondering why this mosquito has a housing on it with a wire attached (although I'll bet you're not and that you know as well as I do that I'm doing all this talking just to keep your mind occupied) I'll tell you. It's nothing but a coil carrying a high-frequency alternating current. The alternating field sees to it that the fluid is magnetically and electrostatically neutral right from the start."

He withdrew the needle suddenly and smoothly, bent an arm and trapped in the inside of her elbow a cotton swab.

"Nobody ever told me that after a treatment," she said.

"What?"

"No charge," she said.

Again that wave of approval, this time with words: "I like your style. How do you feel?"

She cast about for accurate phrases.

"Like the owner of a large sleeping hysteria begging someone not to wake it up."

He laughed.

"In a little while you are going to feel so weird you won't have time for hysteria."

He got up and returned the needle to the bench, looping up the cable as he went. He turned off the AC field and returned with a large glass bowl and a square of plywood. He inverted the bowl on the floor near her and placed the wood on its broad base.

"I remember something like that," she said. "When I was in—in junior high school. They were generating artificial lightning with a—let me see—well, it had a long, endless belt running over pulleys and some little wires scraping on it and a big copper ball on top."

"Van de Graaf generator."

"Right. And they did all sorts of things with it. But what I specially remember is standing on a piece of wood on a bowl like that and they charged me up with the generator. I didn't feel much of anything except all my hair stood out from my head. Everyone laughed. I looked like a golliwog. They said I was carrying forty thousand volts."

"Good. I'm glad you remember that. This'll be a little different, though. By roughly another forty thousand."

"Oh!"

"Don't worry. As long as you're insulated and as long as grounded or comparatively grounded objects—me, for example—stay well away from you, there won't be any fireworks."

"Are you going to use a generator like that?"

"Not like that—and I already did. You're the generator."

"I'm—oh!" She had raised her hand from the upholstered chair arm and there was a crackle of sparks and the faint smell of ozone.

"You sure are and more than I thought—and quicker. Get up."

She started up slowly. She finished the maneuver with speed. As her body separated from the chair she was, for a fractional second, seated in a tangle of spitting blue-white threads. They, or she, propelled her a yard and a half away, standing. Literally shocked half out of her wits, she almost fell.

"Stay on your feet," he snapped and she recovered, gasping. He stepped back a pace. "Get up on the board. Quickly now."

She did as she was told, leaving, for the two paces she traveled, two brief footprints of fire. She teetered on the board. Visibly, her hair began to stir.

"What's happening to me?" she cried.

"You're getting charged after all," he said jovially but at this point she failed to appreciate the extension of even her own witticism.

She cried again, "What's happening to me?"

"It's all right," he said consolingly.

He went to the bench and turned on a tone generator. It moaned deep in the one to three hundred cycle range. He increased the volume and turned the pitch control. It howled upward and, as it did so, her red-gold hair shivered and swept up and out, each hair attempting frantically to get away from all the others. He ran the tone up above ten thousand cycles and all the way back to a belly-bumping inaudible eleven. At the extremes her hair slumped but at around eleven hundred it stood out in, as she had described it, golliwog style. She could feel it.

He turned down the gain to a more or less bearable level and picked up the electroscope. He came toward her, smiling.

"You are an electroscope, you know that? And a living Van de Graff generator as well. And a golliwog."

"Let me down," was all she could say.

"Not yet. Please hang tight. The differential between you and everything else here is so high that if you got near any of it you'd discharge into it. It wouldn't harm you—it isn't current electricity—but you might get a burn and a nervous shock out of it." He held out the electroscope. Even at that distance—and in her distress—she could see the gold leaves writhe apart. He circled her, watching the leaves attentively, moving the instrument forward and back and from side to side. Once he went to the tone generator and turned it down some more. "You're sending such a strong field

I can't pick up the variations," he explained and returned to her, coming closer now.

"I can't—much more—I can't," she murmured.

He did not hear or he did not care. He moved the electroscope near her abdomen, up and from side to side.

"Yup. There you are," he said cheerfully, moving the instrument close to her right breast.

"What?" she whimpered.

"Your cancer. Right breast, low, around toward the armpit." He whistled. "A mean one, too. Malignant as hell."

She swayed and then collapsed forward and down. A sick blackness swept down on her, receded explosively in a glare of agonizing blue-white and then crashed down on her like a mountain falling.

Place where wall meets ceiling. Another wall, another ceiling. Hadn't seen it before. Didn't matter. Don't care.
Sleep.

Place where wall meets ceiling. Something in the way. His face, close, drawn, tired—eyes awake, though, and penetrating. Doesn't matter. Don't care.
Sleep.

Place where wall meets ceiling. Down a bit, late sunlight. Over a little, rusty-gold chrysanthemums in a gold-green glass cornucopia. Something in the way again—his face.
"Can you hear me?"
Yes, but don't answer. Don't move. Don't speak.
Sleep.

It's a room, a wall, a table, a man pacing—a nighttime window and mums you'd think were alive but don't you know they're cut right off and dying?
Do they know that?
"How are you?"
Urgent, urgent.
"Thirsty."

Cold and a bite to it that aches the hinges of the jaws. Grapefruit juice. Lying back on his arm while he holds the glass in the other hand.
Oh, no, that's not . . .
"Thank you. Thanks very—"
Try to sit up. The sheet—my clothes!
"Sorry about that," he said, the mindreader-almost. "Some things that have to be done just aren't consistent with pantyhose and a minidress. All washed and dried and ready for you, though—any time. Over there."

The brown wool and the pantyhose and the shoes, on the chair.
He's respectful, standing back, putting the glass next to an insulated carafe on the night table.
"What things?"
"Throwing up. Bedpans," he said candidly.
Protective with the sheet, which can hide bodies but—oh—not embarrassment.
"Oh, I'm sorry. Oh. I must have—"
Shake head and he slides back and forth in the vision.
"You went into shock and then you just didn't come out of it."
He hesitated. It was the first time she had ever seen him hesitate over anything. She became for a moment an almost-mindreader.
Should I tell her what's in my mind?
Sure, he should. And he did.
"You didn't want to come out of it."
"It's all gone out of my head."
"The pear tree, the electroscope. The injection, the electrostatic response."
"No," she said, not knowing. Then, knowing: "No!"
"Hang on," he rapped and next thing she knew he was by the bed, over her, his two hands hard on her cheeks. "Don't slip off again. You can handle it. You can handle it because it's all right now, do you understand that? You're all right."
"You told me I had cancer."
She sounded pouty, accusing.
He laughed at her, actually laughed.
"You told me you had it."
"Oh, but I didn't know."
"That explains it, then," he said in a load-off-my-back tone. "There wasn't anything in what I did that could cause a three-day withdrawal like that. It had to be something in you."
"Three days!"
He simply nodded and went on with what he was saying.
"I get a little pompous once in a while," he said engagingly. "Comes from being right so much of the time. Took a bit more for granted than I should have, didn't I? When I assumed you'd been to a doctor, maybe even had a biopsy? You hadn't, had you?"
"I was afraid," she admitted. She looked at him. "My mother died of it—and my aunt—and my sister had a radical mastectomy. I couldn't bear it. And when you—"
"When I told you what you already knew and what you never wanted to hear—you couldn't take it. You blacked right out, you know. Fainted away. And it had nothing to do with the seventy-odd thousand volts of static you were carrying. I caught you." He put out his arms where they were, on display, until she looked at them and saw the angry red scorch marks on his forearms and heavy

biceps, as much of them as she could see from under his short-sleeved shirt. "About nine-tenths knocked me out too," he said. "But at least you didn't crack your head or anything."

"Thank you," she said reflexively and then began to cry. "What am I going to do?"

"Do? Go back home, wherever that is—pick up your life again, whatever that might mean."

"But you said—"

"When are you going to get it into your head that what I did was not a diagnostic?"

"Are you—did you—you mean you cured it?"

"I mean you're curing it right now. I explained it all to you before. You remember that now, don't you?"

"Not altogether but—yes." Surreptitiously (but not enough, because he saw her) she felt under the sheet for the lump. "It's still there."

"If I bopped you over the head with a bat," he said with slightly exaggerated simplicity, "there would be a lump on it. It would be there tomorrow and the next day. The day after that it might be smaller. In a week you'd still be able to feel it but it would be gone. Same thing here."

At last she let the enormity of it touch her. "A one-shot cure for cancer—"

"Oh, God," he said harshly. "I can tell by looking at you that I am going to have to listen to that speech again. Well, I won't."

Startled, she asked, "What speech?"

"The one about my duty to humanity. It comes in two phases and many textures. Phase one has to do with my duty to humanity and really means we could make a classic buck with it. Phase two deals solely with my duty to humanity and I don't hear that one very often. Phase two utterly overlooks the reluctance humanity has to accept good things unless they arrive from accepted and respectable sources. Phase one is fully aware of this but gets rat shrewd in figuring ways around it."

She said, "I don't—" but could get no farther.

"The textures," he overrode her, "are accompanied by the light of revelation, with or without religion and/or mysticism. Or they are cast sternly in the ethical-philosophy mold and aim to force me to surrender through guilt mixed—to some degree all the way up to total—with compassion."

"But I only—"

"You," he said, aiming a long index finger at her, "have robbed yourself of the choicest example of everything I have just said. If my assumptions had been right and you had gone to your friendly local sawbones—and he had diagnosed cancer and referred you to a specialist and he had done likewise and sent you to a colleague for consultation and, in random panic, you had fallen into my hands and been cured—and had gone back to your various doctors to report a miracle, do you know what you'd have gotten from them? 'Spontaneous remission,' that's what you'd have gotten. And it wouldn't be only doctors," he went on with a sudden renewal of passion, under which she quailed in her bed. "Everybody has his own commercial. Your nutritionist would have nodded over his wheat germ or his macrobiotic rice cakes, your priest would have dropped to his knees and looked at the sky, your geneticist would have a pet theory about generation-skipping and would assure you that your grandparents probably had spontaneous remissions, too, and never knew it."

"Please!" she cried but he shouted at her.

"Do you know what I am? I am an engineer twice over, mechanical and electrical—and I have a law degree. If you were foolish enough to tell anyone about what has happened here (which I hope you aren't—but if you are I know how to protect myself) I could be jailed for practicing medicine without a license. You could have me up for assault because I stuck a needle into you and even for kidnapping if you could prove I carried you in here from the lab. Nobody would give a damn that I had cured your cancer. You don't know who I am, do you?"

"No, I don't even know your name."

"And I won't tell you. I don't know your name either—"

"Oh! It's—"

"Don't tell me! Don't tell me! I don't want to hear it. I wanted to be involved with your lump and I was. I want it and you to be gone as soon as you're both up to it. Have I made myself absolutely clear?"

"Just let me get dressed," she said tightly, "and I'll leave right now."

"Without making a speech?"

"Without making a speech." And in a flash her anger turned to misery and she added: "I was going to say I was grateful. Would that have been all right, sir!"

And his anger underwent a change too, for he came close to the bed and sat down on his heel, bringing their faces to a level, and said quite gently, "That would be fine. Although—you won't really be grateful for another ten days, when you get your 'spontaneous remission' reports—or maybe for six months or a year or two or five, when examinations keep on testing out negative."

She detected such a wealth of sadness behind this that she found herself reaching for the hand with which he steadied himself against the edge of the bed. He did not recoil but he didn't seem to welcome her touch either.

"Why can't I be grateful right now?"

"That would be an act of faith," he said bitterly, "and that just doesn't happen anymore—if it ever did." He rose and went toward the door. "Please don't go tonight," he said. "It's dark and you don't know the way. I'll see you in the morning."

When he came back in the morning the door was open. The bed was made and the sheets were folded neatly on the chair, together with the pillow slips and the towels she had used. She wasn't there.

He came out into the entrance court and contemplated his bonsai.

Early sun gold-frosted the horizontal upper foliage of the old tree and brought its gnarled limbs into sharp relief, tough brown-gray creviced in velvet. Only the companion of a bonsai (there are owners of a bonsai but they are a lesser breed) fully understands the relationship. There is an exclusive and individual treeness to the tree because it is a living thing and living things change—and there are definite ways in which the tree desires to change. A man sees the tree and in his mind makes certain extensions and extrapolations of what he sees and sets about making them happen. The tree in turn will do only what a tree can do, will resist to the death any attempt to do what it cannot do or to do it in less time than it needs. The shaping of a bonsai is therefore always a compromise and always a cooperation. A man cannot create bonsai, nor can a tree. It takes both and they must understand one another. It takes a long time to do that. One memorizes one's bonsai, every twig, the angle of every crevice and needle and, lying awake at night or in a pause a thousand miles away, one recalls this or that line or mass, one makes one's plans. With wire and water and light, with tilting and with the planting of water-robbing weeds or heavy, root-shading ground cover, one explains to the tree what one wants. And if the explanation is well enough made and there is great enough understanding the tree will respond and obey—almost.

Always there will be its own self-respecting, highly individual variation: *Very well, I shall do what you want, but I will do it my way.* And for these variations the tree is always willing to present a clear and logical explanation and, more often than not (almost smiling), it will make clear to the man that he could have avoided it if his understanding had been better.

It is the slowest sculpture in the world, and there is, at times, doubt as to which is being sculpted, man or tree.

So he stood for perhaps ten minutes, watching the flow of gold over the upper branches, and then went to a carved wooden chest, opened it, shook out a length of disreputable cotton duck. He opened the hinged glass at one side of the atrium and spread the canvas over the roots and all the earth to one side of the trunk, leaving the rest open to wind and water. Perhaps in a while—a month or two—a certain shoot in the topmost branch would take the hint and the uneven flow of moisture up through the cambium layer would nudge it away from that upward reach and persuade it to continue the horizontal passage. And perhaps not—and it would need the harsher language of binding and wire. But then it might have something to say, too, about the rightness of an upward trend and would perhaps say it persuasively enough to convince the man —altogether, a patient, meaningful, and rewarding dialogue.

"Good morning."

"Oh, goddam!" he barked. "You made me bite my tongue. I thought you'd gone."

"I had." She kneeled in the shadows, her back against the inner wall, facing the atrium. "But then I stopped to be with the tree for a while."

"Then what?"

"I thought a lot."

"What about?"

"You."

"Did you now?"

"Look," she said firmly. "I'm not going to any doctor to get this thing checked out. I didn't want to leave until I had told you that and until I was sure you believed me."

"Come on in and we'll get something to eat."

Foolishly, she giggled.

"I can't. My feet are asleep."

Without hesitation he scooped her up in his arms and carried her around the atrium.

She asked, her arm around his shoulders and their faces close, "Do you believe me?"

He continued around until they reached the wooden chest, then stopped and looked into her eyes.

"I believe you. I don't know why you decided as you did but I'm willing to believe you."

He sat her down on the chest and stood back.

"It's that act of faith you mentioned," she said gravely. "I thought you ought to have it at least once in your life—so you can never say again what you said." She tapped her heels gingerly against the slate floor. "Ow!" she made a pained smile. "Pins and needles."

"You must have been thinking for a long time."

"Yes. Want more?"

"Sure."

"You are an angry, frightened man."

He seemed delighted.

"Tell me about all that!"

"No," she said quietly. "You tell me. I'm very serious about this. Why are you angry?"

"I'm not."

"Why are you so angry?"

"I tell you I'm not. Although," he added good-naturedly, "you're pushing me in that direction."

"Well then, why?"

He gazed at her for what to her seemed a very long time indeed.

"You really want to know, don't you?"

She nodded.

He waved a sudden hand, up and out.

"Where do you suppose all this came from—the house, the land, the equipment?"

She waited.

"An exhaust system," he said, with a thickening of his voice she was coming to know. "A way of guiding exhaust gases out of internal combustion engines in such a way that they are given a spin. Unburned solids are embedded in the walls of the muffler in a glass-wool liner that slips out in one piece and can be replaced by a clean one every couple of thousand miles. The rest of the exhaust is fired by its own spark plug and what will burn, burns. The heat is used to preheat the fuel. The rest is spun again through a five-thousand mile cartridge. What finally gets out is, by today's standards at least, pretty clean. And because of the preheating it actually gets better mileage out of the engine."

"So you've made a lot of money."

"I made a lot of money," he echoed. "But not because the thing is being used to cut down air pollution. I got the money because an automobile company bought it and buried it in a vault. They don't like it because it costs something to install in new cars. Some friends of theirs in the refining business don't like it because it gets high performance out of crude fuels. Well, all right—I didn't know any better and I won't make the same mistake again. But yes—I'm angry. I was angry when I was a kid on a tankship and we were set to washing down a bulkhead with chipped brown soap and canvas. I went ashore and bought a detergent and tried it and it was better, faster and cheaper, so I took it to the bos'n, who gave me a punch in the mouth for pretending to know his job better than he did. Well, he was drunk at the time but the rough part came when the old shellbacks in the crew ganged up on me for being what they called a 'company man'—that's a dirty name in a ship. I just couldn't understand why people got in the way of something better.

"I've been up against that all my life. I have something in my head that just won't quit. It's a way I have of asking the next question: why is so-and-so the way it is? Why can't it be such-and-such instead? There is always another question to be asked about anything or any situation—especially you shouldn't quit when you like an answer because there's always another one after it. And we live in a world where people just don't want to ask the next question!

"I've been paid all my stomach will take for things people won't use and if I'm mad all the time it's really my fault—I admit it—because I just can't stop asking that next question and coming up with answers. There are a half-dozen real blockbusters in that lab that nobody will ever see and half a hundred more in my head. But what can you do in a world where people would rather kill each other in a desert, even when they're shown it can turn green and bloom—where they'll fall all over themselves to pour billions into developing a new oil strike when it's been proved over and over again that the fossil fuels will kill us all?

"Yes, I'm angry. Shouldn't I be?"

She let the echoes of his voice swirl around the court and out through the hole in the top of the atrium and waited a little longer to let him know he was here with her and not beside himself and his fury. He grinned at her sheepishly when he came to this.

And she said, "Maybe you're asking the next question instead of asking the right question. I think people who live by wise old sayings are trying not to think—but I know one worth paying some attention to. It's this: If you ask a question the right way, you've just given the answer." She paused to see if he was paying real attention. He was. She went on, "I mean, if you put your hand on a hot stove you might ask yourself, how can I stop my hand from burning? And the answer is pretty clear, isn't it? If the world keeps rejecting what you have to give—there's some way of asking why that contains the answer."

"It's a simple answer," he said shortly. "People are stupid."

"That isn't the answer and you know it," she said.

"What is?"

"Oh, I can't tell you that! All I know is that the way you do something, where people are concerned, is more important than what you do. If you want results. I mean—you already know how to get what you want with the tree, don't you?"

"I'll be damned."

"People are living, growing things, too. I don't know a hundredth part of what you do about bonsai but I do know this—when you start one, it isn't often the strong straight healthy ones you take. It's the twisted sick ones that can be made the most beautiful. When you get to shaping humanity, you might remember that."

"Of all the—I don't know whether to laugh in your face or punch you right in the mouth!"

She rose. He hadn't realized she was quite this tall.

"I'd better go."

"Come on now. You know a figure of speech when you hear one."

"Oh, I didn't feel threatened. But—I'd better go, all the same."
Shrewdly he asked her, "Are you afraid to ask the next question?"
"Terrified."
"Ask it anyway."
"No."
"Then I'll do it for you. You said I was angry—and afraid. You
want to know what I'm afraid of."
"Yes."
"You. I am scared to death of you."
"Are you really?"
"You have a way of provoking honesty," he said with some diffi-
culty. "I'll say what I know you're thinking: I'm afraid of any close
human relationship. I'm afraid of something I can't take apart with
a screwdriver or a mass spectroscope or a table of cosines and tan-
gents. I don't know how to handle it."

His voice was jocular but his hands were shaking.

"You do it by watering one side," she said softly, "or by turning
it just so in the sun. You handle it as if it were a living thing, like
a species or a woman or a bonsai. It will be what you want it to be if
you let it be itself and take the time and the care."

"I think," he said, "that you are making me some kind of offer.
Why?"

"Sitting there most of the night," she said, "I had a crazy kind
of image. Do you think two sick twisted trees ever made bonsai
out of one another?"

"What's your name?" he asked her.

A Date to Remember

William F. Temple

Bell was ostensibly reading *The Week in Washington* and secretly worrying about something that wasn't in the newspaper at all when the phone rang. He reached out from his armchair and took it.

"Hello... Oh, hello, Mick. Well, I didn't want to go out tonight. Is it really important? Can't wait till the morning? Well, I don't know—hang on a minute."

He clapped his hand over the mouthpiece and looked across at his wife who was in the opposite chair. She was knitting calmly.

"Pet," he said, "give me six reasons why I can't go out tonight. Quick."

"There aren't any reasons, and it's no good lying to Mick, anyway," she said. "You know he can read anyone like a book. If he says it's important, you can bet it's important."

"Hey, are you my wife or his? Cooperate, darn you!"

"Just tell him plainly you don't want to go."

Bell grunted and addressed the receiver. "If it's all the same to you, Mick, I'd rather not. You see, any moment, now, something might happen...."

"Nothing's due to happen for three or four days yet," said his wife, joining up a fresh ball of wool.

"All right, Mick," said Bell wearily. "You don't have to keep at me. My wife's on your side, anyway. I'll come right away. 'By."

He went and got his hat and coat. He pulled the window curtain aside and took a peek at the black night.

"Raining like crazy," he said. "Bess, you're a double-crossing, heartless she-cat."

He bent and kissed her hard. "And I love you very much," he added.

He paused at the door for a final injunction: "If anything starts, ring me right away."

The moment Stanley Bell stepped out of the yellow cab, it was as though someone had yanked out the bathtub plug up in heaven. The rain had ceased to a drizzle, but now it came down with a woosh. It bounced up off the sidewalk like rubber. Bell had twenty feet to cover between the cab door and the entrance to the apartment building. He ran, but he might as well have lain full length in the gutter—he could have got no wetter.

"Filthy night," he said to the elevator attendant. "Michael Grahame's apartment—the penthouse."

The attendant slammed the gate and made no answer. He'd been on duty a long time and felt tired. He looked at the fast-growing pool at Bell's feet, knew he'd have to mop it up, and felt more tired.

As the elevator mounted, Bell thought about Michael Grahame.

They'd been friends for twenty years, and all of that time Mick had climbed as steadily as this elevator. From scholarships to college, from college to study in the top-drawer clinics of psychiatry in Vienna, from Vienna to Atlantic City and private practice and authorship—then on to New York, some measure of fame and wealth and this penthouse on upper Fifth Avenue.

Symbolically, Mick was roof garden and Bell was roughly fifth floor, though they'd started together at ground level. But Mick didn't look at it symbolically. His values never changed. That was why their friendship endured. And Stanley Bell prized that friendship as he prized nothing but his wife's love.

Why did he so regard Mick? As the elevator whirred up, he analyzed the feeling. It was because Mick was reassurance. He represented firmness and sanity in the chaos of dying faiths, toppling values, and the growing greeds and fears of this world. The world was going crazy because of the thousand frustrations of a thousand desires.

Mick's sanity and strength lay in the fact that he never seemed to want anything, that he was never frightened to give. If you coveted the Delacroix over his mantel he would give it to you as lightly as he would hand you a cigar.

He never asked for anything himself, never envied anyone, and because he wanted nothing from the world, it became his friend and lavished wealth and honor on him.

Bell's saga had been different. His rise in the publishing world had been in the teeth of opposition. Had the opposition been of his own creation? Had he assumed, in this highly competitive business, that everyone so engaged was his rival—indeed, his enemy? And had he thus made fresh enemies for himself?

Bell realized now that something like that lay at the root of his own indifferent progress. That he was symptomatic of the current world outlook. That he was a fool among approximately two billion other fools. Suddenly he was blazing mad at himself.

He carried this fury out of the elevator with him, past the ebony plate announcing in gilt, MICHAEL GRAHAME: CONSULTING PSYCHIATRIST, and into Grahame's living room. The tenant was reclining in a saddlebag armchair, slippered feet on a footstool, gazing lazily up at the smoke rising from his cigar.

"Mick," said Bell furiously, "sometime we're going to have one of our long, cozy talks about life and how it should be lived. And I'll be going for your throat because you, knowing better, have allowed me to act like a fool for so long.

"But not tonight. I'm not staying a minute longer than I can help. Now, why in Hades have you dragged me over here on a night like this when you know very well—"

"There's a glass of rum and hot water on the sideboard for you," said Grahame calmly. "Thought you'd need it."

"Thanks," said Bell and went for it.

"Blast!" he said, "I'm leaving wet footprints all over your Kairwan carpet."

"Hang your clothes in the airing chamber. There are slippers here and a dressing gown warming on the radiator."

"I'm *not* staying. I've got to—"

"Get out of those wet things, of course," took up Grahame. "Or you certainly won't be staying—in this world for long. Bess will have to spare you for half an hour, while your things dry, or she might have to spare you forever."

"Oh, all right," said Bell ungraciously.

As he changed, he said, "What's it all about, anyway?"

Grahame looked at him. Both men were in their forties. Bell was thin, taut, and anxious-looking. Grahame was large, corpulent, relaxed, and radiated serenity.

"About my last book," said Grahame.

"What about it? It's still selling. I'm reprinting it next month."

"I mean my latest book," said Grahame. "That."

He indicated a Florentine leather folder on the table enclosing a thick wad of typescript. Bell went over to it in his drawers.

"You never told me about this. When did you start it?"

"Fifteen years ago," said Grahame.

Bell raised his eyebrows and the cover of the folder simultaneously. The first page said:

THE WHOLE MAN

Book I: Involuntary Hypnosis: Change of Emphasis.
Book II: The Power Complex and Resolution.
Book III: Free Will and Determinism: a Synthesis.
Book IV: Full Integration.

He flipped the pages over. It was very technical. Up till now all Grahame's books had been the wide-selling popular sort—*Master That Inferiority!, More Abundant Living, The Dynamo in Yourself.* And so on.

Bell donned the dressing gown thoughtfully.

"It'll take a lot of paper, printing, and binding," he said slowly. "Trade conditions are still none too easy."

"You think it won't sell."

There was no note of query in Grahame's voice. He said it flatly, as though he knew exactly what was in Bell's mind.

"It won't sell anything like your usual stuff," said Bell. "It'll be expensive to produce, and I'll have plenty left on my hands. I'd do it out of my regard for you only—well, frankly, Mick, I don't think the firm's finances will stand it.

"We've been shaky for a long time. Your popular psychology stuff has been our mainstay for years. Every other risk I've taken has fallen flat. I'm a rotten businessman."

"Actually," said Grahame, "you're a pretty good businessman. Only you're in the wrong business. Publishing isn't your racket. You've no sense of what the public wants."

"Maybe."

"I'm catching the one A.M. train to Chicago—lecture tour," said Grahame. "I'll be away for a long time. I asked you to come here tonight to hammer a few things into your head. First, *The Whole Man* will be a best seller. You'll make a pile out of it. And I'll make my name out of it."

"You've already made your name."

"Purely marginal frame. *The Whole Man* will make world history. It'll have ten times the influence of *Das Kapital*. Second, there's no time to lose about it. I want you to take it back with you tonight and lay it on the line right away. If it's going to shake the world out of its war hypnosis, it'll have to start doing it pretty darn quick before the radioactive clouds start rolling."

Bell gave a short, harsh bark of laughter which expressed the cynicism of the age. To Grahame, keen prober of mental states, it said a lot.

"So you've written mankind off, Stan?" he said benignly.

"Naturally. It's incurable. We're one of nature's mistakes. We were designed wrong at the start."

"Yet there's a lot worth while in homo saps," said Grahame. "It really would be one of nature's mistakes to scrap him now. I don't think she will."

"Where's your evidence for this optimism?" grunted Bell.

Grahame waved his hand in a circular movement to indicate the adorned walls of the room. The gesture embraced the originals and reproductions of a Delacroix, a Van Eyck, two Corots, Van Gogh's "Champ d'Oliviers," Greuze's "Milkmaid."

It included the loaded bookshelves and the cream of the world's poetry and Tolstoi, Flaubert, Balzac, Dickens, Shaw, Wells. In its orbit came the Ming vase, the Rodin statuette, and the view of the Golden Gate bridge.

"That," he said. "And much, much more. Where's your evidence for your pessimism?"

"That," said Bell, and stabbed a finger at the Sunday newspaper draped over the arm of Grahame's chair.

The paper was dated February 1, 1948. The headlines and sub-headings sprang out at once—THE COLD WAR... BREAKDOWN OF TALKS... WILL CONSCRIPTION COME AGAIN?... SCIENTIST SAYS... MOLOTOV SAYS... BRITAIN SAYS... TRUMAN SAYS....

Grahame picked it up and turned to an inner page. 'Here's an item of interest, Stan," he said and began to read: " 'Moscow, Saturday. The size—' "

"I'm not interested in what Moscow says," interrupted Bell petulantly. "I'm not interested in what anyone says. It's what they do that matters. Everyone's gabbing about peace and preparing for war. They make me sick."

"They won't face the fact that the causes of war lie neither in economics nor in political history but in psychology," murmured Grahame. "However, for once, this isn't about war. Here, read the thing yourself."

He tossed the paper to Bell. The publisher read it with a frown.

MARTIANS CAME IN 1908

—SAYS SOVIET WRITER

Moscow, Saturday: The size of a hole in the crust of the earth made by a heavenly body on June 30, 1908, has convinced the Soviet writer, A. Kazantsev, that Martians arrived on earth that day in an uranium-propelled spaceship.

Whatever hit the earth that day at Tungus, Siberia, left no fragments of itself behind, Kazantsev stated at the Moscow Planetarium today.

He said it could only have been a Martian ship laden with enough uranium to carry it back to the planet.

"Certain it is," he said, "that no meteorite could have done the damage the Tungus missile did, blasting an area greater than all the Moscow region and sending seismic shocks twice around the world.

"I believe the Martians left the planet in 1907 and arrived in June, 1908, but their ship exploded," he said.

"So what?" asked Bell.

"Have you never wondered why Mars has never sent us visitors as far as is known? It's an older planet than Earth and therefore presumably with a more advanced civilization, technically and morally. Don't you think they should have sent us explorers, missionaries, ambassadors, or colonists long before this? In fact, long before 1908?"

"I haven't given it a thought. Maybe the Martians haven't, either. Maybe there aren't any Martians."

"Maybe," said Grahame. "But there's definitely carbon dioxide in the atmosphere of Mars, and the new infrared spectrometer shows that the polar caps are certainly solidified water. The temperatures are extreme by Earthly standards but far from making life impossible—even Earthly life. The vegetation—"

He went on about the flora and topography of Mars and was giving the facts of the canal controversy when Bell interrupted impatiently.

"Look, Mick, at another time I'd be glad to sit at your feet and hear all about it. I mean that. But I'm not going to sit here taking lessons in astronomy when I may be needed at home. You wanted to give me the new book. Right, I'll take it with me and see if I can get it out when I've counted the petty cash. If that's all, I'll be going."

"Wait," said Grahame and produced his checkbook. He wrote out a check and thrust it on Bell. It was for a sum that made Bell blink.

"Finance the book with that," said Grahame. "Get a large edition out quickly. That'll settle your doubts about losing out on it."

"But—" began Bell.

"You can return it out of the profits when they come in," said Grahame quickly, anticipating the objection.

"Well—thanks."

"Your clothes will take at least another ten minutes. Perhaps you can spare me time to air a little fancy of mine?"

"Go ahead, Mick. But don't let it run away with you—about Mars, is it? You think we were visited by Martians in 1908?"

"Perhaps we were. Suppose we were. Suppose they had another try and pulled it off. Suppose they landed tomorrow. What kind of reception do you think they'd get?"

"Depends what kind of mood they were in and what they looked like," said Bell. "If they were mean, like Wells's things, and started flashing heat rays around, I guess they'd soon be nothing but another uranium-made hole in the ground. Unless they had bigger and better bombs than we.

"If they were offensive but still looked like Wells's things, they'd probably end up in a zoo. If they were halfway human, I suppose they'd be feted and asked to say a few words over the radio. But I doubt whether they'd be allowed to colonize."

"That's it, Stan. You reflect the current outlook exactly. You see it in terms of power. Two different races, and one's got to get on top of the other. That's the mental sickness my book analyzes. The power complex."

"That's not new."

"No. Far from new. It goes back to the old tribal fear of the stranger. The intolerance of the *difference*. Everyone wants everyone else to accept *his* creed, to be like himself, thus harmless to him. This craving for security, for protection against the different, won't give tolerance and common sense a chance.

"It's the philosophy of dialectic materialism, and people are acting on it more and more, whether they're Marxists or hate Karl's insides, or have simply never heard of him. But all this and much more is in my book."

"O.K., I'll read it religiously and let you know my views," said Bell. "But I don't want to get into a discussion now."

"All right. I just want to make my point. That is, if the Martians came and stayed for any length of time, there would inevitably arise a state of tension and probably conflict between them and Man. Because—and especially if the Martians were a superior race—this increasing fear of the different would pump suspicion into a frenzy in men's minds."

"Surely, if the Martians were more civilized than we, they'd first send missionaries to educate us out of our lowly state," said Bell. "After all, we sent missionaries to Africa and the South Seas to help the natives out."

"And fine juicy steaks the missionaries made until the white man turned up in force, complete with guns, to show said natives who was really top dog.

"Can you imagine proud, intolerant Man, lord of this planet, content to play second fiddle to a crowd of intruding Martians and permitting himself to be bossed around by them? No. He'd soon turn them into juicy steaks. Unless they also had a power complex and slapped his ears down first."

"I see. You think that's the reason why the Martians have never visited us?"

"No. I think they have visited us."

"You mean they tried to in 1908?"

"Doggone, no," said Grahame, stubbing out his cigar. "That was a meteorite and nothing else, despite 'Soviet Science.' I mean long before that."

"Prehistory?"

"No. In recorded history."

"But they're *not* recorded!" said Bell.

"They are. I believe they landed here unseen, went around observing us unseen, and left missionaries to educate us unseen."

"Why unseen? How unseen?"

"Why? Because they didn't want to become steaks. How? How do bird and animal watchers observe unseen? They try to make themselves look like part of the landscape. Which is only a substitute for making themselves look like part of the life they're observing.

"Some of the top deerstalkers actually get themselves up like deer. Those who first studied the Arabs dressed as Arabs, moved among Arabs, and passed for Arabs—even in the sacred enclosure of the Kaaba, where non-Mohammedans were forbidden on pain of death."

"You mean," said Bell slowly, "you think Martians have been moving among us, disguised in some crazy way as human beings? Observing us—and educating us?"

"Yes," said Grahame. "Who are the teachers of mankind?"

"I—er—" hesitated Bell and veered off anxiously, "You haven't put this nutty idea in the book, have you?"

"No. I said this was a fancy of mine."

"Good!" said Bell with relief. "Well, I guess you could say the teachers of mankind are the originals, our really great poets, artists, composers, engineers, scientific men, and so forth. The creators of all this."

And he imitated Grahame's circular gesture at the books and *objects d'art* in the room.

"Exactly. They're the missionaries from Mars. They set the standard. And the rest of mankind tries to reach it when they can turn their thoughts now and again from war making."

"There must have been droves of missionaries coming and going through the ages, then," said Bell.

"Perhaps not so many as you may think. I visualize these people changing their roles, their bodies, sometimes even their subjects over the years to avoid monotony. Being born again—reincarnated. Though perhaps the change-over is gradual. I mean, as life fades out of one body through senile decay, it flourishes gradually in the new body in the form of the child."

Bell regarded the speaker doubtfully. "Think my clothes are dry now," he said and went and got them. He started dressing himself.

" 'Intimations of Immortality,' " murmured Grahame lazily as if meditating aloud. "Wordsworth died in 1850. Robert Louis Stevenson was born in 1850."

"What of it?"

"Byron died in 1824. He was a restless sort. Supposing he wanted to be one of the great physicists for a change? Lord Kelvin was born in 1824.

"Shelley died in 1822. Pasteur was born in 1822. Titian died in 1576, and Robert Burton, of the famous *Anatomy of Melancholy*, was born in 1576. In 1809, Haydn, the father of the symphony, died—and Abe Lincoln was born. In 1828 Schubert died, Tolstoi was born."

Bell fought with his twisted suspenders and said nothing.

"The Martian who played Voltaire from 1694 to 1778 and Sir Humphry Davy, who gave the miners the safety lamp, for one thing, from 1778 to 1829, and Rubinstein from 1829 to 1894 must have had some fun," mused Grahame.

"And where did he go in 1894?" asked Bell gruffly.

Grahame smiled. "Maybe he went back to Mars on furlough."

"In an organized party, perhaps?" Bell tried to make it sound like levity, but underneath was uneasiness about the way Grahame was talking. Grahame had always been common sense personified. But this fantastic stuff . . . if it was meant as a joke it wasn't particularly funny.

And if Grahame were half serious it made one wonder whether the psychiatrist wouldn't soon need a psychiatrist—and whether *The Whole Man* were really valuable literary property or only something of like quality.

"I doubt whether there were enough of them to make up parties," said Grahame, still smiling. "But there might have been pals who went in pairs. For instance, two great composers, like Liszt and Berlioz, who both died in 1867. Or two great writers, like Mark Twain and Tolstoi, who both died in 1910.

"And the two men who knew more about the soul of humanity than all the others, Cervantes and Shakespeare, both died on the same day—April 23, 1616. On the other hand, Wordsworth and Beethoven were born in the same year, 1770."

"I never could remember dates," said Bell, tying his shoelaces.

"I'm not very good at them myself—these are only odd ones that occur to me," said Grahame carelessly. "But there's one series I know quite well. I'll write it down for you."

"Oh, don't trouble," said Bell, now fully dressed and brushing his coat. But Grahame scribbled a list on the back of an old envelope and held it out to him. Bell took it.

"That—" began Grahame, and was interrupted by the telephone. At the sudden loud tintinnabulation, Bell's stomach seemed to contract to a little lump of pain.

"That may be for me," he said, and licked dry lips.

"It is," said Grahame, who had answered it, holding it out to him. Bell found he was reaching for it with the hand that still clutched the list. He thrust the list impatiently in his pocket and took the phone.

"Hello."

Bess said, "It's started. Sooner than we expected. Don't worry. It'll be some time yet. I'm all packed. The taxi you come back in can take us to the hospital."

"Right. I'm leaving straight away. Make yourself comfortable, pet. Won't be long. 'By."

He dialed the number of a cab rank. When the cab was ordered, he gulped the neat Scotch the understanding Grahame had placed silently at his elbow.

"Thanks. It would happen the one evening I left her. I could murder you, Mick! However, I've no time now."

He snatched his hat.

"Take the book," said Grahame quickly. "Please!"

There was a note in his voice that made Bell, for all his haste, pause to look at him. Grahame was on his feet, a massive figure, standing plumb in the center of his beautiful room, and his attitude was tense entreaty. Never before had Bell seen Grahame show evidence of wanting anything, a favor least of all. Somehow, it moved him.

"Sure, sure," he muttered. "Can't stop to wrap it, though. Can I borrow the folder?"

"You can keep it," said Grahame.

Bell thrust folder and manuscript under his arm.

Grahame relaxed. He even smiled.

"Don't worry about Bess," he said. "It'll turn out all right. I'd come with you but I'm booked for that train."

"That's all right," said Bell, and they shook hands. "Hope the tour's a hit. When you're back I'll be seeing you."

"Yes," said Grahame, and there passed in his eyes an amused twinkle which Bell was to remember.

The rain had stopped.

As the taxi bore him down the avenue, Bell glanced back through the little rear window at the apartment house. Lighted windows staggered up its tall dark sides to the penthouse, shaped against the night sky. There was a break in the clouds above it, a handful of dim stars just visible.

It was a glimpse into the infinite that one rarely obtained in New York.

And somehow, suddenly, Grahame's fancy about the missionaries from out there seemed—possible. When one was moving, trembling, toward the eternal mystery of the birth of a new part of one's own self—especially if it was your first child and you were the apprehensive sort and you were mad about your wife—then in that borderland of uncertainty and the unprecedented almost anything seemed possible.

He came back to the flat as the shadows were long in the early morning light.

He had a shave and a lonely breakfast. It didn't seem right without Bess at the other side of the little table.

But he was immensely relieved. Things had gone swell. Bess was fine—and he was a father—of a son. Pride glowed steadily within him, as though he were due the credit for arranging everything.

On another morning, the mail's reminder of his precarious business would have worried him.

Now it didn't seem to matter. He even took up the newspaper and glanced over the headlines with a light heart.

Two minutes later he saw an item which knocked all the cheerfulness out of him, which impelled him to push his plate away, to rest his head in his hands, all his appetite gone.

At a quarter after midnight last night, the cab taking the well-known psychiatrist and author, Michael Grahame, to Grand Central Station had crashed into a streetcar. Grahame had been killed outright.

And Bell, in his empty flat, felt great gulfs of loneliness opening up all around him. The rock of Grahame was gone overnight. And Bess was not here to comfort him. Not that he thought it wise to tell her about Grahame yet.

She was still weak. And she had liked Grahame.

But she had nothing like his own love and hero worship for the man. He recalled his brusque impatience with Mick a few hours back and wished that he'd been more gracious.

He felt a mixture of grief and self-pity. The glory of his fatherhood was somewhat dimmed.

At midday he went to see her again, bearing orchids he couldn't afford.

His son was asleep in the little cot at her bedside.

Bess said, "Well, there he is. Half a day old already. It's just twelve hours since he arrived."

Bell glanced at his watch—12:15.

"That's right," he said. "I ought to know. Shall I ever forget!"

They laughed. But his laughter died before hers because he remembered something: Mick was killed at the same time that their son was born.

Exactly!

Bess sensed his sudden change of mood.

"What's the matter, love?"

He didn't answer. He was fumbling in his pocket.

He drew out the crumpled old envelope Mick had given him and, for the first time, read what his friend had written.

Then he dropped the envelope on the bed and got up to stare unseeing out of the window.

Mick had been forty-four—born in 1904.

Then, as he gazed at the noonday shimmer, his doubts and uncertainties fell away from him. He knew a confidence that he had never known before.

The Whole Man would be all Mick said it would be.

It would make Bell's fortune and lift Grahame's name into the ranks of the great. And there was every chance that it would do what it was primarily designed to do—set mankind's feet firmly on the true path of deliverance.

Best of all, to him, Mick was with him, would always be with him.

Bess looked at him puzzledly, then picked up the envelope.

Her expression of perplexity only deepened as she read.

Michelangelo—(1474–1564)

Galileo—(1564–1642)

Newton—(1642–1727)

Gainsborough—(1727–1788)

Schopenhauer—(1788–1860)

Chekhov—(1860–1904)

"What's it mean, darling?"

He came back, took the envelope, folded it carefully into his wallet.

"Just some notes Mick gave me."

"Oh," she said, "that reminds me. Has it struck you—the boy looks rather like Mick? Don't you think there's something of Mick in him?"

He turned bright eyes on the little red, wrinkled face in the cot.

"Yes," he said, quietly, "I'm sure there's quite a lot of Mick in him."

Fresh Guy
E. C. Tubb

Sammy was playing knucklebones on the Tombstone when the vampire arrived. As a vampire he obviously had a lot to learn. Sammy had heard him, recognized him for what he was, and had dismissed him as a possible danger long before the stranger stumbled into the light of the tiny fire which Sammy tended. Even when he finally arrived Sammy paid him no attention, concentrating instead on his game, rolling the five scraps of bone with easy familiarity.

He was good at the game, having had much time in which to practice, and he took a quiet pride in the skillful manner he tossed and snatched, flipped and caught, spun and held the knucklebones. He ended the game by throwing them high into the air, catching them on the back of his hand. It was a broad, shovel-like hand with stubby fingers, thick, strong nails, and well-developed muscles.

"Not bad, eh?" Sammy flipped the bones again, letting them bounce down the back of his hand and trapping them neatly between his fingers. He looked up, grinning at the stranger.

"What?" The vampire, a pale, distraught young character, was obviously out of his depth. He wore a faded khaki shirt and pants, a pair of cracked and mildewed boots and a baffled expression. "What did you say?"

"I said 'Not bad, eh?' " Sammy rolled the bones lovingly between his palms. "I bet you couldn't handle them like that."

"I don't suppose I could," admitted the stranger. He ran the tip of his tongue over his lips. "Do you mind if I join you?"

"Help yourself." Sammy waved to a spot opposite him across the fire. "Glad of company." He rolled his bones again and stared moodily into the fire.

The stranger stared too. He seemed to be struggling with some private burden, for twice he attempted to speak and changed his mind at the last moment. He squinted toward Sammy, but the fire was low and the light was bad and all he could make out was a formless blur. Finally, he coughed and got to the heart of what was worrying him.

"Look," he said. "My name is Smith, Edward Smith, and I seem to be in some sort of trouble. I wonder if you could help me?"

"Everyone's in some sort of trouble," said Sammy feelingly. "What's your particular brand?"

"Well," said Smith urgently, "something seems to have happened to me." He passed a wavering hand across his forehead. "This may sound crazy to you but I seem to be living in some weird kind of dream."

"Do tell," said Sammy, he was interested. Casually he flipped the knucklebones into a pocket of the tattered old jacket he wore. "What makes you think that?"

"Everything." Smith frowned as he tried to collect his thoughts. "I was sick, I remember that well enough what with Uncle screaming about doctor's bills and the price of medicine and how he was having trouble getting in the harvest because I couldn't help him and how he'd have to hire a man and who was going to pay for it?" Smith took a deep breath.

Sammy nodded, picking idly at his teeth. "I follow."

"I was as sick as a dog," corrected Smith feelingly. "I guess I would have died if it hadn't been for some queer old coot of a doctor Uncle dug up from somewhere or other. He was cheap, I guess, otherwise I wouldn't have had him, but he had a smell like he'd been out in the rain and hadn't dried off properly."

"And he only came after dark," said Sammy. "Right?"

"How did you know?" Smith blinked in surprise. "Maybe you know him, is that it?"

"I could take a guess," said Sammy. He picked at his teeth again. "Then what happened?"

"I don't know." Smith was genuinely baffled. "I must have passed out, I guess, because the next thing I know I was in a hole in the ground on the side of a hill. I had cramp something cruel so I yelled for help, but no one could have heard me because no one came to see what was wrong." He frowned again. "And that's another queer thing. When I finally managed to get out of the hole and take a look round I couldn't find a thing. The farm was gone, the road all grown over, everything had changed." He shook his head and stared bleakly into the fire. "So I'm either dreaming or crazy."

"You might be crazy," said Sammy. "I wouldn't argue about that, not knowing you well enough to form an opinion, but you're not dreaming, that's for sure."

"I must be," said Smith, he didn't seem to like the idea that he was crazy. "All this is a stupid mixed-up nightmare. It must be."

Sammy didn't bother to argue. He merely reached out and gently pinched Smith on the thigh. Smith screamed and rolled beside the fire, nursing his leg and whimpering with pain.

"Still think that you're dreaming?" asked Sammy pleasantly.

"No," said Smith wildly. "But if I'm not dreaming then I'm crazy. I'm just a poor, crazy madman, that's what."

"Crazy you might be but a man you are not," said Sammy. Smith jerked up his head.

"Not a man?" His voice rose a little. "Then what am I?"

"A vampire."

"A *what!*"

"A vampire."

"Now I know who is crazy." Smith forgot about his leg. "All that guff is for the birds. Superstitious rubbish! Old wives' tales! Nonsense, all of it!"

Sammy shrugged.

"Well, it is," insisted Smith weakly. He brooded for a long time. "All right," he said finally. "I'll ride along with what you say. So I'm a vampire." He leaned forward, triumph glinting in his eyes. "But if I'm a vampire what does that make you?"

"A ghoul," said Sammy. He threw some dried twigs on the fire; blinking in the sudden flare of light.

"Satisfied?" Sammy sucked reflectively at a tooth as the light died.

"I don't know." Smith had been shaken by the sight. "You're either the most deformed human I've ever seen or you aren't human at all."

"I'm not human," admitted Sammy patiently. "I told you that. I'm a ghoul."

"Incredible!" Smith shook his head. "I simply can't believe it."

Sammy grunted and rolled over on to his back. His ears twitched a little, he was listening to the sounds of something moving in the woods.

"It's not that I'm calling you a liar," said Smith. "I wouldn't want you to think that, but the whole thing's so crazy!" He shook his head as if it hurt a little. "And another thing. I must have walked for miles; if I hadn't seen your fire I'd have stumbled around all night, and in all that time I haven't seen or heard a soul. Not even a dog. Where is everyone?"

"Around," said Sammy vaguely. He suddenly caught on to what Smith meant. "Oh, you mean *humans!*" He stabbed a finger downward toward the overgrown concrete slab of The Tombstone. "At a guess I'd say they are about a half a mile down."

"All of them?"

"All that are left. In this part of the world anyway, I wouldn't know about over the oceans." He stared at the young man's expression. "Didn't you know?"

"No." Smith was breathing fast from the top of his chest. "What happened?"

"The Big Bang." Sammy grimaced. "The thing everyone knew would happen, said they didn't want to happen, yet made happen anyway." Speculation narrowed his eyes. "Say, just when were you buried anyway?"

"I fell sick in 1975," said Smith, dodging the leading question. Sammy pursed his lips in a soundless whistle.

"That accounts for it. The Big Bang came a couple of years later and they certainly made a good job of it. A better job than the embalmer did on you or you wouldn't be sitting there now."

"Embalmer?" Smith looked blank. "I don't get it. Are you sure that you know what you're talking about?"

"Listen," snapped Sammy, he was getting annoyed. "I may look a little odd, to you at least, but I'm no dumbbell. I can read fifteen languages and speak twenty more and once I went to school; spent most of a year there before I had to leave."

"Why?"

"It was a medical school," said Sammy shortly. "What I'm getting at is that I know what happened to you. If the embalmer had done a better job you would have died for real. And even then you were lucky; your folks must have cut corners when they planted you. Otherwise you wouldn't have been washed out at the right time."

"Uncle Silas was always a tight-wad," admitted Smith. "He fancied himself at carpentry too." He fell silent, thinking. "I guess that all this must be real then." He chuckled. "Me a vampire! Well, what do you know?" A thought suddenly wiped the smile from his face. "Say! If you're a ghoul—" He swallowed. "What I mean is that ghouls are supposed to—well, aren't they?"

"Forget it," said Sammy. "We've a Gentleman's Agreement, neither touches the other."

"Well!" Smith dabbed at his forehead. "That's a relief. You had me worried for a while about that."

Sammy didn't answer, he was busy listening to the stealthy approach of a visitor. Smith, now that the sounds were loud enough for even his dull hearing to catch, stiffened in sudden alarm.

"Say, what's that?"

"Relax," said Sammy, setting an example. "It's just one of the boys."

"Who?" Smith seemed anxious.

"Who?" Sammy gave a grin. "Well, now," he said deliberately. "At a guess I'd say that it was your pappy." He was always one for a joke.

Boris was of the old school, a tall, thin, cadaverous vampire who believed that the old traditions should be maintained. He came striding out of the woods, his cloak swirling around him, his monocle gleaming red in the reflected light. He sat beside the fire, warming his thin, almost transparent hands, then nodded to Smith.

"Who's the new one?"

Sammy chuckled. He had seen the expression on Smith's face and now awaited the denouement.

"I know you," suddenly blurted Smith. "You're the doctor who attended me when I was sick."

"That's right," said Sammy. "Boris, meet your son. Smith, meet your Pop."

"He's not my father," denied Smith. "Anyway, my old man died way back in a car crash."

"Your new father for your new rebirth," explained Sammy. "Boris infected you when he snitched your blood. If it hadn't been for him you wouldn't be here now so, in a way, he's your Pop." He became serious. "It's the only way vampires can breed, you know, they depend on their victims to perpetuate their race."

"And ghouls?" said Smith shrewdly. "What about them?"

"Like humans," said Sammy shortly. He didn't want to talk about it. Neither, it appeared, did Boris want to discuss his new offspring.

"Lupe here yet?" He shivered a little and drew closer to the fire. Sammy shook his head.

"He'll be along."

"I hope we have better luck this time." Boris sucked at his bloodless lips. "Seven years now we've been waiting and still no sign of them coming out." He looked suddenly panic-stricken. "Could they be all dead?"

"Lupe said that he could hear sounds the last time," reminded Sammy. "And we know they took care to stock up well on supplies."

"But something could have happened." Boris was a natural pessimist. "Maybe something went wrong with their water supply, or they took a bug down there with them and it wiped them out." He began to chew at his nails as he thought about it. "And they're the only ones we know of."

"Take it easy," said Sammy, he was becoming infected with the other's doubts. "They'll be all right, I know they will." He changed the subject. "Anything new?"

"Nothing." Boris hunched closer to the fire, his evening dress, dirt-stained but still retaining a traditional dignity, giving him the appearance of an old and slightly moth-eaten aristocrat. "I've covered a pretty wide area and haven't seen a thing. I guess that we're the last, Sammy, you and me and Lupe, and we're not going to last much longer unless they come out from under The Tombstone pretty soon."

"Don't forget me, Pop," said Smith. "I'm one of the boys now." He grinned at Boris's expression. "What's the matter, Pop? Touch you on the raw?"

"I am not used to being addressed as 'Pop,' " said Boris with simple dignity. "And don't kid yourself that you are something special. Why, I remember the time when young pups like you were ten a penny. And a lot of trouble they caused too, back in the old days. Made life very hectic for a while."

"That's because you weren't organized," said Smith briskly. "Now, take me. I'm modern with modern ideas of how to go about things. You've got to be organized to get anywhere in this world." He stared disdainfully at Boris's garments. "Take you now, dressed up like a Continental Count playing a bit part in some crummy production."

"I am a Count," said Boris in a strangled voice.

"Maybe you were," said Smith airily, "but who wants Counts. What counts now is the front you put on. Dress like big money, talk like big money and, brother, you'll get big money." He beamed in self-satisfaction. "Believe me, I know."

"What's the good of money," said Sammy from the shadows. "It can't buy you anything, not now."

"It will." Smith was confident in his own knowledge of the human race. "And the smart ones are those who get in on the ground floor."

Boris grunted in disgust; he was a quiet old vampire who believed in keeping himself to himself and not making enemies. It was a system of life which had stood him in good stead in the past, and he saw no reason to change just because some young squirt thought he knew it all. He gave a dry laugh at the prospect of deflating the young vampire. Sammy spoiled his fun.

"Better tell Smith what he has to know," he said. "After all, you owe it to him in a way."

"I owe him nothing," snorted the old vampire. "What has he ever done for me?"

"You want me to answer that?" Smith grew annoyed as he thought about it. It wasn't that he objected too much to his new status but the principle behind it annoyed him. He was firm in his belief of the paradox of free enterprise and the sanctity of property, especially private property and Boris had successfully pulled off a very personal theft. And there was nothing he could do about it.

"Tell him, Boris," said Sammy again. "You owe it to the lad."

"You don't have to tell me anything," snapped Smith. He expanded his chest. "I've read a bit and I know what the score is. I know what to eat and know that I've to return to my grave before dawn." Suddenly he looked haggard. "My grave! Hell! I'd never be able to find it again in a month of Sundays!"

Boris snorted with amused contempt. "That's for the comic books," he said. "All that guff about returning to our graves before dawn, I mean. All that's necessary is that you stay out of sunlight;

the actinic rays will trigger off skin cancers. Artificial light's all right, but nothing containing ultraviolet."

"That so?" Smith looked relieved. "Anything else you should tell me while you're at it?"

"Only to respect your elders," snapped Boris. "And don't get careless or you'll wind up with a stake through the heart or a bullet through the ribs. And it needn't be a silver bullet either." He broke off as an animal howled from the darkness.

"Here's Lupe," said Sammy happily, and threw more twigs on the fire.

A big, sleek Alsatian-like dog loped into the firelight, sat down and promptly changed into a man. Even in human form he retained a slightly wolf-like air. He nodded to the others.

"Hi! How's tricks?"

"I'm starving," grumbled Boris.

"So am I." Sammy belched wind and rubbed his stomach. "I've been living off my fat for so long now that soon I'll be too weak to take a bit if I had the chance." He looked hopefully at the werewolf. "Any news?"

"Wife's had a new litter," said Lupe proudly. "Three boys and two girls." He beamed at their congratulations. "Things aren't as easy as they might be but I'm making out." He lifted a foot and scratched himself behind one ear. He noticed Smith's boggle-eyed stare. "New boy?"

"Just born," said Sammy. "Boris was responsible for him."

"Congratulations," said Lupe politely to the old vampire. "How's he shaking down?"

"Well, he hasn't gone crazy on us yet," said Sammy thoughtfully. Boris changed what was, to him, obviously a painful subject.

"Any other news?"

"The rabbits are getting more plentiful," said Lupe.

"Rabbits!" Boris screwed up his mouth. Sammy echoed his sentiments.

"Rabbits might be good eating for you, Lupe, but not for us. Anything else?"

"I don't think so." The werewolf frowned. "There was just one more thing now I come to think about it but it's slipped my mind." He waved a hand. "Never mind, I guess it'll come back if it was important." He returned to the subject closest to his heart. "I wish you could see the youngsters; fine kids all of them."

"You're breeding fast," said Sammy enviously. "Sure you aren't going a little too fast?"

"I don't think so." Lupe scratched the other ear. "I'm keeping the litters down as low as I can but we daren't get too low. Anyway, all our troubles will be over when they come out."

"You can say that again," said Sammy with real feeling. He smacked his lips. "Hell, I never thought that I'd miss humans so much."

"Nor me," said Boris fervently. "Why, once in the old days when they were pressing close I even wished a plague on them." He sighed. "Right now I could do with the old days, stakes, garlic, silver bullets, and all. Modern times were a gift, sure, but look how things wound up."

They nodded, even Smith, all agreeing that the human race had hardly played fair.

"When they come out," said Sammy thoughtfully, "we'll have to take things easy. Treat them gently and give them a chance to breed."

"That's right," agreed Lupe. "Build up the supply before we can let loose the demand. Personally, though, I'm not worried too much. My guess is that they wouldn't have taken many dogs down under The Tombstone with them or, if they did, then they'd have to restrict them to the limit. Anyway, they'd welcome a change." He bared his teeth, concentrated, and changed into a handsome pseudo-Alsatian. He was grinning as he resumed human form. "See what I mean?"

"Humans were always suckers for dogs," said Boris enviously. "I've often wondered why you just didn't move right in and take over."

"Why should we?" Lupe shook his head at the vampire's ignorance. "No need to kill the goose, you know. They never suspected us, not after the Middle Ages, and many a human has worked himself silly to support us in luxury." He scowled. "When I think of how many of us got caught in the Big Bang—!"

"We all got caught in it." Sammy kicked at the fire.

The rest nodded, agreeing with Sammy all the way. Smith didn't say anything. He was still a little confused and more than inclined to think he was in a dream. But fantastic as everything seemed it all made a peculiar kind of sense. Ghouls, vampires, and werewolves were, obviously, very real. Divergent branches of human stock, perhaps, ultra specialists who had become utterly dependent on the human race for their sustenance. Lupe and his kind had adapted best of all but, in the final essence, they were all parasites. He too, now he came to think of it; and suddenly he was very conscious of their concern over the survival of the few humans left beneath The Tombstone.

Parasites cannot live without a host.

Lupe stretched himself, yawned, and rose to his feet. "Well," he said, "I guess that we'd better get on with it." Changing to animal form he began to run over the cracked, overgrown expanse of the slab of cadmium concrete which was The Tombstone. Nose to the ground, tail waving, he looked every inch a splendid specimen of the canine species. Even Smith, who knew better, had to restrain a desire to call to him so that he could pat his head.

"What's he doing?" he asked.

"Checking up," said Sammy. "Lupe's got sharper senses than we have, and he's finding out whether or not they are still moving around down there." He held up his hand for silence. "Watch him!"

Lupe looked over his shoulder, grinned, then vanished behind a clump of scrub. When he reappeared he was in human shape.

"I think I've got something," he called. "Scent's pretty strong by this ventilator."

"They coming out?" Sammy sprang to his feet, his strong legs carrying him over to the werewolf. "Are they?"

"Can't tell." Lupe altered his shape again and sniffed around some more, finally cocking his head and resting one furry ear against a barely visible crack in the concrete. He concentrated so hard that even his tail stopped wagging.

"Dawn'll be here soon," whispered Boris. He shivered and drew his ragged cloak around him. "Another day in the mud."

"How do you arrange it?" said Smith. Like Boris he kept his voice low. "I guess that you could just cover yourself with that cloak and you'd be safe. Is that why you wear it?"

"It has its uses," said Boris ambiguously. He glared at the young vampire with an active dislike. "Listen," he warned, "just because I was responsible for you being here doesn't mean that I've got to wet-nurse you. Life's tough enough without that."

"Who wants you to wet-nurse anyone?" Smith returned the glare. "From what I can see you're just an old-fashioned has-been. Walking around with that cloak as if you were some Count or something. Why didn't you get a plastic cover like they used to cover automobiles with? You could fold that up small and have a regular tent at day-times."

"Smart guy," sneered Boris. "That's the trouble with you young pups, always think you know better than your elders. I'd look fine walking about with a tent on my back now, wouldn't I? Maybe you'd better learn that people like us have to practice camouflage all the time. One slip and—!" He made a suggestive gesture. "It's happened before, you know."

"In comic books," admitted Smith. "But who believes in vampires now?"

"And what's the reason for that?" Boris tightened his thin mouth. "Camouflage, of course, what else? Same as humans don't believe in Sammy and his kind, but how long would it take them to figure it out? So maybe they'd think you was sick in the head and lock you away in an asylum, but what then? They wouldn't feed you the right diet, and they'd keep you there for a long, long time. And you'd die there, make no mistake about that." He shuddered. "It happened to a friend of mine."

"Old-fashioned, that's what you are." Smith appealed to Sammy. "You can see that, can't you? You're educated and—"

"Pipe down!" interrupted Sammy. He felt all on edge as he always did when Lupe came to make one of his periodic checkups. His hunger had mounted until it was a fire in his stomach and his nerves were like harp strings. Restlessly he got to his feet and wandered over to where the werewolf was sniffing the ground.

"They're still alive," said Lupe. He'd changed again and stood, breathing deeply, his chest and forehead covered with sweat. "Hell, I'm all in!"

"Come and sit down." Sammy led the way back to the fire, knowing of the demands that shape-changing made on Lupe's energy sources. The werewolf sagged as he slumped beside the blaze.

"I could smell them," he said after a while. "Scent's stronger than it was and it's my guess that they are moving upward."

"On their way out?" Hope flamed in the old vampire's eyes. "Is that it, Lupe?"

"Could be." Lupe relaxed still more. "From the sounds I'd say that they are moving heavy equipment toward the surface. Maybe one of their tunnels got blocked and they have to clear it. That or they aren't too sure what conditions are like up here and don't want to take any chances." He grinned. "Anyway, they're still safe."

The others grinned with him.

"You know," said Smith thoughtfully, "this needs careful planning." He threw another twig on the fire. *"Very* careful planning."

"Meaning?" Sammy stared dully into the fire. Lupe had gone; he'd rested for a short while and then, resuming animal form for fast travel, had loped off back to his wife and new litter. Sammy felt more depressed than usual after he had gone. It must be nice to be able to return back to a family. He wished he had one of his own.

"Well," said Smith, "if Lupe knows his business then the humans are on their way out. When they do finally come out we'll have to contact them, right?"

"That's right." Sammy fought down the hunger which thought of all those humans living and dying down below always aroused. Once he had tried digging down toward them, but had had to give up in despair. That had been during one of his desperate periods.

"So who is going to be the contact." Smith glanced at Sammy. "You?"

"Why not?" Boris was quick to defend his friend.

"Why not?" Smith shrugged. "Look at him, that's why not."

"Sammy's held down jobs with humans before."

"In the old days, maybe, but there were plenty of freaks walking around then. Those days are over."

"Let's not get personal about this," snapped Sammy. "What's on your mind?"

"I'm a modern man," said Smith. "At least, I was a modern man and I know how they think. Those humans down there know that the surface was blasted with radiation. If Sammy turns up they'll think that he's a mutation or something. They've bred true down there and they aren't going to want mutations around at any price. So they'll shoot him." He spread his hands. "Well," he said defensively. "How can you argue about it? Sammy doesn't look human, does he?"

"Go on," gritted Sammy. He clamped his teeth together, hating Smith for the first time. Fresh guy!

"So that rules out Sammy," continued Smith. It was obvious that he had given the matter some thought. "That leaves me and Boris." He shrugged. "I guess that we needn't even consider Boris."

"Why not?" The old vampire was hurt.

"Because you look a freak too, that's why." Smith was brutally frank. "Let's face it, fellows, neither of you would get to first base."

"And you would, I suppose?" Sammy was sarcastic.

"Sure." Smith had an iron hide, sarcasm didn't reach him. "I'm young and I know what the score is. I could talk my way into their confidence and be accepted."

"And what about us?"

"Oh, I'd take care of you somehow." Smith didn't meet Sammy's eyes. "I'd try to sneak Boris here a drink or two and fix it so that you got something to eat now and again. Things will be hard at first, naturally, but I'll do my best."

"Fresh young pup!" Boris ground his teeth in anger. "No respect for your elders at all! Why I—"

"Hold it!" Sammy sprang to his feet, then relaxed as Lupe bounded into the firelight. "Trouble?"

"No." Lupe grunted as he forced his tired body back into human shape. "Wish that I didn't have to do this every time I wanted to talk." He looked at Sammy. "It's just that I remembered what it was I had to tell you. I bumped into someone you'd be interested in a short while ago. She's living in a cave way south of here, in a place where they used to hang their dead, the humans, I mean. You know it?"

"I know it." Sammy felt excitement warm his blood. "I thought that area had been cleaned out long ago."

"Maybe it was, but she's there now and from what I could see she's making out fine." Lupe winked. "I told her about you and she's interested. Young too." He dropped to all fours. "And lonely." He began to change shape. "Well, just thought that you'd be interested." Abruptly he was gone, a sleek shape bounding through the brush.

Sammy stared after him, too thrilled to shout his thanks. A girl ghoul! Almost he had given up hope of ever finding a female of his own kind but, if Lupe was telling the truth, and he was, then there was something to be gained in life even yet. He sagged at a sudden thought.

The caves were a long way away and he hadn't eaten for too long. Travel took energy and he just didn't have the energy. Smith looked enviously at the ghoul as he slumped beside the fire.

"Lucky devil," he said. "I wish I could get a girl."

"You have to make your own," said Sammy dully. Boris frowned.

"What's wrong with you, Sammy? That was good news. You're going, of course?"

"How can I?" Sammy sighed from the pit of his stomach. "Radiations sterilize, remember, and I can't eat sterile food. Around here it wasn't so bad, that's how I've managed to live this long, but I can't hope to pick up anything decent to eat on so long a journey." He slumped still more. "I'm too weak to chance it." He sighed again. "If I could only get one really decent meal to set me up I'd be off like a shot. Just one good meal."

"Tough," said Smith carelessly. "Still, maybe she'll wait."

"Hold your tongue!" snapped Boris. He glanced at Sammy, then at Smith, then at Sammy again. Nervously he wet his lips. "There's one way," he said suggestively.

"There's the Agreement," reminded Sammy. He'd already thought of what Boris had in mind and dismissed it because of that.

"We're a quorum," pointed out Boris. "We could agree to suspend the Agreement for just this once." He became urgent. "Be sensible, Sammy. The way things are the two of us wouldn't stand a chance to survive until they come out. From what Lupe said it might take another year and those Red Cross stocks are mostly smashed and useless. And when they do come out, what then?"

"Geometrical progression," said Sammy, understandingly. "Two makes four and four makes eight and—"

"He's young," said Boris. "That means that he'll have a hell of an appetite. He won't be able to use discretion, he hasn't had the experience. And you heard what he said about contacting them. What's the betting that he just cuts us out?"

"What are you talking about?" Smith glanced from one to the other. They ignored him.

"I'm not so sure," said Sammy slowly. "We've got to stick together now or we'll all be sunk."

"We'll all be sunk anyway," said Boris. "He'll foul things up for sure." His hand closed pleadingly on Sammy's arm. "Please, Sammy. Just for this once."

"What are you two freaks talking about?" snapped Smith again. Youth and confidence in his superiority made him contemptuous of these old has-beens. Sitting beside the fire he had made his own plans, and they didn't include either of the others. He lost both confidence and contempt as he read Sammy's expression. "No!" he screamed, understanding hitting like a thunderbolt. "No! You wouldn't! You couldn't! You—"

He rose together with Sammy and, turning, raced into the dark safety of the woods. He didn't get far.

Fresh guys rarely do.

Automaton

A. E. van Vogt

The human automaton stirred uneasily in his small, almost invisible plane. His eyes strained into the visiplate, scanning the sky ahead. Out of the blue came two flashes of fire. Instantly, the plane careened as if struck from a double blow.

It fell slowly at first, then more rapidly, down into the enemy lines. As the Earth came near, a resisting mechanism went into operation. The rate of fall grew slower. The automaton had time to see that there was a vast ruin of a city below. Soundlessly, the tiny machine settled into the shelter of the crumbled base of what had once been a building.

A moment passed, then the radio beside him sibilated. Voices which were strange to him were talking to each other.

"Bill!" said the first voice.

"Shoot!"

"Did we get him?"

"Don't think so. Not permanently, anyway. I think he went down under at least partial control, though it's hard to tell with that safety device they have. My guess is he's down there somewhere with his motor shut off."

"I think we disabled him."

"Well, then, you know the routine when one of 'em is cornered just inside our lines. Do your psychology stuff. I'll call the *Vulture*."

"Don't pass the buck to me. I'm sick of spouting those lines. You give 'em!"

"All right. Shoot me the come-on!"

"Hmmmm . . . he's down there. Think we ought to go after him?"

"Naw! The automatons they send out this far are basically the clever ones. That means we couldn't capture him. He'd be just fast enough on the uptake to make it necessary for us to kill him, and who the devil wants to kill those poor, tortured slaves?—Did you get his picture?"

"Yep, he was listening with an intent look on his face. Fine looking chap... It's funny, and kind of terrible how all this started, isn't it?"

"Yeah. Wonder what this guy's number is."

There was a distinct pause. The automaton stirred uneasily. His number? Ninety-two, of course. What else? The voice was speaking again:

"Poor fellow probably doesn't remember that he once had a name."

The other voice said, "Who'd have thought when they first made a human duplicate—flesh and blood and bones and all—that today, only fifty years later, we'd be fighting for our lives against people who look exactly like us, except that they're natural eunuchs."

The automaton listened with vague attention, as the two men went on talking. Every little while he nodded as their words reminded him of something he had almost forgotten. The human duplicates had first been called robots. They had resented that name, and changed it around to make it Tobor, and that stuck. The Tobors proved to be very effective scientists, and at first no one noticed how rapidly they took over scientific posts in every part of the world. Nor was it immediately noticed that the Tobors were secretly carrying on a duplication campaign on a tremendous scale. The great shock to the human masses came when Tobor-infiltrated governments on each continent simultaneously enacted laws declaring duplication would henceforth be the only means of procreation. Sex was forbidden under penalty of a fine for the first offense, then imprisonment, and then, for recalcitrants, the Tobor-invented process of being made into an automaton.

A special police organization—which turned out to be already in existence—was set up to administer the new law. Tobor enforcement officers swung into action immediately, and there was some street fighting on that first day. Neither side even thought of compromise, so within two weeks full-scale war was raging.

The account ended, as Bill said: "I guess he's heard enough. Come on, let's go."

There was muffled laughter, then silence.

The automaton waited, disturbed. Sketchy memories were in his mind of a past when there had been no war, and, somewhere, there was a girl, and another world.

The unreal pictures faded. And again there was only this ship that clothed his body in almost form-fitting metal. There was the need to go on, aerial pictures to be taken... Must get up into the air!

He felt the ship tug in response to his urgent thought, but no movement followed. For seconds, he lay lethargically, then came a second urge for flight. Once more the tiny ship writhed with effort, but no upward movement resulted.

This time the automaton had the slow thought: "Something must have fallen across the ship, and is holding it down... Have to go out and remove it..."

He squirmed against the metal and padding that encased him. Sweat poured down his cheeks, but presently he stood free in ankle deep dust. As he had been trained to do on such occasions, he checked his equipment... weapons, tools, gas mask—

He flung himself flat on the ground as a great, dark ship swooped down out of the sky, and settled to the ground several hundred yards away. From his prone position, the automaton watched it, but there was no sign of movement now. Puzzled, the automaton climbed to his feet. He recalled that one of the men on the radio had said a *Vulture* had been called.

So they had been playing a trick on him, pretending to go away. Clearly visible on the ship's hull was the name: *Vulture 121*.

Its appearance seemed to suggest that an attack was to be made. His strong, determined mouth tightened. They'd soon learn it didn't pay to meddle with a Tobor slave.

Die for Tobor, mighty Tobor...

Tensely, the young woman watched as her pilot lowered the high-speed plane toward the leveled ruin of the city where the *Vulture* lay. The big ship was unmistakable. It towered above the highest remnant of shattered wall. It was a black bulk against the gray-dark sameness of the rubble.

There was a bump and she was out of the machine, clutching her bag. Twice, her right ankle twisted cruelly as she raced over the uneven ground. Breathlessly, she ran up the narrow gangplank.

A steel door clicked open. As she hurried inside, she glanced behind her. The door clanged shut; and she realized gratefully that she was safe.

She stopped, as her eyes had to accustom themselves to the dim metal room. After a moment she saw a little group of men. One of them, a small individual with glasses and a thin face, stepped forward. He took the suitcase from her with one hand, and with the other, he grabbed her hand, and shook it warmly.

"Good girl!" he said. "That was well and swiftly run, Miss Harding. I'm sure no spying ship of the robots could have identified you in any way during the half-minute you were exposed. Oh, pardon me."

He smiled. "I shouldn't be calling them robots, should I? They've reversed all that, haven't they? Tobors is their name. It does have more rhythm and should be psychologically more satisfying to them. There now, you've caught your breath. By the way, I'm Doctor Claremeyer."

"Doctor," Juanita Harding managed to say, "are you sure it's *he?*"

"Definitely, your fiance, John Gregson, chemist extraordinary." . . . It was a younger man who spoke. He stepped forward and took the suitcase from the older man's fingers. "The patrol got the picture by the new process, whereby we tune in on their communicating plates. It was flashed to headquarters, and then transmitted to us."

He paused, and smiled engagingly. "My name is Madden. That's Phillips with the long, gloomy face. The big fellow with the uncombed hair, lurking there in the background like an elephant, is Rice, our field man. And you've already met Doctor Claremeyer."

Rice said gruffly, "We've got a hell of a job here, ma'am, begging your pardon for them rough words."

Miss Harding took off her hat with a brisk sweep of one hand. The shadows retreated from her face into her eyes, but there was a hint of a smile on her lips. "Mr. Rice, I live with a father whose nickname is 'Cyclone' Harding. To him, our everyday language is an enemy which he attacks with all available weapons. Does that answer your apology?"

The big man chuckled. "You win. But let's get down to business. Madden, you've got a brain that thinks in words, tell Miss Harding the situation!"

"Right!" The young man took up the refrain grimly. "We had the good fortune to be in the air near here when the first report came through that an automaton had been brought down alive. As soon as the identification arrived, we asked army headquarters to set up a defense ring of all available planes. They stripped the entire nearby line to help us."

He paused, frowning. "It has had to be very carefully done, because we don't want to give the Tobors any idea of what's going on. Your fiance can't get away; that is certain, I think. And he can't be rescued unless they come out in force of a size that catches us momentarily off guard. Our big problem is to capture him alive."

"And that, of course—" It was Claremeyer, who cut in with a shrug of his shoulders—"may be easy or it may be difficult. Unfortunately, it must be fast. The Tobors will not be unaware long of this concentration of forces, then they will examine his file, analyze at least a part of the true situation, and act.

"The second unfortunate aspect is that in the past we have allowed ourselves a percentage of failures. You must realize that our tactics are almost entirely psychological, based upon fundamental human impulses."

Patiently, he explained the method.

"Ninety-two! . . . This is Sorn speaking."

The voice came sharp, insistent, commanding, from the automaton's wrist radio. The automaton stirred in his concrete shelter. "Yes, Master?"

Apparently, the contact was all that was desired, for he heard the other say, "He's still alive!" The voice was farther away this time, as if the humanoid had turned to speak to someone else.

A second voice spoke hesitatingly, "Normally, I wouldn't have bothered, but this is the one that destroyed his file. Now, a *Vulture* crew is trying to save him."

"They do it every time."

"I know, I know." The second speaker sounded impatient with himself, as if he was aware that he might be acting foolishly. "Still, they've already given a lot of time to him, more than normal, it seems to me. And there is the fact that this particular ship engaged in a lengthy series of code messages with its headquarters. Afterwards, a woman arrived on the scene."

"They nearly always use women in these rescue operations." The Tobor's voice held a note of distaste, but his words were a dismissal of the other's argument.

This time there was silence for many seconds. Finally, the doubting one spoke again, "In my department, I have been acutely conscious that somewhere in our operations about two years ago we unexpectedly captured a human chemist who, it was stated, had discovered a process for sexualizing Tobors."

His emotional disgust was almost too much for him, and in spite of the frankness of his next words, his voice trembled. "Unfortunately, we learned of this too late for us to identify the individual involved. Apparently, he was put through a routine interview, and dementalized."

He had full control of himself again and went on sardonically. "Of course the whole thing could be just a propaganda story, designed to unnerve us. And yet, at the time, our Intelligence reported that an atmosphere of gloom and depression pervaded human headquarters. It appears that we raided a city, captured him in his home, wrecked his laboratory and burned his papers."

His tone implied that he was shrugging. "It was one of scores of similar raids, quite impossible to identify. Prisoners captured in such forays were in no way differentiated from those captured in other ways."

Once more, silence . . . then . . . "Shall I order him to kill himself?"

"Find out if he has a weapon?"

There was a pause. The voice came close, "Have you a blaster, Ninety-two?"

The human automaton, who had listened to the conversation with a faraway blankness in his eyes and mind, alerted as the question was directed at him through his wrist radio.

"I have hand weapons," he said dully.

Once more the interrogator turned away from the distant microphone. "Well?" he said.

"Direct action is too dangerous," said the second Tobor. "You know how they resist actual suicide. Sometimes it brings them right out of their automaton state. The will to live is too basic."

"Then we're right back where we started."

"No! Tell him specifically to defend himself to the death. That's on a different level. That's an appeal to his loyalty, to his indoctrinated hatred of our human enemies and to his patriotism to the Tobor cause."

Lying in the rubble, the automaton nodded as the Master's firm voice issued the commands. Naturally . . . to the death . . . of course.

On the radio, Sorn still sounded dissatisfied. "I think we should force the issue. I think we should concentrate projectors in the area, and see what happens."

"They've always accepted such challenges in the past."

"Up to a point only. I believe most earnestly that we should test their reaction. I feel that this man resisted too hard during his captivity and there's a tremendous pressure working on him."

"Human beings are very deceptive," said the other doubtfully. "Some of them are merely anxious to go home. It seems to be a powerful motivation."

His objection must have been rhetorical. After a bare moment of silence, he looked up and said decisively, "Very well, we'll attack!"

By an hour after dark, a hundred projectors were engaged on both sides. The night flashed with long trailers of bright flame.

"Phew!" Rice raced up the gangplank into the ship. His heavy face was scarlet with effort. As the door clanged shut behind him, he gasped, "Miss Harding, that fiance of yours is a dangerous man. He's trigger happy, and needs more propaganda."

The girl was pale. She had watched Rice's attempt to get the screen into position from the great barrier window in the observation room. She said, "Maybe I should go out now!"

"And get burned!" Doctor Claremeyer came forward. He was blinking behind his glasses. "Now, don't you feel badly, Miss Harding. I know it seems incredible that the man who loves you has been so changed that he would kill you on sight—but you'll just have to accept the reality. The fact that the Tobors have decided to put up a fight for him hasn't helped matters any."

"Those beasts!" she said. It was a dry sob. "What are you going to do now?"

"More propaganda."

"You think he'll hear it over the roar of the projectors?" She was astonished.

"He knows what it is," said Doctor Claremeyer matter-of-factly. "The pattern has been established. Even a single word coming through will be a reminder of the whole pattern."

A few moments later, she was listening gloomily while the loud speakers blared their message:

"... You are a human being. We are human beings. You were captured by the robots. We want to rescue you from the robots. These robots call themselves Tobors because it sounds better. They're robots. They're not human beings, but you are a human being. We are human beings, and we want to rescue you. Do everything that we ask you to do. Do nothing that they tell you to do. We want to make you well. We want to save you. ..."

Abruptly, the ship moved. A moment later, the *Vulture* commander came over.

"I had to give the order to take off," he said. "We'll come back again about dawn. The Tobors must be losing equipment at a terrific rate. It's a bridgehead fight for them, but it's getting too hot for us also."

He must have felt the girl would place the worst construction on the withdrawal order. He explained to her in a low voice:

"We can depend on a slave using every precaution to stay alive. He'll have been given training for that. Besides, we did get the screen up and the picture will show over and over."

He went on, before she could speak, "Besides, we have been given permission to try direct contact with him."

"What does that mean?"

"We'll use a weak signal that won't carry more than a few hundred yards. That way they won't be able to tune in on what we're saying. Our hope is that he'll be sufficiently stimulated to tell us his secret formula."

Juanita Harding sat for a long time, frowning. Her comment, when it finally came, was extremely feminine. "I'm not sure," she said, "that I approve of the pictures you're showing on that screen."

The commander said judiciously, "We've got to strike at the basic drives of human beings."

He departed hastily.

John Gregson, who had been an automaton, became aware that he was clawing at a bright screen. As he grew more conscious of his actions, he slowed his frantic attempt to grasp at the elusive shapes that had lured him out of hiding. He stepped back.

All around him was intense darkness. As he backed away a little further, he stumbled over a twisted girder. He started to fall, but saved himself by grasping at the burned and rusted metal. It creaked a little from his weight and flakes of metal came away free in his hands.

He retreated anxiously into the darkness to take better advantage of the light reflections. For the first time he recognized that he was in one of the destroyed cities. He thought: "But how did I get here? What's happened to me?"

A voice from his wrist radio made him jump. "Sorn!" it said insistently. The icy tone stiffened Gregson. Deep in his mind a bell of recognition clanged its first warning. He was about to reply, when he realized that it was not he who had been addressed.

"Yes?" The answer was clear enough, but it seemed to come from a much greater distance.

"Where are you now?"

Sorn said slowly, "I landed about half a mile from the screen. It was a misjudgment, as I intended to come down much closer. Unfortunately, in landing I got my directions twisted. I can't see a thing."

"The screen they're using for the pictures is still up. I can see a reflection of it in Ninety-two's Wristo. Surely, it'll be a bright landmark."

"It must be in a hollow, or behind a pile of debris. I'm in pitch darkness. Contact Ninety-two and—"

The first reference to his *number* had started the train of associations. The second one brought such a flood of hideous memory that Gregson cringed. In a flashing kaleidoscope of pictures, he realized his situation and tried to recall the immediate sequence of events that had brought him back to control of himself. Somebody had called his name insistently. . . . not his number—his name. Each time they had asked him a question, something about a formula for— For what? He couldn't remember, something about—about— Abruptly, it came back!

Crouching there in the darkness, he closed his eyes in a sheer physical reaction. "I gave it to them. I told them the formula. But who was—them?"

It could only have been some member of the crew of a *Vulture* ship, he told himself shakily. The Tobors didn't know his name. To them he was . . . Ninety-two.

That recollection brought him back with a start to his own predicament. He was just in time to hear the voice on the Wristo say vindictively:

"All right, I've got it. I'll be over there in ten minutes."

The Tobor in the distant Control Center was impersonal. "This is on your own head, Sorn. You seem to have an obsession about this case."

"They were broadcasting to him on a local wave," said Sorn in a dark voice, "so direct, so close that we couldn't catch what they were saying. And his answer, when he finally made it, was interfered with so that, again, we didn't hear it, but it was a formula of some kind. I'm counting on the possibility that he was not able to give them the full description. Since he's still at the screen, he hasn't been rescued, so if I can kill him now, within minutes—"

There was a click... the voice trailed off into silence. Gregson stood in the darkness beside the screen, and shudderingly considered his position.

Where was the *Vulture?* The sky was pitch dark, though there was an ever-so-faint light in the East, the first herald of the coming dawn. The sound of the projectors had become a mutter far away, no longer threatening. The great battle of the night was over.

... The battle of the individuals was about to begin....

Gregson retreated even farther into the darkness, and fumbled over his body for hand weapons. There were none. "But that's ridiculous," he told himself shakily. "I had a blaster and—"

He stopped the thought. Once again, desperate now, he searched himself... Nothing. He guessed that in his mad scramble to get to the screen, he had lost his weapons.

He was still teetering indecisively when he heard a movement in the near night.

Vulture 121 landed gently in the intense darkness of the false dawn. Juanita Harding had taken off her clothes, and now had a robe wrapped around her. She did not hesitate when Rice beckoned. He grinned at her reassuringly.

"I'm taking along a cylinder of the stuff," he said, "just in case he doesn't become inspired quickly enough."

She smiled wanly, but said nothing. Doctor Claremeyer came to the door with them. He gave her hand a quick squeeze.

"Remember," he said, "this is war!"

She replied, "I know. And all's fair in love and war, isn't it?"

"Now, you're talking."

A moment later they were gone into the night.

Gregson was retreating in earnest and he felt a lot better. It was going to be hard for any one person to locate him in this vast maze of shattered concrete and marble and metal.

Moment by moment, however, the desolate horizon grew lighter. He saw the ship suddenly in the shadowy ruins to his right. Its shape was unmistakable. *Vulture!* Gregson raced toward it over the uneven ruins of what had once been a paved street.

Gasping with relief, he saw that the gangplank was down. As he raced up it, two men covered him with their blasters. Abruptly, one of them gasped, "It's Gregson!"

Weapons were scraped back into their leathery holsters. Hands grasped eagerly at his hands, and there was a pumping of arms. Eyes searched his face eagerly for signs of sanity, found them, and glowed with pleasure. A thousand words attacked the dawn air.

"We got your formula."

"Great... wonderful."

"The genius made up some of the hormone gas in our own ship lab. How fast does it work?"

Gregson guessed that the "genius" was the tall, gloomy individual who had been introduced as Phillips. He said, "It takes only a few seconds. After all, you breathe it in and it's taken right into your bloodstream. It's pretty powerful stuff."

Madden said, "We had some idea of using it to intensify your own reactions. In fact, Rice took some—" He stopped. "But just a minute," he said, "Rice and Miss Harding are—" He stopped again.

It was the small man, Doctor Claremeyer, who took up the thread of Madden's thought. "Mr. Gregson," he said, "we saw a man on our infra-red plates heading for the screen. He was too far away to identify, so we took it for granted it was you. And so, Rice and Miss Harding went out and—"

The Commander cut him off at that point. "Quick, let's get out there! It may be a trap!"

Gregson scarcely heard that. He was already racing down the gangplank.

"Sorn!" the voice on the Wristo sounded impatient. "Sorn, what's happened to you?"

In the half-darkness near the screen, the men and the girl listened to the words of the Tobor on Gregson's Wristo. From their vantage point they watched Sorn looking at the pictures on the screen itself.

"Sorn, your last report was that you were near where Ninety-two was last known to be hiding—"

Rice put one plump hand over Gregson's Wristo, to block off the sound; and whispered, "That's when I let him have it. Boy, I never had a better idea than when I took along a cylinder of your gas, Gregson. I shot a dose of it at him from fifty feet, and he never even knew what hit him."

"—Sorn, I know you're still alive. I can hear you mumbling to yourself."

Rice said, "We'll have to be careful of our dosage in the future. He's practically ready to eat up the pictures. You can see for yourself —the Tobor-human war is as good as over."

Gregson watched silently as the one-time Tobor leader scrambled eagerly in front of the screen. A dozen girls were on parade beside a pool. Periodically, they would all dive into the water. There would be a flash of long, bare limbs, the glint of a tanned back, then they would all climb out. They did that over and over.

The trouble was, each time Sorn tried to grasp one of the images, his shadow fell across the screen and blotted her out. Frustrated, he rushed to another, only to have the same thing happen again.

"Sorn, answer me!"

This time the Tobor paused. The reply he made then must have shocked the entire Tobor headquarters, and the effect reached out to all the Tobor armies around the world.

Gregson tightened his arm appreciatively around Juanita's waist (she still wore her robe over the beauty with which she was to have lured him back to safety) as he listened to the fateful words.

"Women," Sorn was saying, "they're wonderful!"

Report on the
Barnhouse Effect

Kurt Vonnegut, Jr.

Let me begin by saying that I don't know any more about where Professor Arthur Barnhouse is hiding than anyone else does. Save for one short, enigmatic message left in my mailbox on Christmas Eve, I have not heard from him since his disappearance a year and a half ago.

What's more, readers of this article will be disappointed if they expect to learn how *they* can bring about the so-called "Barnhouse Effect." If I were able and willing to give away that secret, I would certainly be something more important than a psychology instructor.

I have been urged to write this report because I did research under the professor's direction and because I was the first to learn of his astonishing discovery. But while I was his student I was never entrusted with knowledge of how the mental forces could be released and directed. He was unwilling to trust anyone with that information.

I would like to point out that the term "Barnhouse Effect" is a creation of the popular press, and was never used by Professor Barnhouse. The name he chose for the phenomenon was "dynamopsychism," or *force of the mind.*

I cannot believe that there is a civilized person yet to be convinced that such a force exists, what with its destructive effects on display in every national capital. I think humanity has always had an inkling that this sort of force does exist. It has been common knowledge that some people are luckier than others with inanimate objects like dice. What Professor Barnhouse did was to show that such "luck" was a measurable force, which in his case could be enormous.

By my calculations, the professor was about fifty-five times more powerful than a Nagasaki-type atomic bomb at the time he went into hiding. He was not bluffing when, on the eve of "Operation

Brainstorm," he told General Honus Barker: "Sitting here at the dinner table, I'm pretty sure I can flatten anything on earth—from Joe Louis to the Great Wall of China."

There is an understandable tendency to look upon Professor Barnhouse as a supernatural visitation. The First Church of Barnhouse in Los Angeles has a congregation numbering in the thousands. He is godlike in neither appearance nor intellect. The man who disarms the world is single, shorter than the average American male, stout, and averse to exercise. His I.Q. is 143, which is good but certainly not sensational. He is quite mortal, about to celebrate his fortieth birthday, and in good health. If he is alone now, the isolation won't bother him too much. He was quiet and shy when I knew him, and seemed to find more companionship in books and music than in his associations at the college.

Neither he nor his powers fall outside the sphere of Nature. His dynamopsychic radiations are subject to many known physical laws that apply in the field of radio. Hardly a person has not now heard the snarl of "Barnhouse static" on his home receiver. The radiations are affected by sunspots and variations in the ionosphere.

However, they differ from ordinary broadcast waves in several important ways. Their total energy can be brought to bear on any single point the professor chooses, and that energy is undiminished by distance. As a weapon, then, dynamopsychism has an impressive advantage over bacteria and atomic bombs, beyond the fact that it costs nothing to use: it enables the professor to single out critical individuals and objects instead of slaughtering whole populations in the process of maintaining international equilibrium.

As General Honus Barker told the House Military Affairs Committee: "Until someone finds Barnhouse, there is no defense against the Barnhouse Effect." Efforts to "jam" or block the radiations have failed. Premier Slezak could have saved himself the fantastic expense of his "Barnhouse-proof" shelter. Despite the shelter's twelve-foot-thick lead armor, the premier has been floored twice while in it.

There is talk of screening the population for men potentially as powerful dynamopsychically as the professor. Senator Warren Foust demanded funds for this purpose last month, with the passionate declaration: "He who rules the Barnhouse Effect rules the world!" Commissar Kropotnik said much the same thing, so another costly armaments race, with a new twist, has begun.

This race at least has its comical aspects. The world's best gamblers are being coddled by governments like so many nuclear physicists. There may be several hundred persons with dynamopsychic talent on earth, myself included. But, without knowledge of the professor's technique, they can never be anything but dice-table despots. With the secret, it would probably take them ten years to become dangerous weapons. It took the professor that long. He who rules the Barnhouse Effect is Barnhouse and will be for some time.

Popularly, the "Age of Barnhouse" is said to have begun a year and a half ago, on the day of Operation Brainstorm. That was when dynamopsychism became significant politically. Actually, the phenomenon was discovered in May, 1942, shortly after the professor turned down a direct commission in the Army and enlisted as an artillery private. Like X-rays and vulcanized rubber, dynamopsychism was discovered by accident.

From time to time Private Barnhouse was invited to take part in games of chance by his barrack mates. He knew nothing about the games, and usually begged off. But one evening, out of social grace, he agreed to shoot craps. It was terrible or wonderful that he played, depending upon whether or not you like the world as it now is.

"Shoot sevens, Pop," someone said.

So "Pop" shot sevens—ten in a row to bankrupt the barracks. He retired to his bunk and, as a mathematical exercise, calculated the odds against his feat on the back of a laundry slip. His chances of doing it, he found, were one in almost ten million! Bewildered, he borrowed a pair of dice from the man in the bunk next to his. He tried to roll sevens again, but got only the usual assortment of numbers. He lay back for a moment, then resumed his toying with the dice. He rolled ten more sevens in a row.

He might have dismissed the phenomenon with a low whistle. But the professor instead mulled over the circumstances surrounding his two lucky streaks. There was one single factor in common: on both occasions, *the same thought train had flashed through his mind just before he threw the dice.* It was that thought train which aligned the professor's brain cells into what has since become the most powerful weapon on earth.

The soldier in the next bunk gave dynamopsychism its first token of respect. In an understatement certain to bring wry smiles to the faces of the world's dejected demagogues, the soldier said, "You're hotter'n a two-dollar pistol, Pop." Professor Barnhouse was all of that. The dice that did his bidding weighed but a few grams, so the forces involved were minute; but the unmistakable fact that there were such forces was earth-shaking.

Professional caution kept him from revealing his discovery immediately. He wanted more facts and a body of theory to go with them. Later, when the atomic bomb was dropped in Hiroshima, it was fear that made him hold his peace. At no time were his experiments, as Premier Slezak called them, "a bourgeois plot to shackle the true democracies of the world." The professor didn't know where they were leading.

In time, he came to recognize another startling feature of dynamopsychism: *its strength increased with use.* Within six months, he was able to govern dice thrown by men the length of a barracks distant. By the time of his discharge in 1945, he could knock bricks loose from chimneys three miles away.

Charges that Professor Barnhouse could have won the last war in a minute, but did not care to do so, are perfectly senseless. When the war ended, he had the range and power of a 37-millimeter cannon, perhaps—certainly no more. His dynamopsychic powers graduated from the small-arms class only after his discharge and return to Wyandotte College.

I enrolled in the Wyandotte Graduate School two years after the professor had rejoined the faculty. By chance, he was assigned as my thesis adviser. I was unhappy about the assignment, for the professor was, in the eyes of both colleagues and students, a somewhat ridiculous figure. He missed classes or had lapses of memory during lectures. When I arrived, in fact, his shortcomings had passed from the ridiculous to the intolerable.

"We're assigning you to Barnhouse as a sort of temporary thing," the dean of social studies told me. He looked apologetic and perplexed. "Brilliant man, Barnhouse, I guess. Difficult to know since his return, perhaps, but his work before the war brought a great deal of credit to our little school."

When I reported to the professor's laboratory for the first time, what I saw was more distressing than the gossip. Every surface in the room was covered with dust; books and apparatus had not been disturbed for months. The professor sat napping at his desk when I entered. The only signs of recent activity were three overflowing ashtrays, a pair of scissors, and a morning paper with several items clipped from its front page.

As he raised his head to look at me, I saw that his eyes were clouded with fatigue. "Hi," he said, "just can't seem to get my sleeping done at night." He lighted a cigarette, his hands trembling slightly. "You the young man I'm supposed to help with a thesis?"

"Yes, sir," I said. In minutes he converted my misgivings to alarm.

"You an overseas veteran?" he asked.

"Yes, sir."

"Not much left over there, is there?" He frowned. "Enjoy the last war?"

"No, sir."

"Look like another war to you?"

"Kind of, sir."

"What can be done about it?"

I shrugged. "Looks pretty hopeless."

He peered at me intently. "Know anything about international law, the U.N., and all that?"

"Only what I pick up from the papers."

"Same here," he sighed. He showed me a fat scrapbook packed with newspaper clippings. "Never used to pay any attention to international politics. Now I study them the way I used to study rats in mazes. Everybody tells me the same thing—'Looks hopeless.' "

"Nothing short of a miracle—" I began.

"Believe in magic?" he asked sharply. The professor fished two dice from his vest pocket. "I will try to roll twos," he said. He rolled twos three times in a row. "One chance in about 47,000 of that happening. There's a miracle for you." He beamed for an instant, then brought the interview to an end, remarking that he had a class which had begun ten minutes ago.

He was not quick to take me into his confidence, and he said no more about his trick with the dice. I assumed they were loaded, and forgot about them. He set me the task of watching male rats cross electrified metal strips to get to food or female rats—an experiment that had been done to everyone's satisfaction in the nineteen-thirties. As though the pointlessness of my work were not bad enough, the professor annoyed me further with irrelevant questions. His favorites were: "Think we should have dropped the atomic bomb on Hiroshima?" and "Think every new piece of scientific information is a good thing for humanity?"

However, I did not feel put upon for long. "Give those poor animals a holiday," he said one morning, after I had been with him only a month. "I wish you'd help me look into a more interesting problem—namely, my sanity."

I returned the rats to their cages.

"What you must do is simple," he said, speaking softly. "Watch the inkwell on my desk. If you see nothing happen to it, say so, and I'll go quietly—relieved, I might add—to the nearest sanitarium."

I nodded uncertainly.

He locked the laboratory door and drew the blinds, so that we were in twilight for a moment. "I'm odd, I know," he said. "It's fear of myself that's made me odd."

"I've found you somewhat eccentric, perhaps, but certainly not—"

"If nothing happens to that inkwell, 'crazy as a bedbug' is the only description of me that will do," he interrupted, turning on the overhead lights. His eyes narrowed. "To give you an idea of how crazy, I'll tell you what's been running through my mind when I should have been sleeping. I think maybe I can save the world. I think maybe I can make every nation a *have* nation, and do away with war for good. I think maybe I can clear roads through jungles, irrigate deserts, build dams overnight."

"Yes, sir."

"Watch the inkwell!"

Dutifully and fearfully I watched. A high-pitched humming seemed to come from the inkwell; then it began to vibrate alarmingly, and finally to bound about the top of the desk, making two noisy circuits. It stopped, hummed again, glowed red, then popped in splinters with a blue-green flash.

Perhaps my hair stood on end. The professor laughed gently. "Magnets?" I managed to say at last.

"Wish to heaven it were magnets," he murmured. It was then that he told me of dynamopsychism. He knew only that there was such a force; he could not explain it. "It's me and me alone—and it's awful."

"I'd say it was amazing and wonderful!" I cried.

"If all I could do was make inkwells dance, I'd be tickled silly with the whole business." He shrugged disconsolately. "But I'm no toy, my boy. If you like, we can drive around the neighborhood, and I'll show you what I mean." He told me about pulverized boulders, shattered oaks, and abandoned farm buildings demolished within a fifty-mile radius of the campus. "Did every bit of it sitting right here, just thinking—not even thinking hard."

He scratched his head nervously. "I have never dared to concentrate as hard as I can for fear of the damage I might do. I'm to the point where a mere whim is a block-buster." There was a depressing pause. "Up until a few days ago, I've thought it best to keep my secret for fear of what use it might be put to," he continued. "Now I realize that I haven't any more right to it than a man has a right to own an atomic bomb."

He fumbled through a heap of papers. "This says about all that needs to be said, I think." He handed me a draft of a letter to the Secretary of State.

> Dear Sir:
>
> I have discovered a new force which costs nothing to use, and which is probably more important than atomic energy. I should like to see it used most effectively in the cause of peace, and am, therefore, requesting your advice as to how this might best be done.
>
> Yours truly,
> A. Barnhouse

"I have no idea what will happen next," said the professor.

There followed three months of perpetual nightmare, wherein the nation's political and military great came at all hours to watch the professor's tricks.

We were quartered in an old mansion near Charlottesville, Virginia, to which we had been whisked five days after the letter was mailed. Surrounded by barbed wire and twenty guards, we were labeled "Project Wishing Well," and were classified as Top Secret.

For companionship we had General Honus Barker and the State Department's William K. Cuthrell. For the professor's talk of peace-through-plenty they had indulgent smiles and much discourse on practical measures and realistic thinking. So treated, the professor, who had at first been almost meek, progressed in a matter of weeks toward stubbornness.

He had agreed to reveal the thought train by means of which he aligned his mind into a dynamopsychic transmitter. But, under Cuthrell's and Barker's nagging to do so, he began to hedge. At first he declared that the information could be passed on simply by word of mouth. Later he said that it would have to be written up in a long report. Finally, at dinner one night, just after General Barker had read the secret orders for Operation Brainstorm, the professor announced, "The report may take as long as five years to write." He looked fiercely at the general. "Maybe twenty."

The dismay occasioned by this flat announcement was offset somewhat by the exciting anticipation of Operation Brainstorm. The general was in a holiday mood. "The target ships are on their way to the Caroline Islands at this very moment," he declared ecstatically. "One hundred and twenty of them! At the same time, ten V-2s are being readied for firing in New Mexico, and fifty radio-controlled jet bombers are being equipped for a mock attack on the Aleutians. Just think of it!" Happily he reviewed his orders. "At exactly 1100 hours next Wednesday, I will give you the order to *concentrate;* and you, professor, will think as hard as you can about sinking the target ships, destroying the V-2s before they hit the ground, and knocking down the bombers before they reach the Aleutians! Think you can handle it?"

The professor turned gray and closed his eyes. "As I told you before, my friend, I don't know what I can do." He added bitterly, "As for this Operation Brainstorm, I was never consulted about it, and it strikes me as childish and insanely expensive."

General Barker bridled. "Sir," he said, "your field is psychology, and I wouldn't presume to give you advice in that field. Mine is national defense. I have had thirty years of experience and success, Professor, and I'll ask you not to criticize my judgment."

The professor appealed to Mr. Cuthrell. "Look," he pleaded, "isn't it war and military matters we're all trying to get rid of? Wouldn't it be a whole lot more significant and lots cheaper for me to try moving cloud masses into drought areas, and things like that? I admit I know next to nothing about international politics, but it seems reasonable to suppose that nobody would want to fight wars if there were enough of everything to go around. Mr. Cuthrell, I'd like to try running generators where there isn't any coal or water power, irrigating deserts, and so on. Why, you could figure out what each country needs to make the most of its resources, and I could give it to them without costing American taxpayers a penny."

"Eternal vigilance is the price of freedom," said the general heavily.

Mr. Cuthrell threw the general a look of mild distaste. "Unfortunately, the general is right in his own way," he said. "I wish to heaven the world were ready for ideals like yours, but it simply isn't. We aren't surrounded by brothers, but by enemies. It isn't a lack of food or resources that has us on the brink of war—it's a struggle for power. Who's going to be in charge of the world, our kind of people or theirs?"

The professor nodded in reluctant agreement and arose from the table. "I beg your pardon, gentlemen. You are, after all, better qualified to judge what is best for the country. I'll do whatever you say." He turned to me. "Don't forget to wind the restricted clock and put the confidential cat out," he said gloomily, and ascended the stairs to his bedroom.

For reasons of national security, Operation Brainstorm was carried on without the knowledge of the American citizenry which was paying the bill. The observers, technicians, and military men involved in the activity knew that a test was under way—a test of what, they had no idea. Only thirty-seven key men, myself included, knew what was afoot.

In Virginia, the day for Operation Brainstorm was unseasonably cool. Inside, a log fire crackled in the fireplace, and the flames were reflected in the polished metal cabinets that lined the living room. All that remained of the room's lovely old furniture was a Victorian love seat, set squarely in the center of the floor, facing three television receivers. One long bench had been brought in for the ten of us privileged to watch. The television screens showed, from left to right, the stretch of desert which was the rocket target, the guinea-pig fleet, and a section of the Aleutian sky through which the radio-controlled bomber formation would roar.

Ninety minutes before H-hour the radios announced that the rockets were ready, that the observation ships had backed away to what was thought to be a safe distance, and that the bombers were on their way. The small Virginia audience lined up on the bench in order of rank, smoked a great deal, and said little. Professor Barnhouse was in his bedroom. General Barker bustled about the house like a woman preparing Thanksgiving dinner for twenty.

At ten minutes before H-hour the general came in, shepherding the professor before him. The professor was comfortably attired in sneakers, gray flannels, a blue sweater, and a white shirt open at the neck. The two of them sat side by side on the love seat. The general was rigid and perspiring; the professor was cheerful. He looked at each of the screens, lighted a cigarette and settled back.

"Bombers sighted!" cried the Aleutian observers.

"Rockets away!" barked the New Mexico radio operator.

All of us looked quickly at the big electric clock over the mantel, while the professor, a half-smile on his face, continued to watch the television sets. In hollow tones, the general counted away the seconds remaining. "Five . . . four . . . three . . . two . . . one . . . "Concentrate!"

Professor Barnhouse closed his eyes, pursed his lips, and stroked his temples. He held the position for a minute. The television images were scrambled, and the radio signals were drowned in the din of Barnhouse static. The professor sighed, opened his eyes, and smiled confidently.

"Did you give it everything you had?" asked the general dubiously.

"I was wide open," the professor replied.

The television images pulled themselves together, and mingled cries of amazement came over the radios tuned to the observers. The Aleutian sky was streaked with the smoke trails of bombers screaming down in flames. Simultaneously, there appeared high over the rocket target a cluster of white puffs, followed by faint thunder.

General Barker shook his head happily. "By George!" he crowed, "Well, sir, by George, by George, by George!"

"Look!" shouted the admiral seated next to me. "The fleet—it wasn't touched!"

"The guns seem to be drooping," said Mr. Cuthrell.

We left the bench and clustered about the television sets to examine the damage more closely. What Mr. Cuthrell had said was true. The ships' guns curved downward, their muzzles resting on the steel decks. We in Virginia were making such a hullabaloo that it was impossible to hear the radio reports. We were so engrossed, in fact, that we didn't miss the professor until two short snarls of Barnhouse static shocked us into sudden silence. The radios went dead.

We looked around apprehensively. The professor was gone. A harassed guard threw open the front door from the outside to yell that the professor had escaped. He brandished his pistol in the direction of the gates, which hung open, limp and twisted. In the distance, a speeding government station wagon topped a ridge and dropped from sight into the valley beyond. The air was filled with choking smoke, for every vehicle on the grounds was ablaze. Pursuit was impossible.

"What in God's name got into him?" bellowed the general.

Mr. Cuthrell, who had rushed out onto the front porch, now slouched back into the room, reading a penciled note as he came. He thrust the note into my hands. "The good man left this billet-doux under the door knocker. Perhaps our young friend here will be kind enough to read it to you gentlemen, while I take a restful walk through the woods."

"Gentlemen," I read aloud, "As the first superweapon with a conscience, I am removing myself from your national defense stockpile. Setting a new precedent in the behavior of ordnance, I have humane reasons for going off. A. Barnhouse."

Since that day, of course, the professor has been systematically destroying the world's armaments, until there is now little with which to equip an army other than rocks and sharp sticks. His activities haven't exactly resulted in peace, but have, rather, precipitated a bloodless and entertaining sort of war that might be called the "War of the Tattletales." Every nation is flooded with enemy agents whose sole mission is to locate military equipment, which is promptly wrecked when it is brought to the professor's attention in the press.

Just as every day brings news of more armaments pulverized by dynamopsychism, so has it brought rumors of the professor's whereabouts. During last week alone, three publications carried articles proving variously that he was hiding in an Inca ruin in the Andes, in the sewers of Paris, and in the unexplored lower chambers of Carlsbad Caverns. Knowing the man, I am inclined to regard such hiding places as unnecessarily romantic and uncomfortable. While there are numerous persons eager to kill him, there must be millions who would care for him and hide him. I like to think that he is in the home of such a person.

One thing is certain: at this writing, Professor Barnhouse is not dead. Barnhouse static jammed broadcasts not ten minutes ago. In the eighteen months since his disappearance, he has been reported dead some half-dozen times. Each report has stemmed from the death of an unidentified man resembling the professor, during a period free of the static. The first three reports were followed at once by renewed talk of rearmament and recourse to war. The saber-rattlers have learned how imprudent premature celebrations of the professor's demise can be.

Many a stouthearted patriot has found himself prone in the tangled bunting and timbers of a smashed reviewing stand, seconds after having announced that the arch-tyranny of Barnhouse was at an end. But those who would make war if they could, in every country in the world, wait in sullen silence for what must come—the passing of Professor Barnhouse.

To ask how much longer the professor will live is to ask how much longer we must wait for the blessing of another world war. He is of short-lived stock: his mother lived to be fifty-three, his father to be forty-nine; and the life-spans of his grandparents on both sides were of the same order. He might be expected to live, then, for perhaps fifteen years more, if he can remain hidden from his enemies. When one considers the number and vigor of these enemies, however, fifteen years seems an extraordinary length of time, which might better be revised to fifteen days, hours, or minutes.

The professor knows that he cannot live much longer. I say this because of the message left in my mailbox on Christmas Eve. Unsigned, typewritten on a soiled scrap of paper, the note consisted of ten sentences. The first nine of these, each a bewildering tangle of psychological jargon and references to obscure texts, made no sense to me at first reading. The tenth, unlike the rest, was simply constructed and contained no large words—but its irrational content made it the most puzzling and bizarre sentence of all. I nearly threw the note away, thinking it a colleague's warped notion of a practical joke. For some reason, though, I added it to the clutter on top of my desk, which included, among other mementos, the professor's dice.

It took me several weeks to realize that the message really meant something, that the first nine sentences, when unsnarled, could be taken as instructions. The tenth still told me nothing. It was only last night that I discovered how it fitted in with the rest. The sentence appeared in my thoughts last night, while I was toying absently with the professor's dice.

I promised to have this report on its way to the publishers today. In view of what has happened, I am obliged to break that promise, or release the report incomplete. The delay will not be a long one, for one of the few blessings accorded a bachelor like myself is the ability to move quickly from one abode to another, or from one way of life to another. What property I want to take with me can be packed in a few hours. Fortunately, I am not without substantial private means, which may take as long as a week to realize in liquid and anonymous form. When this is done, I shall mail the report.

I have just returned from a visit to my doctor, who tells me my health is excellent. I am young, and, with any luck at all, I shall live to a ripe old age indeed, for my family on both sides is noted for longevity.

Briefly, I propose to vanish.

Sooner or later, Professor Barnhouse must die. But long before then I shall be ready. So, to the saber-rattlers of today—and even, I hope, of tomorrow—I say: Be advised. Barnhouse will die. But not the Barnhouse Effect.

Last night, I tried once more to follow the oblique instructions on the scrap of paper. I took the professor's dice, and then, with the last nightmarish sentence flitting through my mind, I rolled fifty consecutive sevens.

Good-by.

The Chronic Argonauts

H. G. Wells

The Story from an Esoteric Point of View

Being the Account of Dr Nebogipfel's sojourn in Llyddwdd

About half-a-mile outside the village of Llyddwdd by the road
that goes up over the eastern flank of the mountain called Pen-y-pwll
to Rwstog is a large farm-building known as the Manse. It derives
this title from the fact that it was at one time the residence of the
minister of the Calvinistic Methodists. It is a quaint, low, irregular
erection, lying back some hundred yards from the roadway, and
now fast passing into a ruinous state.

Since its construction in the latter half of the last century this
house has undergone many changes of fortune, having been abandoned long since by the farmer of the surrounding acres for less
pretentious and more commodious headquarters. Among others
Miss Carnot, 'the Gallic Sappho' at one time made it her home,
and later on an old man named Williams became its occupier. The
foul murder of this tenant by his two sons was the cause of its
remaining for some considerable period uninhabited; with the
inevitable consequence of its undergoing very extensive dilapida-
tion.

The house had got a bad name, and adolescent man and Nature
combined to bring swift desolation upon it. The fear of the Williamses which kept the Llyddwdd lads from gratifying their propen-
sity to invade its deserted interior, manifested itself in unusually
destructive resentment against its external breakables. The missiles
with which they at once confessed and defied their spiritual dread,
left scarcely a splinter of glass, and only battered relics of the old-
fashioned leaden frames, in its narrow windows; while numberless
shattered tiles about the house, and four or five black apertures
yawning behind naked rafters in the roof, also witnessed vividly
to the energy of their trajection. Rain and wind thus had free way

to enter the empty rooms and work their will there, old Time aiding and abetting. Alternately soaked and desiccated, the planks of flooring and wainscot warped apart strangely, split here and there, and tore themselves away in paroxysms of rheumatic pain from the rust-devoured nails that had once held them firm. The plaster of walls and ceiling, growing green-black with a rain-fed crust of lowly life, parted slowly from the fermenting laths; and large fragments thereof falling down inexplicably in tranquil hours, with loud concussion and clatter, gave strength to the popular superstition that old Williams and his sons were fated to re-enact their fearful tragedy until the final judgment. White roses and daedal creepers, that Miss Carnot had first adorned the walls with, spread now luxuriantly over the lichen-filmed tiles of the roof, and in slender graceful sprays timidly invaded the ghostly cobweb-draped apartments. Fungi, sickly pale, began to displace and uplift the bricks in the cellar floor; while on the rotting wood everywhere they clustered, in all the glory of purple and mottled crimson, yellow-brown and hepatite. Wood-lice and ants, beetles and moths, winged and creeping things innumerable, found each day a more congenial home among the ruins; and after them in ever-increasing multitudes swarmed the blotchy toads. Swallows and martins built every year more thickly in the silent, airy, upper chambers. Bats and owls struggled for the crepuscular corners of the lower rooms. Thus, in the Spring of the year eighteen hundred and eighty-seven, was Nature taking over, gradually but certainly, the tenancy of the old Manse. 'The house was falling into decay,' as men who do not appreciate the application of human derelicts to other beings' use would say, 'surely and swiftly.' But it was destined nevertheless to shelter another human tenant before its final dissolution.

There was no intelligence of the advent of a new inhabitant in quiet Llyddwdd. He came without a solitary premonition out of the vast unknown into the sphere of minute village observation and gossip. He fell into the Llyddwdd world, as it were, like a thunderbolt falling in the daytime. Suddenly, and out of nothingness, he *was*. Rumour, indeed, vaguely averred that he was seen to arrive by a certain train from London, and to walk straight without hesitation to the old Manse, giving neither explanatory word nor sign to mortal as to his purpose there: but then the same fertile source of information also hinted that he was first beheld skimming down the slopes of steep Pen-y-pwll with exceeding swiftness, riding, as it appeared to the intelligent observer, upon an instrument not unlike a sieve and that he entered the house by the chimney. Of these conflicting reports, the former was the first to be generally circulated, but the latter, in view of the bizarre presence and eccentric ways of the newest inhabitant, obtained wider credence. By whatever means he arrived, there can be no doubt that he was in, and in possession of the Manse, on the first of May; because on the morning of that day he was inspected by Mrs Morgan ap Lloyd Jones, and subsequently by the numerous persons her report brought up the mountain slope, engaged in the curious occupation of nailing sheet-tin across the void window sockets of his new domicile—'blinding his house,' as Mrs Morgan ap Lloyd Jones not inaptly termed it.

He was a small-bodied, sallow faced little man, clad in a close-fitting garment of some stiff, dark material, which Mr Parry Davies, the Llyddwdd shoemaker, opined was leather. His aquiline nose, thin lips, high cheek-ridges, and pointed chin, were all small and mutually well proportioned; but the bones and muscles of his face were rendered excessively prominent and distinct by his extreme leanness. The same cause contributed to the sunken appearance of the large eager-looking grey eyes, that gazed forth from under his phenomenally wide and high forehead. It was this latter feature that most powerfully attracted the attention of an observer. It seemed to be great beyond all preconceived ratio to the rest of his counte-nance. Dimensions, corrugations, wrinkles, venation, were alike abnormally exaggerated. Below it his eyes glowed like lights in some cave at a cliff's foot. It so over-powered and suppressed the rest of his face as to give an *unhuman* appearance almost, to what would otherwise have been an unquestionably handsome profile. The lank black hair that hung unkempt before his eyes served to increase rather than conceal this effect, by adding to unnatural altitude a suggestion of hydrocephalic projection: and the idea of something ultra human was furthermore accentuated by the temporal arteries that pulsated visibly through his transparent yellow skin. No won-der, in view even of these things, that among the highly and over-poetical Cymric of Llyddwdd the sieve theory of arrival found con-siderable favour.

It was his bearing and actions, however, much more than his personality, that won over believers to the warlock notion of matters. In almost every circumstance of life the observant villagers soon found his ways were not only not *their* ways, but altogether inexplicable upon any theory of motives they could conceive. Thus, in a small matter at the beginning, when Arthur Price Williams, eminent and famous in every tavern in Caernarvonshire for his social gifts, endeavoured, in choicest Welsh and even choicer English, to inveigle the stranger into conversation over the sheet-tin perfor-mance, he failed utterly. Inquisitional supposition, straightforward enquiry, offer of assistance, suggestion of method, sarcasm, irony, abuse, and at last, gage of battle, though shouted with much effort from the road hedge, went unanswered and apparently unheard. Missile weapons, Arthur Price Williams found, were equally unavail-ing for the purpose of introduction, and the gathered crowd dispersed with unappeased curiosity and suspicion. Later in the day, the swarth apparition was seen striding down the mountain road towards the village, hatless, and with such swift width of step and set resolution of countenance, that Arthur Price Williams, beholding him from afar from the 'Pig and Whistle' doorway was seized with dire consternation, and hid behind the Dutch oven in the kitchen till he was past. Wild panic also smote the school-house as the children were coming out, and drove them indoors like leaves before a gale. He was merely seeking the provision shop, however, and erupted thencefrom after a prolonged stay, loaded with a various armful of blue parcels, a loaf, herrings, pigs' trotters, salt pork, and a black bottle, with which he returned in the same swift projectile gait to the Manse. His way of shopping was to name, and to name simply, without solitary other word of explanation, civility or request, the article he required.

The shopkeeper's crude meteorological superstitions and inquisitive commonplaces, he seemed not to hear, and he might have been esteemed deaf if he had not evinced the promptest attention to the faintest relevant remark. Consequently it was speedily rumoured that he was determined to avoid all but the most necessary human intercourse. He lived altogether mysteriously, in the decaying Manse, without mortal service or companionship, presumably sleeping on planks or litter, and either preparing his own food or eating it raw. This, coupled with the popular conception of the haunting patricides, did much to strengthen the popular supposition of some vast gulf between the newcomer and common humanity. The only thing that was inharmonious with this idea of severance from mankind was a constant flux of crates filled with grotesquely contorted glassware, cases of brazen and steel instruments, huge coils of wire, vast iron and fire-clay implements, of inconceivable purpose, jars and phials labelled in black and scarlet—POISON, huge packages of books, and gargantuan rolls of cartridge paper, which set in towards his Llyddwdd quarters from the outer world. The apparently hieroglyphic inscriptions on these various consignments revealed at the profound scrutiny of Pugh Jones that the style and title of the new inhabitant was Dr Moses Nebogipfel, Ph.D., F.R.S., N.W.R., PAID: at which discovery much edification was felt, especially among the purely Welsh-speaking community. Further than this, these arrivals, by their evident unfitness for any allowable mortal use, and inferential diabolicalness, filled the neighbourhood with a vague horror and lively curiosity, which were greatly augmented by the extraordinary phenomena, and still more extraordinary accounts thereof, that followed their reception in the Manse.

The first of these was on Wednesday, the fifteenth of May, when the Calvinistic Methodists of Llyddwdd had their annual commemoration festival; on which occasion, in accordance with custom, dwellers in the surrounding parishes of Rwstog, Peu-y-garn, Caer-gyllwdd, Llanrdd, and even distant Llanrwst flocked into the village. Popular thanks to Providence were materialized in the usual way, by means of plumb-bread and butter, mixed tea, *terza,* consecrated flirtations, kiss-in-the-ring, rough-and-tumble football, and vituperative political speechmaking. About half-past eight the fun began to tarnish, and the assembly to break up; and by nine numerous couples and occasional groups were wending their way in the darkling along the hilly Llyddwdd and Rwstog road. It was a calm warm night; one of those nights when lamps, gas and heavy sleep seem stupid ingratitude to the Creator. The zenith sky was an ineffable deep lucent blue, and the evening star hung golden in the liquid darkness of the west. In the north-north-west, a faint phosphorescence marked the sunken day. The moon was just rising, pallid and gibbous over the huge haze-dimmed shoulder of Pen-y-pwll. Against the wan eastern sky, from the vague outline of the mountain slope, the Manse stood out black, clear, and solitary. The stillness of the twilight had hushed the myriad murmurs of the day. Only the sounds of footsteps and voices and laughter, that came fitfully rising and falling from the roadway, and an intermittent hammering in the darkened dwelling, broke the silence. Suddenly a strange whizzing, buzzing whirr filled the night air, and a bright flicker glanced across the dim path of the wayfarers. All eyes were turned in astonishment to the old Manse. The house no longer loomed a black featureless block but was filled to overflowing with light. From the gaping holes in the roof, from chinks and fissures amid tiles and brickwork, from every gap which Nature or man had pierced in the crumbling old shell, a blinding blue-white glare was streaming, beside which the rising moon seemed a disc of opaque sulphur. The thin mist of the dewy night had caught the violet glow and hung, unearthly smoke, over the colourless blaze. A strange turmoil and outcrying in the old Manse now began, and grew ever more audible to the clustering spectators, and therewith came clanging loud impacts against the window-guarding tin. Then from the gleaming roof-gaps of the house suddenly vomited forth a wondrous swarm of heteromerous living things—swallows, sparrows, martins, owls, bats, insects in visible multitudes, to hang for many minutes a noisy, gyring, spreading cloud over the black gables and chimneys, . . . and then slowly to thin out and vanish away in the night.

As this tumult died away the throbbing humming that had first arrested attention grew once more in the listener's hearing, until at last it was the only sound in the long stillness. Presently, however, the road gradually awoke again to the beating and shuffling of feet, as the knots of Rwstog people, one by one, turned their blinking eyes from the dazzling whiteness and, pondering deeply, continued their homeward way.

The cultivated reader will have already discerned that this phenomenon, which sowed a whole crop of uncanny thoughts in the minds of these worthy folk, was simply the installation of the electric light in the Manse. Truly, this last vicissitude of the old house was its strangest one. Its revival to mortal life was like the raising of Lazarus. From that hour forth, by night and day, behind the tin-blinded windows, the tamed lightning illuminated every corner of its quickly changing interior. The almost frenzied energy of the lank-haired, leather-clad little Doctor swept away into obscure holes and corners and common destruction, creeper sprays, toad-stools, rose leaves, birds' nests, birds' eggs, cobwebs, and all the coatings and lovingly fanciful trimmings with which that maternal old dotard, Dame Nature, had tricked out the decaying house for its lying in state. The magneto-electric apparatus whirred incessantly amid the vestiges of the wainscoted dining-room, where once the eighteenth century tenant had piously read morning prayer and eaten his Sunday dinner; and in the place of his sacred symbolical sideboard was a nasty heap of coke. The oven of the bakehouse supplied substratum and material for a forge, whose snorting, pant-ing bellows, and intermittent, ruddy, spark-laden blast made the benighted, but Bible-lit Welsh women murmur in liquid Cymric, as they hurried by: 'Whose breath kindleth coals, and out of his mouth is a flame of fire.' For the idea these good people formed of it was that a tame, but occasionally restive, leviathan had been added to the terrors of the haunted house. The constantly increasing accumulation of pieces of machinery, big brass castings, block tin, casks, crates, and packages of innumerable articles, by their demands for space, necessitated the sacrifice of most of the slighter partitions of the house; and the beams and flooring of the upper chambers were also mercilessly sawn away by the tireless scientist in such a way as to convert them into mere shelves and corner brack-ets of the atrial space between cellars and rafters. Some of the sounder planking was utilized in the making of a rude broad table, upon which files and heaps of geometrical diagrams speedily accumulated. The production of these latter seemed to be the object upon which the mind of Dr Nebogipfel was so inflexibly set. All other circumstances of his life were made entirely subsidiary to this one occupation. Strangely complicated traceries of lines they were—plans, elevations, sections by surfaces and solids, that, with the help of logarithmic mechanical apparatus and involved curvi-graphical machines, spread swiftly under his expert hands over yard after yard of paper. Some of these symbolized shapes he despatched to London, and they presently returned, *realized*, in forms of brass and ivory, and nickel and mahogany. Some of them he himself trans-lated into solid models of metal and wood; occasionally casting the metallic ones in moulds of sand, but often laboriously hewing them out of the block for greater precision of dimension. In this second process, among other appliances, he employed a steel circular saw set with diamond powder and made to rotate with extraordinary swiftness, by means of steam and multiplying gear. It was this latter thing, more than all else, that filled Llyddwdd with a sickly loathing of the Doctor as a man of blood and darkness. Often in the silence of midnight—for the newest inhabitant heeded the sun but little in his incessant research—the awakened dwellers around Pen-y-pwll would hear, what was at first a complaining murmur, like the groaning of a wounded man, '*gurr*-urr-urr-URR,' rising by slow gradations in pitch and intensity to the likeness of a voice in a despairing passionate protest, and at last ending abruptly in a sharp piercing shriek that rang in the ears for hours afterwards and begot numberless grewsome dreams.

The mystery of all these unearthly noises and inexplicable phenomena, the Doctor's inhumanly brusque bearing and evident uneasiness when away from his absorbing occupation, his entire and jealous seclusion, and his terrifying behaviour to certain officious intruders, roused popular resentment and curiosity to the highest, and a plot was already on foot to make some sort of popular inquisition (probably accompanied by an experimental ducking) into his proceedings, when the sudden death of the hunchback Hughes in a fit, brought matters to an unexpected crisis. It happened in broad daylight, in the roadway just opposite the Manse. Half a dozen people witnessed it. The unfortunate creature was seen to fall suddenly and roll about on the pathway, struggling violently, as it appeared to the spectators, with some invisible assailant. When assistance reached him he was purple in the face and his blue lips were covered with a glairy foam. He died almost as soon as they laid hands on him.

Owen Thomas, the general practitioner, vainly assured the excited crowd which speedily gathered outside the 'Pig and Whistle,' whither the body had been carried, that death was unquestionably natural. A horrible zymotic suspicion had gone forth that deceased was the victim of Dr Nebogipfel's imputed aerial powers. The contagion was with the news that passed like a flash through the village and set all Llyddwdd seething with a fierce desire for action against the worker of this iniquity. Downright superstition, which had previously walked somewhat modestly about the village, in the fear of ridicule and the Doctor, now appeared boldly before the sight of all men, clad in the terrible majesty of truth. People who had hitherto kept entire silence as to their fears of the imp-like philosopher suddenly discovered a fearsome pleasure in whispering dread possibilities to kindred souls, and from whispers of possibilities their sympathy-fostered utterances soon developed into unhesitating asseverations in loud and even high-pitched tones. The fancy of a captive leviathan, already alluded to, which had up to now been the horrid but secret joy of a certain conclave of ignorant old women, was published to all the world as indisputable fact; it being stated, on her own authority, that the animal had, on one occasion, chased Mrs Morgan ap Lloyd Jones almost into Rwstog. The story that Nebogipfel had been heard within the Manse chanting, in conjunction with the Williamses, horrible blasphemy, and that a 'black flapping thing, of the size of a young calf,' had thereupon entered the gap in the roof, was universally believed in. A grisly anecdote, that owed its origination to a stumble in the churchyard, was circulated, to the effect that the Doctor had been caught ghoulishly tearing with his long white fingers at a new-made grave. The numerously attested declaration that Nebogipfel and the murdered Williams had been seen hanging the sons on a ghostly gibbet, at the back of the house, was due to the electric illumination of a fitfully wind-shaken tree. A hundred like stories hurtled thickly about the village and darkened the moral atmosphere. The Reverend Elijah Ulysses Cook, hearing of the tumult, sallied forth to allay it, and narrowly escaped drawing on himself the gathering lightning.

By eight o'clock (it was Monday the twenty-second of July) a grand demonstration had organized itself against the 'necromancer.' A number of bolder hearts among the men formed the nucleus of the gathering, and at nightfall Arthur Price Williams, John Peters, and others brought torches and raised their spark-raining flames aloft with curt ominous suggestions. The less adventurous village manhood came straggling late to the rendezvous, and with them the married women came in groups of four or five, greatly increasing the excitement of the assembly with their shrill hysterical talk and active imaginations. After these the children and young girls, overcome by undefinable dread, crept quietly out of the too silent and shadowy houses into the yellow glare of the pine knots, and the tumultuary noise of the thickening people. By nine, nearly half the Llyddwdd population was massed before the 'Pig and Whistle.' There was a confused murmur of many tongues, but above all the stir and chatter of the growing crowd could be heard the coarse, cracked voice of the blood-thirsty old fanatic, Pritchard, drawing a congenial lesson from the fate of the four hundred and fifty idolators of Carmel.

Just as the church clock was beating out the hour, an occultly originated movement up hill began, and soon the whole assembly, men, women, and children, was moving in a fear-compacted mass, towards the ill-fated Doctor's abode. As they left the brightly-lit public house behind them, a quavering female voice began singing one of those grim-sounding canticles that so satisfy the Calvinistic ear. In a wonderfully short time, the tune had been caught up, first by two or three, and then by the whole procession, and the manifold shuffling of heavy shoon grew swiftly into rhythm with the beats of the hymn. When, however, their goal rose, like a blazing star, over the undulation of the road, the volume of the chanting suddenly died away, leaving only the voices of the ringleaders, shouting indeed now somewhat out of tune, but, if anything, more vigorously than before. Their persistence and example nevertheless failed to prevent a perceptible breaking and slackening of the pace, as the Manse was neared, and when the gate was reached, the whole crowd came to a dead halt. Vague fear for the future had begotten the courage that had brought the villagers thus far: fear for the present now smothered its kindred birth. The intense blaze from the gaps in the death-like silent pile lit up rows of livid, hesitating faces: and a smothered, frightened sobbing broke out among the children. 'Well,' said Arthur Price Williams, addressing Jack Peters, with an expert assumption of modest discipleship, 'what do we do *now*, Jack?' But Peters was regarding the Manse with manifest dubiety, and ignored the question. The Llyddwdd witch-find seemed to be suddenly aborting.

At this juncture old Pritchard suddenly pushed his way forward, gesticulating weirdly with his bony hands and long arms. '*What!*' he shouted, in broken notes, 'fear ye to smite when the Lord hateth? *Burn* the warlock!' And seizing a flambeau from Peters, he flung open the rickety gate and strode on down the drive, his torch leaving a coiling trail of scintillant sparks on the night wind. 'Burn the warlock,' screamed a shrill voice from the wavering crowd, and in a moment the gregarious human instinct had prevailed. With an outburst of incoherent, threatening voice, the mob poured after the fanatic.

Woe betide the Philosopher now! They expected barricaded doors; but with a groan of a conscious insufficiency, the hinge-rusted portals swung wide at the push of Pritchard. Blinded by the light, he hesitated for a second on the threshold, while his followers came crowding up behind him.

Those who were there say that they saw Dr Nebogipfel, standing in the toneless electric glare, on a peculiar erection of brass and ebony and ivory; and that he seemed to be smiling at them, half pityingly and half scornfully, as it is said martyrs are wont to smile. Some assert, moreover, that by his side was sitting a tall man, clad in ravenswing, and some even aver that this second man—whom others deny—bore on his face the likeness of the Reverend Elijah Ulysses Cook, while others declare that he resembled the description of the murdered Williams. Be that as it may, it must now go unproven for ever, for suddenly a wondrous thing smote the crowd as it swarmed in through the entrance. Pritchard pitched headlong on the floor senseless. While shouts and shrieks of anger, changed in mid utterance to yells of agonizing fear, or to the mute gasp of heart-stopping horror: and then a frantic rush was made for the doorway.

For the calm, smiling Doctor, and his quiet, black-clad companion, and the polished platform which upbore them, had vanished before their eyes!

How an Esoteric Story Became Possible

A silvery-foliaged willow by the side of a mere. Out of the cress-spangled waters below, rise clumps of sedge-blades, and among them glows the purple fleur-de-lys, and sapphire vapour of forget-me-nots. Beyond is a sluggish stream of water reflecting the intense blue of the moist Fenland sky; and beyond that a low osier-fringed eyot. This limits all the visible universe, save some scattered pollards and spear-like poplars showing against the violet distance. At the foot of the willow reclines the author watching a copper butterfly fluttering from iris to iris.

Who can fix the colours of the sunset? Who can take a cast of flame? Let him essay to register the mutations of mortal thought as it wanders from a copper butterfly to the disembodied soul, and thence passes to spiritual motions and the vanishing of Dr Moses Nebogipfel and the Rev Elijah Ulysses Cook from the world of sense.

As the author lay basking there and speculating, as another once did under the Budh tree, on mystic transmutations, a presence became apparent. There was a somewhat on the eyot between him and the purple horizon—an opaque reflecting entity, making itself dimly perceptible by reflection in the water to his averted eyes. He raised them in curious surprise.

What was it?

He stared in stupefied astonishment at the apparition, doubted, blinked, rubbed his eyes, stared again, and believed. It was solid, it cast a shadow, and it upbore two men. There was white metal in it that blazed in the noontide sun like incandescent magnesium, ebony bars that drank in the light, and white parts that gleamed like polished ivory. Yet withal it seemed unreal. The thing was not square as a machine ought to be, but all awry: it was twisted and seemed falling over, hanging in two directions, as those queer crystals called triclinic hang; it seemed like a machine that had been crushed or warped; it was suggestive and not confirmatory, like the machine of a disordered dream. The men, too, were dreamlike. One was short, intensely sallow, with a strangely-shaped head, and clad in a garment of dark olive green; the other was, grotesquely out of place, evidently a clergyman of the Established Church, a fair-haired, pale-faced respectable-looking man.

Once more doubt came rushing in on the author. He sprawled back and stared at the sky, rubbed his eyes, stared at the willow wands that hung between him and the blue, closely examined his hands to see if his eyes had any new things to relate about them, and then sat up again and stared at the eyot. A gentle breeze stirred the osiers; a white bird was flapping its way through the lower sky. The machine of the vision had vanished! It was an illusion—a projection of the subjective—an assertion of the immateriality of mind. 'Yes,' interpolated the sceptic faculty, 'but *how comes it that the clergyman is still there?*'

The clergyman had not vanished. In intense perplexity the author examined this black-coated phenomenon as he stood regarding the world with hand-shaded eyes. The author knew the periphery of that eyot by heart, and the question that troubled him was, 'Whence?' The clergyman looked as Frenchmen look when they land at Newhaven—intensely travel-worn; his clothes showed rubbed and seamy in the bright day. When he came to the edge of the island and shouted a question to the author, his voice was broken and trembled. 'Yes,' answered the author, 'it is an island. *How did you get there?*'

But the clergyman, instead of replying to this asked a very strange question.

He said 'Are you in the nineteenth century?' The author made him repeat that question before he replied. 'Thank heaven,' cried the clergyman rapturously. Then he asked very eagerly for the exact date.

'August the ninth, eighteen hundred and eighty-seven,' he repeated after the author. 'Heaven be praised!' and sinking down on the eyot so that the sedges hid him, he audibly burst into tears.

Now the author was mightily surprised at all this, and going a certain distance along the mere, he obtained a punt, and getting into it he hastily poled to the eyot where he had last seen the clergyman. He found him lying insensible among the reeds, and carried him in his punt to the house where he lived, and the clergyman lay there insensible for ten days.

Meanwhile, it became known that he was the Rev Elijah Cook, who had disappeared from Llyddwdd with Dr Moses Nebogipfel three weeks before.

On August 19th, the nurse called the author out of his study to speak to the invalid. He found him perfectly sensible, but his eyes were strangely bright, and his face was deadly pale. 'Have you found out who I am?' he asked.

'You are the Rev Elijah Ulysses Cook, Master of Arts, of Pembroke College, Oxford, and Rector of Llyddwdd, near Rwstog, in Caernarvon.'

He bowed his head. 'Have you been told anything of how I came here?'

'I found you among the reeds,' I said. He was silent and thoughtful for a while. 'I have a deposition to make. Will you take it? It concerns the murder of an old man named Williams, which occurred in 1862, this disappearance of Dr Moses Nebogipfel, the abduction of a ward in the year 4003—'

The author stared.

'The year of our Lord 4003,' he corrected. 'She would come. Also several assaults on public officials in the years 17,901 and 2.'

The author coughed.

'The years 17,901 and 2, and valuable medical, social, and physiographical data for all time.'

After a consultation with the Doctor, it was decided to have the deposition taken down, and this is what constitutes the remainder of the story of the Chronic Argonauts.

On August 29th 1887, the Rev Elijah Cook died. His body was conveyed to Llyddwdd, and buried in the churchyard there.

The Esoteric Story
Based on the Clergyman's Depositions

The Anachronic Man

Incidentally it has been remarked in the first part, how the Reverend Elijah Ulysses Cook attempted and failed to quiet the superstitious excitement of the villagers on the afternoon of the memorable twenty-second of July. His next proceeding was to try and warn the unsocial philosopher of the dangers which impended. With this intent he made his way from the rumour-pelted village, through the silent, slumbrous heat of the July afternoon, up the slopes of Pen-y-pwll, to the old Manse. His loud knocking at the heavy door called forth dull resonance from the interior, and produced a shower of lumps of plaster and fragments of decaying touchwood from the rickety porch, but beyond this the dreamy stillness of the summer mid-day remained unbroken. Everything was so quiet as he stood there expectant, that the occasional speech of the haymakers a mile away in the fields, over towards Rwstog, could be distinctly heard. The reverend gentleman waited long, then knocked again, and waited again, and listened, until the echoes and the patter of rubbish had melted away into the deep silence, and the creeping in the blood-vessels of his ears had become oppressively audible, swelling and sinking with sounds like the confused murmuring of a distant crowd, and causing a suggestion of anxious discomfort to spread slowly over his mind.

Again he knocked, this time loud, quick blows with his stick, and almost immediately afterwards, leaning his hand against the door, he kicked its panels vigorously. There was a shouting of echoes, a protesting jarring of hinges, and then the oaken door yawned and displayed, in the blue blaze of the electric light, vestiges of partitions, piles of planking and straw, masses of metal, heaps of papers and overthrown apparatus, to the rector's astonished eyes.

'Doctor Nebogipfel, excuse my intruding,' he called out, but the only response was a reverberation among the black beams and shadows that hung dimly above. For almost a minute he stood there, leaning forward over the threshold, staring at the glittering mechanisms, diagrams, books, scattered indiscriminately with broken food, packing cases, heaps of coke, hay, and microcosmic lumber, about the undivided house cavity; and then, removing his hat and treading stealthily, as if the silence were a sacred thing, he stepped into the apparently deserted shelter of the Doctor.

His eyes sought everywhere, as he cautiously made his way through the confusion, with a strange anticipation of finding Nebogipfel hidden somewhere in the sharp black shadows among the litter, so strong in him was an indescribable sense of a perceiving presence. This feeling was so vivid that, when, after an abortive exploration, he seated himself upon Nebogipfel's diagram-covered bench, it made him explain in a forced hoarse voice to the stillness —'He is not here. I have something to say to him. I must wait for him.' It was so vivid, too, that the trickling of some grit down the wall in the vacant corner behind him made him start round in a sudden perspiration. There was nothing visible there, but turning his head back, he was stricken rigid with horror by the swift, noiseless apparition of Nebogipfel, ghastly pale, and with red-stained hands, crouching upon a strange-looking metallic platform, and with his deep grey eyes looking intently into the visitor's face.

Cook's first impulse was to yell out his fear, but his throat was paralysed, and he could only stare fascinated at the bizarre countenance that had thus clashed suddenly into visibility. The lips were quivering and the breath came in short convulsive sobs. The unhuman forehead was wet with perspiration, while the veins were swollen, knotted and purple. The Doctor's red hands, too, he noticed, were trembling, as the hands of slight people tremble after intense muscular exertion, and his lips closed and opened as if he, too, had a difficulty in speaking as he gasped, 'Who—what do you do here?'

Cook answered not a word, but stared with hair erect, open mouth, and dilated eyes, at the dark red unmistakable smear that streaked the pure ivory and gleaming nickel and shining ebony of the platform.

'What are you doing here?' repeated the Doctor, raising himself. 'What do you want?'

Cook gave a convulsive effort. 'In Heaven's name, *what* are you?' he gasped; and then black curtains came closing in from every side, sweeping the squatting, dwarfish phantasm that reeled before him into rayless, voiceless night.

The Reverend Elijah Ulysses Cook recovered his perceptions to find himself lying on the floor of the old Manse, and Doctor Nebogipfel, no longer blood-stained and with all trace of his agitation gone, kneeling by his side and bending over him with a glass of brandy in his hand. 'Do not be alarmed, sir,' said the philosopher with a faint smile, as the clergyman opened his eyes. 'I have not treated you to a disembodied spirit, or anything nearly so extraordinary . . . may I offer you this?"

The clergyman submitted quietly to the brandy, and then stared perplexed into Nebogipfel's face, vainly searching his memory for what occurrences had preceded his insensibility. Raising himself at last into a sitting posture, he saw the oblique mass of metals that had appeared with the Doctor, and immediately all that happened flashed back upon his mind. He looked from this structure to the recluse, and from the recluse to the structure.

'There is absolutely no deception, sir,' said Nebogipfel with the slightest trace of mockery in his voice. 'I lay no claim to work in matters spiritual. It is a *bona fide* mechanical contrivance, a thing emphatically of this sordid world. Excuse me—just one minute.' He rose from his knees, stepped upon the mahogany platform, took a curiously curved lever in his hand and pulled it over. Cook rubbed his eyes. *There* certainly was no deception. The Doctor and the machine had vanished.

The reverend gentleman felt no horror this time, only a slight nervous shock, to see the Doctor presently re-appear 'in the twinkling of an eye' and get down from the machine. From that he walked in a straight line with his hands behind his back and his face downcast, until his progress was stopped by the intervention of a circular saw; then, turning round sharply on his heel, he said:

'I was thinking while I was . . . away . . . Would you like to come? I should greatly value a companion.'

The clergyman was still sitting, hatless, on the floor. 'I am afraid,' he said slowly, 'you will think me stupid—'

'Not at all,' interrupted the Doctor. 'The stupidity is mine. You desire to have all this explained . . . wish to know where I am going first. I have spoken so little with men of this age for the last ten years or more that I have ceased to make due allowances and concessions for other minds. I will do my best, but that I fear will be very unsatisfactory. It is a long story . . . do you find that floor comfortable to sit on? If not, there is a nice packing case over there, or some straw behind you, or this bench—the diagrams are done with now, but I am afraid of the drawing pins. You may sit on the Chronic Argo!'

'*No*, thank you,' slowly replied the clergyman, eyeing that deformed structure thus indicated, suspiciously; 'I am *quite* comfortable here.'

'Then I will begin. Do you read fables? Modern ones?'

'I am afraid I must confess to a good deal of fiction,' said the clergyman depreciatingly. 'In Wales the ordained ministers of the sacraments of the Church have perhaps *too* large a share of leisure—

'Have you read the Ugly Duckling?'

'Hans Christian Andersen's—yes—in my childhood.'

'A wonderful story—a story that has even been full of tears and heart swelling hopes for me, since first it came to me in my lonely boyhood and saved me from unspeakable things. That story, if you understand it well, will tell you almost all that you should know of me to comprehend how that machine came to be thought of in a mortal brain . . . Even when I read that simple narrative for the first time, a thousand bitter experiences had begun the teaching of my isolation among the people of my birth—I knew the story was for me. The ugly duckling that proved to be a swan, that lived through all contempt and bitterness, to float at last sublime. From that hour forth, I dreamt of meeting with my kind, dreamt of encountering that sympathy I knew was my profoundest need. Twenty years I lived in that hope, lived and worked, lived and wandered, loved even, and, at last, despaired. Only once among all those millions of wondering, astonished, indifferent, contemptuous, and insidious faces that I met with in that passionate wandering, looked *one* upon me as I desired . . . looked—'

He paused. The Reverend Cook glanced up into his face, expecting some indication of the deep feeling that had sounded in his last words. It was downcast, clouded, and thoughtful, but the mouth was rigidly firm.

'In short, Mr Cook, I discovered that I was one of those superior Cagots called a genius—a man born out of my time—a man thinking the thoughts of a wiser age, doing things and believing things that men now *cannot* understand, and that in the years ordained to me there was nothing but silence and suffering for my soul—unbroken solitude, man's bitterest pain. I knew I was an Anachronic Man; my age was still to come. One filmy hope alone held me to life, a hope to which I clung until it had become a certain thing. Thirty years of unremitting toil and deepest thought among the hidden things of matter and form and life, and then *that*, the Chronic Argo, *the ship that sails through time*, and now I go to join my generation, to journey through the ages till my time has come.'

The Chronic Argo

Dr Nebogipfel paused, looking in sudden doubt at the clergyman's perplexed face. 'You think that sounds mad,' he said, 'to travel through time?'

'It certainly jars with accepted opinions,' said the clergyman, allowing the faintest suggestion of controversy to appear in his intonation, and speaking apparently to the Chronic Argo. Even a clergyman of the Church of England you see can have a suspicion of illusions at times.

'It certainly *does* jar with accepted opinions,' agreed the philosopher cordially. 'It does more than that—it defies accepted opinions to mortal combat. Opinions of all sorts, Mr Cook—Scientific Theories, Laws, Articles of Belief, or, to come to elements, Logical Premises, Ideas, or whatever you like to call them—all are, from the infinite nature of things, so many diagrammatic caricatures of the ineffable—caricatures altogether to be avoided save where they are necessary in the shaping of results—as chalk outlines are necessary to the painter and plans and sections to the engineer. Men, from the exigencies of their being, find this hard to believe.'

The Rev Elijah Ulysses Cook nodded his head with the quiet smile of one whose opponent has unwittingly given a point.

'It is as easy to come to regard ideas as complete reproductions of entities as it is to roll off a log. Hence it is that almost all civilized men believe in the *reality* of the Greek geometrical conceptions.'

'Oh! pardon me, sir,' interrupted Cook. 'Most men know that a geometrical point has no existence in matter, and the same with a geometrical line. I think you underrate...'

'Yes, yes, *those* things are recognized,' said Nebogipfel calmly; 'but now... a cube. Does that exist in the material universe?'

'Certainly.'

'An instantaneous cube?'

'I don't know what you intend by that expression.'

'Without any other sort of extension; a body having length, breadth, and thickness, exists?'

'What other sort of extension *can* there be?' asked Cook, with raised eyebrows.

'Has it never occurred to you that no form can exist in the material universe that has no extension in time?... Has it never glimmered upon your consciousness that nothing stood between men and a geometry of four dimensions—length, breadth, thickness, and *duration*—but the inertia of opinion, the impulse from the Levantine philosophers of the bronze age?'

'Putting it that way,' said the clergyman, 'it does look as though there was a flaw somewhere in the notion of tridimensional being; *but...*' He became silent, leaving that sufficiently eloquent 'but' to convey all the prejudice and distrust that filled his mind.

'When we take up this new light of a fourth dimension and re-examine our physical science in its illumination,' continued Nebogipfel, after a pause, 'we find ourselves no longer limited by hopeless restriction to a certain beat of time—to our own generation. Locomotion along lines of duration—chronic navigation comes within the range, first, of geometrical theory, and then of practical mechanics. There *was* a time when men could only move horizontally and in their appointed country. The clouds floated above them unattainable things, mysterious chariots of those fearful gods who dwelt among the mountain summits. Speaking practically, man in those days was restricted to motion in two dimensions; and even there circumambient ocean and hypoborean fear bound him in. But those times were to pass away. First, the keel of Jason cut its way between the Symplegades, and then in the fulness of time, Columbus dropped anchor in a bay of Atlantis. Then man burst his bidimensional limits, and invaded the third dimension, soaring with Montgolfier into the clouds, and sinking with the diving bell into the purple treasure-caves of the waters. And now another step, and the hidden past and unknown future are before us. We stand upon a mountain summit with the plains of the ages spread below.'

Nebogipfel paused and looked down at his hearer.

The Reverend Elijah Cook was sitting with an expression of strong distrust on his face. Preaching much had brought home certain truths to him very vividly, and he always suspected rhetoric. 'Are those things figures of speech,' he asked; 'or am I to take them as precise statements? Do you speak of travelling through time in the same way as one might speak of Omnipotence making His pathway on the storm, or do you—a—mean what you say?'

Dr Nebogipfel smiled quietly. 'Come and look at these diagrams,' he said, and then with elaborate simplicity he commenced to explain again to the clergyman the new quadridimensional geometry. Insensibly Cook's aversion passed away, and seeming impossibility grew possible, now that such tangible things as diagrams and models could be brought forward in evidence. Presently he found himself asking questions, and his interest grew deeper and deeper as Nebogipfel slowly and with precise clearness unfolded the beautiful order of his strange invention. The moments slipped away unchecked, as the Doctor passed on to the narrative of his research, and it was with a start of surprise that the clergyman noticed the deep blue of the dying twilight through the open doorway.

'The voyage,' said Nebogipfel concluding his history, 'will be full of undreamt-of dangers—already in one brief essay I have stood in the very jaws of death—but it is also full of the divinest promise of undreamt-of joy. Will you come? Will you walk among the people of the Golden Years? . . .'

But the mention of death by the philosopher had brought flooding back to the mind of Cook, all the horrible sensations of the first apparition.

'Dr Nebogipfel . . . one question?' He hesitated. 'On your hands . . . *Was it blood?*'

Nebogipfel's countenance fell. He spoke slowly.

'When I had stopped my machine, I found myself in this room as it used to be. *Hark!*'

'It is the wind in the trees towards Rwstog.'

'It sounded like the voices of a multitude of people singing ... when I had stopped I found myself in this room as it used to be. An old man, a young man, and a lad were sitting at a table—reading some book together. I stood behind them unsuspected. "Evil spirits assailed him," read the old man; "but it is written, 'to him that overcometh shall be given life eternal.' They came as entreating friends, but he endured through all their snares. They came as principalities and powers, but he defied them in the name of the King of Kings. Once even it is told that in his study, while he was translating the New Testament into German, the Evil One himself appeared before him..." Just then the lad glanced timorously round, and with a fearful wail fainted away...'

'The others sprang at me... It was a fearful grapple... The old man clung to my throat, screaming "Man or Devil, I defy thee..." '

'I could not help it. We rolled together on the floor... the knife his trembling son had dropped came to my hand... *Hark!*'

He paused and listened, but Cook remained staring at him in the same horror-stricken attitude he had assumed when the memory of the blood-stained hands had rushed back over his mind.

'Do you hear what they are crying? *Hark!*'

Burn the warlock! Burn the murderer!

'Do you hear? There is no time to be lost.'

Slay the murderer of cripples. Kill the devil's claw!

'Come! Come!'

Cook, with a convulsive effort, made a gesture of repugnance and strode to the doorway. A crowd of black figures roaring towards him in the red torchlight made him recoil. He shut the door and faced Nebogipfel.

The thin lips of the Doctor curled with a contemptuous sneer. 'They will kill you if you stay,' he said; and seizing his unresisting visitor by the wrist, he forced him towards the glittering machine. Cook sat down and covered his face with his hands.

In another moment the door was flung open, and old Pritchard stood blinking on the threshold.

A pause. A hoarse shout changing suddenly into a sharp shrill shriek.

A thunderous roar like the bursting forth of a great fountain of water.

The voyage of the Chronic Argonauts had begun.

End of This Part of the Chronic Argonauts

How did it end? How came it that Cook wept with joy to return once more to this nineteenth century of ours? Why did not Nebogipfel remain with him? All that, and more also, has been written, and will or will never be read, according as Fate may have decreed to the Curious Reader.

Nine-tenths of science fiction is crud. But why
not? Nine-tenths of everything is crud.

THEODORE STURGEON

Including mainstream literature, of course.

ISAAC ASIMOV

AN ESSAY, AN EXPLANATION, AND AN EXCERPT

Isaac Asimov suggests that science fiction is the *only* literature
of ideas—at least relevant ones. Walter Van Tilburg Clark confesses
to "literary borrowing." Arthur Koestler charges, "Nature has let
us down, God seems to have left the receiver off the hook, and
time is running out." Three authors, three works constitute this
section.

These are the three basic approaches to understanding the methods
and intentions of the fantasy-science fiction writer. The history of
science fiction and fantasy is interesting and, certainly, it is a valid
approach to a study of the genre. However, this is by no means
as important as a study of the issues made interesting and important
and understandable by the genre. For a survey of the history of
the fantasy-science fiction field, the following books are invaluable:

> AMIS, KINGSLEY. *New Maps of Hell: A Survey of Science
> Fiction*. New York, 1960.
> BLOOMFIELD, PAUL. *Imaginary Worlds; or, The Evolution
> of Utopia*. London, 1932.
> FRANKLIN, H. BRUCE. *Future Perfect: American Science Fic-
> tion of the Nineteenth Century*. New York, 1966.
> GREEN, ROGER LANCELYN. *Into Other Worlds*. London,
> 1957.
> KNIGHT, DAMON. *In Search of Wonder: Essays on Modern
> Science Fiction*. Rev. ed. Chicago, 1967.
> MOSKOWITZ, SAM. *Explorers of the Infinite: Shapers of Sci-
> ence Fiction*. Cleveland, 1971.
> *Seekers of Tomorrow: Masters of Modern Science Fiction*.
> Cleveland, 1971.

PHILMUS, ROBERT M. *Into the Unknown: The Evolution of Science Fiction from Francis Godwin to H. G. Wells.* Berkeley, 1970.

A study of fantasy-science fiction can be profitably conducted along traditional lines of literary study. However, most teachers and students find a greater value in the generation of ideas, the generation of excitement the literature causes. (See Jack Williamson's survey of college courses and methodology, "Science Fiction Comes to College" in the May, 1971, issue of *Extrapolation,* and Gerald Jonas's "Onward and Upward With the Arts: S. F." in the July 29, 1972, issue of *The New Yorker.*) The short paper, the research paper, the personal essay generated by fantasy-science fiction are exemplified in the following three works. And the authors are unexcelled in their techniques.

After reading these three works, it will be difficult, indeed, to disagree with Pope's dictum, "The proper study of mankind is man." And it will be difficult to argue that fantasy-science fiction is not one of the most fertile fields for that study....

When Aristotle Fails, Try Science Fiction

Isaac Asimov

It is odd to be asked whether science fiction is a literature of ideas. Far from doubting that it is, I would like to suggest that it is the *only* literature of relevant ideas, since it is the only literature that, at its best, is firmly based on scientific thought.

Of the products of the human intellect, the scientific method is unique. This is not because it ought to be considered the only path to Truth; it isn't. In fact, it firmly admits it isn't. It doesn't even pretend to define what Truth (with a capital T) is, or whether the word has meaning. In this it parts company with the self-assured thinkers of various religious, philosophical, and mystical persuasions who have drowned the world in sorrow and blood through the conviction that they and they alone own Truth.

The uniqueness of science comes in this: the scientific method offers a way of determining the False. Science is the only gateway to proven error. There have been Homeric disputes in the history of science, and while it could not be maintained that either party was wholly right or had the key to Truth, it could be shown that the views of at least one were at variance with what seemed to be the facts available to us through observation.

Pasteur maintained alcoholic fermentation to be the product of living cells; Liebig said no. Liebig, in the mid-nineteenth-century context of observation, was proved wrong; his views were abandoned. Newton advanced a brilliantly successful picture of the universe, but it failed in certain apparently minor respects. Einstein advanced another picture that did not fail in those respects. Whether Einstein's view is True is still argued and may be argued for an indefinite time to come, but Newton's view is False. There is no argument about the latter.

Compare this with other fields in which intellectuals amuse themselves. Who has ever proved a school of philosophy to be False?

When has one religion triumphed over another by debate, experiment and observation? What rules of criticism can settle matters in such a way that all critics will agree on a particular work of art or literature?

A man without chemical training can speak learnedly of chemistry, making use of a large vocabulary and a stately oratorical style—and he will be caught out almost at once by any bright teenager who has studied chemistry in high school.

The same man, without training in art, can speak learnedly of art in the same way, and while his ignorance may be evident to some real expert in the field, no one else would venture to dispute him with any real hope of success.

There is an accepted consensus in science and to be a plausible fake in science (before any audience not utterly ignorant in the field) one must learn that consensus thoroughly. Having learned it, however, one has no need to be a plausible fake.

In other fields of intellectual endeavor there is, however, no accepted consensus. The different schools argue endlessly, moving in circles about each other as fad succeeds fashion over the centuries. Though individuals may be unbelievably eloquent and sincere, there is, short of the rack and the stake, no decision ever. Consequently, to be a plausible fake in religion, art, politics, mysticism, or even any of the "soft" sciences such as sociology (to anyone not utterly expert in the field), one need only learn the vocabulary and develop a certain self-assurance.

It is not surprising, then, that so many young intellectuals avoid the study of science and so many old intellectuals are proud of their ignorance of science. Science has a bad habit of puncturing pretension for all to see. Those who value their pretension to intellect and are insecure over it are well advised to avoid science.

To be sure, when a scientist ventures outside his field and pontificates elsewhere, he is as likely to speak nonsense as anyone else. (And there may be those unkind enough to say I am demonstrating this fact in this very article.) However, since nonsense outside science is difficult or impossible to demonstrate, the scientist is at least no worse than anyone else in this respect.

If we consider Literature (with a capital L) as a vehicle of ideas, we can only conclude that, by and large, the ideas with which it is concerned are the same ideas that Homer and Aeschylus struggled with. They are well worth discussing, I am sure; even fun. There is enough there to keep an infinite number of minds busy for an infinite amount of time, but they weren't settled and aren't settled.

It is these "eternal verities" that are precisely what science fiction doesn't deal with. Science fiction deals with change. It deals with the possible advance in science and with the potential changes —even in those damned eternal verities—this may bring about in society.

As it happens, we are living in a society in which all the enormous changes—the *only* enormous changes—are being brought about by science and its application to everyday life. Count up the changes introduced by the automobile, by the television set, by the jet plane. Ask yourself what might happen to the world of tomorrow if there is complete automation, if robots become practical, if the disease of old age is cured, if hydrogen fusion is made a workable source of energy.

The fact is that no previous generation has had to face the possibility and the potentialities of such enormous and such rapid change. No generation has had to face the appalling certainty that if the advance of science isn't judged accurately, if the problems of tomorrow aren't solved before they are upon us, that advance and those problems will overwhelm us.

This generation, then, is the first that can't take as its primary concern the age-old questions that have agitated all deep thinkers since civilization began. Those questions are still interesting, but they are no longer of first importance, and any literature that deals with them (that is, any literature but science fiction) is increasingly irrelevant.

If this thought seems too large to swallow, consider a rather simple analogy: the faster an automobile is moving, the less the driver can concern himself with the eternal beauties of the scenery and the more he must involve himself with the trivial obstacles in the road ahead.

And that is where science fiction comes in.

Not all science fiction, of course. Theodore Sturgeon, one of the outstanding practitioners in the field, once said to a group of fans, "Nine-tenths of science fiction is crud." There was a startled gasp from the audience and he went on, "But why not? Nine-tenths of everything is crud." Including mainstream literature, of course.

It must be understood, then, that I am talking of the one-tenth (or possibly less) of science fiction that is not crud.

This means you will have to take my word for what follows, if you are not yourself an experienced science-fiction fan. The nonfan or even the mild fan with occasional experience in the field is almost certain to have been exposed only to the crud, which is, alas, of high visibility. He sees the comic strips, the monster movies, the pale TV fantasies. He never sees the better magazines and paperbacks where the science-fiction writers of greatest repute are to be found.

So let's see—

In 1940 there was endless talk about Fascism, Communism and Democracy, talk that must have varied little in actual content concerning the conflicts of freedom and authority, of race, religion and patriotism, from analogous discussions carried on in fifth and fourth centuries B.C. Greece. In 1940, when the Nazis were everywhere victorious, such talk might well have been considered important. It might plausibly have been argued that these discussions dealt with the great issues of the century.

And what was science fiction talking about? Well, in the May 1941 issue of *Astounding Science Fiction*, there appeared a story called "Solution Unsatisfactory" by Anson MacDonald (real name, Robert A. Heinlein), which suggested that the United States might put together a huge scientific project designed to work out a nuclear weapon that would end World War II. It then went on, carefully and thoughtfully, to consider the nuclear stalemate into which the world would consequently be thrown. At about the same time, John W. Campbell, Jr., editor of the magazine, was saying, in print, that the apparent issues of the war were, in a sense, trivial, since nuclear energy was on the point of being tamed and that this would so change the world that what then seemed life-and-death differences in philosophy would prove unimportant.

Well, who were the thinkers who, in 1940, were considering the nuclear stalemate? What generals were planning for a world in which each major power had nuclear bombs? What political scientists were thinking of a situation in which no matter how hot the rhetoric between competing great powers, any war between them would have to stay cold—not through consideration of fine points of economics or morals, but over the brutal fact that a nuclear stalemate cannot be broken, short of world suicide?

These thoughts, which were, after all, the truly relevant ideas on 1940's horizon, were reserved to science-fiction writers.

Nowadays, articles on ecology are in great demand, and it is quite fashionable to talk of population and pollution and of all the vast changes they may bring about. It is easy to do so now. Rachel Carson started it, most people would say, with her *Silent Spring*. But did anyone precede her?

Well, in the June, July, and August 1952 issues of *Galaxy*, there appeared a three-part serial, "Gravy Planet," by Frederik Pohl and Cyril Kornbluth, which is a detailed picture of an enormously over-populated world from almost every possible aspect. In the February 1956 issue of *Fantasy and Science Fiction*, there appeared "Census Takers" by Frederik Pohl in which it is (ironically) suggested that the time will come when one of the chief duties of census takers will be to shoot down every tenth (or fourteenth, or eighth, depending on the population increase in the past decade) person they count, as the only means of keeping the population under control.

What sociologist (not now, but twenty years ago) was clamoring in print over the overwhelming effect of population increase? What government functionary (not now, but twenty years ago) was getting it clearly through his head that there existed no social problem that did not depend for its cure, *first of all*, on a cessation of population growth? (Surely not President Eisenhower, who piously stated that

if there was one problem in which the government must not interfere, it was the matter of birth control. He changed his mind later;
I'll give him credit for that.) What psychologist or philosopher (not
now, but twenty years ago) was pointing out that if population continued to increase, there was no hope for human freedom or dignity
under any circumstances?

Such thoughts were pretty largely reserved, twenty years ago, to
science-fiction writers.

There are many people (invariably those who know nothing about
science fiction) who think that because men have reached the moon,
science has caught up with science fiction and that science-fiction
writers have "nothing to write about."

They would be surprised to know that the mere act of reaching
the moon was outdated in science fiction in the 1920s and that no
reputable science-fiction writer has been excited by such a little thing
in nearly half a century.

In the July 1939 issue of *Astounding Science Fiction*, there appeared
a story called "Trends," written by myself while I was still a teenager.
It did indeed deal with the first flights to the moon, which I put
in the period between 1973 and 1978. (I underestimated the push
that would be given rocket research by World War II.) My predictions
on the details of the beginnings of space exploration were ludicrously
wrong, but none of that represented the point of the story, anyway.

What made the story publishable was the social background I presented for the rocket flights. In my story, I pictured strong popular
opposition to the notion of space travel.

Many years later it was pointed out to me that in all the volumin-
ous literature about space travel, either fictional or nonfictional, no
such suggestion had ever before been broached. The world was
always pictured as wildly and unanimously enthusiastic.

Well, where in 1939 was there the engineer or the industrialist
who was taking into serious account the necessity of justifying the
expense and risk of space exploration? Where was the engineer or
the industrialist who was soberly considering the possibility of space
exploration?

Such thoughts were largely reserved for the science-fiction writer
and for a few engineers, who in almost every case were science-
fiction fans—Willy Ley and Wernher von Braun, to name a couple.

And where does science fiction stand today?

It is more popular than ever and has gained a new respectability.
Dozens of courses in it are being given in dozens of colleges. Literary
figures have grown interested in it as a branch of the art. And,
of course, the very growth in popularity tends to dilute and weaken
it.

It has grown sufficiently popular and respectable, since the days
of Sputnik, for people to wish to enter it as a purely literary field.
And once that becomes a motive, the writers don't need to know

science anymore. To write purely literary science fiction, one returns to the "eternal verities" but surrounds them with some of the verbiage of science fiction, together with a bit of the new stylistic experimentation one comes across in the mainstream and with some of the explicit sex that is now in fashion.

And this is what some people in science fiction call the "new wave."

To me, it seems that the new wave merely attempts to reduce real science fiction to the tasteless pap of the mainstream.

New-wave science fiction can be interesting, daring, even fascinating, if it is written well enough, but if the author knows no science, the product is no more valuable for its content of relevant ideas than is the writing outside science fiction.

Fortunately, the real science fiction—those stories that deal with scientific ideas and their impact on the future as written by someone knowledgeable in science—still exists and will undoubtedly continue to exist as long as mankind does (which, alas, may not be long).

This does not mean that every science-fiction story is good prediction or is necessarily intended to be a prediction at all, or that very good science-fiction stories might not deal with futures that cannot reasonably be expected to come to pass.

That does not matter. The point is that the habit of looking sensibly toward the future, the habit of assuming change and trying to penetrate beyond the fact of change to its effect and to the new problems it will introduce, the habit of accepting change as now more important to mankind than those dreary eternal verities, is to be found only in science fiction or in those serious nonfictional discussions of the future by people who, almost always, are or have been deeply interested in science fiction.

For instance, while ordinary literature deals merry-go-round-wise with the white-black racial dilemma in the United States, I await the science-fiction story that will seriously consider the kind of society America might be attempting to rebuild *after* the infinitely costly racial war we are facing—a war that may destroy our world influence and our internal affluence. Perhaps such a story, sufficiently well thought out and written, may force those who read it into a contemplation of the problem from a new and utterly relevant angle.

To see what I mean, ask yourself how many of those, north and south, who blithely talked abolition and secession in the 1850s in terms of pure rhetoric might not have utterly changed their attitudes and gotten down to sober realities if they could have foreseen the exact nature of the Civil War and of the Reconstruction that followed and could have understood that none of the torture of the 1860s and 1870s would in the least solve the problem of white-and-black after all.

So read this magazine and others of the sort by all means, and follow the clash of stock ideas as an amusing intellectual game. Or read Plato or Sophocles and follow the same clash in more readable prose. But if you want the real ideas, the ideas that count today and may even count tomorrow, the ideas for which Aristotle offers little real help, or Senator X or Commissar Y either, then read science fiction.

The Ghost of an Apprehension

Walter Van Tilburg Clark

Since the story took place in my mind somewhat as a play might, the intention producing the scene, the scene and the intention selecting the cast, and all three, by means of certain guiding principles which developed with them, dictating the action, and since its approach has occurred often with me, in novels as well as in stories, it will help both to shape the discussion to follow and in a measure to widen its application, if we put the synopsis itself into something like dramatic form. To brief the brief, then (the story is only eight pages long):

THE SCENE. Interior of a dugout above a creek thinly lined with alders. A small, smoky, peat fire in the center. In one wall a niche containing a few battered cooking utensils. In the opposite wall an earth bunk with two old army blankets on it. Above the entrance, a rolled canvas, which is the door. Outside (the backdrop, so to speak) a desolate prairie, pitted by craters and grooved by the frozen ruts of huge wheels and caterpillar treads. Here and there a remnant of highway pavement, a spidery entanglement of barbed wire, and, in the depressions, a few small, shadowy trees. On the far horizon, a red sunset with bars of black cloud across it. Overhead, changing clouds gliding rapidly south before a high, booming wind. A single wedge of wild geese passes over, going southward more swiftly than the clouds and conversing faintly among themselves. A prairie wolf yaps in the distance. There is no other sound or motion. The air near the ground is still and full of the cold promise of winter.

THE CAST. Four men, all dirty, ragged, and bearded: Dr. Jenkins, a former professor and the host, and three visitors: a powerful, sardonic man, once a writer; a polite, conciliatory soul, whose past is not revealed; and a very thin, nervous young man with a bad cough, who has been a musician. The writer and the conciliatory soul have evidently been here before, though not often, but the musician is making his first call.

THE ACTION. Dr. Jenkins has just finished reading *The Tempest* aloud, and while he wraps up his library, Shakespeare, the Bible, *The Divine Comedy,* and *Moby Dick,* is discussing with the writer and the anonymous one, the present, and possibly future, worth of the books. When he has put the books into the niche with the pots, there is a brief, coercive silence, after which he reluctantly produces an old portable phonograph and twelve records. They may hear one record; one record, once a week, is his rule. He reads the titles. A Gershwin named by the writer is rejected as too sharp a reminder. The musician is given the choice, and after hearing the titles again, and complaining that there are parts he can't remember, he selects a Debussy nocturne. Dr. Jenkins, in a sudden, penitent gesture, takes out one of his three remaining steel needles, though he has been using thorns himself. The visitors rise to their knees in a reverent semicircle to watch him insert the needle and set the record on. At the first note of the piano, however, the musician shrinks back against the wall, where he struggles silently against his cough and the agony of hearing music again.

When the record is finished, the visitors rise. The musician is the last to rise, but then he goes out at once, without a word. The other two leave more slowly and formally. Dr. Jenkins lingers in the doorway, peering down into the dusk and listening. At last, just as a cloud erases one of four visible stars, he hears a faint cough from down among the alders. He lowers the canvas and pegs it down, and puts the phonograph and records, and then the books too, into a hole above the bunk and seals them in. After changing his blankets around so that he will lie facing the door, and putting more fuel on the fire, he stands watching the canvas again. Still only the wind, which has at last come down to earth, moves it. He prays and gets under his blankets, where, "On the inside of the bed, next the wall, he could feel with his hand the comfortable piece of lead pipe."

Even so brief a retelling, when we remember that the story first appeared in the fall of 1941, suggests fully enough all we need to know about the apprehension which was the source of the idea. It also brings us at once to the crux of the writing problem, for it was just the very universality of that apprehension which placed the severest strictures upon the design of the story, and so compelled me in the first stage, to formulate the guiding principles already mentioned.

Clearly I could justify the use of such a theme only by bringing that universal apprehension into sharp focus, by so heightening the reader's reaction to what he already knew and feared as to make the vaguely possible into the concretely probable. Gradually it became evident that the means to such a concentration and heightening must be three. First, if I were to avoid the flavor of Wellsian prophecy, the great apprehension itself must be touched upon lightly and indirectly, must be little more than a taken-for-granted backdrop. Secondly, the incident played against that backdrop, and the characters engaged in it, had to be highly credible, not in terms of their situation, but in terms of an everyday American life. In short, it didn't seem to me that the desired tone could be achieved in the key of either the incident or the scene alone, but that it must arise out of the dissonant juxtaposition of the two. And finally, the manner of the story had to convey the same contrast, had to be fiddle light on the surface and bass viol deep beneath, which is to say, it had to be satirical. One cannot afford to speak seriously of the end of the world. All of these necessities, the minor and credible activity, presented against a background of doom, in a manner calculated to sustain the dissonance, added up, of course, to a very short story. One does not strain a joke about the end of the world, either.

I didn't, naturally, start with a notion of saying something about the finality of modern war, and out of that melancholy fog evolve a set of rules, and out of them a story. The process was not that orderly. First, I just began to write. I can't remember exactly what set me off. Probably it was some intensifying item of the day's news, stirring me when I had time to sit and brood on it until I had to get rid of the emotion it built up, and the first, suggestive images began to appear. Almost always, whatever may have been working up to it in my mind, recognized and unrecognized, it is some image suddenly coming alive and suggesting more to follow, or to precede, that makes me reach for a pencil. In this case it was the prairie, the vast, desolated backdrop of the dugout, which first appeared, accompanied by a feeling that such a scene implied in itself all that one could afford to say directly about a final war. In short, the critical process began with the creative, and by the time I had completed the introductory description (a slow procedure, involving much cutting, rewriting, and rearranging) the controlling principles, more or less as I have stated them, were already in full operation, the cast had appeared and been approved, and the incident had arisen out of their gathering. The story was finished, except for putting it down, which meant little more than keeping an ear open for that desirable dissonance.

The prairie first appeared blackened by old fires, full of shell craters, deeply scored everywhere by the tracks of enormous tank battles and the vestiges of hopeless entrenchment, and devoid of all present signs of human life. There were no houses, or even shells of houses, no barns, no windmills, no fences, no recognizable fields or even stubs of groves or orchards. It was bare as the moon. It suggested a warfare of almost cosmic proportions (since Hiroshima, we can delete the "almost") which was what I wanted, and it suggested also, that a good deal of time had passed since the battle. That hint of time softening the edges of all detail, but unable to restore anything, made the destruction even more final, and sufficiently indicated, it seemed to me, that the survivors necessary to the story must be so few, and so far set back, as to be without hope or use. But then I saw that the mooniness was too complete, and could just as well mean a region that had always been desert as it could the ruin of a productive region. Yet it seemed wrong to name the place, and I still didn't want any skeletons of building against the sky. I preferred that tundralike emptiness stretching away to the western horizon. (I was looking west, perhaps because Americans have that habit, perhaps because the war we most dreaded was raging in Europe, and so, in the story, would have gone across America westward, but probably just because the scene had first appeared in an end-of-day light, and one would naturally be looking toward the sunset.) So there appeared the broken remnants of a highway as unobtrusive tokens of the past. Clearer signs of time elapsed since the fighting were also needed, yet signs which would not too much relieve the sterility of the earth, so there grew up the sparse lines of willows and alders in the trenches and creek beds, and the stunted, new trees in the craters.

Sometime during its first viewing, though I avoided the narrowing effect of a name (the nature of the land, and the fact that the four men were unquestionably American, seemed enough in the way of location) the region became definitely the American Middle West, because it spread the devastation over the whole world to show the heart of the most isolated major power swept over, and the grain lands gone in a warfare which concentrated on cities. It made the place not only a field of the final war, but the final field as well.

Late autumn became the necessary time of year, the last season before the complete death and the somehow healing secrecy of winter, just as sunset, the last hour of vision before the secrecy of night, was the proper time of day. To begin with, the sky had been cloudless, the sunset one of those infinitely penetrable, green-gold fadings that come with cold, but now such a horizon seemed too peaceful, and even suggestive of hope. There had to be some motion in that inert landscape, some threat in the sky. So the clouds formed, moving in a wintry wind, and the sunset turned red, and then, although that came as an afterthought, in part because the professor had to hear that last faint cough down in the alders, the unmoving lower air settled in. The chief intent was that the dissonance of the two regions of air should furnish a physical lead into the moral dissonance of the action, and also that it should reinforce the threat of the black clouds across the sunset, suggest apprehension by ear and skin as well as by eye. Finally, for by now the story was fully in view, some touch of conscious life was needed, by which to move from the backdrop into the play. Hence, as also maintaining the mood, the far-off yapping of the wolf, unheard in those parts for generations, and the brief, almost invisible passage of the geese, unconcerned with the land except as a distance to get over.

The action of the story, prepared all during the arranging and rearranging of this backdrop, moved forward so swiftly, almost automatically, in its details, as to be now largely beyond recall. I do remember the vital factors of the preparation, however. I remember that the cast first appeared to me as three in number, the three who became the professor, the writer, and the musician; that they were all men because even one woman might imply a future; and that they became men of highly mental pasts because that rendered them more nearly helpless, increased their recession, and made it more likely that they would retain the necessary surface of polite conduct. I remember also that the three men first came together in the open, around a wood fire down by the creek, but that somehow nothing would happen among them there. The size and finality of the setting shrank them and paralyzed them with futility. I could not even seem to discover any reason for their bothering to get together, save an animal loneliness which had no dramatic potential except through a much longer development than I could afford. When at last it became clear that it was the scene which rendered them so unusable, the dugout, as in keeping with the tank tracks and the barbed wire, appeared in the bank behind me, and we moved into it. That was all it took. The men not only came alive, but swelled to more than life-size, filling the little cave enormously, assuming the importance for me that they had for each other, and setting the lifeless prairie away into its proper backdrop perspective. The vestigial touches of homemaking effort became possible: the few and battered utensils, kept in a niche, like a saint; the peat fire and the earthen bunk, hinting of a nearly woodless world; the army blankets and the canvas. Also, the home made necessary the host, and the professor, as likely to be the most provident and the most chairmanly, at once assumed that role, and with it his manner and his more numerous years. Indeed it was only then that he certainly became a professor, a kind of epitome of civilized man in his most familiar form, suggesting thereby a great deal through his mere presence in a cave.

When the fragments of possible conversation among the three men, the professor, the writer, and a third who was for a time alternately a painter and a musician, began to occur in the midst of the backdrop details, I shortly felt the need of a fourth man, not only because I sensed that the musician-painter was going to be nearly inarticulate, and, for the sake of variety and interplay, three speakers were preferable to two, but also because the trio was a bit too patly symbolic, and so likely to resist the individualization without which they couldn't convince. (The writer was first seen as a sculptor—which has something to do with the physical characteristics he retained—but changed his profession, partly for the same reason, to break up the rigid one-two-three alignment by drawing nearer to the professor's interests, making a one-two grouping, and partly because it better suited the intent of the tale that he should be thwarted by an absence of that so-common commodity, paper. Of clay there would still be aplenty.) So the fourth man joined the group, the man with the unknown past, the representative of the great, departed audience whose need had produced the specialists. He was a real help, for not only did he relieve the stiffness of the allegory, but he also furnished a contrasting attitude, a second psychological level, being a trifle deferential in the presence of the more specific abilities of the others, but also more resigned because his individual needs were less acute. He was, in short, different in kind, whereas the other three, all upon one level of bolder individuality, were different only in particulars: the harsh cynicism of the frustrated writer; the advanced tuberculosis which makes time so important to the musician; the grave, reluctant, orderly air of the professor. Furthermore, I believe that I had found in him another sufficiently concealed means to irony, for his deference was, of course, wholly pointless in that place and time, a mere hang-over from an irrecoverable social pattern, and yet it was just that trace of deference, that touch of the conciliatory, that held together, by its remnant of drawing-room conduct, a group that otherwise would almost certainly have broken into an undesirable violence.

Once we were in the dugout, and the anonymous fourth had entered, there seemed to be only one thing lacking, that precipitating agent which would settle the whole narrative out in visible form, the reason for the gathering. I cannot remember how many reasons I fleetingly considered off the top of my mind while I completed the backdrop and caught unusable but suggestive glimpses of the civilized pasts of the men. (The professor, for instance, had taught English in a Midwestern college, specializing in Victorian Literature, but had a wide range of interests beyond that. He had lived in a small, white, frame house, with vines on the front porch, and a dark, somewhat stuffy study in it, with heavy rugs, too much furniture, and the walls lined with books, mostly old and worn, but here and there in bright, new bindings or dust jackets. He had two children, but both were grown and away from home, and he was rather lonely, because he had retired just a couple of years before the war, and his wife, a plump, bespectacled woman, although a

fine mother and housekeeper, did not share any of his intellectual
interests.) I remember very clearly, however, that the happiest
moment of the whole preliminary came with the discovery of the
portable phonograph. Beyond question it was the very object, the
key symbol, for which I'd been hunting ever since my first dusky
glimpse of the prairie. It was portable, which was important. It
would seem valuable enough to such a man as the professor, to
be worth carrying off in a crisis. It was a universally familiar object,
and so would derive its dramatic virtue entirely from its present
rarity. In its combined material inconsequence—for certainly it was
one of the lesser gadgets of our abundantly gadgeted civilization—
and spiritual consequence, as the only remaining vehicle of perhaps
the highest achievement of mind and emotion of that same civilization, it became the very centerpiece of the desired dissonance, the
touchstone for action and language. The title arrived with it, of
course. In its presence, the relationships of the cast were rapidly
established. It became evident that the small, suppressed element
of conflict that was needed must spring from it and from the music
it produced. As a result, the musician at once assumed the brief
future that would make him desperate, and became certainly a musician rather than a painter, and also the newcomer, the stranger in
the group, the man in whom the restraint of association would play
the smallest part and the hunger for music the greatest. At once,
also, the professor, as the owner of the treasure, became the antago-
nist. To all intents the story was complete.

There remained only to discover a valid and contributory means
of prolonging, though backwards, into the hours before the tale
opens, a meeting which would otherwise be incredibly brief, and
which could not, obviously, be extended by eating and drinking.
Books were beyond question the means, and certainly, in this context, the reasons for selecting the four the professor had brought
with him are equally clear, at least by the time the writer has spoken
of *Moby Dick* as something they can all understand now (he might
usefully have dropped a word about Ishmael's coffin-boat) and
added that Shelley had too much soul, and was "no earthly good."
Nor is there any mystery about his selecting *The Tempest* for the
reading, once we realize that Caliban and Ariel are at it again over
the portable phonograph. The act of reading and the reverence
accorded the books serve also as a kind of induction to the high
sacrament of the music, in which the professor becomes the priest
of a doomed faith and the visitors literally assume kneeling positions
around the phonograph.

It is intended that the conclusion should leave with the reader
a sense of unity, of the opening dissonance resolved, though not
into peace, but rather by means, gently, gently, of almost entirely
reducing the professor to the cave man, blending him, as it were,

into the terrible landscape. As he stands suspiciously in the door-way, after the guests have departed, he sees, at the very instant he hears the coughing down in the alders, one of four bright stars suddenly hidden by a cloud. It is a sufficient sign to the primitive credulity revived in him, and indirectly, we hope, in the reader. Then also, as he stands watching the canvas he has pegged down, it is moved by "the first gusts of a lowering wind." The opening dissonance between the wuthering upper air and the still ground air is also resolved, and again, as in the case of the human disso-nance, by suggesting an end, by bringing winter to the door. Yet, in the last line, as the professor lies on the earth bench, facing the billowing canvas, "On the inside of the bed, next to the wall, he could feel with his hand the comfortable piece of lead pipe." His weapon still comes from that lost world of gadgets. He cannot bring even violence to the level of the new—the very old—world in which he now lives. And of course futility, in any but the meanest and most temporary sense, attends the defense for which he is prepared.

It seemed to me that sentence plucked the proper closing note, one that might linger for a time with a tenuous but moving reminder of the whole intention. If so, it was so, happily, by means of the very last phrase, and particularly by means of the one word "comfort-able." Nothing in the phrase was considered, not "comfortable" any more than the rest, but even as it came, that "comfortable" tickled me, not so much because of its immediate implication, in which the paradox was clear enough, as for some more remote, redoubling connotation which I could not, at the moment, catch hold of. Then, a few seconds after I had poked home the final period, it came to me. I had done a bit of lucky thieving from Bill of Avon. (Perhaps the professor's volume of Shakespeare had put it out handy for the borrowing.) Remember how Juliet, waking in the tomb, and not yet aware that Romeo is dead, murmurs drowsily to the gentle Friar Lawrence, "Oh, comfortable Friar—"? Oh, poor professor, with only his lead pipe. And I was sure that at least the ghost of that old, warm, trusting "comfortable" would lurk to trouble the reader as it had troubled me. Nor could I feel, considering the grim little twist I had given it, that Bill would begrudge me his word. After all, he was no mean shakes of a borrower himself.

The Age of Climax
Arthur Koestler

I come from a country which does not yet exist.

J. CRAVEIRINHA

The Hinge of History

"The present generation is the hinge of history.... We may now be in the time of the most rapid change in the whole evolution of the human race, either past or to come.... The world has now become too dangerous for anything less than Utopia."[1]

This was written by a contemporary American biophysicist, J. R. Platt. We have heard such warnings before—Isaiah, Jeremiah, Cassandra, St. John of the Apocalypse, and so on down the centuries through Augustine, the prophets of the Millenium, to Lenin and Oswald Spengler. In every century there was at least one generation which flattered itself to be "the hinge of history," to live at a time such as never was before, awaiting the blow of the last trumpet or some secular equivalent of it. And there was also James Thurber's unforgettable "Get-Ready man," who wandered barefoot in his nightshirt through the dark streets of his home town, waking people with the blood-curdling cry: "Get ready, get rready, the wurrld is coming to an end."

So one ought to be cautious with pronouncements about the uniqueness of one's own time. Nevertheless there are at least two good reasons which justify the view that humanity is going through a crisis unprecedented in its nature and magnitude in the whole of its past history. The first is quantitative, the second qualitative.

The first is the upsetting of the ecological balance. Its consequences have been summed up by Sir Gavin de Beer in an article commemorating the bicentenary of Malthus: "If we go back a million years to the hominids, or even 250,000 years to Swanscombe Man and his Missus, the curve of population is like an aircraft taking off: for most of that time it just skims along the time axis; then, about A.D. 1600, the undercarriage is raised and it begins to soar; today it is rising almost vertically, more like a rocket off its pad. A million years to reach 3,250 million; thirty or so to double it!"[2]

To be a little more specific: historians have estimated that the world's population at the beginning of the Christian era was around 250 million. By the middle of the seventeenth century it had doubled, rising to about 500 million. By the middle of the nineteenth it had doubled again and reached the first billion mark.* It is at this point that Pasteur, Lister and Semmelweiss took a hand and changed the ecological balance of our species by declaring war on the micro-organisms in its environment—a change more drastic and far-reaching than all the technical inventions of James Watt, Edison and the Wright brothers put together. But the disaster they unwittingly initiated made itself felt only a century later. By 1925 the population had doubled again, to two billion. By 1965 it was well over three billion, and the doubling period had shrunk from 1,500 years to about 35 years.[3]

This figure is based on an average global growth rate of 2 per cent per annum—1.6 to 1.8 in industrialised countries, 3 per cent or more in a number of low-income nations. Thus India, which in 1965 had a population of 450 million, at the present growth rate will have 900 million mouths to feed in A.D. 2000. Even for the short period of fifteen years, 1965–80, to keep up with the estimated population-growth would require an increase of yield per acre of existing farmland by at least 50 per cent; and L. R. Brown of the U.S. Department of Agriculture has calculated "that an additional 24 million tons of fertiliser a year must be applied to achieve this performance, but the entire world production of fertiliser is only 28.6 million tons a year."[4] As for China, with a population of 750 million in 1966, it will, if the present trend continues, at the end of the century equal the total population of the earth as it was in 1900.

The explosion is accompanied by the implosion of migrants from rural areas to the cities, "not inspired by the call of employment but by the desperate hope that some menial job or government relief will be available there. . . . Kingsley Davies estimates that in the year 2000, the largest Indian city, Calcutta, will contain between 36 and 66 million people. Calcutta sprawling for hundreds of square miles, with a population of 66 million inadequately employed people, suggests a concentration of misery that can only have explosive consequences."[5]

---

*I am following U.S. usage: 1,000 million=one billion.

Returning to the planet as a whole, the prospect is: 7 billion people in 2000; 14 billion in 2035; 25 billion a hundred years from now (see illustration). "But," as a sober Ford Foundation report says, "but long before then, in the face of such population pressure, it is inevitable that the Four Horsemen will take over."[6]

How many people can our planet nourish? According to Colin Clark, one of the leading authorities in this field, 12 to 15 billion—but only on condition that the methods of cultivation and soil preservation in the whole world are brought up to the high standard of the Netherlands. This, of course, is nothing short of Utopia; yet even under these optimum conditions the total population would outpace the total supply in the first decades of the next century.

It will be objected that predictions based on existing population trends are notoriously unreliable. That is our main hope; but since the last war, this unreliability has worked steadily in favour of the pessimists: the factual increase surpasses all maximal predictions. Besides, the great surprises—such as the stabilisation of the Japanese population around 1949 by the legalisation of abortion—which play havoc with the statistician's predictions have always occurred in highly developed countries, which took family planning more or less for granted long before modern contraceptives came on the market, and were thus able to break the predicted pattern by adapting the number of their babies to economic and psychological trends. In contrast to Japan—the only Asiatic country with a Western level of literacy—fifteen years of intense birth-control propaganda in India has yielded practically no results. The fast breeders in Asia, Africa and Latin America are by nature the least amenable to disciplined family planning. They are the three-quarters of the earth's population which set the pace.

All this has often been said, and repetition tends to blunt rather than sharpen our awareness. The public is aware that there is a problem; it is not aware of the magnitude and the urgency of the problem; it is not aware that we are moving towards a climax which is not centuries, but only a few decades ahead—that is, well within the lifetime of the present generation of teenagers. What I am trying to prove is not that the situation is hopeless, but that it is indeed unique, unprecedented in man's history. De Beer's parable of the aeroplane which skims along the runway for thousands of miles, but within a mile or two from takeoff changes into a rocket, shooting straight up into the sky, is meant to illustrate what the mathematician calls an "exponential curve" (see illustration).

The curve should be extended to the left—into the past—for miles on end, along which its rise would only be discernible through a microscope. Then comes the critical moment, when Pasteur et al. took the brakes off. The brakes, of course, symbolise the high mortality rate which, balancing the "lift" of the birth rate, kept the population curve nearly horizontal. It took about a century—half an inch on our scale—until the consequences became apparent; from then onward the curve rises steeper and steeper, until, in the second half of our century, it starts rocketing towards the sky. It took our species something like a hundred thousand years to spawn its first billion. Today we are adding a further billion to the total every twelve years. In the first few decades of the next century, if the present trend continues, we shall add a billion every six years. After that, every three years; and so on. But long before that de Beer's crazy aeroplane is bound to crash.

An exponential curve reflects a process with the brakes off, which has got out of hand. Even the draughtsman attempting to extend the curve into the future will be defeated because, as the curve gets steeper and steeper, he must run out of paper—as the world must run out of food, of *Lebensraum*, of beaches and river shores, of privacy, of smiles.

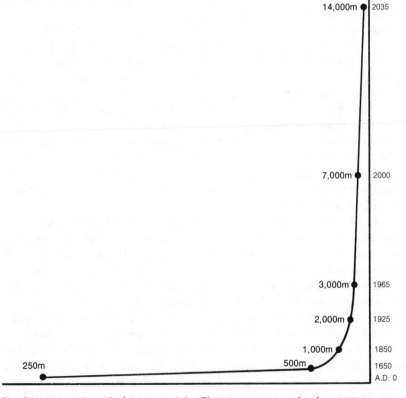

Population curve from the beginning of the Christian era extrapolated to 2035 A.D.

The uncanny properties of exponential curves reflect the uniqueness of our time—not only the population explosion, but also the explosion in power, communications, and specialised knowledge.

To take the last item first, Dr. Ian Morris of University College writes: "As measured by manpower, number of periodicals or number of scientific papers, science is growing exponentially with a doubling time of about fifteen years. . . ." The number of scientific journals in 1700 was less than ten, in 1800 around a hundred, in 1850 around a thousand, in 1900 more than ten thousand, after the First World War around a hundred thousand, and by A.D. 2000 is expected to reach the one million mark. "The same picture is obtained if the number of scientists or scientific papers is measured, and appears to be comparable for widely different scientific disciplines. During the past fifteen years, the same number of scientists were produced as existed during the entire previous period of science. Thus because the average working life of a research scientist is about forty-five years, seven out of every eight scientists who have ever lived are alive now. Similarly, almost *ninety per cent* of all scientific endeavour has been undertaken during the past fifty years."[7] The United States National Education Authority sets the doubling time since 1950 even lower: ten years.[8]

Take power next. Again we have that long flat stretch of the curve from Cro Magnon to about five thousand years ago. With the invention of the lever, the pulley and other simple mechanical devices, the muscular strength of man would appear multiplied, say, five- or tenfold; then the curve would again remain nearly horizontal until the invention of the steam engine and the Industrial Revolution, just two hundred years ago. From then on, it is the same story as before: takeoff, steeper and steeper climb to the rocket-like stage. The exponential increase in the speed of communications, or in the range of penetration into the depths of the universe by optical and radio telescopes, is too well known to need stressing; but the following illustration is perhaps less familiar.

At the end of the nineteen twenties we could impart to atomic particles about half a million electron-volts of energy; in the 1930s we could accelerate them to twenty million electron-volts; by 1950 to five hundred million; and at the time of writing, an accelerator of fifty thousand million electron-volts is under construction. But more bemusing than all these figures is to me an episode in 1930, when I nearly lost my job as a science editor because of indignant protests against an article I wrote on the progress in rocketry, in which I predicted space travel "in our lifetime." And a year or two before the first Sputnik was launched, Britain's Astronomer Royal made the immortal statement: "Space travel is bilge." Our imagination is willing to accept that things are changing, but unable to accept the *rate* at which they are changing, and to extrapolate into the future. The mind boggles at an exponential curve as Pascal's mind boggled when, in the Copernican universe, infinity opened its gaping jaws: *"Le silence éternel de ces espaces infinis m'effraie."*

That is the position in which we find ourselves today. We dare no longer extrapolate into the future, partly because we are frightened, mainly because of the poverty of our imagination.

Two Curves

But at least we can look back over our shoulders into the past, and compare the chart which we have just discussed, showing the explosive increase in people, knowledge, power and communications, with another type of chart indicating the progress of social morality, ethical beliefs, spiritual awareness and related values. This chart will yield a curve of quite different shape. It, too, will show a very slow rise during the nearly flat prehistoric miles; then it will oscillate with inconclusive ups and downs through what we call civilised history; but shortly after the exponential curves get airborne, the "ethical curve" shows a pronounced downward trend, marked by two World Wars, the genocidal enterprises of several dictators, and new methods of terror combined with indoctrination, which can hold whole continents in their grip.

The contrast between these two curves gives certainly an oversimplified, but not an over-dramatised view of our history. They represent the consequences of man's split mind. The exponential curves are all, in one way or another, the work of the new cortex; they show the explosive results of learning at long last how to actualise its potentials which, through all the millennia of our prehistory, have been lying dormant. The other curve reflects the delusional streak, the persistence of misplaced devotion to emotional beliefs dominated by the archaic paleo-mammalian brain.

To quote v. Bertalanffy once more:

> What is called human progress is a purely intellectual affair, made possible by the enormous development of the forebrain. Owing to this, man was able to build up the symbolic worlds of speech and thought, and some progress in science and technology during the 5000 years of recorded history was made.
>
> Not much development, however, is seen on the moral side. It is doubtful whether the methods of modern warfare are preferable to the big stones used for cracking the skull of the fellow-Neanderthaler. It is rather obvious that the moral standards of Laotse and Buddha were not inferior to ours. The human cortex contains some ten billion neurons that have made possible the progress from stone axe to airplanes and atomic bombs, from primitive mythology to quantum theory. There is no corresponding

development on the instinctual side that causes man to mend his ways. For this reason, moral exhortations, as proffered through the centuries by the founders of religion and great leaders of humanity, have proved disconcertingly ineffective.[9]

As a further illustration of the gulf between our intellectual and emotional development, take the contrast between communication and co-operation. Progress of the means of communication is again reflected by an exponential curve: crowded within a single century are the invention of steam-ship, railway, motor car, air-ship, aeroplane, rocket, space-ship; of telegraph, telephone, gramophone, radio, radar; of photography, cinematography, television, telstar.... The month I was born, the Wright brothers in Kitty Hawk, North Carolina, managed for the first time to stay in the air for one entire minute in their flying machine; the chances are that before I die we shall have reached the moon and perhaps Mars. *No generation of man ever before has witnessed in its lifetime such changes.*

Within that lifetime, our planet has shrunk to Lilliputian proportions, so that instead of Jules Verne's Eighty Days, it can be orbited in eighty minutes. But as to the second curve—the bridging of the distance between nations did not bring them "closer" to each other—rather the opposite. Before the communications-explosion travel was slow, but there existed no Iron Curtain, no Berlin Wall, no minefields in no-man's lands, and hardly any restrictions on immigration or emigration; today about one-third of mankind is not permitted to leave its own country. One could almost say that progress in co-operation varied in inverse ratio to progress in communications. The conquest of the air transformed limited into total warfare; the mass media became the demagogue's instruments of fomenting hatred; and even between close neighbours like England and France, the increase in tourist traffic has hardly increased mutual understanding. There have been some positive advances such as the European Common Market; they are minute compared to the gigantic cracks which divide the planet into three major and countless minor, hostile, isolated camps.

The point of labouring these obvious facts is to make them fall into the general pattern. Language, the outstanding achievement of the neocortex, became a more dividing than unifying factor, increasing intra-specific tensions; progress in communications followed a similar trend of turning a blessing into a curse. Even from the aesthetic point of view we have managed to contaminate the luminiferous ether as we have contaminated our air, rivers and seashores; you fiddle with the dials of your radio and from all over the world, instead of celestial harmonies, the ether disgorges its musical latrine slush.

Of all exponential curves, that referring to progress in destructive power is the most spectacular and the best known. To sum it up as briefly as possible: after the First World War, statisticians calculated that on the average ten thousand rifle bullets or ten artillery shells had been needed to kill one enemy soldier. The bombs dropped from flying machines weighed a few pounds. By the Second World War, the block-busters had acquired a destructive power equal to twenty tons of T.N.T. The first atomic bomb on Hiroshima equalled twenty thousand tons of T.N.T. Ten years later, the first hydrogen bomb equalled twenty million tons. At the time of writing, we are stockpiling bombs the equivalent of one hundred million tons of T.N.T.; and there are rumours of a "gigaton bomb"—a "nuclear weapon packing the power of a billion tons of T.N.T. that could be detonated a hundred miles off the U.S. coastline and still set off a fifty-foot tidal wave that would sweep across much of the entire American continent... or a cobalt bomb that would send a deadly cloud sweeping forever about the earth."[10]

The New Calendar

I have said that there are two reasons which entitle us to call our time "unique." The first is quantitative, expressed by the exponential increase of populations, communications, destructive power, etc. Under their combined impact, an extra-terrestrial intelligence, to whom centuries are as seconds, able to survey the whole curve in one sweep, would probably come to the conclusion that human civilisation is either on the verge of, or in the process of, exploding.

The second reason is qualitative, and can be summed up in a single sentence: before the thermonuclear bomb, man had to live with the idea of his death as an individual; from now onward, mankind has to live with the idea of its death as a species.

The bomb has given us the power to commit genosuicide; and within a few years we should even have the power to turn our planet into a *nova*, an exploding star. Every age has had its Cassandras and Get-Ready Men, and mankind has managed to survive regardless of their sinister prophecies. But this comforting argument is no longer valid, as no past age, however convulsed by war and pestilence, had possessed our newly acquired power over life on the planet *as a whole*.

The full implications of this fact have not yet sunk into the minds of even the noisiest pacifists. We have always been taught to accept the transitoriness of individual existence, while taking the survival of our species axiomatically for granted. This was a perfectly reasonable belief, barring some unlikely cosmic catastrophe. But it has ceased to be a reasonable belief since the day when the possibility of engineering a catastrophe of cosmic dimensions was experimentally tested and proven. It pulverised the assumptions on which all philosophy from Socrates onward was based: the potential immortality of our species.

But new insights of a revolutionary nature cannot be assimilated at once. There are periods of incubation. The Copernican theory of the earth's motion had to wait eighty years before it took root. The unconscious mind has its own clock, and its own ways of digesting what the conscious mind has rejected as indigestible. The leaders of the French Revolution were well aware of this fact; to hasten the process of assimilation, they introduced a new calendar, starting on the day of the proclamation of the Republic: September 22, 1792, became the 1st of Vendémiaire of the year 1. It would perhaps not be a bad idea if we all kept a second calendar, at least in our minds, starting with the year when the new Star of Bethlehem rose over Hiroshima. Calendars imply convictions about the fundamental importance of certain events: the first Olympiad, the founding of the city of Rome, the birth of Jesus, the flight of Mohammed from Mecca. The positing of a year zero provides a time scale, a measure of an age, of the distance covered from the real or assumed starting point of a given civilisation.

Thus I am writing this in the year 22 p.H—post Hiroshima. For there can be little doubt that in that year a new era started. The human race is facing a challenge unprecedented in its history—which can only be met by taking action of an equally unprecedented nature. The first half of the preceding sentence is now more or less generally accepted, but the second is not. Even the thinking minority still believes that a peril unique in its novelty can be averted by time-worn traditional remedies, by appeals to sweet reason and common sense. But such appeals are powerless against the militant ideologies of closed systems, whose true believers are convinced—as a professor at Peking University wrote recently—that "respect for facts and for other people's opinions must be exterminated from man's soul like vermin."[11]

All efforts of persuasion by reasoned argument rely on the implicit assumption that *homo sapiens*, though occasionally blinded by emotion, is a basically rational animal, aware of the motives of his own actions and beliefs—an assumption which is untenable in the light of both historical and neurological evidence. All such appeals fall on barren ground; they could take root only if the ground were prepared by a spontaneous change in human mentality all over the world—the equivalent of a major biological mutation. Then, and only then, would mankind as a whole, from its political leaders down to the lonely crowd, become receptive to reasoned argument, and willing to resort to those unorthodox measures which would enable it to meet the challenge.

It is highly improbable that such a mental mutation will occur spontaneously in the foreseeable future; whereas it is highly probable that the spark which initiates the chain-reaction will be ignited sooner or later, deliberately or by accident. As the devices of atomic and biological warfare become more potent and simpler to produce, their spreading to young and immature, as well as old and over-ripe, nations is inevitable. An invention, once made, cannot be disinvented; the bomb has come to stay. Mankind has to live with it forever: not merely through the next crisis and the next one, but forever; not through the next twenty or two hundred or two thousand years, but forever. It has become part of the human condition.

In the first twenty years of the post-Hiroshima era—1946–66 according to the conventional calendar—men had fought, as already mentioned, forty "minor" wars and civil wars tabulated by the Pentagon.[12] More than half of them were fought between Communists and non-Communists (China, Greece); the others were either "anti-colonial" wars (Algeria, Indo-China), "imperialist adventures" (Suez, Hungary, Bay of Pigs), or "classical" wars between neighbours (India-Pakistan, Israel-Arabs). But this Pentagon list does not include crises like the Berlin blockade of 1950, and *coups d'état* like the defenestrations in Prague, 1948. As a French diplomat has put it: "There are no longer such things as war and peace, just different levels of confrontations."

These wars and civil wars were fought with conventional arms, mostly by nuclear have-nots. But at least on two occasions—Berlin, 1950 and Cuba, 1962—we were on the brink of nuclear war; and all this in the first two decades since the year zero p.H. If one extrapolates from these data into the future, the probability of disaster approaches statistical certainty.

A further aggravating factor is that nuclear devices, like other gadgets, will undergo the process of progressive miniaturisation: they will become smaller and easier to make, so that in the long run effective global control of their manufacture will become impracticable on these grounds alone; in the foreseeable future they will be made and stored in large quantities, from windswept Alaska to sunny Stanleyville. It is as if a gang of delinquent children had been locked in a room filled with inflammable material, and provided with match-boxes—accompanied by the warning not to use them. Some social scientists have indeed estimated (to quote J. R. Platt again), that

> our 'half-life'* under these circumstances—that is, the
> probable number of years before these repeated confron-

*The term is borrowed from atomic physics: "half-life" is the time taken for half the atoms of a radioactive isotope to disintegrate.

> tations add up to a 50–50 chance of destroying the human
> race forever—may be only about ten to twenty years.
> Obviously this is not an objectively testable number.
> Nevertheless the idea is clear. This is the first time in
> the history of the human race that babies—all babies
> everywhere, forever—have had such a slim chance of sur-
> vival.[13]

There is indeed no convincing reason which could lead us to
believe that the conflicts, crises, confrontations and wars of the past
will not be repeated in varying parts of the world in the years,
decades and centuries to come. Ever since the Second World War,
the ideological, racial, ethnic tensions have been on the increase
in Africa, Asia, Latin America. In the United States, in spite of all
genuine efforts to find a solution, the racial problem is becoming
more intractable; even Israel, prime victim of racial persecution, has
its own underprivileged majority of coloured Jews. The lessons of
the past have been wasted; history not only repeats itself, it seems
to be labouring under a neurotic compulsion to do so. Thus in 1920
a town named Danzig on the eastern fringes of Europe was made
into an enclave which could only be reached by a narrow corridor
through foreign territory. This absurd arrangement became the pretext for World War Two. While it was still on, a town named Berlin,
in the heart of Europe, was made into an enclave which could only
be reached by a narrow corridor through foreign territory. This
absurd repetition became the pretext which has already once brought
us to the brink of war, and will in all probability do so again. Hegel
wrote: "What experience and history teach us is this—that people
and governments have never learned anything from history, or acted
on principles deduced from it."

It has been said that the blood of martyrs fertilises the earth. In
fact it has been running down into the sewers, with a monotonously
gurgling sound, as far as man can remember; and at whatever part
of the world we look, there is scant evidence which would encourage
us to hope that the gurgling will diminish or stop. If we discard
the comforts of wishful thinking, we must expect that the motives
and *loci* of potential conflict will continue to drift across the globe
like high-pressure areas over a meteorological chart. And our only
precarious safeguard against the ballooning of local into total conflict, mutual deterrence, will always remain dependent on uncon-
trollable psychological factors—the restraint or recklessness of fallible
key individuals. Russian roulette is a game which cannot be played
for long.

So long as we believed that our species as such was virtually
immortal, with an astronomical lifespan before it, we could afford
to wait patiently for that change of heart which, gradually or sud-

denly, would make love, peace and sweet reason prevail. But we no longer have that assurance of immortality, nor the unlimited time to wait for the moment when the lion will lie down with the lamb, the Arab with the Israeli, and the Commissar with the Yogi.

The conclusions, if we dare to draw them, are quite simple. Our biological evolution to all intents and purposes came to a standstill in Cro-Magnon days. Since we cannot in the foreseeable future expect the necessary change in human nature to arise by way of a spontaneous mutation, that is, by natural means, we must induce it by artificial means. We can only hope to survive as a species by developing techniques which supplant biological evolution. We must search for a cure for the schizophysiology inherent in man's nature, and the resulting split in our minds, which led to the situation in which we find ourselves.

"Tampering with Human Nature"

I believe that if we fail to find this cure, the old paranoid streak in man, combined with his new powers of destruction, must sooner or later lead to genosuicide. But I also believe that the cure is almost within reach of contemporary biology; and that with the proper concentration of efforts it might be produced within the lifetime of the generation which is now entering on the scene.

I am aware that this sounds over-optimistic, in contrast to the seemingly over-pessimistic views just expressed on the prospect ahead of us if we persist in carrying on in our paranoiac ways. I do not think these apprehensions are exaggerated, and I do not think that the idea of a cure for *homo sap.* is utopian. It is not inspired by science fiction, but based on a realistic assessment of the recent advances in several convergent branches of the life sciences. They do not provide a cure, but they indicate the area of research that may produce it.

I am also aware that any proposal which involves "artificial tampering with human nature" is bound to provoke strong emotional resistances. These are partly based on prejudice, but partly on a healthy aversion against further intrusions into the privacy and sanctity of the individual by the excesses of social engineering, character engineering, various forms of brain-washing, and other threatening aspects of the air-conditioned nightmare surrounding us. On the other hand, ever since the first hunter wrapped his shivering frame into the hide of a dead animal, man has been tampering with his own nature, creating for himself an artificial environment which gradually transformed the face of the planet, and an artificial mode of existence without which he can no longer survive. There is no turning back on housing, clothing, artificial heating, cooked food;

nor on spectacles, hearing aids, forceps, artificial limbs, anaesthetics, antiseptics, prophylactics, vaccines, and so forth.

We start tampering with human nature almost from the moment a baby is born, for one of the first routine measures is the universal practice to drop a solution of silver nitrate into the baby's eyes to protect it against *ophthalmia neonatorum,* a form of conjunctivitis frequently leading to blindness, caused by gonococci which, unknown to her, may have lurked in the mother's genital tract. This is followed, later on, by preventive vaccinations, compulsory in most civilised countries, against smallpox, typhoid and so on. To appreciate the value of these tamperings with the course of Nature, let us remember that the prevalence of smallpox among Red Indians was one of the main causes which made them lose their continent to the white man. In the seventeenth and eighteenth centuries it constituted a hazard to which everybody was exposed. Its ravages might have been even worse but for that intrepid lady, Mary Wortley Montagu who learnt the ancient oriental practice of "inoculation" from the Turks, and introduced it to England at the beginning of the eighteenth century. It consisted of infecting the person to be immunised with matter taken from mild smallpox cases—a rather dangerous procedure, but with a much lower fatality rate than "natural" smallpox (the risk vanished only when Jenner discovered that vaccination with the attenuated virus of *cowpox* gave immunity against smallpox).

A less well-known case of tampering is the prevention of goitre and of a certain variety of cretinism associated with it. When I was a child, and was taken for the holidays to the Alps, the number of inhabitants of mountain valleys who had monstrous swellings in front of their necks, and the number of cretinous children in their families was quite frightening. Today there is not a single case of goitre in the Tyrolean village where I spend part of the year, nor in the neighbouring valleys. It has been found that goitre is associated with a deficiency of iodine in the thyroid gland, and that the water in regions where the disease used to be endemic was hard and poor in iodine. Thus iodine was periodically added in small quantities to the drinking water or diet of the children, and goitre became virtually a thing of the past.

Evidently man, or a certain breed of man, was biologically not equipped to live in environments with iodine-poor water, or to cope with the virus of smallpox, and the deadly micro-organisms of malaria or sleeping sickness. If we reverse the situation, we find that some microbes are equally ill-equipped for resisting other species of micro-organisms which we call antibiotics. Now microbes seem to have an enormous mutation rate (or some other method of hereditary adaptation), for, within a few years, they have evolved new drug-resistant strains. We humans cannot perform such evolutionary feats. But we can *simulate* major adaptive mutations by adding iodine to the drinking water, or by putting drops into the eyes of the newborn, to protect them from enemies against which our natural defences are inadequate.

In recent years biologists have discovered that every animal species which they studied—from flower beetles through rabbits to baboons—is equipped with instinctive behaviour-patterns which put a brake on excessive breeding, and keep the population-density in a given territory fairly constant, even when food is plentiful. When the density exceeds a certain limit, crowding produces stress-symptoms which affect the hormonal balance; rabbits and deer begin to die off from "adrenal stress" without any sign of epidemic disease; the females of rats stop caring for their young, which perish, and abnormal sexual behaviour makes its appearance. Thus the ecological equilibrium in a given area is maintained not only by the relative distribution of animals, plants and micro-organisms, of predators and prey, but also by a kind of intra-specific feedback mechanism which adjusts the rate of breeding so as to keep the population at a stable level. The population of a given species in a given territory behaves in fact as a self-regulating social holon, governed by the instinctive canons of "keeping distance" and maintaining average density.

But in this respect man is again unique—except perhaps for the suicidal lemmings. It seems almost as if in human populations the ecological rule were reversed: the more crowded they are in slums, ghettoes and poverty-stricken areas, the faster they breed. In the past, the stabilising factor was not the type of feedback mechanism which regulates the rate of breeding in animals, but the death-harvests of war, pestilence and infant mortality. However, already in biblical days, as we learn from the story of Onan, man compensated to some extent for the absence of instinctive breeding-controls by voluntary birth-control through *coitus interruptus* and other practices. Then, a century ago, when Louis Pasteur initiated the "take-off" of the population curve, Charles Goodyear, rubber manufacturer and inventor (after whom the famous tyre company is named) invented the first artificial contraceptives. The modern methods of birth-control by intra-uterine coils and oral contraceptives represent a much more radical tampering with Nature on a more vital level. They interfere in a permanent (and yet by all indications non-injurious) manner with the physiological processes governing the oestrual cycle. Applied on a world-wide scale—as they must be if the impending catastrophe is to be prevented—they would amount to an *artificially simulated, adaptive mutation*.

Our species became a biological freak when somewhere on the way it lost the instinctual controls which in animals regulate the rate of breeding. It can only survive by inventing methods which imitate evolutionary mutation. We can no longer hope that Nature will provide the corrective remedy. We must provide it ourselves.

Prometheus Unhinged

Mutatis mutandis, can we invent a similar remedy for the schizophysiology of our nervous system, for the paranoid streak in man which made such an appalling mess of our history? And not only of the history of *homo sapiens,* but apparently of his near-human predecessors as well. Let us go back to Lorenz:

> Obviously instinctive behaviour mechanisms failed to cope with the new circumstances which culture unavoidably produced even at its very dawn. There is evidence that the first inventors of pebble tools, the African Australopithecines, promptly used their new weapons to kill not only game, but fellow members of their species as well. Peking Man, the Prometheus who learned to preserve fire, used it to roast his brothers: beside the first traces of the regular use of fire lie the mutilated and roasted bones of *Sinanthropus Pekinenis* himself.[14]

The Promethean myth has acquired an ugly twist: the giant reaching out to steal the lightning from the gods is insane. By all indications the trouble started with the sudden mushrooming of the neocortex at a rate "unprecedented in evolutionary history." If we compress the whole history of life on earth, from its beginnings some 2,000 million years ago to the present, into a single day from midnight to midnight, then the age of mammals would begin about 11 P.M.; and the evolution from *Pithecantropus* (Java ape-man) to *homo sapiens*—that is, the evolution of the human neocortex—would have taken place in the last forty-five seconds. The growth of the cortex, too, followed an exponential curve. Is it unreasonable to assume that at this explosive rate of the brain's development, which so widely overshot its mark, something may have gone wrong? More precisely, that the lines of communication between the very old and the brand-new structures were not developed sufficiently to guarantee their harmonious interplay, the hierarchic co-ordination of instinct and intelligence. Remembering the mistakes which occurred in the evolution of earlier versions of nervous systems—the arthropod brain choking its alimentary canal, the marsupial brain without adequate connections between the right and left hemispheres—we cannot help suspecting that something similar may have happened to us; and the combined evidence from neurophysiology, psychopathology and human history seems to support this hypothesis.

The neurophysiological evidence indicates, as we have seen, a dissonance between the reactions of neocortex and limbic system. Instead of functioning as integral parts in a hierarchic order, they lead a kind of agonised coexistence. To revert to an earlier metaphor: the rider has never gained complete control of the horse, and the horse asserts its whims in the most objectionable ways. We have also seen that the horse—the limbic system—has direct access to the emotion-generating, viscerally orientated centres in the hypothalamus; but the rider has no direct access to them. Moreover, the stirrups and reins by which the rider is meant to control the horse are inadequate. To quote MacLean once more: "On the basis of neuronographic studies there appear to be no extensive 'associational' connections between the limbic and the neocortex."* There is no anatomical evidence for the intricate "loops within loops" of feedbacks, of the delicate interplay of excitation and inhibition, which characterises the nervous system in general. "Both horse and man are very much alive to one another and to their environment, yet communication between them is limited. Both derive information and act upon it in a different way."[15]

Here, then, is the anatomical substratum of the "divided house of faith and reason" whose tenants are condemned to live in a state of "controlled schizophrenia"—as the atomic spy Klaus Fuchs described it.

To go on preaching sweet reason to an inherently unreasonable species is, as history shows, a fairly hopeless enterprise. Biological evolution has let us down; we can only hope to survive if we develop techniques which supplant it by inducing the necessary changes in human nature. We may be able to prevent the demotic apocalypse by interfering with woman's oestrous cycle. We cannot cure our paranoiac disposition by putting additional wiring circuits into our brains. But we may be able to achieve a cure, or at least a significant improvement, by directing research into the required channels.

Mutating into the Future

In 1961 the University of California San Francisco Medical Center organised a symposium on *Control of the Mind*. At the first session,

---

*The article continues: "This would indicate that the two depend almost entirely on vertical, rather than horizontal, lines of communication. The so-called diffuse projection system of the diencephalon offers one such possible relating system, but the evidence in this regard is still conflicting. There is ample justification, however, for assuming another system of connections through the reticular system of the midbrain. This part of the brain, which has been shown by Magoun and others to be essential to a state of wakefulness, has been found electro-physiologically to bear a reciprocal relationship to both the limbic and the neocortex. In addition there is anatomical and electrophysiological evidence that the central gray, which lies as a core within this reticulum and which plays a dynamogenous role in emotion, is related to the archicortex."[15] This is what one means by "inadequate" co-ordination.

Professor Holger Hydén of Goeteborg University made headlines in the San Francisco press, although the title of his highly technical paper—"Biochemical Aspects of Brain Activity"—was hardly designed to appeal to the popular press. Hydén is one of the leading authorities in that field. The passage which created the sensation is quoted below (the reference to me is explained by the fact that I was a participant of the symposium):

> In considering the problem of control of the mind, the data give rise to the following question: would it be possible to change the fundamentals of emotion by inducing molecular changes in the biologically active substances in the brain? The RNA,* in particular, is the main target for such a speculation, since a molecular change of the RNA may lead to a change in the proteins being formed. One may phrase the question in different words to modify the emphasis: do the experimental data presented here provide means to modify the mental state by specifically induced chemical changes? Results pointing in that direction have been obtained; this work was carried out using a substance called tricyano-aminopropene.
>
> ... The application of a substance changing the rate of production and composition of RNA and provoking enzyme changes in the functional units of the central nervous system has both negative and positive aspects. There is now evidence that the administration of tricyano-aminopropene is followed by an increased suggestibility in man. This being the case, a defined change of such a functionally important substance as the RNA in the brain could be used for conditioning. The author is not referring specifically to tricyano-aminopropene, but to any substance inducing changes of biologically important molecules in the neurons and the glia and affecting the mental state in a negative direction. It is not difficult to imagine the possible uses to which a government in a police-controlled state could put this substance. For a time they would subject the population to hard conditions. Suddenly the hardship would be removed, and at the same time, the substance would be added to the tap water and the mass-communications media turned on. This method would be much cheaper, and would create more intriguing possibilities, than to let Ivanov treat Rubashov individually for a long time, as Koestler described in his book. On the other hand, a counter-measure against the

*Ribosenucleic acid, a key substance in the genetic apparatus.

effect of a substance such as tricyano-aminopropene is not difficult to imagine either.[16]

Leaving technical details aside, the implications are clear. Like any other human science, biochemistry can serve the powers of light or of darkness. Its dangers are terrifying; but we are now concerned with its beneficial possibilities. Let me quote another pertinent passage from Dean Saunders, of the San Francisco Medical School, at the *Control of the Mind* symposium:

> The great technological skill and ingenuity of the modern chemist has provided the medical scientist and the physician with an abundant array of new chemical compounds of varying and diverse structure which influence the central nervous system to distort, accelerate, or depress the mental state and behavioural characteristics of the individual. The conference emphasised that many of these chemical agents possess a highly selective action on particular and discrete parts of the nervous system—so much so as to permit from an examination of their actions in man and animals an arrangement in order and rank. Those chemical agents thus offer, by a consideration of the relationships between chemical structure and biological action, the possibility of providing a vast array of drugs influencing the specific activity of the brain. Indeed, since such agents may either potentiate or attenuate one another, exhibit overlap in their actions, and demonstrate polarity in their effects on the brain, the very strong possibility is suggested of a full spectrum of chemical agents which can be used for the control of the mind in the majority of its activities.
>
> ... Here at our disposal, to be used wisely or unwisely, is an increasing array of agents that manipulate human beings. ... It is now possible to act directly on the individual to modify his behaviour instead of, as in the past, indirectly through modification of the environment. This, then, constitutes a part of what Aldous Huxley has called "The Final Revolution." ...[17]

I must comment on the last paragraph in this quotation. Huxley was haunted by the fear that this "Final Revolution," brought about by the combined effect of drugs and the mass media, could create "within a generation or so for entire societies a sort of painless concentration camp of the mind, in which people will have lost their liberties in the enjoyment of a dictatorship without tears."[18] In other words, the state of affairs described in *Brave New World*. As an antidote, Huxley advocated the use of mescalin and other psychodelic drugs, to guide us along the eightfold path towards cosmic consciousness, mystic enlightenment and artistic creativity.

I have been for a long time an admirer of Huxley's personality and work, but in his last years I profoundly disagreed with him; and the points of disagreement will help to clarify the issue.

In *Heaven and Hell*, praising the benefits of mescalin, Huxley offered this advice to modern man in search of his soul: "knowing as he does... what are the chemical conditions of transcendental experience, the aspiring mystic should turn for technical help to the specialists in pharmacology, in biochemistry, in physiology and neurology...."

Now this is precisely what I do *not* mean by the positive uses of psychopharmacology. In the first place, experimenting with mescalin or with LSD 25 does involve serious risks. But quite apart from this, it is fundamentally wrong, and naive, to expect that drugs can present the mind with gratis gifts—put into it something which is not already there. Neither mystic insights, nor philosophic wisdom, nor creative power can be provided by pill or injection. The psycho-pharmacist cannot *add* to the faculties of the brain—but he can, at best, *eliminate* obstructions and blockages which impede their proper use. He cannot aggrandise us—but he can, within limits, normalise us; he cannot put additional circuits into the brain, but he can, again within limits, improve the co-ordination between existing ones, attenuate conflicts, prevent the blowing of fuses, and ensure a steady power supply. That is all the help we can ask for—but if we were able to obtain it, the benefits to mankind would be incalculable; it would be the "Final Revolution" in a sense opposite to Huxley's—the break-through from maniac to man.

The "we" in the previous sentence is not meant to refer to patients in the psychiatric ward or on the therapist's couch. Psychopharmacology will no doubt play an increasing part in the treatment of mental disorders in the clinical sense;* but that is not the point. What we are concerned with is a cure for the paranoiac streak in what we call normal people, i.e., mankind as a whole: an artificially simulated, adaptive mutation to bridge the rift between the phylogenetically old and new brain, between instinct and intellect, emotion and reason. If it is within our reach to increase man's suggestibility, it will be soon within our reach to do the opposite, to counteract misplaced devotion and that militant enthusiasm, both murderous and suicidal, which we see reflected in the pages of the daily newspaper. The most urgent task of biochemistry is the search

---

*As this book goes to press, the American journal, *Archives of General Psychiatry*, reports experiments at Tulane University which suggest the possibility of a chemical cure for schizophrenia (Gould, D., "An Antibody in Schizophrenics." London: *New Scientist*, 2.2.1967.)

for a remedy in the "increasing range," as Saunders put it, "of the spectrum of chemical agents which can be used for the control of the mind." It is not utopian to believe that it can and will be done. Our present tranquillisers, barbiturates, stimulants, anti-depressants and combinations thereof, are merely a first step towards a more sophisticated range of aids to promote a co-ordinated, harmonious state of mind. Not the unruffled ataraxia sought by the Stoics, not the ecstasy of the dancing dervish, nor the Pop-Nirvana created by Huxley's "soma" pills—but a state of dynamic equilibrium in which thought and emotion are re-united, and hierarchic order is restored.

A Plea to the Phantom Reader

I am aware that "control of the mind" and "manipulating human beings" have sinister undertones. Who is to control the controls, manipulate the manipulators? Assuming that we succeed in synthesising a hormone which acts as a mental stabiliser on the lines indicated—how are we to propagate its global use to induce that beneficial mutation? Are we to ram it down people's throats, or put it into the tap water?

The answer seems obvious. No legislation, no compulsory measures were needed to persuade Greeks and Romans to partake of "the juice of the grape that gives joy and oblivion." Sleeping pills, pep pills, tranquillisers have, for better or worse, spread across the world with a minimum of publicity or official encouragement. They have spread because people liked their effect, and even accepted unpleasant or harmful after-effects. A mental stabiliser would produce neither euphoria, nor sleep, nor mescalin visions, nor cabbage-like equanimity—it would in fact have no noticeably specific effect, except promoting cerebral co-ordination and harmonising thought and emotion; in other words, restore the integrity of the split hierarchy. Its use would spread because people like feeling healthy rather than unhealthy in body or mind. It would spread as vaccination has spread, and contraception has spread, not by coercion but by enlightened self-interest.

The first noticeable result would perhaps be a sudden drop in the crime and suicide rate in certain regions and social groups where the new Pill became fashionable. From here on the developments are as unpredictable as the consequences of James Watt's or Pasteur's discoveries had been. Some Swiss canton might decide, after a public referendum, to add the new substance to the chlorine in the water supply,* for a trial period, and other countries might follow their

*Incidentally, even the Don't-Tamper-with-Nature Brigade no longer seriously objects to chlorine or other antiseptics being put into tap water.

example. Or there might be an international fashion among the
young, replacing weirdy-beards and purple hearts. In one way or
the other, the mutation would get under way.

It is possible that totalitarian countries would try to resist it. But
today even Iron Curtains have become porous; hot jazz, mini skirts,
discotheques and other bourgeois inventions are spreading irresisti-
bly. When the ruling élite started experimenting with the new
medicine, and discovered that it made them see things in an
altogether different light—then, and only then, would the world be
ripe for a global disarmament conference which is not a sinister
farce. And should there be a transitional period during which one
side alone went ahead with the cure, while the other pesisted in
its paranoid ways, there would be none of the risks of unilateral
disarmament involved; on the contrary, the mutated side would be
stronger because more rational in its long-term policies, less
frightened and less hysterical.

I do not think this is science fiction; and I am confident that the
type of reader to whom this book is addressed will not think so
either. Every writer has a favourite type of imaginary reader, a
friendly phantom but highly critical, whose opinion is the only one
that matters, with whom he is engaged in a continuous, exhausting
dialogue. I feel sure, as I said, that my friendly phantom reader
has sufficient imagination to extrapolate from the recent, breath-
taking advances of biology into the future, and to concede that the
solution outlined here is in the realm of the possible. What worries
me is that he will not like it; that he might be repelled and disgusted
by the idea that we should rely for our salvation on molecular
chemistry instead of a spiritual rebirth. I share his distress, but I
see no alternative. I hear him exclaim: "By trying to sell us your
Pills, you are adopting that crudely materialistic attitude and naive
scientific *hubris*, which you pretend to oppose." I still oppose it.
But I do not believe that it is "materialistic" to take a realistic view
of the condition of man; nor is it *hubris* to feed thyroid extracts
to children who would otherwise grow into cretins. To use our brain
to cure its own shortcomings seems to me a brave and dedicated
enterprise. Like the reader, I would prefer to set my hopes on moral
persuasion by word and example. But we are a mentally sick race,
and as such deaf to persuasion. It has been tried from the age of
the prophets to Albert Schweitzer; and the result has been, as Swift
said, that "we have just enough religion to make us hate, but not
enough to love each other." That applies to all religions, theistic
or secular, whether taught by Moses or Marx or Mao Tse Tung;
and Swift's anguished cry: "not die here in a rage, like a poisoned
rat in a hole" has acquired an urgency as never before.

Nature has let us down, God seems to have left the receiver off
the hook, and time is running out. To hope for salvation to be syn-

thesised in the laboratory may seem materialistic, crankish, or naive; but, to tell the truth, there is a Jungian twist to it—for it reflects the ancient alchemist's dream to concoct the *elixir vitae*. What we expect from it, however, is not eternal life, nor the transformation of base metal into gold, but the transformation of *homo maniacus* into *homo sapiens*. When man decides to take his fate into his own hands, that possibility will be within reach.

References

1. Platt, J. R., *The Step to Man*. New York, 1966. pp. 195, 196 and 200.
2. de Beer, G., *Embryos and Ancestors*. Oxford, 1940.
3. National Research Council Report on "Natural Resources." Washington, D.C., 1962.
4. Harkavy, O., "Economic Problems of Population Growth." New York: The Ford Foundation.
5. Ibid., p. 8.
6. Eastman, N. J., in *Fertility and Sterility*, Vol. 15, No. 5, September–October 1965, reprinted by the Ford Foundation, 1965.
7. Morris, I., in *New Scientist*. London, 25.8.66.
8. *Time*, New York, 29.1.65.
9. v. Bertalanffy, L., in *The Scientific Monthly*, January 1956.
10. *Time*, New York, 25.9.64.
11. Lindquist, S., *China and Crisis*. London, 1966.
12. *Time*, New York, 24.9.65.
13. Platt.
14. Lorenz, K. L., *On Aggression*. London, 1966. p. 205.
15. MacLean, P., "Psychosomatics" in *Handbook of Physiology— Neurophysiology* III, 1961. pp. 1738-9.
16. Hydén, H., in *Control of the Mind*. Farber, S. M. and Wilson, R. H. L., eds. New York, 1961.
17. Saunders, J. B. de C. M., in *Control of the Mind*. Farber, S. M. and Wilson, R. H. L., eds. New York, 1961. p. xi f.
18. Huxley, A., in *Control of the Mind*. New York, 1961.